Statistical Methods

for the Behavioral Sciences

■ **Books by ALLEN L. EDWARDS**

Experimental Design in Psychological Research

Statistical Analysis for Students in Psychology and Education

Statistical Methods for the Behavioral Sciences

■ ALLEN L. EDWARDS

Professor of Psychology
University of Washington

Statistical Methods for the Behavioral Sciences

■ RINEHART & COMPANY, INC. *New York*

Library of Congress Catalog Card Number: 54-9561

to Steven

Preface

To say that the behavioral sciences involve a high degree of empiricism is not to deny that theory often plays an important role in these sciences. Rather it is to emphasize that the behavioral sciences are intimately associated with the raw stuff of empiricism—observational data. Theory may be the guide to the choice of observations to be made. Theory may also assist in the integration of conclusions drawn from data with current knowledge. But the first concern of the behavioral sciences is still with research based upon data and with the conclusions to be drawn from such data.

Any research worker in the behavioral sciences knows, however, that raw data are seldom in a form such that the conclusions to be drawn from the data are either immediate or obvious. Observations must first be processed, analyzed, or operated upon. In these activities of the behavioral scientist, statistical methods play an important role. It is primarily as a consequence of the application of statistical methods to data that the behavioral scientist decides what conclusions are warranted and what the alternatives are to the decisions made.

This text is intended for students of the behavioral sciences, and it describes the applications of statistical methods to the data of these sciences. If it were possible to assume that students of the behavioral sciences had equivalent degrees of mathematical training or—more important—mathematical knowledge, this book could have been written at a different level. For reasons that I have expressed in my other books dealing with statistical methods, I do not think this assumption can be made at the present time. Consequently, I have tried to present statistical techniques and methods in such a way that the student with a minimum amount of mathematical knowledge can follow the discussion.

This minimum amount of mathematical knowledge is presented in Chapter 2, Survey of Rules and Principles. The student who masters this chapter should be able to follow subsequent developments. In the examples at the end of the chapters I have occasionally included problems that the more advanced student may find of interest. The answers to all examples are given in the appendix.

I well know, after some ten years of teaching statistical methods to students of the behavioral sciences, that there is no problem in making the content of the course sufficiently difficult. There is a problem, however, in attempting a presentation that is sufficiently simple and accurate to be followed by those with a minimum of mathematical training. It is this problem which has interested me and which I have tried to keep constantly before me in writing this text.

In reading this and other statistical books it would be difficult indeed for the research worker not to be aware of the stress that is placed upon the notion of normality of distribution. In brief, this notion means that in the application of statistical methods to data of the real world the assumption is made that the data, the observations, are themselves drawn from a population that is normally distributed. When this assumption is justified, the research worker has available a number of powerful statistical methods for the analysis of his data. This text is primarily concerned with these methods.

It not infrequently happens, however, that when the research worker meets with data of the real world, the assumption of normality of distribution is clearly not justified. What is to be done when this happens? The problem has not gone unrecognized by statisticians. Methods of statistical analysis, free from the assumption of normality of distribution, have been developed. These methods are variously known as nonparametric or distribution-free methods.

It has been my experience, as a result of close association with active research workers in psychology, sociology, and education, that distribution-free methods are extremely useful in the analysis of much of the data obtained from these fields. I believe that they deserve more attention than has commonly been given to them in applied statistical texts. I have tried, therefore, to integrate a variety of these methods into the text along with the more commonly used methods of statistical analysis involving the assumption of normality of distribution.

In the preparation of this book, many individuals have contributed in one way or another. In particular the comments of A. W. Bendig, Irwin Child, Cletus J. Burke, Don Fiske, David Grant, Paul Horst, Lyle Jones,

William Kruskal, Moncrieff H. Smith, Jr., and the late H. M. Johnson on my previous books, *Statistical Analysis* and *Experimental Design in Psychological Research*, have proved helpful. In addition, Paul Horst read the complete manuscript of the present text and provided many valuable suggestions.

I am indebted to Sir Ronald A. Fisher and to Messrs. Oliver and Boyd Ltd., Edinburgh, for permission to reprint Tables IV, V, and VI from their book, *Statistical Methods for Research Workers*. Table I is reproduced by permission of M. G. Kendall and B. B. Smith and the Royal Statistical Society. Portions of Table II have been taken from *Handbook of Statistical Nomographs, Tables, and Formulas* by permission of J. W. Dunlap and A. K. Kurtz. Table VIII has been reproduced from G. W. Snedecor's book, *Statistical Methods*, by permission of the author and his publisher, the Iowa State College Press. Table IX is reprinted from *Elementary Mathematical Tables* by permission of D. E. Smith, W. D. Reeve, and E. L. Morss and their publishers, Ginn and Company. Table X is reprinted by permission of M. D. Davidoff and H. W. Goheen and the Psychometric Society. Table XIII was made possible by permission of E. G. Olds and the Institute of Mathematical Statistics. Table XV is reprinted by permission of Colin White and the Biometric Society.

To various authors and to the publishers of *Personnel Psychology, Journal of Experimental Education, Journal of Social Psychology, American Psychologist, Journal of Applied Psychology, Journal of Experimental Psychology, Psychological Review, Journal of Abnormal and Social Psychology, American Journal of Psychology, Journal of the Royal Statistical Society, Biometrika, Journal of the American Statistical Association, Annals of Mathematical Statistics, Biometrics, and Psychometrika*, I am indebted for permission to quote material and to make use of data published in these journals.

A. L. E.

Seattle, Washington
June, 1954

Contents

CHAPTER ONE

Introduction

Approached from the point of view that *statistical techniques are tools* to be used in experimentation and research, and in the discovery of new facts, the study of statistical methods can be an interesting as well as a valuable subject. As social scientists, are we interested in descriptions? Then statistical methods can assist us in making our descriptions more precise. Are we interested in differences between individuals and groups? Then statistical methods can assist us in describing and evaluating the reliability of observed differences. Are we interested in discovering whether there is any relationship between two traits, two abilities, or between information and attitude, or between juvenile-delinquency rates and distance of residence from the center of the city? Statistical methods again come to our assistance. These are applications of statistical methods to problems, and there is no reason why such applications cannot be learned at the same time that the techniques are learned. That is the point of view stressed in this book.

The Text and the Student

Not everyone who uses a stop watch is interested, or need be, in the detailed construction of the watch. The stop watch is a tool, an instrument, which can be used for measuring, describing, or evaluating time intervals. In similar fashion statistical methods may be regarded as techniques for measuring, describing, and evaluating data. Learning to apply elementary statistical techniques does not require elaborate previous mathematical preparation. The field of mathematical statistics is so highly developed that not every worker in the field of psychology or education can be expected to be a specialist in both fields.

Automobile manufacturers publish two different sets of instructions to accompany the automobiles they produce; one book is intended for the driver of the car and the other is intended for the mechanic. Needless to say, the contents of the two books are not the same. The mechanic's book explains the working of the engine and other details. The driver's book tells him how to operate the car. The driver himself may never see the engine that makes his car go, but he takes it for granted that it is there and in good working order. Of course, if the car breaks down, then the driver must take it to the mechanic to get it repaired.

This text is more like the automobile book for drivers than like the one for mechanics. If while reading it you become interested in getting a better knowledge of the mathematical bases behind the techniques presented, then books such as those by Hoel (1947) and Mood (1950) may be consulted.[1] You will find, however, that these books, dealing with the mathematical theory of statistics, require at least a knowledge of advanced calculus.

Examples and Problems

It is a generally recognized principle in psychology and education that one learns by doing. That is the purpose of the exercises and examples scattered throughout the text. As far as possible these examples have been selected for simplicity, but some are more complicated than others. Emphasis in the text is placed upon the procedures to be followed in making various computations and in interpreting the results of these computations. It is possible to learn to do this just as well with numbers that are small as with numbers that are large. In the few cases where large numbers have been used, you will find that Chapter 4, on "simplifying computations," will enable you to "code" these numbers, that is, to reduce their size, so that computations will be facilitated.

Use of Tables

In the back of the book you will find a number of tables you will have occasion to refer to constantly. It is important that you know how to use these tables accurately. Each one will be explained in detail when it is first introduced into the discussion. Some of these tables are designed to simplify your work, such as the table of squares, square roots, and reciprocals. This table will enable you to obtain square roots easily and will also give you the squares of numbers so that you may avoid unnecessary multiplication.

[1] References are cited by author and by date and may be found in the list beginning on page 441.

Symbols and Formulas

A word or two should be said about the use of symbols. They are relatively few, and each one has a specialized meaning. These symbols are in reality a form of shorthand, a simplified way of expressing something that would otherwise have to be written out in longhand. Some of these symbols stand for quantities, and others stand for operations to be performed. It is much easier, for example, to write "$2 + 2 = 4$" than it is to write: "The quantity 'two' plus the quantity 'two' gives the sum of four."

Here is a slightly different example and one that may be unfamiliar: $R = X_h - X_l$. If we were to put this into words we would say: "The range of measurements is equal to the highest measurement minus the lowest measurement." In the symbolic treatment, $R = X_h - X_l$, R stands for range, X_h stands for the highest measurement, and X_l stands for the lowest measurement. Once having memorized the symbolic statement we can use it over and over again in place of the longer definition. In essence, then, symbols enable us to say a lot with little effort. Take them in stride, memorize each one as it is introduced, and you will find that they will give you little trouble.[2]

What we have just said with respect to symbols applies also to formulas which are stated in terms of symbols. If you think of each formula as consisting of symbols that stand for quantities and operations to be performed, and if you see it as merely an abbreviated way of saying something, you will soon realize the value of formulas. The purpose of a formula is to simplify your work, not to make it more complicated.

In everyday speech we have found that there is more than one way of saying essentially the same thing. This is true of formulas also. We shall find that it is possible to write different formulas that say the same thing. Some of these formulas are introduced because they make clear the notion or idea we wish to present. But the formula that most clearly expresses an idea is not always the formula that is easiest to use for calculative purposes. Thus one formula may be used because of the simplicity and clarity of its expression, and we may then say the same thing with another formula that can be used more conveniently in calculations.

Daily Preparation

A book written about the subject of statistical techniques and a course in statistical techniques may not be quite like the usual texts and courses

[2] It is unfortunate, but true, that different writers use different symbols to mean the same thing. In some texts, for example, you will find that the symbol M is used for the arithmetic mean. In other texts, you will find $\bar{X}$ or $\bar{x}$ used to represent the mean. We have tried, in general, to use symbols in such a way that they are consistent and in accord with current and growing practice.

to which you are accustomed. Some courses do not require daily preparation, and many students get into the habit of waiting until just before an examination before getting down to work. By cramming they may succeed in absorbing a sufficient amount of knowledge, temporarily at least, to pass an objective or essay type of examination. But research in the problem of retention of material learned in this fashion indicates that it is soon forgotten. Students may not consider this too great a handicap if they find that an understanding of later topics is not dependent on what has come before.

This is not the case with statistical methods. They cannot be successfully learned or mastered by cramming. Nor can the student, once having taken an examination, afford to forget the material studied and still expect to understand what is to come later. If you have any doubts about this, try reading some of the later chapters in this book now. You will find things presented there that you cannot possibly understand unless you are already familiar with the subject matter of the earlier chapters.

Statistical methods, as presented in this book, start from scratch: the assumption is that the student knows nothing at all about the subject. But there is continuity of development, each new topic or section being built upon the foundation established by previous sections. In certain respects this approach is like the construction of a house, in which the site is prepared, the foundation laid, the sides erected, and finally the roof put on. No good contractor attempts to put a roof on a house until he is sure of his foundation and sides. The first few chapters of this book are the foundation of everything that appears later. Don't make the mistake of rushing through them because they may seem familiar or easy. The chances are very good that many of the questions you may ask about later developments have their answers in one of the earlier chapters.

Empirical Approach

For practically every topic developed in this book there are several possible approaches. There is an algebraic development, a geometrical development, and an "empirical" or, as some prefer to call it, "arithmetical" development. By the empirical approach is meant the actual working through of a simple set of arithmetical computations to see that certain theorems or statements check as they should. More will be said about the empirical approach in the third chapter, where we take up the subject of "averages and measures of variability." The empirical approach is stressed throughout the discussion so that the student without much previous knowledge of mathematics can follow the development of various topics. When an algebraic development is presented, it is done in sufficient detail for you to follow it.

If you have trouble with any of the algebraic presentations, then you will want to review the material in Chapter 2 quite thoroughly. If you can understand the material in Chapter 2, then there is no reason why you should not be able to understand the material in subsequent chapters. It is not the intention of this book to make things difficult for you, although this perhaps would have been an easier task than trying to make things simple. But even the learning of simple things will require some effort and cooperation on your part. You can get off to a good start by reviewing the material in Chapter 2.

Statistical Terms and Statements

Averages

In our daily conversation we often use the term "average." We say that "John is better than average" when someone questions us about his golfing ability. Or that "Mary is slightly below average as a dancer" and "slightly above average in height." Some of our college courses we say we like "better than average." Some of the shoes we buy are "poorer than average." And, although in our own thinking we may not have defined the term as precisely as a statistician would, we have some general understanding of the concept. We may be vaguely aware that our statements concerning averages are based upon a series of observations or measurements and that each of these observations or measurements taken singly may not be the same as the average we have in mind. We perhaps have some scale in mind when we refer to John's ability as a golfer or Mary's height, and our average represents some middle position or value. The statements that "John is better than average" and that "Mary is slightly above average" indicate that we do not believe that they represent this middle position.

We can find statements similar to these in books on psychology, education, and the social sciences, but they are usually expressed more precisely than the statements we make about averages in our daily conversation.

"A group of 50 high-school students, after viewing a motion picture that presented the Chinese in a very favorable light, showed an average shift toward the favorable end of a scale measuring attitude toward the Chinese of 2.5 scale points. A control group that had not seen the motion picture showed a shift of only 1.2 scale points."

"The average reading-comprehension-test score for 200 sixth-grade students was 82.3, while the average score on the same test for a group of 200 seventh-grade students was 96.8."

"A group of subjects that had practiced simple arithmetic computations one hour daily for five days made an average of 13.3 errors on a speed test. Another group with ten days of daily practice made an average of 8.4 errors on the same test."

All of these statements concerning averages were made possible by statistical methods.

Variability

We encounter another kind of statement that is made possible by statistical methods. In their simplest form such statements may appear as follows:

"The individual shifts in attitude scores for the group viewing the motion picture ranged from .8 to 7.3. For the group that did not see the motion picture the shifts ranged from .2 to 3.4 points."

"The range of scores on the reading comprehension test for the sixth-grade students was from 30 to 101; for the seventh-grade students the range was from 39 to 135."

"The number of errors for the group with five days of practice ranged from 2 to 21, while for the group with ten days of practice the range was from 2 to 11."

These statements indicate something of the spread or differences among measures of individual performance. They tell us, taken in conjunction with statements about averages, that some of the measurements were above average and that others were below. These differences are as much a matter of interest as are the averages, so much so to some psychologists that entire books have been devoted to the subject.[3] But we experience variability also outside our books in daily life. We note that not all incomes are the same but that some are very high and others very low; that the temperature is not the same but varies from hour to hour, from day to day, and from month to month. Not all synthetic tires have the same life span; some give more mileage than others. Not all individuals are equally good at golf, dancing, and other skills.

Relationships

Sometimes we find statements that are not directly about averages or differences, but about relations between averages or differences. For example, in connection with the previous statements about reading comprehension scores for the 200 sixth graders, we might find something like this:

"Those students who were above average on the reading-comprehension test also tended to be above average in intelligence, as measured by an

[3] See, for example, Tyler (1947), Anastasi (1937), and Gilliland and Clark (1939).

intelligence test, while those who were below average on one test also tended to be below average on the other. There was, in other words, a decided relationship between performance on the two tests, the *correlation coefficient* being .78."

You need not concern yourself at this time with the meaning of "correlation coefficient" other than to note that it is a measure of relationship or association. Our interest here is in pointing out that relationships are also a subject of discussion in psychology and education. Statements concerning relationships probably appear as often in these fields as do statements concerning averages and differences. They too are made possible by statistical methods.

We also make constant reference to relationships in daily life, although these statements, like those about averages and differences, are not expressed as precisely as the statistician would like to express them. We note that a person's income may be related to the number of years of education he has; or that the amount of rainfall is related to the season of the year; or that an individual's opinions on political questions may be related to the section of the country in which he lives. Or we might say about John's golf: "He's good. He practices a great deal." In this case we would indicate that we thought there was some relationship between his ability and the amount of practice.

■ Functions of Statistical Methods

Precise Description

If you have followed the rather elementary discussion up to this point, then you are already familiar with some of the chief functions of statistical methods. In the behavioral and social sciences (and the examples in this book are selected largely from these fields) statistical methods enable us to study and to describe precisely averages, differences, and relationships. The problem of studying averages and differences may seem simple enough. If we are interested in the performance of college freshmen on a test of verbal facility, for example, we give a group of freshmen the test and find some measure of average performance and some measure of variability or individual differences. We shall have more to say about this problem later, but now let us see how we might investigate relationships.

Study of Relationships

One obvious method of studying relationships is making comparisons. We might compare the average performance of freshmen on our test with the average performance of college sophomores to determine whether there is any relationship between year in college and performance. If we found that sophomores made a higher average score than freshmen, then we might assume that such a relationship does exist. We might feel even more confident of our assumption if we had also tested a group of juniors and a group of seniors and found that average performance increased from year to year. If we were so inclined, we might even carry our investigation on down through the various grades in high school.

On some occasions we may not find any basis upon which to classify individuals to get more than two groups. If we were interested in the relationship between sex and performance on our test of verbal facility we should have to be content with classifying our subjects as men or women and studying the average performance of each of these two groups on our test.

There is another method of approaching the problem of relationships. Instead of studying average differences between groups, we study the difference or relationship between paired measurements. Some examples with which you are probably already familiar are the relationship between grades earned in college and scores on an academic-aptitude test, the relationship between height and weight, the relationship between motivation and learning. The problem here is similar to that discussed above, except that all of our subjects are considered as members of a single group. For each subject we have a pair of measurements and we determine the relationship between these pairs

Planning of Experiments

It is sometimes possible for an investigator to control various factors in which he is interested and to manipulate others experimentally in order to study the relationships between them. This situation may be called an *experiment*. The example cited earlier concerning the influence of a motion picture on attitudes is a case in point. The factor introduced into the situation was the motion picture about the Chinese. By testing the attitudes before and after children had seen it, the influence of the picture on attitudes could be measured. Subjects may be given practice periods of different lengths in order to study the relationship between the amount of practice and performance. The behavior of children may be observed under normal play conditions, and then factors designed to produce frustration in the children may be introduced into the situation in order to observe whether these factors result in changes in play behavior.

Usually this approach to the study of differences and relationships involves an *experimental* and a *control group*, and the behavior or performance of the two groups is compared. The experimental group is the group for which some factor (practice, frustration) is varied while the control group does not experience the factor. The factor that is introduced into the experimental situation is ordinarily called the *experimental* or *independent variable;* the variable for which we observe changes is called the *dependent variable.*

There are various techniques for selecting, assigning, and equating the members of the experimental and control groups so that various factors pertinent to the problems under investigation may be controlled. If we had reason to believe that, in a particular investigation, age might be related to the behavior under study, then obviously we would want to have some assurance that this factor would not account for the results of our experiment. One way in which we might accomplish this would be by matching each individual in our experimental groups with another individual of the same age in the control group.

Sometimes a particular experiment demands that our groups already differ with respect to a variable in which we are interested. This might be the case if we wished to study the effects of differing attitudes upon the learning and retention of different kinds of prose. For example, will individuals who favor a given issue learn material that presents a favorable picture of the issue more readily than material opposed to it? Will the opposite tendency be present in individuals who are opposed to the issue? In this instance we might select for study groups that differ with respect to the attitude they hold on the issue, but that are matched with respect to some other variable, such as level of intelligence.

Statistical methods play a very important part in the planning of experiments as well as in the evaluation of the results of experiments. Setting up an experiment so that the most advantageous analysis of the results is possible is called a problem in *experimental design.*[4] A sound experimental design is like a good blueprint; it gives confidence that the various parts are going to fit together at the end.

Statistical Inference

Having conducted an experiment or having made a series of observations and having described such things as averages, differences, and relationships, and having quantified these descriptions, we find that statistical methods enable us to take another step. We are often interested in knowing how reliable our descriptions are. If we repeated the experiment with other groups, to what extent would the new averages, measures of variation, and relationships differ from those we obtained the first time? Statistical methods enable us to determine the reliability of observed differences and relationships so that we may make generalizations with a

[4] The books by Fisher (1942), Cochran and Cox (1950), Kempthorne (1952), Edwards (1950*a*), Lindquist (1940), Snedecor (1946), Johnson (1949), and Mather (1947) deal with the problems of experimental design in detail.

given *degree of confidence*. The process by which we arrive at such generalizations is known as *statistical inference*.

Prediction

Suppose that we had studied a group of workmen operating a particular machine and that we had then constructed a test that we believed to be capable of measuring performance on the machine itself. On the test a group of "good" workmen make an average score of so many points and a group of "poor" workmen make a much lower average score. Could we then predict from the scores of a new group of workmen how well they would probably perform on the machine in question? If we find the relationship between a scholastic-aptitude test and college grades, then how accurately can we predict the average grades of other individuals, knowing only their scholastic-aptitude-test scores before they have taken any college work? Accurate prediction is the final function of statistical methods with which we shall be concerned.

■ Summary

In summary, we now know something about the kinds of problems to which statistical methods can be applied. The chapters that follow discuss in greater detail the use of statistical methods: (1) in making precise descriptions of averages, differences, and relationships; (2) in planning and designing experiments; (3) in determining the degree of confidence we may place in certain generalizations about our observations; and (4) in making predictions.

As a final note to this introduction and survey of what is to come, we might add that there are a number of statistical problems peculiar to testing and test construction which are dealt with by various statistical techniques. But this is a field that has expanded so rapidly that it requires separate treatment. It is also true that familiarity with elementary methods of statistical analysis is a prerequisite for understanding statistical techniques in testing and test construction. We shall deal with some of the problems of testing, but the treatment by Conrad (1948), Goodenough (1949), Guilford (1936), Adkins (1947), Thurstone (1935), and Gulliksen (1950) is much more complete.

■ CHAPTER TWO

Survey of Rules and Principles

The rules and principles outlined in this chapter are extremely simple as well as extremely important.[1] They deal with fractions, decimals, positive and negative numbers, radicals, exponents, logarithms, and simple equations. The material may be familiar to many students, but merely being able to work the examples is not sufficient. Working a problem when it is expressed in simple form is one thing, but unless you clearly understand the rule or principle that guided you in determining the answer, you may not be able to apply it to some of the formulas developed later. We shall not point out at this time the specific applications of the materials in this chapter to subsequent developments. However, we shall have occasion to refer to this chapter quite frequently in later discussions.

■ Symbols

The symbols $+$, $-$, $\div$, and $\times$ refer to the operations of addition, subtraction, division, and multiplication, respectively. Parentheses and brackets may also be used to indicate multiplication. For example, if we write (3)(4), this means to multiply 3 and 4. Often we have no need for any multiplication sign, and the product of a and b is simply written ab. Nor do we have much use for $\div$ as a sign of division. Instead, division will

[1] The very excellent book *Mathematics essential for elementary statistics* by Helen Walker (1951) is both an introduction to and a review of elementary algebra. The student who needs additional assistance should obtain a copy for thorough study.

usually be indicated by a bar. Thus, to indicate a divided by b, we would write either a/b or $\frac{a}{b}$.

We shall have occasion to use the two symbols $<$ and $>$ quite frequently. The symbol $<$ means "is less than," and the symbol $>$ means "is greater than." Thus "$p < .05$" is read "p is less than .05," and "$p > .05$" is read "p is greater than .05." If we write "$p \leqq .05$," this is read "p is less than or equal to .05," and "$p \geqq .05$" is read "p is greater than or equal to .05."

Additional symbols will be defined when they are first introduced into the text.

Fractions

A fraction is one method of stating that we are dealing with a sum that has been divided into a number of equal parts. The numerator of the fraction indicates the number of parts considered, and the denominator indicates the equal parts. For example, 3/4 indicates that a given sum or number has been divided into four equal parts and that we are dealing with three of these four parts.

Rule 1. The numerator and denominator of a fraction may be multiplied or divided by the same number or symbol without changing the value of the fraction. Thus, starting with the fraction on the left and multiplying both the numerator and denominator by the same value, we get the following *equivalent fractions*:

$$\frac{4}{5} = \frac{8}{10} = \frac{24}{30} = \frac{48}{60}$$

$$\frac{2x}{3y} = \frac{4x}{6y} = \frac{12x}{18y} = \frac{24xy}{36y^2}$$

Rule 2. Observe, however, that adding or subtracting the same number or symbol from the numerator and denominator of a fraction will, in general, change the value of the fraction. If we subtract 1 from both the numerator and denominator of the fraction 4/5, we get 3/4 which is not the same value as the original fraction. If we add 3 to the numerator and denominator of the fraction 2/3, we get 5/6 which is not the same value as our first fraction. An exception to this rule would occur when the numerator of the fraction is equal to the denominator. Thus subtracting 3 from the numerator and denominator of 9/9 gives 6/6 which does not change the value of the original fraction; and adding 2 to both the numerator and denominator of 3/3 gives 5/5 which is also equal to the original value.

Rule 3. We cannot add or subtract fractions until they have first been transformed so that they have a common denominator. The transformation may be made by Rule 1. For example, if we wish to add 1/2 and 1/4 we may multiply both the numerator and denominator of the fraction 1/2 by 2. This will give us the equivalent fraction 2/4, and the fractions to be added will have a common denominator of 4. We then add or subtract the numerators only; the denominator of the answer is the common denominator of the group of fractions added or subtracted. Thus

$$\frac{1}{2} + \frac{1}{4} = \frac{2 \times 1}{2 \times 2} + \frac{1}{4} = \frac{2}{4} + \frac{1}{4} = \frac{3}{4}$$

$$\frac{a}{b} + \frac{c}{d} = \frac{ad}{bd} + \frac{bc}{bd} = \frac{ad + bc}{bd}$$

Rule 4. To multiply fractions merely multiply the numerators and multiply the denominators. This, in effect, serves to reduce them all to a common denominator. Thus

$$\frac{2}{3} \times \frac{3}{4} \times \frac{5}{6} \times \frac{4}{5} = \frac{2 \times 3 \times 5 \times 4}{3 \times 4 \times 6 \times 5} = \frac{120}{360} = \frac{1}{3}$$

$$\frac{a}{b} \times \frac{c}{d} \times \frac{x}{y} = \frac{acx}{bdy}$$

Rule 5. To divide fractions, invert the divisor and multiply according to Rule 4. Thus

$$\frac{2}{3} \div \frac{1}{2} = \frac{2}{3} \times \frac{2}{1} = \frac{4}{3} = 1\frac{1}{3}$$

$$\frac{a}{b} \div \frac{c}{d} = \frac{a}{b} \times \frac{d}{c} = \frac{ad}{bc}$$

Rule 6. If 1 is divided by any number n, this fraction or its quotient is called the *reciprocal* of n. Thus 1/4 or .25 is the reciprocal of the number 4. If a number a is to be divided by another number n, we can obtain the same quotient by multiplying a by the reciprocal of n. Thus

$$\frac{a}{n} = a \times \frac{1}{n}$$

$$\frac{8}{50} = 8 \times \frac{1}{50} = (8)(.02) = .16$$

Table II, in the Appendix, gives the reciprocals of numbers from 1 to 1,000.

Decimals

Common fractions, as we have seen above, may have different denominators. Decimals or decimal fractions, on the other hand, always have a denominator of 10 or some power of 10 such as 100, 1,000, 10,000, 100,000, and so on. Thus .3 = 3/10, .03 = 3/100, .003 = 3/1,000, and .0003 = 3/10,000. Common fractions such as 1/2, 3/4, and 2/5 may be written as decimal fractions by dividing the numerator by the denominator. Thus 1/2, 3/4, and 2/5 may also be written .5, .75, and .4, respectively.

Rule 1. When adding or subtracting decimals, keep the decimal points in a straight line and the decimal point in the answer directly under the decimal points of the figures added or subtracted. Thus

$$\begin{array}{r} .82 \\ .90 \\ \hline 1.72 \end{array} \qquad \begin{array}{r} .333 \\ 1.222 \\ \hline 1.555 \end{array} \qquad \text{and} \qquad \begin{array}{r} 1.28 \\ -.05 \\ \hline 1.23 \end{array} \qquad \begin{array}{r} .83 \\ -.11 \\ \hline .72 \end{array}$$

Rule 2. In multiplying numbers involving decimals, point off as many decimal places in the product as there are decimal places in the multiplier and multiplicand together. The answer, in other words, will have as many decimal places as the sum of those in the two numbers multiplied. Thus

$$\begin{array}{r} .03 \\ .09 \\ \hline .0027 \end{array} \qquad \begin{array}{r} .222 \\ .10 \\ \hline .02220 \end{array} \qquad \begin{array}{r} 2.20 \\ .03 \\ \hline .0660 \end{array} \qquad \begin{array}{r} .0005 \\ .2 \\ \hline .00010 \end{array}$$

Rule 3. When one decimal is divided by another, the number of decimal places in the dividend minus the number of decimal places in the divisor equals the number of decimal places in the answer. Thus

$$\frac{.004}{.2} = .02 \qquad \frac{4.2}{.2} = 21 \qquad \frac{.008}{.02} = .4 \qquad \frac{.90}{.03} = 30$$

We must always have at least the same number of decimal places in the dividend as in the divisor—and we may need more in order to complete the division. If the dividend has fewer decimal places than the divisor, then we may add 0's to the right of the decimal point in the dividend. Thus

$$\frac{8}{10} = \frac{8.0}{10} = .8 \qquad \frac{.4}{.25} = \frac{.400}{.25} = 1.6$$

$$\frac{.42}{.002} = \frac{.420}{.002} = 210 \qquad \frac{42}{.2} = \frac{42.0}{.2} = 210$$

■ Proportions and Per Cents

Rule 1. To find what proportion of a sum or total a given number is, divide the number by the sum or total. If, in a class of 60 students, 15 students receive a grade of C, and we wish to find the proportion receiving this grade, we divide 15 by 60 and our answer is .25. If, in an experiment, 35 subjects out of a total of 70 show a characteristic in which we are interested, and we wish to know the proportion showing the characteristic, we divide 35 by 70 and our answer is .5.

Rule 2. To translate a proportion into a per cent, multiply the proportion by 100. In the example above, the proportion of subjects showing the characteristic is .5 and the per cent showing the characteristic is $.5 \times 100 = 50$ per cent. We see from this also that if we wish to translate a per cent into a proportion, we must divide the per cent by 100.

Rule 3. To find the number that a given proportion of a total equals, multiply the total by the proportion. If, in a group of 40 students, the proportion receiving a grade of B is .1, the number receiving this grade is $(40)(.1) = 4$. The same rule applies to a per cent, the per cent being changed to a proportion or decimal.

Rule 4. Just as the sum of all per cents of a given total is equal to 100, so also the sum of all proportions of any given total is equal to 1.00.

■ Positive and Negative Numbers

Perhaps the simplest illustration of the meaning of negative numbers can be given in terms of readings on a thermometer. Suppose that the temperature is now 20 degrees above zero, and the weather man says that we can expect a drop of 25 degrees by nightfall. What temperature will it be then? On the thermometer we have numbers above and below zero, and if the weather man's prediction comes true, we would say that the temperature is 5 degrees below zero, or -5 degrees. Temperatures above zero are represented by a plus sign and those below zero by a minus sign. Ordinarily, we omit the plus sign for numbers above zero, but whenever the number is below zero we write a minus sign in front of it.

Just as minus and plus signs can be used to indicate temperatures above and below zero, they can also be used to indicate *directions* or *deviations* from some value other than zero. For example, knowing that the average height of a group of students is 67 inches, we could describe an individual with a height of 69 inches as being 2 inches above the average and an individual with a height of 65 inches as being 2 inches below the average. For these two values we could write 2 and -2 respectively. All values above the average could be written as deviations without any sign, the plus sign being understood. Each value below the average could also be written as a deviation, but each of these values would have a minus sign.

Rule 1. To add numbers with the same sign, we merely add and give the sum the common sign. Thus, adding the following, we get

$$2 + 3 + 4 + 6 + 8 = 23$$

$$(-2) + (-3) + (-4) + (-6) + (-8) = -23$$

Rule 2. To add two numbers with unlike signs, take the difference between the two numbers and attach the sign of the larger number. Thus, adding the following pairs, we get

$$\begin{array}{r} -2 \\ 6 \\ \hline 4 \end{array} \qquad \begin{array}{r} 4 \\ -8 \\ \hline -4 \end{array} \qquad \begin{array}{r} -10 \\ 9 \\ \hline -1 \end{array} \qquad \begin{array}{r} 8 \\ -9 \\ \hline -1 \end{array} \qquad \begin{array}{r} -5 \\ 6 \\ \hline 1 \end{array}$$

Rule 3. To add a group of numbers with unlike signs, add the positive and negative numbers separately, following Rule 1, and then take the difference between the two sums and attach the sign of the larger quantity, following Rule 2. Thus

$$2 - 3 - 7 - 5 - 1 + 4 = 6 - 16 = -10$$

$$10 - 4 - 6 + 5 - 5 + 5 = 20 - 15 = 5$$

Rule 4. To subtract one signed number from another, change the sign of the subtrahend and add according to the rules above. Thus, subtracting the following pairs, remembering that the sign of the number is written only when the number is negative, we get

$$\begin{array}{rrrrrrrr} 5 & 4 & -4 & -4 & -4 & -4 & 4 & 6 \\ \underline{-3} & \underline{-6} & \underline{-3} & \underline{-8} & \underline{3} & \underline{8} & \underline{5} & \underline{2} \\ 8 & 10 & -1 & 4 & -7 & -12 & -1 & 4 \end{array}$$

Rule 5. The multiplication of numbers with like signs gives a positive product; the multiplication of numbers with unlike signs gives a negative product. Thus, multiplying the following pairs, remembering that the sign of the number is written only when it is negative, we get

$$6 \times -3 = -18 \qquad -4 \times -2 = 8 \qquad 3 \times -3 = -9$$

$$2 \times -4 = -8 \qquad 4 \times 2 = 8 \qquad -5 \times 2 = -10$$

$$-1 \times -5 = 5 \qquad -5 \times -5 = 25 \qquad -3 \times -3 = 9$$

Rule 6. The division of numbers with like signs gives a positive quotient; the division of numbers with unlike signs gives a negative quotient. Thus, dividing the following pairs, remembering that the sign of the number is written only when the number is negative, we get

$$\frac{-6}{-3} = 2 \qquad \frac{-6}{2} = -3 \qquad \frac{6}{3} = 2 \qquad \frac{4}{-2} = -2$$

■ Order of Operations and Symbols of Grouping

Rule 1. Numbers in a series involving only the operation of multiplication or the operation of addition may be multiplied or added in any order without changing the answer. Thus

$$\frac{2 \times 3 \times 4}{2 \times 3} = \frac{24}{6} = 4 \qquad \text{and} \qquad \frac{4 \times 2 \times 3}{3 \times 2} = \frac{24}{6} = 4$$

$$\frac{2 + 3 + 4}{5 + 6} = \frac{9}{11} \qquad \text{and} \qquad \frac{4 + 2 + 3}{6 + 5} = \frac{9}{11}$$

Rule 2. When the operations of division and multiplication are involved along with the operations of subtraction and addition, the multiplication and division should be performed first. Thus

$$2 + 3 \times 8 = 26$$

$$3 \times 2 - 1 = 5$$

$$4 + \frac{4}{2} = 6$$

$$4 + 8 \times 2 - 2 \times 1 = 18$$

Rule 3. In order to prevent ambiguity in the operations performed and their order, we make use of symbols of grouping. Parentheses and brackets are commonly used symbols. When symbols of grouping are used, the terms within the symbols should be treated as a single number. Thus

$$(2 + 4) + (8 - 3) + 2(4 + 1) = 6 + 5 + 10 = 21$$

$$(2 + 4)/2 = 6/2 = 3$$

$$(5 + 4)/(2 + 1) = 9/3 = 3$$

$$2[(5 + 4)/(2 + 1)] = (2)(9/3) = 6$$

Rule 4. When numbers or symbols are enclosed in parentheses or brackets without any intervening signs, the operation of multiplication is indicated, as we have pointed out earlier. Thus

$$(2)(4 + 5) = (2)(9) = 18$$

$$\left[\frac{(2)(2)}{4} + 4\right][(3)(6) - 2] = (5)(16) = 80$$

Rule 5. If a minus sign precedes the parentheses and the parentheses are removed, the sign of every term within the parentheses must be changed. Thus

$$(8 + 2 - 1) - (6 + 4 - 3) = 8 + 2 - 1 - 6 - 4 + 3 = 2$$

Operations with Zero

Rule 1. If we add or subtract zero from any number, the result is the number itself. Thus

$$2 + 0 = 2$$

$$8 - 0 = 8$$

Rule 2. The product of zero and any other number or numbers is equal to zero. Thus

$$(8)(0) = 0$$

$$(8)(4)(0)(2)(1) = 0$$

$$(8)(4) - (6)(0) = 32 - 0 = 32$$

Rule 3. If a is not equal to zero, then $0/a$ is equal to zero, regardless of the value of a.

Rule 4. The use of zero as a divisor is an operation that is not permitted.

Operations with Radicals

In this text we shall frequently have occasion to deal with *radicals*. A radical is any expression such as $c = \sqrt[n]{a}$. The number c is said to be the nth root of a, the symbol $\sqrt{\ }$ is called a radical sign, and a is called the radicand. The bar used with the radical sign is a symbol of grouping and means that the complete expression under the bar must be treated as a single number. We shall be concerned only with square roots, that is, where n is equal to 2, and it is customary to write the radical sign without the value of n when this is the case.

The expression $c = \sqrt{a}$ implies that $c^2 = a$, and it is obvious that a has two roots, for $(-c)(-c) = c^2$ and $(c)(c) = c^2$. We shall have occasion to deal with only the principal or positive square root of a, unless otherwise noted.

Rule 1. To multiply two radicals, multiply their radicands. To divide one radical by another, divide the radicand of the first by the radicand of the second. Thus

$$\sqrt{a}\,\sqrt{b} = \sqrt{ab}$$

$$\sqrt{5}\,\sqrt{7} = \sqrt{35}$$

$$\frac{\sqrt{a}}{\sqrt{b}} = \sqrt{\frac{a}{b}}$$

$$\frac{\sqrt{7}}{\sqrt{8}} = \sqrt{\frac{7}{8}}$$

Rule 2. To multiply or divide a radical by any number, multiply or divide the radicand by the square of the number. Thus

$$a\sqrt{b - \frac{c}{d}} = \sqrt{a^2\left(b - \frac{c}{d}\right)} = \sqrt{a^2b - \frac{a^2c}{d}}$$

$$5\sqrt{3 - \frac{4}{5}} = \sqrt{25\left(3 - \frac{4}{5}\right)} = \sqrt{75 - 20} = \sqrt{55}$$

$$\frac{\sqrt{a}}{c} = \frac{\sqrt{a}}{\sqrt{c^2}} = \sqrt{\frac{a}{c^2}}$$

$$\frac{\sqrt{3}}{2} = \frac{\sqrt{3}}{\sqrt{2^2}} = \sqrt{\frac{3}{4}}$$

■ Table of Squares and Square Roots

Table II, in the Appendix, contains the squares and square roots of numbers from 1 to 1,000. It is important that you know how to use this table correctly and how to locate approximate values for the square roots of numbers with over four figures. After you have practiced with a few examples, you will find this fairly easy to do.

To find the square root of any number from 1 to 1,000, find the number in the column headed N and read the square root in the column headed $\sqrt{N}$. To find the square of any number from 1 to 1,000, find the number in the column headed N and read the answer in the column headed N^2.

Suppose you wished to find the square root of 625. Finding 625 in the column headed N; the square root obtained from the column headed $\sqrt{N}$ is 25. Now look in the N column for the number 25. Across the table in the N^2 column you will find the number 625. This should give you an indication of a second way of finding the square root of a number, a method that is particularly valuable when you have to find the square root of a number larger than any of those given in the N column. If 25 squared is 625, then the square root of 625 is 25. Therefore, if you have a number larger than 1,000 or with four or more figures, look for the closest approximation of it in the N^2 column and read the square root in the N column. In this way you can find a good approximation of the square root of any number with as many as six figures.

Before using Table II to find the square root of a number, always point off the number in pairs, starting at the decimal point. Thus 30.8025 and 2,520.04, when pointed off, would be 30 .80 25 and 25 20 .04, respectively. When the number of figures to the right or left of the decimal point is odd, assume that a zero has been added. Thus the numbers given on the left below would be pointed off as shown on the right below:

63,001.	06 30 01.
2,294.4	22 94. 40
778.41	07 78. 41
21.068	21. 06 80
1.400	01. 40 00

For convenience, you may assume that the square root will have one figure for every pair in the number, as pointed off, the decimal point being located according to the number of pairs on each side of it in the number for which you are seeking the square root. Thus, taking the square roots of the numbers shown above, we get

$\sqrt{06\ 30\ 01.} = 251$ since there are three pairs to the left of the decimal point

$\sqrt{22\ 94\ .40} = 47.9$ since there are two pairs to the left and one pair to the right of the decimal point

$\sqrt{07\ 78\ .41} = 27.9$ since there are two pairs to the left and one pair to the right of the decimal point

$\sqrt{21\ .06\ 80} =$	4.59	since there is one pair to the left and two pairs to the right of the decimal point
$\sqrt{01\ .40\ 00} =$	1.18	since there is one pair to the left and two pairs to the right of the decimal point

The square root of any number less than 1 is always greater than the number itself, and the square of a number less than 1 is always less than the number itself. Thus

$$\sqrt{.81} = .9 \qquad (.4)^2 = .16$$

$$\sqrt{.64} = .8 \qquad (.03)^2 = .0009$$

$$\sqrt{.0025} = .05 \qquad (.14)^2 = .0196$$

Exponents

If we have n factors each equal to a given number a, where a is not equal to zero, then the product

$$a^n$$

is called the nth power of a. The number n is called the *exponent* of the power, and the number a is called the *base*. Thus

$$a^5 = (a)(a)(a)(a)(a)$$

Rule 1. Any number a, not equal to zero, but with zero exponent, is defined as

$$a^0 = 1$$

Then any value of a not equal to zero may also be defined as

Rule 2. $$a^{-n} = \frac{1}{a^n}$$

Rule 3. $$a^{1/n} = \sqrt[n]{a}$$

Rule 4. $$a^{-1/n} = \frac{1}{\sqrt[n]{a}}$$

Letting a equal 10 and n equal 2, we have for the above three expressions:

$$10^{-2} = \frac{1}{10^2}$$

$$10^{1/2} = \sqrt{10}$$

$$10^{-1/2} = \frac{1}{\sqrt{10}}$$

We also have the following rules for exponents:

Rule 5. $$(a^m)(a^n) = a^{m+n}$$

Rule 6. $$(a^m)^n = a^{mn}$$

Rule 7. $$(ab)^n = (a^n)(b^n)$$

Rule 8. $$\left(\frac{a}{b}\right)^n = \frac{a^n}{b^n}$$

Letting $a = 10$, $b = 5$, $m = 3$, and $n = 2$, we have for the above four expressions:

$$(10^3)(10^2) = 10^5$$

$$(10^3)^2 = 10^6$$

$$(10 \times 5)^2 = (10^2)(5^2)$$

$$\left(\frac{10}{5}\right)^2 = \frac{10^2}{5^2}$$

■ Logarithms

If we have $$n = b^a$$

then $$\log_b n = a$$

Thus the logarithm of a number n to the base b is the exponent that must be applied to b to obtain n. If base 10 is used, so that

$$100 = 10^{2.0000}$$

then $$\log_{10} 100 = 2.0000$$

Logarithms to base 10 are called *common logarithms*, and for common logarithms it is customary to omit the base and simply write $\log 100 = 2.0000$.

The common logarithm of any positive number consists of two parts, an integer called the *characteristic* and a decimal fraction called the *mantissa*. The characteristic depends only upon the position of the decimal point in the number, and the mantissa depends only upon the particular sequence of digits in the number. In the example above, for $\log 100 = 2.0000$, 2 is the characteristic and .0000 is the mantissa.

If a number is larger than 1, the characteristic of its logarithm will be positive and 1 less than the number of digits to the left of the decimal point. If the number is positive, but less than 1, then the characteristic of its logarithm will be negative and 1 more than the number of zeros between the decimal point and the first nonzero digit. Thus

Number	*Characteristic of Logarithm*
1,000.	3
100.	2
10.	1
1.	0
.1	−1
.01	−2
.001	−3
.0001	−4

The characteristic of the logarithm of a number can be determined, as shown above, by inspection of the position of the decimal point. The mantissa of the logarithm of a number can be found from a table of logarithms. Table IX, in the Appendix, gives the mantissas of the logarithms of any three-digit number. The first two digits of the number are given in the column headed N, the third digit of the number is given at the top of the table. The mantissa is given in the body of the table. To find log 27.7, we first observe that the characteristic is 1. Then from Table IX we find that the mantissa is .4425. Thus

$$\log 27.7 = 1.4425$$

Note also that $\log 277 = 2.4425$, $\log 2.77 = .4425$, $\log .277 = .4425 - 1$, and $\log .0277 = .4425 - 2$. In the case of negative characteristics, the characteristic is written at the right of the mantissa, with a negative sign attached. It is fairly common practice to add *and* subtract a number from the logarithm so that it becomes a positive number minus 10 or some multiple of 10. For example, if we have

$$a - b = a - b$$

then $$a - b = n + a - b - n$$

and therefore $$\log .277 = .4425 - 1 = 9.4425 - 10$$

$$\log .0277 = .4425 - 2 = 8.4425 - 10$$

It is possible to find the mantissa of the logarithm of any four-digit positive number from Table IX also. The method of doing this is explained at the bottom of Table IX, and we shall not repeat the explanation here.

Given a logarithm, we can find the *antilogarithm* or number corresponding to it by proceeding in the reverse of the way in which we find a logarithm. For example, to find the antilogarithm of 8.4425 − 10, we see from the table of logarithms that the mantissa .4425 corresponds to the sequence of digits 277. Since the characteristic is 8 − 10, or −2, the number is less than unity and will have one zero between the decimal point and the first figure. Thus antilog 8.4425 − 10 = .0277.

Rule 1. The logarithm of a product is equal to the sum of the logarithms of the numbers multiplied. For example, to find the product of a and b, we find the logarithm of a and the logarithm of b and sum the logarithms. The antilogarithm of the sum will be the product. Thus

$$a = bc$$

and $$\log a = \log b + \log c$$

Letting $b = 3$ and $c = 4$, then

$$a = (3)(4)$$

$$\log a = \log 3 + \log 4$$

$$= .4771 + .6021$$

$$= 1.0792$$

and antilog 1.0792 = 12.

Rule 2. The logarithm of the quotient of two numbers is equal to the logarithm of the numerator minus the logarithm of the denominator. For example, to divide one number by another, we find the logarithm of the numerator and subtract from this the logarithm of the denominator. The antilogarithm of the remainder will be the quotient. Thus

$$a = \frac{b}{c}$$

and

$$\log a = \log b - \log c$$

Letting $b = 12$ and $c = 3$, then

$$a = \frac{12}{3}$$

$$\log a = \log 12 - \log 3$$

$$= 1.0792 - .4771$$

$$= .6021$$

and antilog $.6021 = 4$.

Rule 3. The logarithm of the power of a number is equal to the product of the exponent and the logarithm of the number. For example, to find the square of a number, we find the logarithm of the number and multiply this by the exponent 2. Then the antilogarithm of the product will be the square of the number. Thus

$$a = b^n$$

and

$$\log a = n \log b$$

Letting $b = 3$ and $n = 2$, then

$$a = 3^2$$

$$\log a = 2 \log 3$$

$$= 2(.4771)$$

$$= .9542$$

and antilog $.9542 = 9$.

Summation

To summate means to add. When, for example, we summate a *variable* (a quantity that may assume a succession of values or, simply, that which varies) such as X for a given series of n measurements, we merely add all of the n values of X in the series. This operation is indicated by Σ, the Greek capital letter *sigma*. Thus

$$\Sigma X = X_1 + X_2 + X_3 + X_4 + \cdots + X_n$$

A more precise method of indicating the summation in this instance would be to write it $\sum_{i=1}^{n} X_i$. These additional symbols above and below the summation sign would indicate the limits of the summation and may be necessary in order to avoid confusion when the summation might not extend over the entire series of observations. However, since the summation in most elementary statistical problems is over the entire series of n observations, the limits will not, in general, be written, but will be understood to be from 1 to n.

Rule 1. The summation of a *constant* (a value that does not change for a given series) is obtained by multiplying the constant by n, the number of times the constant appears in the series. For example, if we let a equal a constant, then

$$\Sigma a = na$$

If a is equal to 3 and n is equal to 6, then

$$\Sigma a = a_1 + a_2 + a_3 + a_4 + a_5 + a_6 = na$$

$$\Sigma a = 3 + 3 + 3 + 3 + 3 + 3 = (6)(3)$$

Rule 2. The summation of an algebraic sum of two or more terms is the same as the algebraic sum of the sums of these terms taken separately. What this rather complicated-sounding rule means is that it is possible to write

$$\Sigma(a + b - x) = \Sigma a + \Sigma b - \Sigma x$$

If we let a and b be constants and x be a variable, then

$$\Sigma(a + b - x) = na + nb - \Sigma x$$

$$= n(a + b) - \Sigma x$$

Rule 3. If we have a variable that is multiplied by a constant, then the sum of these products will be equal to the constant times the summation of the variable. For example, if a is a constant and x is a variable, then

$$\sum ax = a\sum x$$

Rule 4. If we have a variable that is divided by a constant, then the sum of these quotients may be obtained by summing the variable and dividing the sum by the constant. For example, if a is a constant and x is a variable, then

$$\sum \frac{x}{a} = \frac{\sum x}{a}$$

Equations

In performing operations upon equations there is one simple rule: whatever is done to one side of the equation must also be done to the other side. If you multiply one side by a number or symbol, then you must also multiply the other side by the same number or symbol. The same rule applies to division, addition, subtraction, squaring, and taking the square root. The following examples illustrate this rule very simply:

1. If $a = bc$	then dividing both sides by b	$\frac{a}{b} = c$
2. If $a = b + c$	then subtracting b from both sides	$a - b = c$
3. If $a = b + c$	then squaring both sides	$a^2 = (b + c)^2 = b^2 + 2bc + c^2$
4. If $a = b - c$	then squaring both sides	$a^2 = (b - c)^2 = b^2 - 2bc + c^2$
5. If $a = b - c$	then adding c to both sides	$a + c = b$
6. If $a = b + c$	then multiplying both sides by d	$da = d(b + c) = db + dc$
7. If $a^2 = \frac{b}{c}$	then taking the square root of both sides	$a = \sqrt{\frac{b}{c}}$

8. If $a = b + c$ then dividing both sides by b

$$\frac{a}{b} = \frac{b + c}{b} = \frac{b}{b} + \frac{c}{b} = 1 + \frac{c}{b}$$

9. If $a + b = c + d$ then dividing both sides by n

$$\frac{a + b}{n} = \frac{c + d}{n}$$

10. If $-a - b = c - d$ then multiplying both sides by -1

$$a + b = -c + d$$

EXAMPLES

2.1—Add each of the following.

(*a*) $\begin{array}{r} -8 \\ -3 \\ \hline \end{array}$ (*b*) $\begin{array}{r} 4 \\ -2 \\ \hline \end{array}$ (*c*) $\begin{array}{r} 8 \\ -9 \\ \hline \end{array}$ (*d*) $\begin{array}{r} 20 \\ -10 \\ \hline \end{array}$ (*e*) $\begin{array}{r} 10 \\ -8 \\ \hline \end{array}$ (*f*) $\begin{array}{r} -6 \\ 2 \\ \hline \end{array}$

(*g*) $\begin{array}{r} -6 \\ 3 \\ \hline \end{array}$ (*h*) $\begin{array}{r} -9 \\ 1 \\ \hline \end{array}$ (*i*) $\begin{array}{r} 0 \\ -16 \\ \hline \end{array}$ (*j*) $\begin{array}{r} -4 \\ -2 \\ \hline \end{array}$ (*k*) $\begin{array}{r} -4 \\ 7 \\ \hline \end{array}$

2.2—Subtract each of the following.

(*a*) $\begin{array}{r} -8 \\ -3 \\ \hline \end{array}$ (*b*) $\begin{array}{r} 4 \\ -2 \\ \hline \end{array}$ (*c*) $\begin{array}{r} 8 \\ -9 \\ \hline \end{array}$ (*d*) $\begin{array}{r} 20 \\ -10 \\ \hline \end{array}$ (*e*) $\begin{array}{r} 10 \\ -8 \\ \hline \end{array}$ (*f*) $\begin{array}{r} -6 \\ -2 \\ \hline \end{array}$

(*g*) $\begin{array}{r} -6 \\ -3 \\ \hline \end{array}$ (*h*) $\begin{array}{r} -9 \\ -1 \\ \hline \end{array}$ (*i*) $\begin{array}{r} 0 \\ -16 \\ \hline \end{array}$ (*j*) $\begin{array}{r} -4 \\ -2 \\ \hline \end{array}$ (*k*) $\begin{array}{r} -4 \\ 7 \\ \hline \end{array}$

2.3—Multiply each of the following.

(*a*) $(-3)(-8)$	(*e*) $(-1)(0)$	(*i*) $(.28)(-.006)$
(*b*) $(2)(-5)$	(*f*) $(.02)(.02)$	(*j*) $(-.004)(-.02)$
(*c*) $(-3)(2)$	(*g*) $(.1)(.1)$	(*k*) $(.44)(.002)$
(*d*) $(-1)(-6)$	(*h*) $(.61)(.3)$	(*l*) $(-.12)(.1)$

2.4—Divide each of the following.

(*a*) $-8/2$
(*b*) $8/-2$
(*c*) $9/-3$
(*d*) $.04/.02$
(*e*) $.04/.002$
(*f*) $.04/2$
(*g*) $.4/.01$
(*h*) $.3/.5$
(*i*) $.06/.03$
(*j*) $2.4/.003$
(*k*) $-.846/-.02$
(*l*) $.63/-.03$

2.5—Perform the operations indicated.

(*a*) $(6 + 1)^2$
(*b*) $(2 - 3)^2$
(*c*) $(4 + 1 - 2)^2$
(*d*) $(2/3)(4 - 1)$
(*e*) $2 - 6 - 3 + 4$
(*f*) $(-4)(-6 - 2)$
(*g*) $(3/4) + (1/8)$
(*h*) $(2/4) - (3/6)$
(*i*) $(-2/4)/(6/2)$
(*j*) $(2/8)(6/12)$
(*k*) $(8 + 4) - (-3 + 5)$
(*l*) $(8)(4) + (2)(0)$
(*m*) $(36/4) + 3$
(*n*) $(18/6)(4 + 2) - 3$
(*o*) $(42)(3)(0)(1)$
(*p*) $(2)(4 - 4) + 2$

2.6—Find the square roots of the following numbers, using Table II, in the Appendix.

(*a*) 337,561
(*b*) 76,176
(*c*) 778.4
(*d*) 15.2881
(*e*) .04
(*f*) .0016
(*g*) .000025
(*h*) .4624
(*i*) .90
(*j*) 1,024
(*k*) 5.9536
(*l*) 10.0489
(*m*) .09
(*n*) .009
(*o*) 37.21
(*p*) 38,809
(*q*) 30,276
(*r*) 966,289

2.7—Find the logarithms of the numbers as indicated, using Table IX, in the Appendix.

(*a*) log 679
(*b*) log 8.04
(*c*) log .0034
(*d*) log 56.05
(*e*) log .000437
(*f*) log 845.6
(*g*) log 76.05
(*h*) log 752

2.8—Find the antilogarithms of the following, using Table IX, in the Appendix.

(*a*) antilog .9299

(*b*) antilog .7404

(*c*) antilog 1.7419

(*d*) antilog 2.4843

(*e*) antilog 8.9340 − 10

(*f*) antilog 9.6803 − 10

2.9—Check each of the following by marking (1) if true or (2) if false.

(*a*) $(49 + 8)/7 = 7 + 8$

(*b*) $(1/4)(4)(6) = (4/4)(6/4)$

(*c*) $(4 + 2)/4 = 2$

(*d*) $(6)(2)(2)/2 = (3)(2)(2)$

(*e*) $(6)(5)/(2)(3) = (6/2)(5/3)$

(*f*) $2x/2y = x/y$

(*g*) $4x/3y = 12x/9y$

(*h*) $(2/6)/(1/3) = (2/18)$

(*i*) $(x - y)^2 = x^2 + y^2 + 2xy$

(*j*) $(3/4)/(1/4) = (12/4)$

(*k*) $(2/3)/(2/3) = 1$

(*l*) $(8 - 3)/2 = 4 - 3$

(*m*) $4^0 = 0$

(*n*) $1/10^2 = 10^{-2}$

(*o*) $(a/b)^n = a^n/b^n$

(*p*) $10^{-1/2} = \sqrt{10}$

(*q*) $(a^m)(a^n) = a^{mn}$

(*r*) $(ab)^n = a^nb^n$

(*s*) $(3^4)(3^6) = 3^{10}$

(*t*) $(2/3)^2 = 4/9$

(*u*) $\sqrt{a}/a = \sqrt{1/a}$

(*v*) $\sqrt{a}/b = \sqrt{a/b^2}$

(*w*) $\sqrt{9}\sqrt{36} = \sqrt{324}$

(*x*) $2\sqrt{25} = \sqrt{100}$

(*y*) $\sqrt{45}/\sqrt{5} = 3$

2.10—Solve each of the following as indicated.

(*a*) If $ab = c$, then $a =$

(*b*) If $a/b = x/y$, then $ay =$

(*c*) If $a/b = x/y$ then $a =$

(*d*) If $abc = xy/n$, then $a =$

(*e*) If $a^2 = y^2(1 - r^2)$, then $a =$

(*f*) If $x = \sqrt{4a + 9c}$, then $c =$

(*g*) If $(4a/3) - (x/4) + a = 10$, then $x =$

(*h*) If $16x^2 + 4c^2 = a^2$, then $a =$

(*i*) If $25a^2 - 16b^2 = c^2$, then $a =$

(*j*) If $(6x + 3a)(2) = r$, then $a =$

(*k*) If $(14 - 2 + 5)(3 - 12) = a + 2$, then $a =$

2.11—If 15 of 60 students receive a grade of B in a class, what proportion of the students receive a B?

2.12—If 16 of 64 students pass an item on a test, what proportion of the students fail the item?

2.13—If 60 per cent of a sample of 200 students vote no on an issue, how many students are there voting no?

CHAPTER THREE

Measures of Central Tendency and Variability

Changes in performance or behavior of members of the same group under differing sets of conditions or before and after they have experienced some variable that the experimenter has introduced make a simple and effective experimental design. When factors that might have influenced the results have been excluded or equated, any observed changes may be assumed to be the result of the differing conditions. In this way one might study the influence of motion pictures upon attitudes, the effect of a course in propaganda analysis upon ability to analyze propaganda, and, in general, the effect upon behavior of any variable or set of conditions that the experimenter may introduce.

When it is not possible or feasible to study the behavior of the same individuals under differing conditions, the experimenter may resort to a matching procedure in order to select two comparable groups for observation. Individuals might be matched upon the basis of intelligence-test scores, reading-comprehension scores, attitudes, or some other variable that may be related to the variable under study. We need not concern ourselves at this point with why this particular type of experimental design is efficient; the reasons for this must await discussion of the development of correlational techniques and tests of significance. We have mentioned the subject by way of introduction to a hypothetical experiment, the data of which we wish to discuss.

An Experiment in Retention

Suppose that on some nights we read a sociology text just before going to bed and that on other occasions we do our reading in the morning. After several weeks we have the impression that our memory of what we have read is much better when our period of study has been followed by sleep than when it has been followed by waking activity. In order to investigate the problem further, we design a simple experiment to test retention under the two conditions.

We have as subjects for our experiment two groups of 20 subjects each. Each individual in one group has been matched with another individual in the second group on the basis of an academic-aptitude test which we already have reason to believe is a variable related to retention and learning. Our experimental procedure is to have both groups of subjects learn a list of 20 words by the *method of paired associates.* In this method words are presented in pairs, and the subject is supposed to learn to respond with the second member of a pair when the first is presented.

We have all of our subjects go through the list until they achieve one perfect trial, that is, one trial with no errors. This learning period in the case of one of our groups is followed by eight hours of sleep and in the case of the other group is followed by eight hours of uncontrolled waking activity. At the end of the eight-hour period both groups are retested. The figures given in columns (2) and (3) of Table 3.1[1] show the number of correct responses on this second test.

The Range as a Measure of Variation

In this hypothetical experiment, 16 of the differences in retention, as shown in column (4) of Table 3.1, favor the member of the "sleep" group and 4 of the differences favor the member of the "wake" group.[2] Observe, however, the variation exhibited by the difference scores.

If the difference scores were all the same, we would have no need of statistical methods nor would we have any need to observe more than one pair of subjects. Suppose, for example, that a constant difference of 4 points was found in favor of the subject in the "sleep" group. Then the difference in retention for a single pair of subjects would, under these circumstances, give us complete information, since all additional pairs of subjects would show the same constant difference in retention of 4 points in favor of the member of the "sleep" group.

Constant differences of the kind described, however, are seldom, if ever, found in research work. Instead, the tendency of individual measure-

---

[1] Tables in the body of the text are numbered serially by chapters. Table 3.1 means Chapter 3, Table 1. Table 3.2 is the second table in Chapter 3. Figures appearing in the text are also numbered in this manner, as are the examples at the end of chapters.

[2] The data cited are hypothetical for purposes of illustration and simplicity, but see the study by Jenkins and Dallenbach (1924).

Table 3.1—Retention Scores of Paired Individuals Following Eight Hours of Differing Degrees of Activity

Pair	*Group*		*Difference between Pairs*	*Deviations and Squared Deviations*					
	Sleep	*Wake*							
(1)	(2) X	(3) Y	(4) D	(5) x	(6) x^2	(7) y	(8) y^2	(9) d	(10) d^2
1	14	18	−4	0	0	7	49	−7	49
2	8	12	−4	−6	36	1	1	−7	49
3	15	10	5	1	1	−1	1	2	4
4	16	9	7	2	4	−2	4	4	16
5	8	14	−6	−6	36	3	9	−9	81
6	15	10	5	1	1	−1	1	2	4
7	15	9	6	1	1	−2	4	3	9
8	17	11	6	3	9	0	0	3	9
9	18	13	5	4	16	2	4	2	4
10	13	6	7	−1	1	−5	25	4	16
11	10	16	−6	−4	16	5	25	−9	81
12	19	14	5	5	25	3	9	2	4
13	20	16	4	6	36	5	25	1	1
14	17	8	9	3	9	−3	9	6	36
15	14	8	6	0	0	−3	9	3	9
16	10	8	2	−4	16	−3	9	−1	1
17	14	9	5	0	0	−2	4	2	4
18	15	10	5	1	1	−1	1	2	4
19	13	11	2	−1	1	0	0	−1	1
20	9	8	1	−5	25	−3	9	−2	4
Σ	280	220	60	0	234	0	198	0	386

ments, and of differences between pairs of measurements, to vary is a fundamental fact of nature. That is one reason why we need the assistance of statistical methods in evaluating data.

A simple measure of the variation present in each group would be the *range*, which we have already defined as being the difference between the highest and lowest measurement. For the "sleep" group the highest score is 20 and the lowest score is 8; the range is therefore 12. For the "wake" group the highest score is 18 and the lowest score is 6; the range is therefore also 12. We could find a similar measure of spread or variation for the *differences* in retention scores between pairs of subjects. The spread of these differences is from 9 to −6; the range is therefore 15. Symbolically, we define the range as[3]

$$R = X_h - X_l \tag{3.1}$$

where R = the range
X_h = the highest measurement in the series
X_l = the lowest measurement in the series

The Mean as a Measure of Concentration

Note that despite the spread or variability of the scores within each group, there is also a tendency for the various scores to cluster around the middle values rather than at the extremes. A single score toward the middle of the range would be more representative of *all* of the scores than a value selected from either extreme. The statistics we use to measure this concentration are known as *averages* or *measures of central tendency.* The statistician may not always mean by average, however, the measure you may have in mind. The measure of which you are thinking is probably the *mean,* which is found by adding all of the scores and dividing the sum by the number of scores. The mean is only one among several possible kinds of averages.

Let us find the mean for the "sleep" group, the "wake" group, and for the differences between pairs of measurements. The totals or sums of the scores for each series are given at the bottom of Table 3.1. For the "sleep" group the total is 280, and, since this sum is based on 20 observations, we divide 280 by 20 and find the mean score for the group to be 14.0. Similarly, we determine that the mean for the "wake" group is 11.0 and that the mean of the differences is 3.0. Note that *the difference between the two means is equal to the mean of the differences.*

Some Basic Symbols

Let us see how it is possible to indicate symbolically the computations involved in finding the mean. We shall let n equal the number of scores in a given series and let X represent the scores themselves. Then the individual scores might be represented by $X_1, X_2, X_3, X_4, \cdots, X_n$, where the subscripts $1, 2, 3, 4, \cdots, n$ stand for the particular measures. In the example under consideration we may let X represent scores for the "sleep" group. Similarly, we may let Y represent scores for the "wake" group, with Y_1

[3] Formulas, like tables, are numbered serially by chapters for convenient reference. Thus a reference to formula (3.4) would mean the fourth formula in Chapter 3.

corresponding to X_1, Y_2 to X_2, and so on for each matched pair of subjects. The differences between the paired values of X and Y may be represented by D, and particular values of D may be represented by D_1, D_2, D_3, and so forth.

Since n is the same for the X, Y, and D scores, we do not need to worry about a separate symbol for indicating the number of cases in each series. We shall use the symbol $\bar{X}$ to represent the mean of the X series, $\bar{Y}$ to represent the mean of the Y series, and $\bar{D}$ to represent the mean of the differences. We need one more symbol, one that we shall use very frequently, $\sum$, which is the Greek capital *sigma*. This symbol is an operational as well as a descriptive symbol and means to sum. Thus $\sum X$ would mean "to sum the variable X," or simply "summation X," or "sum of the X's." $\sum Y$ would mean "to sum the variable Y," or "summation Y," and $\sum D$ would mean "to sum the variable D."

In terms of the symbols we have just discussed, it would now be possible for us to represent the mean of the X series by the following formula:

$$\bar{X} = \frac{X_1 + X_2 + X_3 + X_4 + X_5 + \cdots + X_n}{n} \qquad \textbf{(3.2)}$$

But since we have the symbol $\sum$, meaning to sum, we may merely write, in abbreviated form,

$$\bar{X} = \frac{\sum X}{n} \qquad \textbf{(3.3)}$$

where $\bar{X}$ = the mean
$\sum$ = the sum of
X = each of the individual measurements or scores
n = the number of measurements in the series

Formula (3.3) is the generalized formula for the mean. We need only substitute Y for X to apply it to the Y series or D for X if we wished to find the mean of the D series. We have already pointed out that symbols and formulas are a kind of shorthand. You may observe, in this instance, how much more quickly, and with how much less space, $\bar{X} = \dfrac{\sum X}{n}$ can be written than the statement for which it stands: "The mean of a series is equal to the sum of the individual measures in the series divided by the number of measures in the series."

We should note the following identity. From formula (3.3) we have

$$\bar{X} = \frac{\sum X}{n}$$

Then, multiplying both sides by n, we obtain

$$n\bar{X} = \sum X \tag{3.4}$$

Consequently, we may, in any expression involving $\sum X$, substitute $n\bar{X}$ without changing the meaning of the expression. In the same way, $\sum X$ may, if we so desire, be substituted for $n\bar{X}$.

The Average Deviation as a Measure of Variation

We are now ready for a new symbol. The new symbol we want is one that will represent the *deviation* of an observed measure from the mean of the series. We shall use the symbol x to designate a deviation of X from the mean of the X series. Thus

$$x = X - \bar{X} \tag{3.5}$$

where x = a deviation from the mean
X = the original measurement
$\bar{X}$ = the mean

Similarly, we could use y to represent the deviation of a Y score from the mean of the Y's and d to represent the deviation of a difference score D from the mean of the differences.

If we were to subtract the mean of the X scores from each of the X scores and sum for the series, in other words, find $\sum(X - \bar{X})$ or $\sum x$, as we have done in column (5) of Table 3.1, we should find that *the sum of the deviations from the mean equals zero.* An algebraic proof of this is quite simple. From formula (3.5) we have

$$x = X - \bar{X}$$

and summating $\qquad \sum x = \sum X - n\bar{X}$

Since we have already shown in formula (3.4) that $n\bar{X} = \sum X$, therefore

$$\sum x = 0 \tag{3.6}$$

Formula (3.6) expresses a basic statistical theorem. You will find that it holds true for any series of measurements and can easily be verified in the case of the Y and D distributions of scores of Table 3.1. This is the reason why we cannot simply add the deviations from the mean and divide by n in order to get a measure of the average deviation or spread of scores from the mean. The simple average deviation would always equal zero and consequently would be of no value as a measure of variability.

We could, however, ignore the *signs* of the deviations and find the sum of the *absolute values* and divide this sum by n. The resulting value is called the *average deviation*. Symbolically, we would write

$$AD = \frac{\Sigma|x|}{n} \tag{3.7}$$

where AD = the average deviation
$|x|$ = the absolute value of x
n = the number of measures in the series

The average deviation is one of the easiest measures of variability to understand and had great popularity at one time. It is still of value if one must describe variation to a group of statistically inexperienced individuals, but it has been found to be of limited utility in statistical theory. You may wonder, if the average deviation is of so little value, why we have bothered to mention it. Why not simply use the range as our measure of variability? The answer to the first question is that the average deviation provides an introduction to the standard deviation and variance, the measures of variability that we shall use most often. The answer to the second question is that the range also has its disadvantages. It is determined by only two scores, and the information provided by the other $n - 2$ scores is discarded. The range also fluctuates much more from one series of observations to another than do the other measures of variation such as the average deviation or standard deviation. If we were to repeat our experiment in the effect of sleeping and waking periods on retention, for example, the range for each group and for the differences between pairs might differ greatly from the values we got the first time.

■ The Variance and Standard Deviation

The most valuable measure of variability is the *variance* or the square root of the variance which is called the *standard deviation*. The variance is computed from the squares of the deviations from the mean and is represented by the symbol s^2. We have already pointed out that ignoring the signs of the deviations, as we did in calculating the average deviation, does not lead to the development of any very significant statistical techniques. Ignoring the signs of the deviations means that we lose desirable algebraic properties of the individual deviations and of any measure based upon them. Squaring the deviations will maintain the algebraic properties and, incidentally, all of the squared deviations will be positive in sign. Furthermore, as we shall show later, *the sum of squared deviations from the mean is less than the sum of squared deviations from any other value not equal to the mean.*[4] Squared deviations, as we shall see, form the basis of much of statistical theory.

If we square each of the deviations from the mean, sum, and divide by $n - 1$, we obtain the *mean square* or variance which is symbolized by s^2. This definition of the variance may be written as

$$s^2 = \frac{\sum(X - \bar{X})^2}{n - 1} = \frac{\sum x^2}{n - 1} \tag{3.8}$$

The standard deviation is simply the square root of the variance. Thus the standard deviation is equal to $\sqrt{s^2}$, or, as it is more commonly expressed,

$$s = \sqrt{\frac{\sum(X - \bar{X})^2}{n - 1}} = \sqrt{\frac{\sum x^2}{n - 1}} \tag{3.9}$$

where s = the standard deviation
x^2 = the square of a deviation from the mean
$\sum$ = the sum of
n = the number of cases

The calculation of the standard deviation may be summarized in the following steps:

1. Find the mean $\qquad \bar{X} = \frac{\sum X}{n}$
2. Find the deviation of each score from the mean $\qquad x = X - \bar{X}$
3. Square each deviation $\qquad x^2 = (X - \bar{X})^2$
4. Find the sum of the squared deviations (sum of squares) $\qquad \sum x^2 = \sum(X - \bar{X})^2$

---

[4] See the answer to Example 4.14 of Chapter 4.

5. Divide the sum of squares by $n - 1$ to find the variance or mean square $\qquad s^2 = \dfrac{\sum x^2}{n-1}$

6. Extract the square root to find the standard deviation $\qquad s = \sqrt{\dfrac{\sum x^2}{n-1}}$

Extracting the square root (Step 6) returns us to our original unit of measurement. For example, if the original values of X were in terms of inches, the standard deviation would be in terms of inches also. You may follow the steps in the calculation of the standard deviation in Table 3.1. There we show the calculation of the standard deviations of the X, Y, and D series of measurements. For the D series, for example, column (4) gives the scores that we sum to find the mean. Column (9) gives the deviations of each of these scores from the mean, and column (10) gives the squares of the deviations. The sum of the squared deviations is 386, which, when divided by $n - 1 = 19$, gives the variance 20.3158. The standard deviation is the square root of 20.3158, and from Table II, in the Appendix, we find this to be equal to approximately 4.51.

We may note the following identity. From formula (3.8), we have

$$s^2 = \frac{\sum x^2}{n-1}$$

Then, multiplying both sides by $n - 1$, we obtain

$$(n-1)(s^2) = \sum x^2 \tag{3.10}$$

It will be useful in later discussions to know that we may interchange $(n-1)s^2$ and $\sum x^2$ in a given expression without changing the meaning of the expression.

The Normal-Distribution Curve

You may already be familiar with the concept of a *normal distribution* from other sources. A normal distribution is represented by a bell-shaped symmetrical frequency curve with very few measurements at the extremes and more and more as you move in toward the middle. It will look something like the curve shown in Figure 3.1.

Suppose that this distribution curve represented measurements of differences in retention for 10,000 pairs of subjects. That is, suppose that instead of merely 20 pairs, as we had in the experiment mentioned earlier, we had 10,000. We would not expect all of the differences in retention to be the same for these 10,000 pairs any more than they were for our 20 pairs. If we had 10,000 pairs of subjects we might obtain differences in favor of a member of the "sleep" group greater than any of those we observed in our 20 pairs of observations. And we might also obtain differences in favor of a member of the "wake" group greater than any of the differences we observed with our small group of 20 pairs of observations. But, in terms of what we have already observed, we would expect most of these 10,000 differences to

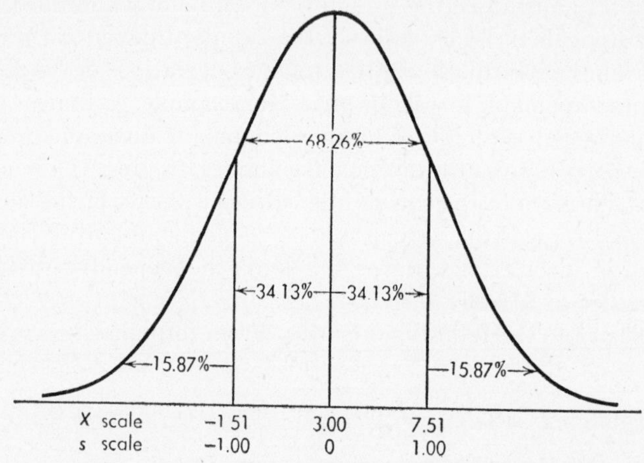

Fig. 3.1—Normal distribution curve with mean equal to 3.00 and standard deviation equal to 4.51.

tend toward the middle or mean of the distribution, and we may further assume that this distribution would be normal in form as shown in Figure 3.1.

If the mean and standard deviation of this new distribution were the same as the mean and standard deviation of our 20 observations, then between the mean and plus-one standard deviation would fall approximately 34.13 per cent of these 10,000 differences. Similarly, between the mean and minus-one standard deviation would fall approximately 34.13 per cent of the differences. In other words, between 3.0 ± 4.51 or between -1.51 and 7.51 would fall approximately 68.26 per cent of the cases, and outside these limits would lie approximately 31.74 per cent of the differences. About 15.87 per cent of the differences would be greater than 7.51 and about 15.87 per cent would fall below -1.51. We can make these statements because the equation for the normal curve is known, and tables have been prepared that enable us to find the proportion or per cent of cases between the mean and any given distance from the mean expressed in terms of standard-deviation units. These tables are discussed in detail in a later chapter.

The Median as a Measure of Central Tendency

In general, if a distribution is approximately normal, the mean is the appropriate measure to use to describe the central tendency of the group. If the distribution departs very much from the normal form so that scores are piled up at one end or the other of the scale, then another measure of central tendency may be used to supplement the description provided by the mean. This measure of central tendency is called the *median* and is defined as that point in a distribution of measurements above which and below which 50 per cent of the measurements lie. The median would also be the appropriate measure of central tendency to use if a distribution is truncated, that is, cut off at one end so that we know only the number but not the exact values of the measures at this end, as, for example, in a distribution of incomes where we might have at one end 7 cases that are simply recorded as $15,000 *and over*. In a perfectly normal distribution the mean and median coincide, they have the same value.

Table 3.2—Frequency of Ratings on a Five-Point Scale

(1) *Ratings*	(2) *Limits*	(3) *f*
5	4.5–5.5	4
4	3.5–4.5	3
3	2.5–3.5	2
2	1.5–2.5	1
1	.5–1.5	1

To illustrate the calculation of the median, let us suppose that we have a number of ratings on a 5-point scale and that we wish to find the median value of the ratings. Our first step is to *arrange the ratings in order of magnitude from lowest to highest.* But instead of writing out the value of each rating, we shall simply list the 5 possible values, in order of magnitude under the heading "Ratings" and then under *f* list the *frequency* or number of times each value occurs, as in Table 3.2. The rating "5," for example, occurs 4 times, the rating "4" occurs 3 times, and so on. Measurements arranged in the manner of Table 3.2 are called *frequency distributions.*

Since we have defined the median as a point, we shall have to pause for a moment to consider whether a score or rating can be considered a precise point or not. It is customary in statistical work to think of a measurement, regardless of the instrument used in making it, as representing an *interval* ranging from half a unit below to half a unit above the given value. A height reported in terms of inches, for example, may be considered as representing an interval ranging from one-half inch below to one-half inch above the reported value. A height of 61 inches, in other words, may indicate a value ranging from 60.5 to 61.5. Even if the height were reported to the nearest 1/10 inch, 61.8 inches, for example, it might still represent an interval ranging from 61.75 to 61.85. This is because there are limits to the accuracy of any measuring instrument. Regardless of how fine we may make our units of measurement, that is, how many decimal places may be used in reporting them, we still do not know the *precise value* of the final number. Considered in this fashion, a rating of 5 may mean a value from 4.5 to 5.5, and a rating of 1 may mean a value from .5 to 1.5.

To find the median we must first find out how many ratings we have under consideration. This we do by adding the frequencies, 1, 1, 2, 3, and 4. We find that n is 11 and we wish to find the point above which and below which exactly 50 per cent or 5.5 of these 11 cases will fall. If we start counting upward from the lowest rating, we find that $1 + 1 + 2$ will give us 4 of the needed 5.5 cases. This carries us through the rating 3, the upper limit of which is 3.5. We have moved up the scale, in other words, to the point 3.5 and have found 4 cases below here. But this is not sufficient; we need 5.5 cases or 1.5 more than the 4 we have so far. The rating 4 occupies the interval from 3.5 to 4.5, and there are 3 cases located within this interval. We do not know how these 3 cases are distributed in the interval 3.5 to 4.5, but for convenience *we may assume that they are distributed evenly throughout the interval.* We must move up into this interval until we have 1.5 more cases.

To interpolate into the interval, we merely divide the needed number of cases by the number of cases within the interval and multiply the result by the size of the interval. Since we need 1.5 additional cases, and the number of cases within the interval is 3, and since the size of the interval, which we may designate by i, is from 3.5 to 4.5 or 1, we have

$$\left(\frac{1.5}{3}\right)1 = .5$$

We add the value obtained above, .5, to the lower limit, 3.5, of the interval in which we know the median falls, and this gives us the value of the median, 4.0. This is the point on the rating scale below which and above which 50 per cent of the cases fall.

We may, if we wish, check the value of the median by counting down from the highest rating. We have 4 cases for the rating 5 which extends *down* to 4.5. We still need 1.5 more cases in order to get our 50 per cent. We need to go down into the interval 4.5 to 3.5 far enough to include 1.5 of the 3 cases that we assume to be distributed evenly throughout the interval. And $(1.5/3)i$ gives us .5, since i, the size of the interval, is equal to 1. We now *subtract* .5 (we are moving downward on the scale) from the *upper* limit, 4.5, of the interval in which we know the median falls, and arrive at the same value as before, 4.0, for the median.

Sometimes in computing the median where we have an even number of cases, we may find that 50 per cent of the measurements or scores take us exactly through a given score but that there is a gap between the upper limit of this score and the next score. By a gap is meant that the possible values between the two scores are missing or do not occur. For example, suppose we had the following measurements: 8, 18, 16, 7, 5, 10, 14, 17. Rearranging these measurements in order of size, we have, from the lowest to the highest:

5, 7, 8, 10, 14, 16, 17, 18

For this example, n is equal to 8 and 50 per cent of n is equal to 4. We need to find the point on the score continuum above which and below which 4 scores will fall. Counting up from the bottom or lowest score we find that the first four scores take us through 10, the upper limit of which is 10.5. It is true that 50 per cent of the scores do fall below the point 10.5, and that 50 per cent fall above this point. But it is also true that 50 per cent fall above and below any other point we might choose to select between 10.5 and 13.5. Under these circumstances *we assume that the value which best represents the median is the midpoint of the gap*, 10.5 to 13.5. The range of the gap is equal to $13.5 - 10.5 = 3$. One half of three is equal to 1.5, and 1.5 added to the upper limit of 10.5 gives us a value of 12 for the median. You may check this value by counting down from the top, only, in this instance, since you are moving downward, you would have to subtract 1.5 from the lower limit of the score 14. The value of the median remains the same, regardless of whether we calculate it by counting up or down.

If, in the distribution above, there were no gap, that is, if 10 had been followed by 11 rather than by 14, then the median would become *the dividing point between these two scores.* Since the upper limit of 10 is 10.5 and the lower limit of 11 is 10.5, the value arrived at for the median would be 10.5.

The following formula for computing the median will handle all situations except when the median falls in a gap in the distribution of measurements.

$$Mdn = l + \left(\frac{\frac{n}{2} - \sum f_b}{f_w} \right) i \tag{3.11}$$

where Mdn = the median
l = the lower limit of the interval containing the median
n = the total number of scores
$\sum f_b$ = the sum of the frequencies or the number of scores below the interval containing the median
f_w = the frequency or number of scores within the interval containing the median
i = the size or range of the interval (In the illustrations considered, since i has always equaled 1, it may be ignored; we include it here because this is a more generalized formula which can be used later.)

When the median falls within a gap, its value can readily be determined in the manner described earlier, and no formula is necessary. Formula (3.11) is applicable to measures arranged in a frequency distribution as in Table 3.2 or to measures that have merely been arranged in order of size without a frequency distribution.

The value of the median obtained with formula (3.11) may be checked, in the manner indicated earlier, by working from the top interval down. The formula in this case becomes

$$Mdn = u - \left(\frac{\frac{n}{2} - \sum f_a}{f_w} \right) i \tag{3.12}$$

where u = the upper limit of the interval containing the median and
$\sum f_a$ = the sum of the frequencies or the number of scores *above* the interval containing the median

You may note, from the definition of the median as a point below which and above which 50 per cent of the scores fall, that the median is not influenced by the magnitude or numerical value of the scores falling on each side of it. The median, for example, would be unchanged if we arbitrarily added 100 points to a score falling above it. The mean, on the other hand, is the center of balance of the scores, and changing the value of any single score in a distribution would influence the mean. Since the sum of the deviations from the mean is equal to zero, the mean must fall at that point in the distribution of scores where the sum of the negative deviations balances exactly or is equal to the sum of the positive deviations. Changing any single score will move the center of balance and result in a new value for the mean.

■ The Semi-Interquartile Range

The measure of variation generally used in connection with the median is the *semi-interquartile range* or Q. To find the value of Q, two other values must be computed: Q_1, the first quartile, and Q_3, the third quartile. These two values are also points on a scale, Q_1 being the point below which 25 per cent of the measurements fall and above which 75 per cent fall, and Q_3 being the point below which 75 per cent fall and above which 25 per cent fall. To obtain Q_1 we modify formula (3.11) as follows:

$$Q_1 = l + \left(\frac{\frac{n}{4} - \sum f_b}{f_w}\right) i$$

where Q_1 = the first quartile
l = the lower limit of the interval containing Q_1
n = the total number of scores
$\sum f_b$ = the sum of the frequencies or number of scores *below* the interval containing Q_1
f_w = the frequency or number of scores within the interval containing Q_1
i = the size or range of the interval

It is important to note that the symbols, l, $\sum f_b$, and f_w now refer to Q_1 rather than the median. To find Q_3, we would substitute $3n/4$ or 75 per cent of n for $n/2$ in formula (3.11). The symbols l, $\sum f_b$, and f_w would now refer to Q_3 rather than the median.

The interval $Q_3 - Q_1$ contains the middle 50 per cent of the measurements and is known as the *interquartile range.* The semi-interquartile range is one half of the range of the middle 50 per cent of the cases and is given by the following formula

$$Q = \frac{Q_3 - Q_1}{2} \tag{3.13}$$

where Q = the semi-interquartile range
Q_3 = the third quartile
Q_1 = the first quartile

Centiles

Just as we used formula (3.11) to find the median or point above which and below which 50 per cent of the cases fall, and to find Q_1 and Q_3, so also it can be used, with slight modifications, to find the point in a distribution above which and below which any given per cent of the cases fall. Such points are commonly called *centiles* and may be symbolized by C with an appropriate subscript. The 80th centile, for example, would be indicated by C_{80}. Since the median marks the point below which 50 per cent of the cases fall, it is also the 50th centile or C_{50}. The 25th centile is C_{25} and is the same as Q_1, and the 75th centile is C_{75} and is the same as Q_3. The points dividing the distribution into tenths are also given special names; they are called *deciles*. Thus C_{10}, the 10th centile, is also the first decile, and C_{20}, the 20th centile, is also the second decile, and so forth.

If we wish to find a given centile, we need only substitute that per cent of the total number of scores or measures for $n/2$ in formula (3.11), remembering that l, $\sum f_b$, and f_w *will now refer to the particular centile being found rather than the median.* Thus if we wish to find the 80th centile, which would be the point below which 80 per cent of the cases fall, $n/2$ would be replaced by $80n/100$ or by $4n/5$. To find the 33rd centile we would substitute $33n/100$ for $n/2$ in formula (3.11). The 50th centile, the median, would be, of course, $50n/100$, which, simplified, is $n/2$.

Centiles are often used to describe an individual's relative position in a group with respect to some variable, For example, if we were told that John's score on a reading test was 49, and this was all that we were told, we would know no more about his ability than if we had not been told his score. If we knew that the mean score for college freshmen on the test was 40, we would at least know that he performed better than the average freshman. But if we were told that his score corresponded to the 75th centile, we would know that he does better than 75 per cent of the students who take the test.

One major difficulty with centiles as a means of expressing relative position is that, when distributions are fairly normal, individual differences relatively near the center of the distribution are exaggerated in comparison with the extremes. The actual measured differences represented by the centile range 40 to 60, for example, are not as great as the actual measured differences represented by the centile ranges 1 to 21 and 79 to 99. This is because, as we know from our earlier discussion of the normal curve, frequencies are greater in the center of the distribution than at the extremes.

Other Measures of Central Tendency and Variability

There are other kinds of averages than those we have mentioned. One is the *mode*, or measure that occurs most frequently in a distribution of measurements. Another is the *geometric mean* which is the nth root of the product of the n values in a series. The geometric mean of 3 and 12, for example, would be $\sqrt{(3)(12)} = \sqrt{36} = 6$, whereas the arithmetic mean would be 7.5. We shall have occasion to refer again briefly to the geometric mean in connection with measures of relationships. Another measure of central tendency is the *harmonic mean*, which is defined as the reciprocal of the arithmetic mean of the reciprocals of the measurements. A reciprocal of a given value, you will recall from the discussion in Chapter 2, is 1 divided by that value. The harmonic mean is used in problems involving the averaging of rates, but we shall have no need to refer to it again in this text.

There are also other measures of variability in addition to those we have described. One such is the *middle 80 per cent range* or the spread of scores between the 10th and 90th centiles. Another is the *probable deviation* or *probable error* which was widely used in the past, but which is practically never used now to describe variability. The probable deviation is approximately 2/3 the size (more precisely, .6745) of the standard deviation. In a normal distribution the interval established by the mean plus and minus one probable deviation contains the middle 50 per cent of the measures and is therefore equivalent to $Q_3 - Q_1$.

The measures of central tendency and variability that we have treated briefly in this section are used very infrequently in psychology and education, and, with the exception of the geometric mean, have little bearing upon the statistical methods developed later. We shall consequently say no more about them. Our basic measure of central tendency will be the mean, and our basic measure of variability will be the standard deviation or its square, the variance. We shall refer to these measures constantly. Be sure that you thoroughly understand their calculation.

Samples and Statistics

We have more or less avoided the use of the term "sample" up to this point, but to continue to do so would prove awkward. In your own experience you have "sampled" foods and then made judgments or based future reactions on your experience with these samples, that is, you may ask for more or you may refuse more because you assume that the remainder of the food will be very much like the sample you tasted. An observer would probably note that you do two things when you sample: (1) you deal with only a part or portion of some whole, and (2) you assume that this part or portion is in some way representative of the whole. This is very similar to the meaning of a sample in statistics.

The statistical sample consists of the particular group of observations that has been selected for investigation, and, generally, the sample under study is assumed to be representative of some larger group from which the sample was selected. The larger group is called a *population* or *universe*. A measure derived from a sample such as the mean or standard deviation is called a *statistic*. The corresponding mean or standard deviation that would be obtained if the population instead of the sample had been studied is called a *parameter*. Since parameters are based upon all existing cases, they have fixed, single values. Since statistics, on the other hand, are based upon only a part of the total population, they may vary from sample to sample.

Statistics, in the absence of any other information, are the best *estimates* we have of the population parameters. Two statistics which we have discussed in this chapter, the mean and the variance, are, as we have emphasized previously, basic. To find them you need to compute but two sums: the sum of scores, $\sum X$, and the sum of squares, $\sum x^2$. The sum of scores is necessary for the mean, and the sum of squares for the variance. Later we shall find that there are easier ways of computing these statistics when we have to deal with either a large number of observations or when the measures have large numerical values.

■ A Note to the Student

At this point, statistical analysis may seem utterly complex and confusing. If so, part of the difficulty is that in this chapter we have introduced, briefly, a number of important concepts and symbols that are new and strange to you. It will require some time, study, and practice in manipulation before these concepts and symbols become familiar and you feel at ease with them. You will then know at sight that x means a deviation from the mean of the distribution without having to stop and think about its meaning. And so it will be with the other symbols and concepts.

Many of the topics introduced in this chapter had to be treated in very brief fashion. To have gone into them in greater detail would have forced us to digress from our main purpose of *introducing* you to the topics discussed. You may have questions about the normal distribution which have been left unanswered. You may wonder whether any conclusions could be drawn from the experiment on retention after a period of sleep and after a period of waking activity. You probably have other questions, such as why we divided by $n - 1$ instead of by n in formula (3.8) in finding the variance. To have answered these and other questions at this time would result in nothing but additional confusion. We shall come back to them in later chapters.

In reading other texts you may become disturbed by the differences in notation you encounter. You will find, for example, that some writers use M instead of $\bar{X}$ for the mean—and some even use both, with little apparent reason. In some cases you will find $\bar{x}$ used to designate the mean. Some writers use S instead of $\sum$ to indicate summation. The notation in statistics has not become standardized to the extent that each writer uses exactly the same symbols with exactly the same meaning. From the point of view of the student who is just beginning to learn one notation this is unfortunate and undoubtedly a source of confusion. It can only be said here that we have tried to use a notation that will result in as little confusion as possible when you read some other text. In other words, we have tried to use symbols in the same way as a fair number of other texts use them. But, since each writer is something of an individualist, idiosyncrasies and individual differences will be found.

■ EXAMPLES

3.1—A class in applied psychology made the following scores on a weekly quiz. Find the mean of the scores.

30	28	26	25	23	21	20
29	28	26	24	23	21	20
29	27	26	24	22	21	19
29	27	25	24	22	20	19
28	26	25	24	21	20	18

3.2—Find the median for each of the following distributions. Check your calculations by counting down from the top.

(*a*) 23, 23, 22, 22, 22, 20, 17, 17, 17, 17, 15, 15, 13, 13, 13, 12, 12

(*b*) 20, 20, 19, 17, 17, 17, 15, 15, 15

(*c*) 15, 13, 11, 9, 6, 4, 2

(*d*) 24, 22, 19, 17, 16, 14, 8, 6

(*e*) 38, 35, 34, 33, 30, 28, 20, 17

(*f*) 95, 94, 90, 88, 87, 85, 83, 80, 78, 70

(*g*) 14, 12, 11, 11, 10, 9, 9, 9, 9, 9, 8, 8, 4

(*h*) 170, 164, 160, 160, 159, 158, 158, 158, 158, 157, 156, 154, 150, 150

(*i*) 25, 24, 24, 23, 23, 22, 22, 22, 22, 21, 21, 21, 21, 20, 20, 20, 19, 19, 18, 17 (*j*) 50, 48, 45, 42, 40, 36, 34, 31, 29, 28

(*k*) 4, 4, 4, 4, 4, 4, 4, 3, 3, 3, 1, 0

(*l*) 25, 22, 18, 17, 16, 15, 14, 10, 8, 5, 5, 4, 3

(*m*) 14, 10, 8, 8, 8, 2, 1, 0, 0, 0

3.3—Find the mean, variance, and standard deviation of the following distribution of measurements.

25	24	22	21	20	19	18	17	14
25	24	22	21	20	19	18	15	
25	24	22	21	20	18	17	15	
25	23	21	21	19	18	17	14	
24	23	21	20	19	18	17	14	

3.4—Find the median, Q_1, and Q_3 for the distribution of scores in Example 3.3.

3.5—Find the median, 60th centile, and 13th centile for the following distribution of scores.

30, 30, 29, 27, 25, 23, 23, 23, 22, 21, 19, 18, 17, 16, 15, 14, 13, 13

3.6—Two sections in psychology were given an intelligence test. The scores for each group were as follows.

Section 1				*Section 2*			
82	84	80	90	74	84	66	68
80	82	80	82	74	80	62	80
76	86	76	88	72	86	68	76
90	78	78	78	70	78	74	76
88	78	84	80	82	78	68	64

(*a*) Find the mean, average deviation, variance, and standard deviation for each section.

(*b*) Which group is more homogeneous with respect to intelligence as measured by the test?

(*c*) Other factors being equal, which group would you predict to have the higher average score on the final examination in the course?

(*d*) How many scores are more than 3 standard deviations above the mean or 3 standard deviations below the mean in Section 1?

3.7—Write a symbolic equivalent for each of the following. For example, $X - \bar{X}$ could also be written x.

(*a*) $X - \bar{X}$ (*h*) $\frac{\sum X}{n}$

(*b*) ΣX	(*i*) s
(*c*) Σx^2	(*j*) $n\bar{X}$
(*d*) $\bar{X}$	(*k*) x
(*e*) $(X - \bar{X})^2$	(*l*) $\dfrac{\Sigma x^2}{n - 1}$
(*f*) s^2	
(*g*) $(n - 1)s^2$	(*m*) $\Sigma(X - \bar{X})$

3.8—Show, algebraically, that the sum of the deviations from the mean is equal to zero.

3.9—Show, algebraically, that if observations are paired so that if $D = X_1 - X_2$, then the mean of the differences $\bar{D}$ is equal to the difference between the means $\bar{X}_1 - \bar{X}_2$.

3.10—If we know the means, $\bar{X}_1$ and $\bar{X}_2$, of two sets of observations and also the number of observations, n_1 and n_2, in each set, then we can find the mean of the combined sets. Write the formula that would be used in finding this mean. Note that the formula could be extended to any number of sets of observations.

3.11—Translate each of the verbal statements given below so that it is expressed in terms of the statistical symbols used in the chapter. For example, the statement "if every score in a distribution is squared and the sum of all of these squared scores is obtained and from this sum there is subtracted n times the square of the mean of the scores, the result will be $n - 1$ times the variance" could be written as follows:

$$\Sigma X^2 - n\bar{X}^2 = (n - 1)s^2$$

(*a*) If the mean is subtracted from each of the scores in a distribution and the remainder is squared, the sum of all such squares will be $n - 1$ times the variance.

(*b*) If the mean is subtracted from each of the scores in a distribution, the sum of the remainders will be zero.

(*c*) If the number 10 is subtracted from each score in a distribution, the mean of these remainders will be 10 less than the mean of the original scores.

(*d*) If each score in a distribution is increased by 1 and the result squared, the sum of these squares will be equal to the sum of three terms, namely, the sum of the squares of the original scores, twice the sum of the original scores, and the number of observations in the distribution.

(*e*) If we subtract the mean of a distribution from a given score and square this deviation, it will be equal to the original score squared minus 2 times the original score times the mean, plus the mean squared.

(*f*) If each score in a distribution is multiplied by a constant k and the products are summed, the result will be equal to the constant value times the sum of the original scores.

■ CHAPTER FOUR

Simplifying Statistical Computations

The computation of the mean and standard deviation is quite simple as long as we are dealing with relatively few measurements or when the numerical size of the measurements is small. But when we have a great many scores and when the values of these are large, as may often be the case, then we need some method for simplifying our work. This is achieved through *coding*, a means of reducing scores or measurements.

■ The Approximate Nature of Measurements

You may recall that in the last chapter we touched briefly upon the meaning of a measurement or score when we considered the calculation of the median. At that time we pointed out that measurements are made and reported to the nearest unit, whatever that unit happens to be. Height, for example, may be reported to the nearest inch despite the fact that there is not a jump from one inch to the next, but a *theoretically* infinite gradation of units between each. The distance between 61 and 62 inches, for example, might be divided into tenths and reported 61.1, or divided into hundredths and reported 61.01, or thousandths and reported 60.001, and so on. A height, then, reported simply as 61 inches is not the precise value upon close examination that it might at first seem to be. But then neither would a reported value of 61.001 inches be an exact figure, for, regardless of the units of measurement, theoretically an instrument might be constructed that would measure with a greater degree of precision.

This is true of all measurement. Time may be measured in terms of years, months, weeks, days, hours, minutes, seconds, milliseconds, and so on, each succeeding unit being more precise than the one before, but even milliseconds are not exact values but only approximate. What we have said about time applies also to other measurements with which you may be familiar: temperature, weight, brightness, intensity of sound, and so forth.

Because of the approximate nature of measurements, we customarily, in statistics, regard a height reported in terms of the nearest inch, such as 61 inches, as representing an interval ranging from 60.5 to 61.5, that is, half a unit above and half a unit below the value reported. We regard psychological-test scores and other measurements in the same manner. An intelligence-test score of 82 is taken to mean from 81.5 to 82.5; an attitude-test score of 23 is considered as representing an interval from 22.5 to 23.5. It is conceivable in each instance that, if our units of measurement on these scales had been more refined, the obtained values might have been somewhat higher or somewhat lower than the scores, 82 and 23, indicate. If this disturbs your previous beliefs about the accuracy of figures, then you might take comfort in the thought that most of our units of measurements are precise enough for the situations in which we are interested.

Significant Figures

A question that students frequently ask is: How many decimal places shall I carry in my computations? There is no exact answer to this question as it is phrased. More properly, the question should be: How many *significant figures* should I carry? But even here there is no exact answer, but only "good" or established practice and "poor" or not common practice—like "good" and "bad" usage in English. In view of what we have said concerning the approximate nature of measurements, the figures 28, 280, and 2,800 each contains but two significant figures. That is because the zeros used in the second and third numbers are merely used to locate decimal points, they are "fillers." The first value, 28, represents a range from 27.5 to 28.5; the second, 280, a range from 275 to 285; and the third, 2,800, a range from 2,750 to 2,850. However, if 280 and 2,800 had been written 280. and 2,800., with a decimal point, then the zeros would have been considered significant figures, and the range would be 279.5 to 280.5 and 2,799.5 to 2,800.5, respectively. In the measurements used throughout this book, we shall follow the fairly common practice of *not writing the decimal point* after figures such as 70 or 60 or 210, but *assume that it is understood.* When a score is written as 60, for example, it will be assumed that this represents a range from 59.5 to 60.5.

There are "rules" governing the number of significant figures in the answers to problems involving multiplication, division, addition, and subtraction, but, as Snedecor (1946, p. 96) has pointed out, they would have to be discarded when an involved series of operations must be performed. Following rigidly any single set of rules would involve "exaggerations of inaccuracies." The best single principle to follow is to carry along more figures in various computations than you intend to retain in the final answer, and then to round back to a reasonable number of places in reporting your answer. Let us consider first what we mean by a "reasonable" number of places in an answer before turning to the techniques of "rounding."

Common Practice in Reporting Statistics

An examination of the research literature in a given field will indicate current practice. In psychology, education, and the social sciences, since many or most of our measures are concerned with scores usually reported in terms of whole numbers and seldom in terms of decimals or fractions, the following is common practice:

1. The mean is usually reported to one or two decimal places.
2. The median is usually reported to one or two decimal places.
3. The variance is usually reported to three or four decimal places.
4. The standard deviation is usually reported to one or two decimal places.
5. Standard errors, which we have not discussed as yet, are usually reported to two and ordinarily not more than three decimal places.
6. Correlation coefficients are usually reported to two and sometimes to three decimal places.
7. Per cents, written as decimal fractions, are seldom reported to more than four places and usually to two or three places.
8. Proportions are seldom reported to more than four decimal places and usually to two or three places.
9. Ratios, used in tests of significance, which we shall take up later, are usually reported to two or sometimes to three decimal places.

When the number of observations with which we are dealing is very large, we might report the statistics listed above to another decimal place, but when the number of observations is small, say less than 100, such "professed accuracy" is apt to be looked upon as misleading. If you are going to report the mean of a sample to two decimal places, then you should carry the division $\sum X/n$ to three places and round back to two. This practice should be followed in computing all other statistics also: carry along two or three extra figures in making your computations and then round back in your final answer.

Rounding Figures

In rounding numbers to the nearest whole number, we proceed as follows: 8.4 becomes 8; 7.1 becomes 7; 3.2 becomes 3; 7.6 becomes 8; 7.8 becomes 8; and 6.6 becomes 7. What is the rule we have followed? If the decimal fraction was less than .5 we dropped it and let the number stand; if the decimal fraction was over .5, we raised the number by one. If we round to one decimal we follow the same rule: 8.46 becomes 8.5; 7.32 becomes 7.3; 6.11 becomes 6.1; and 4.654 becomes 4.7.

Difficulties in rounding are apt to arise when we are asked to round numbers such as these: 5.5 and 4.5 to the nearest whole number; 8.550 and 5.650 to one decimal place. The answers may surprise you: 5.5 becomes 6; 4.5 remains 4; 8.550 becomes 8.6; and 4.65 remains 4.6. All of these numbers involve the dropping of a 5, which is right on the border line. The rule by common practice is this: if the number preceding the 5 which is to be dropped is an even number, then we do not change it, but if the number preceding the 5 is odd, then it is raised by one. This is an arbitrary rule, to be sure, and it could just as well be the other way around. Either one would work and would tend to balance out errors that might be present in rounding if we had a long series to work with.

Raw-Score Formula for the Sum of Squares

Consider the set of scores on a Thurstone attitude scale listed in column (1) of Table 4.1. The mean of this distribution is 75/15 = 5. In column (2) we

Table 4.1—A Set of Scores on a Thurstone Attitude Scale Illustrating Coding by Subtraction

	(1) X	(2) x	(3) x^2	(4) X^2	(5) $X-4$	(6) $X-3$	(7) $(X-4)^2$
	11	6	36	121	7	8	49
	8	3	9	64	4	5	16
	5	0	0	25	1	2	1
	2	−3	9	4	−2	−1	4
	4	−1	1	16	0	1	0
	7	2	4	49	3	4	9
	1	−4	16	1	−3	−2	9
	2	−3	9	4	−2	−1	4
	5	0	0	25	1	2	1
	9	4	16	81	5	6	25
	7	2	4	49	3	4	9
	1	−4	16	1	−3	−2	9
	4	−1	1	16	0	1	0
	5	0	0	25	1	2	1
	4	−1	1	16	0	1	0
Σ	75	0	122	497	15	30	137

have $x = X - \bar{X}$ or the deviations of the scores from the mean. Column (3) gives the squares of these deviations and summing the squares we obtain

$$\sum x^2 = 122$$

The sum of squares is one of the quantities we shall have occasion to calculate frequently, and we want now to develop some simple methods for obtaining it. The following algebra involves nothing more than the application of the rules of Chapter 2. We shall indicate each step in detail so that you may follow the development. The final result is a basic formula in statistical analysis.

By definition	$x = X - \bar{X}$
Squaring	$x^2 = (X - \bar{X})^2$
Or	$x^2 = X^2 - 2X\bar{X} + \bar{X}^2$
Summating	$\sum x^2 = \sum X^2 - 2\bar{X}\sum X + n\bar{X}^2$
Substituting an identity	$\sum x^2 = \sum X^2 - 2\bar{X}n\bar{X} + n\bar{X}^2$
And	$\sum x^2 = \sum X^2 - 2n\bar{X}^2 + n\bar{X}^2$
Then combining terms	$\sum x^2 = \sum X^2 - n\bar{X}^2$
Substituting an identity	$\sum x^2 = \sum X^2 - n\left(\frac{\sum X}{n}\right)\left(\frac{\sum X}{n}\right)$

We obtain

$$\sum x^2 = \sum X^2 - \frac{(\sum X^2)}{n} \tag{4.1}$$

Substituting the appropriate values from Table 4.1 in formula (4.1), we get

$$\sum x^2 = 497 - \frac{(75)^2}{15}$$

$$= 497 - \frac{5{,}625}{15}$$

$$= 497 - 375$$

$$= 122$$

which is the same value we obtained when we worked with the actual deviations from the mean of the distribution.

We see from the above that it is possible to obtain the sum of squares directly from the original measures without first subtracting the mean. All that is necessary is to square the original measures and to sum them. Then from this sum we subtract the square of the sum of scores, divided by n. The result is the sum of squares. The term $(\sum X)^2/n$ is called the *correction term for the sum of squares*. It is necessary because we have not actually worked with deviations from the mean of the distribution.

Coding by Subtraction

We are now ready to consider some of the techniques of coding measurements. Consider again the scores listed in column (1) of Table 4.1. Suppose, without knowing what the mean of the distribution was, we had subtracted 5 from each of these scores and then summed the resulting deviations. The fact that this sum would be equal to zero should tell us immediately that the value we have subtracted is actually the mean.[1]

Now try subtracting 4 from each of the scores as we have done in column (5) of Table 4.1. The sum of the deviations is now no longer zero but 15. If you were to divide this value by n, which is equal to 15, the result would be 1, which is just the amount you need to add to the value 4, which you subtracted from each score, in order to obtain the mean. Try subtracting 3 from each score, as we have done in column (6) of the table, and you will now find that the sum of the deviations is equal to 30. And 30 divided by n gives 2, which is just the amount you need to add to 3, the value subtracted from each score, in order to obtain the mean.

As a matter of fact, any value at all could be subtracted from these scores, and you could still find the mean by summing the deviations from the value subtracted. Judging from the examples given above, all that you would need to do would be to sum the deviations, divide this sum by n, and add it to the value which you have subtracted from each score. The result would be the mean of the distribution.

Calculation of the Mean

We are going to have to resort to some more symbols. The deviations we have just used may be symbolized by X'. This means that the deviation is not from the actual mean $\bar{X}$ of the distribution, but from some other

[1] A theorem introduced earlier (p. 38) showed that the sum of the deviations from the mean is equal to zero.

point of arbitrary origin, symbolized by M'. That is,

$$X' = X - M' \tag{4.2}$$

where X' = a score coded by subtraction of a constant
X = the original score
M' = some arbitrary constant

We can now arrive at an equation for the mean, using the coded scores defined by formula (4.2).

By definition $$X' = X - M'$$

Summating $$\sum X' = \sum X - nM'$$

Dividing by n $$\frac{\sum X'}{n} = \frac{\sum X}{n} - M'$$

Substituting an identity $$\frac{\sum X'}{n} = \bar{X} - M'$$

And adding M' to both sides we obtain

$$\bar{X} = M' + \frac{\sum X'}{n} \tag{4.3}$$

where $\bar{X}$ = the mean
M' = an arbitrary constant subtracted from each score
X' = a score coded by the subtraction of an arbitrary constant M'
n = the number of scores

If we let M' be equal to 3, then we find from column (6) of Table 4.1 that $\sum X'$ is equal to 30. Substituting in formula (4.3), we obtain

$$\bar{X} = 3 + \frac{30}{15}$$

$$= 3 + 2$$

$$= 5$$

The value $(\sum X')/n$ is called the *correction term for the mean*, when we work with measures that have been coded by the subtraction of a constant. If M' turned out to be the mean, then $(\sum X')/n$ would, of course, be zero and we would have $\bar{X} = M'$.

Calculation of the Sum of Squares

Perhaps you are wondering whether the X' values can be squared, summed, and then corrected in some fashion to arrive at the sum of squares, that is $\sum x^2$. The answer is yes. All that we need to do to obtain the sum of squares is to subtract $(\sum X')^2/n$ from $\sum X'^2$. In other words

$$\sum x^2 = \sum X'^2 - \frac{(\sum X')^2}{n} \qquad \textbf{(4.4)}$$

The algebra by which we arrived at formula (4.4) is given in answer to one of the examples at the end of the chapter. You might try working out a proof before looking at the one given there.

The correction term $(\sum X')^2/n$ in formula (4.4) is for failure to take the deviation from the actual mean, not for the process of subtraction as such. Measures of variation, such as the standard deviation and the range, are uninfluenced by subtraction or addition of a constant. The variation in a set of measurements will remain the same, regardless of whether we add a constant value to each one or whether we subtract a constant value from each one. For example, if the lowest score in a set was 20 and the highest was 40, the range would be 20. If a constant such as 10 was subtracted from every score in the series, the lowest score would become 10, the highest score would become 30, and the range would remain 20. If 10 was added to each score, the lowest score would become 30, the highest 50, and the range would be the same as before. The standard deviation would also remain the same, regardless of the constant which is subtracted or added.

We may illustrate formula (4.4) with the series of Thurstone attitude-scale scores we have used before. Column (3) of Table 4.1 shows that the sum of squared deviations from the mean is equal to 122. In column (5) we give the values of X' where X' is equal to $X - 4$, and we find that $\sum X'$ is equal to 15. The squares of X' are given in column (7) and we see that this sum is equal to 137. Then substituting in formula (4.4) we obtain

$$\sum x^2 = 137 - \frac{(15)^2}{15}$$

$$= 137 - \frac{225}{15}$$

$$= 137 - 15$$

$$= 122$$

which is the same as the value we obtained by squaring the deviations from the mean.

We now have several different ways of finding the sum of squares: we may work with deviations from the actual mean; we may subtract some value other than the mean and apply a correction term to the resulting sum of squared deviations; or we may work with the measurements as they stand. This last method is particularly valuable if you have a calculating machine to assist you in your computations.

■ Coding by Division

We have just seen how we may subtract a constant from a series of scores, thus reducing the numerical size of the scores. We found also that we could work with these reduced or "coded" scores and, by applying a correction term, arrive at the same value for the *sum of scores* and for the *sum of squares* that we would have obtained working with the original measures. We shall now see how division, too, can be used to reduce the size of scores.

In Table 4.2 column (1) we have a set of original measurements, the

Table 4.2—Coding Scores by Division

	(1) X	(2) x	(3) x^2	(4) $x' = X/2$	(5) $x'^2 = (X/2)^2$
	12	2	4	6	36
	10	0	0	5	25
	8	−2	4	4	16
	10	0	0	5	25
	14	4	16	7	49
	6	−4	16	3	9
	8	−2	4	4	16
	16	6	36	8	64
	6	−4	16	3	9
	10	0	0	5	25
Σ	100	0	96	50	274

sum of which is 100. Since n is equal to 10, the mean of these scores is 100/10 or 10. Column (2) gives the deviation of each score from the mean, and the sum of this column is zero, as it should be. Column (3) gives the deviations squared, and the sum of squares is equal to 96. In column (4) we have divided each X by 2, and we shall symbolize this coded score by x'. Column (5) contains the squares of the coded scores or $x'^2 = \left(\frac{X}{2}\right)^2$.

Calculation of the Mean

We shall let i represent any constant by which each score has been divided. Then

$$x' = \frac{X}{i} \tag{4.5}$$

where x' = a score coded by division
X = the original score
i = any constant

We develop a formula for the mean as follows:

By definition $\quad x' = \frac{X}{i}$

Summating $\quad \Sigma x' = \frac{\Sigma X}{i}$

Multiplying by i $\quad i\Sigma x' = \Sigma X$

Dividing by n we obtain

$$\bar{X} = \left(\frac{\Sigma x'}{n}\right) i \tag{4.6}$$

We thus see that if we have reduced scores by dividing each one by the same constant, we may sum these coded scores, divide by n, and multiply the result by i, the value by which we divided each score, to arrive at the mean. Substituting the appropriate numerical values from Table 4.2 in formula (4.6) we obtain

$$\bar{X} = \left(\frac{50}{10}\right) 2$$

$$= (5)(2)$$

$$= 10$$

which is the value of the mean we obtained by working with the original measures.

Calculation of the Sum of Squares

The formula for the sum of squares now requires a *correction term for coding* as well as one for failure to take the deviations from the mean of the series. Measures of variation, although uninfluenced by subtraction or addition, are changed by multiplication or division. Note, for example, that the range of scores in column (4) of Table 4.2 is no longer the same as that of the original measurements in column (1). The formula we need is

$$\Sigma x^2 = \left[\Sigma x'^2 - \frac{(\Sigma x')^2}{n}\right] i^2 \tag{4.7}$$

where x = a deviation of the original score from the mean
x' = a score coded by division or X/i
i = the constant by which each score is divided
n = the number of measures in the series

The proof of formula (4.7) is given as an answer to one of the examples at the end of the chapter.[2] Substituting in formula (4.7) with the appropriate values taken from Table 4.2, we obtain

$$\Sigma x^2 = \left[274 - \frac{(50)^2}{10}\right] 2^2$$

$$= (274 - 250)4$$

$$= 96$$

which is precisely the value we obtain when we sum the squared deviations from the mean shown in column (3) of Table 4.2.

Coding by Subtraction and Then by Division

Calculation of the Mean

It is possible to code measures by first subtracting some constant M' and then to code the obtained values of X' by dividing each one by some constant i. Scores or measures that have been coded by both operations in

[2] Sometimes we shall give a proof in the text and at other times it will be given in the answers to the examples that appear at the end of the chapters.

the order described will also be designated by the symbol x'. Formula (4.6) for the mean will now require that we add the subtracted constant M' to the right-hand side in order to find the mean. Thus

$$\bar{X} = M' + \left(\frac{\sum x'}{n}\right) i \tag{4.8}$$

Calculation of the Sum of Squares

The sum of squares, as we have pointed out before, will be uninfluenced by the subtraction of a constant from each measure, and, as you might guess, formula (4.7) will apply. We need only take into account the constant i by which each score has been divided. Thus if scores have first been coded by subtracting a constant and then by dividing by a constant, we have

$$\sum x^2 = \left[\sum x'^2 - \frac{(\sum x')^2}{n}\right] i^2$$

where the terms have the same meaning as in formula (4.7).

■ Summary of Coding Formulas

You may not quite grasp, at this time, the value of the coding techniques we have described. That is perhaps because the problems and data we have had to work with up to now have been selected for simplicity and ease of computation. In each illustration the mean has been a whole number and the figures have been small rather than large. But suppose that the mean for a distribution of over 100 scores turned out to be 152.67. If you tried to compute the standard deviation by working with deviations from this mean, the computations would involve squaring four- or five-place figures. Coding the series by subtracting some integer and reducing it even more by dividing by a constant would simplify your computations.

It should be pointed out that it is also possible to code measures by multiplication and addition, but we seldom have need for these coding techniques in handling the data of the social sciences. The rules are these: the mean is influenced by every operation; the standard deviation or sum of squares is influenced only by multiplication and division. When more than one operation has been performed, for example, subtraction and then division, the coded results must be decoded with the inverse operation (the inverse operation of subtraction is addition, of division, multiplication) and in reverse order. If we subtracted 5 and then divided each measure by 2, we must decode the resulting mean by first multiplying by 2 and then adding 5. The sum of squares, being influenced only by the one operation, division, must be multiplied by the square of the value by which each measure was divided.[3]

The various coding formulas are summarized below for convenient reference:

1. When we deal with the original measures, then

$$\bar{X} = \frac{\sum X}{n} \qquad \text{and} \qquad \sum x^2 = \sum X^2 - \frac{(\sum X)^2}{n}$$

2. When scores have been coded by subtraction only, with $X' = X - M'$, then

$$\bar{X} = M' + \left(\frac{\sum X'}{n}\right) \qquad \text{and} \qquad \sum x^2 = \sum X'^2 - \frac{(\sum X')^2}{n}$$

3. When scores have been coded by division only, with $x' = X/i$, then

$$\bar{X} = \left(\frac{\sum x'}{n}\right) i \qquad \text{and} \qquad \sum x^2 = \left[\sum x'^2 - \frac{(\sum x')^2}{n}\right] i^2$$

4. When scores have been reduced first by subtraction of a constant and then by division by a constant, with $x' = (X - M')/i$, then

$$\bar{X} = M' + \left(\frac{\sum x'}{n}\right) i \qquad \text{and} \qquad \sum x^2 = \left[\sum x'^2 - \frac{(\sum x')^2}{n}\right] i^2$$

The formulas given above are basic. Memorize them and make sure that you know what every term means and what every term does.

Grouping Measures into Classes

The most common method of coding scores or other measurements is by "grouping" them into "classes" to form a frequency distribution. You may recall that earlier in this chapter we discussed "precision of measurement." Grouping may be thought of as the equivalent of using a less precise measuring instrument and is most valuable when we have

---

[3] If we added 5 and then multiplied each measure by 2, we must decode the resulting mean by first dividing by 2 and then subtracting 5. The sum of squares, again being influenced by only the one operation, division, must be divided by the square of the coding constant.

a large number of measurements. Instead of treating each measurement separately, we group them into a number of equal intervals, classes, or steps. We then assign a single numerical value to all of the scores in a given class. By coding these class values by means of subtraction and division we simplify our computations considerably.

Examine the scores of Table 4.3. They are hypothetical, but we shall

Table 4.3—Hypothetical Scores Made by Students on an Objective Type of Examination

87	76	73	70	67	66	64	63	61	60
85	75	72	69	67	65	64	62	61	60
82	74	71	69	67	65	63	62	61	60
78	74	71	68	66	65	63	62	61	60
77	74	70	68	66	64	63	62	61	60
60	59	58	57	56	54	52	50	46	43
60	59	58	57	55	54	52	49	46	42
60	59	58	57	55	53	51	49	46	38
60	59	58	56	55	53	51	48	45	35
60	59	57	56	54	53	50	47	44	33

assume that they were made by a class in psychology on an objective examination. These scores, as they stand, do not give a very concise description of the performance of the group—and one of the purposes of statistics is to summarize and describe. Nor are these scores, as they stand, very convenient to use in computations.

The Number of Intervals or Classes

The first thing we need to do in making a frequency distribution is to determine how we shall group the scores. We could group the scores of Table 4.3 in terms of an *interval* of 1 by placing numbers ranging from 87, the highest value in the table, to 33, the lowest value in the table, at the left-hand side of a sheet of paper and then making a tally mark (/) each time one of these numbers was found in the distribution. This, however, would still leave the scores spread out; we would have 55 *possible* scores recorded at the left with the scores being recorded in terms of an interval of 1 or the original unit of measurement. With an interval of 1, we have as many classes as there are possible values of the scores.[4]

[4] The number of *possible* values that a set of measurements might take is equal to the range plus 1. Thus if the range of scores in a set is from 7 to 4, we have 3 + 1 = 4 possible values, that is, 7, 6, 5, and 4.

Fortunately, experience has shown that quite accurate results can be obtained in statistics when, for purposes of computation, we work with a much smaller number of classes or intervals, say from 10 to 20. Our first suggestion for grouping scores, then, will be that we group them so as to have from 10 to 20 classes or groups. The larger the number of intervals or classes, the more precise will be the computations, but also the more complicated the computations. Consequently, the number of class intervals we decide to work with will be dictated by our desire for accuracy and also by our desire for convenience.

Size of the Class Interval

One method that might be used to determine the appropriate size of the class interval to use in grouping measures is first to find the range and then to divide the range by the number of class intervals with which you wish to work. In the present problem, if we wished to work with approximately 10 classes, we would divide the range, 54, by 10, and the quotient would be 5.4. This quotient rounded off to the nearest integer would be 5 which suggests the size of the interval to use in order to obtain approximately 10 classes.

If we wished to work with approximately 15 class intervals, we would divide the range by 15 and this quotient would be 3.6, which, when rounded, suggests 4 as the size interval to use. A class interval of 2 would give slightly more than 20 classes, and an interval of 3 would give slightly less than 20 classes.

Limits of the Intervals

It is customary in psychology and education to start class intervals so that the lowest score of the interval is some multiple of the size of the class interval.[5] For example, when the size of the interval is 3, intervals are started with some multiple of 3 such as 6, 9, 12, or 15, and so forth. However, if there is any apparent tendency for the original measures to cluster about particular values, then the limits of the intervals might be established in such a way that these clusters will fall toward the middle of the various intervals. Since this will not necessarily be the case and since we desire some uniformity in the procedures to be used, we shall always begin the class intervals with a multiple of the size of the interval.

For the data of Table 4.3 we shall use a class interval of 5. Since the lowest score in the table falls between 30 and 35, we shall have to begin the first interval with 30 in order to include this score.

[5] This is an arbitrary practice but has certain advantages if computations are to be done on a machine with coded scores and the coding is to be done without first making a frequency distribution. We shall discuss this technique later.

Although it is customary to record the limits of the intervals as 30–34, 35–39, 40–44, and so forth, for a class interval of 5, we must remember what we have previously said about the meaning of a score, that is, that it represents a range extending .5 of a unit above and below the recorded value. The same reasoning applies to class intervals; the *theoretical limits* of the interval 30–34 are 29.5–34.5, that is, .5 of a unit below and .5 of a unit above the *recorded limits.*

Tallying the Scores

The next step in making a frequency distribution, after the size of the interval and the limits of the first interval have been determined, is to tally the scores. The various class intervals are listed as in Table 4.4

Table 4.4—Frequency Distribution of Scores Given in Table 4.3

(1) *Scores*	(2) *Tally Marks*	(3) *f*
85–89	//	2
80–84	/	1
75–79	////	4
70–74	/𝍸/ ////	9
65–69	/𝍸/ /𝍸/ ///	13
60–64	/𝍸/ /𝍸/ /𝍸/ /𝍸/ /𝍸/ /	26
55–59	/𝍸/ /𝍸/ /𝍸/ ////	19
50–54	/𝍸/ /𝍸/ //	12
45–49	/𝍸/ ///	8
40–44	///	3
35–39	//	2
30–34	/	1

according to the accepted practice of placing the highest interval at the top. As the scores are taken one at a time, a tally mark is placed opposite the interval in which each score falls. When four tally marks (////) have been made in a given interval, the fifth is made as a cross tally, thus (/𝍸/). The sum of the tally marks for each interval gives the *frequency* of scores within the interval. The sum of all of the frequencies gives the total number of measurements or *n*.

Assumptions concerning Grouped Scores

What assumption can we make concerning the scores as they are now grouped? A convenient assumption is that *the best single value to represent all of the scores within a given interval is the midpoint of that interval.* We shall find that the mean and standard deviation based upon this assumption will not be seriously in error.[6]

Locating the midpoints of the intervals is an easy process. The midpoint of an interval is halfway between the lower theoretical limit and the upper theoretical limit of the interval. The lower limit of the interval 30–34 is 29.5, and the upper limit is 34.5, a range of 5. Half of 5 is 2.5, and this value added to the lower limit of the interval gives the midpoint, 32. The midpoint of any interval, in other words, is the lower limit of the interval plus $i/2$, where i is the size of the interval. It is important not to forget that the lower limit of an interval extends .5 of a unit below the recorded value, and the upper limit .5 of a unit above.

The midpoints of the class intervals are shown in column (2) of Table 4.5. We assume that the two scores falling within the interval 85–89 can both be represented by the midpoint 87. A similar assumption is made concerning the scores in each of the other intervals.

Coding the Midpoints

You will note that by letting the midpoints of the intervals represent all of the scores within the interval, we have reduced the number of numerical values that we have to deal with to 12, the number of midpoints. These scores still range in size from 32 to 87, however, and we shall now proceed to reduce their numerical values by means of the coding techniques we have already studied. We shall, in other words, code the midpoints. This coding will not change the values of the mean and standard deviation except for the slight errors already introduced by grouping, if we take into consideration the proper corrections for origin and coding.

A convenient constant to subtract from each midpoint is the midpoint of the lowest class interval. If we subtract the value of this midpoint, 32, from each of the other midpoints, we obtain the X' values shown in column (3) of Table 4.5. Remember that this coding operation will have no influence upon the sum of squares or standard deviation, but only upon the mean. If we now further code the values in column (3) by dividing each one by i, the size of the class interval, we obtain the coded x' values shown in column (5). It is with these measures that we shall do all of our calculations. Obviously, calculations with measurements ranging in size from

---

[6] In general, it can be said that the errors resulting from grouping measures into classes will have no systematic influence upon the mean, but they will tend to increase the variance and standard deviation over the values that would be obtained from the ungrouped measures. There is a correction, known as Sheppard's correction, that can be applied to the variance or standard deviation obtained from the grouped measures. For a discussion of the properties of this correction, see Fisher (1936, pp. 50–51).

Table 4.5—Calculation of the Mean and Standard Deviation from Scores Coded by Grouping

(1) *Scores*	(2) *Midpoint*	(3) X'	(4) f	(5) x'	(6) fx'	(7) fx'^2
85–89	87	55	2	11	22	242
80–84	82	50	1	10	10	100
75–79	77	45	4	9	36	324
70–74	72	40	9	8	72	576
65–69	67	35	13	7	91	637
60–64	62	30	26	6	156	936
55–59	57	25	19	5	95	475
50–54	52	20	12	4	48	192
45–49	47	15	8	3	24	72
40–44	42	10	3	2	6	12
35–39	37	5	2	1	2	2
30–34	32	0	1	0	0	0
Σ			100		562	3,568

0 to 11, as do the values in column (5), will be much easier than calculations with the original scores as they appear in Table 4.3.

Calculation of the Mean

To obtain the sum of the coded scores, we first multiply each coded score x' by the corresponding frequency f with which the score occurs. The values of fx' are given in column (6) of Table 4.5. Summing the fx' values will then give the sum of the coded scores. The formula for the mean then becomes

$$\bar{X} = M' + \left(\frac{\Sigma fx'}{n}\right) i \qquad \textbf{(4.9)}$$

Substituting the appropriate values from Table 4.5 in formula (4.9), we obtain

$$\bar{X} = 32 + \left(\frac{562}{100}\right) 5$$

$$= 32 + (5.62)(5)$$

$$= 32 + 28.1$$

$$= 60.1$$

Calculation of the Sum of Squares

In column (7) of Table 4.5 we have multiplied the squares of the coded scores by their corresponding frequencies. The entries in column (7) are most easily obtained by multiplying the values in column (6) by those in column (5) to give $x'fx' = fx'^2$. The sum of squares will then be given by

$$\Sigma x^2 = \left[\Sigma fx'^2 - \frac{(\Sigma fx')^2}{n}\right] i^2 \qquad \textbf{(4.10)}$$

Substituting the appropriate values from Table 4.5 in formula (4.10), we obtain

$$\Sigma x^2 = \left[3{,}568 - \frac{(562)^2}{100}\right] 5^2$$

$$= (3{,}568 - 3{,}158.44)\ (25)$$

$$= (409.56)\ (25)$$

$$= 10{,}239$$

Then the variance, as defined by formula (3.8), will be

$$s^2 = \frac{10{,}239}{100 - 1}$$

$$= 103.42$$

and the standard deviation, which is the square root of the variance, will be

$$s = \sqrt{\frac{10{,}239}{100 - 1}}$$

$$= 10.2$$

Using a Different Value for M'

You may note several things from Table 4.5. In the first place, it is not necessary to go through all of the steps we have described in arriving at the coded x' values shown in column (5). If the same coding procedure that we have described is used, all that is necessary is to number the lowest class interval 0 and to assign the values 1, 2, 3, 4, 5, and so on, to the successive class intervals. This will apply to all distributions coded in the manner described. There is no necessity, in other words, to subtract the midpoint of the lowest class interval from the other midpoints and then to divide each of these coded values by i. We have gone through these steps in the table merely to indicate the nature of the coded scores shown in column (5).

A second thing to observe is that it would have been possible to subtract some midpoint other than that of the lowest class interval. We could have subtracted, for example, the midpoint of some interval toward the center of the distribution from the other midpoints before dividing by i. If we had subtracted the midpoint of the class interval 60–64, then the coded x' value for this interval would be 0. The interval directly above would have a coded x' value of 1, the next interval a coded x' value of 2, and so on. The interval directly below 60—64 would have a coded x' value of -1, the next a coded x' value of -2, and so on. This coding procedure would give us slightly smaller figures to deal with, but would have introduced some negative values into our computations. Regardless of which midpoint we subtract, the resulting mean and standard deviation will be the same. As a general practice, it is convenient to start the lowest class interval with 0 and to number up from there. This procedure makes coding a routine affair.

The "Charlier Checks"

There are checks on the accuracy of your computations. They are known as the "Charlier checks" and in the present problem may be made by adding 1 to each coded x' value in column (5) of Table 4.5. We may designate these new coded values as x''. Now find $\sum fx''$ and $\sum fx''^2$ as before. If the computations in the first and second instance have both been correctly made, then the following relations will hold

$$\sum fx'' = \sum fx' + n \tag{4.11}$$

and

$$\sum fx''^2 = \sum fx'^2 + (2)(\sum fx') + n \tag{4.12}$$

As an illustration of the Charlier checks, we may examine the computations in Table 4.6. Substituting the appropriate values from this table in formula (4.11), we obtain

$$\sum fx'' = 65 = 45 + 20$$

$$= 65 = 65$$

Table **4.6**—Illustration of the "Charlier Checks"

(1) *Scores*	(2) f	(3) x'	(4) fx'	(5) fx'^2	(6) f	(7) x''	(8) fx''	(9) fx''^2
30–32	1	5	5	25	1	6	6	36
27–29	2	4	8	32	2	5	10	50
24–26	5	3	15	45	5	4	20	80
21–23	7	2	14	28	7	3	21	63
18–20	3	1	3	3	3	2	6	12
15–17	2	0	0	0	2	1	2	2
Σ	20		45	133			65	243

Substituting in formula (4.12), we obtain

$$\Sigma fx''^2 = 243 = 133 + (2)(45) + 20$$

$$= 243 = 243$$

Calculation of the Median

The median, Q_1, Q_3, and other centiles can also be found from a frequency distribution. Formula (3.11) given earlier will work without any change. But if we have our scores grouped in intervals greater than 1, as will usually be the case, the value within the parentheses must be multiplied by the size of the interval i. For purposes of illustration, we may find the median of the distribution of scores shown in Table 4.5. Substituting in formula (3.11) we have

$$Mdn = l + \left(\frac{\frac{n}{2} - \Sigma f_b}{f_w}\right) i$$

$$= 59.5 + \left(\frac{50 - 45}{26}\right) 5$$

$$= 59.5 + .96$$

$$= 60.46$$

Summary of Steps in Coding in a Frequency Distribution

Here is a summary of the steps in coding measurements by grouping them in a frequency distribution.

1. Determine the range of scores.

2. Divide the range by the number of class intervals you wish to work with, say 15. This figure, when rounded, gives the appropriate size of the class interval i.

3. Begin the lowest interval with some multiple of the size of the class interval—a multiple which is equal to or just below the lowest measure in the series.

4. Code the lowest class interval 0, the next 1, the next 2, and so forth until the highest interval has been coded.

5. Apply formula (4.9) for the mean and formula (4.10) for the sum of squares.

If you are working with a calculating machine, you may not want to record the scores in a frequency distribution, but may still wish to code them. This is easily accomplished. Follow the procedure above through the third step. Then take the lower limit (recorded limit) of the first interval and divide this by i (the size of the interval). This will be a whole number since the lower recorded limit is a multiple of i and may be designated as k. Now divide each measurement by i, discarding any remainder. Subtract the value of k, and this will give you the coded value of the score. This coded value will be identical with the coded value you would obtain if you had grouped the scores into a frequency distribution.

To illustrate the above procedure, we may consider a few of the scores from Table 4.3. We have decided to use an interval of 5, and the lower limit of the first interval is 30. This limit divided by the size of the interval gives the value of k, which is 6. The score 33 divided by i gives 6 and a remainder of 3 which we discard. Then subtracting $k = 6$, we obtain a coded score of 0. The score 56 divided by i gives 11 and a remainder of 1 which we discard. Then, subtracting $k = 6$, we obtain the coded score of 5. We would proceed in similar fashion for the other scores in Table 4.3. You may observe that the coded scores obtained in this way are exactly the same as those that would be obtained from the frequency distribution of Table 4.5.

■ EXAMPLES

4.1—Here is an easy set of measurements for coding.

29 28 27 25 24 22 20

(*a*) Find the mean and sum of squares using deviations from the mean.

(*b*) Subtract 22 from each score and find the mean and sum of squares of the original values using these coded scores.

(*c*) Find the sum of squares using formula (4.1).

4.2—By making a frequency distribution, code the following scores made by a class in general psychology on an objective examination. Let $i = 3$ and begin the first interval with 6.

(*a*) Find the mean and standard deviation.
(*b*) Check your computations by means of the Charlier checks.

44	40	35	34	32	31	30	29	27
43	40	35	34	31	31	30	29	27
42	37	35	33	31	30	29	29	27
40	36	34	33	31	30	29	28	26
40	35	34	32	31	30	29	28	26
26	25	24	24	23	23	22	22	22
26	25	24	23	23	23	22	22	22
26	25	24	23	23	23	22	22	22
25	25	24	23	23	23	22	22	22
25	25	24	23	23	22	22	22	22
22	21	20	20	20	19	18	18	18
22	21	20	20	19	18	18	18	17
21	21	20	20	19	18	18	18	17
21	21	20	20	19	18	18	18	17
21	20	20	20	19	18	18	18	17
17	17	16	15	14	14	13	12	9
17	17	16	15	14	14	13	12	9
17	16	16	15	14	14	13	12	9
17	16	16	15	14	14	13	11	8
17	16	15	15	14	13	12	11	7

4.3—Find the mean, median, and standard deviation of the following distribution.

Scores	f	x'
60–62	1	8
57–59	3	7
54–56	2	6
51–53	7	5
48–50	11	4
45–47	10	3
42–44	9	2
39–41	5	1
36–38	5	0

4.4—Find the mean, median, and standard deviation of the following distribution.

Scores	*f*
27–29	1
24–26	2
21–23	4
18–20	5
15–17	3
12–14	2
9–11	2
6– 8	1

4.5—Make a frequency distribution of the following scores. Let $i = 3$ and begin the first interval with 15. Find the mean, median, 30th centile, and standard deviation.

42	16	38	29	33	35	40	32	34
43	19	26	27	33	38	20	37	34
46	36	25	23	30	42	38	20	
40	36	24	22	32	45	22	18	
39	37	28	31	32	22	20	35	
20	18	42	35	35	35	35	31	

4.6—Marks (1943) gave a test, designed to measure attitude toward Negroes, to 2,096 Negro youth living in rural sections of the south. A low score on the test indicates a favorable attitude, and a high score indicates an unfavorable attitude. Find the mean and standard deviation of the distribution of scores.

Scores	*f*
14	12
13	53
12	96
11	152
10	219
9	273
8	255
7	227
6	203
5	172
4	144
3	117
2	86
1	54
0	33

4.7—Kelly and Fiske (1950) gave the Miller Analogies Test to 367 Veterans Administration trainees in clinical psychology. The distribution of scores was as given below. Find the mean and standard deviation.

Scores	*f*
95–99	2
90–94	20
85–89	36
80–84	55
75–79	59
70–74	59
65–69	56
60–64	23
55–59	27
50–54	12
45–49	3
40–44	10
35–39	3
30–34	1
25–29	1

4.8—If $X' = X - M'$, then prove that

$$\bar{X} = M' + \frac{\sum X'}{n}$$

4.9—Prove that

$$\sum x^2 = \sum X^2 - \frac{(\sum X)^2}{n}$$

4.10—We have proved in Example 4.9 that $\sum x^2 = \sum X^2 - \dfrac{(\sum X)^2}{n}$. We now let $X' = X - M'$ and we can show that

$$\sum X^2 = \sum X'^2 + 2M'\sum X' + nM'^2$$

and that

$$\frac{(\sum X)^2}{n} = \frac{(\sum X' + nM')^2}{n}$$

With these identities and the proof from Example 4.9, show that

$$\sum x^2 = \sum X'^2 - \frac{(\sum X')^2}{n}$$

4.11—If we define $x' = X/i$, then we can show that

$$\sum x'^2 = \frac{\sum X^2}{i^2} \qquad \text{and that} \qquad (\sum x')^2/n = (\sum X)^2/ni^2$$

With these identities and the proof from Example 4.9, show that

$$\left[\sum x'^2 - \frac{(\sum x')^2}{n}\right] i^2 = \sum x^2$$

4.12—If $x' = (X - M')/i$, show that

$$\bar{X} = M' + \left(\frac{\sum x'}{n}\right) i$$

4.13—Show that: (a) $\sum fx'' = \sum fx' + n$
(b) $\sum fx''^2 = \sum fx'^2 + 2\sum fx' + n$.

4.14—Let $X' = X - M'$, $x = X - \bar{X}$, and $d = \bar{X} - M'$. Show that $\sum x^2 < \sum X'^2$ unless $d = 0$, in which case $\sum x^2 = \sum X'^2$.

CHAPTER FIVE

Graphical Representation of Frequency Distributions

A frequency distribution of scores on the Minnesota Psycho-Analogies Test for 158 students majoring in psychology is shown in Table 5.1. There are two forms of the Psycho-Analogies Test, *A* and *B*, and each form consists of 75 items. The scores given in Table 5.1 are on Form *A*. The following is an example of the type of problem contained in the test, with the correct response given in italics:

Orchestra : Violinist :: Test : (1) Battery; (2) Item Analysis;
(3) *Item*; (4) Validity.

Levine (1950) reports data showing that mean scores on the Psycho-Analogies Test rise successively from 51.7 for graduating seniors to 66.6 for third-year graduate students in psychology. Advanced students in psychology, in other words, actually do perform better on the average on the test than less advanced students in psychology.

The scores in Table 5.1 are grouped in a class interval of 3, and the frequency distribution is based upon a combined group of seniors, and first-, second-, and third-year graduate students. The frequency distribution, with its mean of 59.3 and standard deviation of 8.1, gives a concise description of the 158 scores.

■ The Histogram

The frequency distribution of Table 5.1 can also be portrayed by means of a *histogram*. The histogram enables one to obtain a picture of the distri-

Table 5.1—Frequency Distribution of Scores on Form *A* of Minnesota Psycho-Analogies Test for 158 Students Majoring in Psychology*

$(\bar{X} = 59.3;\ s = 8.1)$

(1) *Class Interval*	(2) *Midpoints of Intervals*	(3) *f*	(4) *p*	(5) *cf*	(6) *cp*	(7) *Upper Limits of Intervals*
72–74	73	4	.03	158	1.00	74
69–71	70	15	.09	154	.97	71
66–68	67	21	.13	139	.88	68
63–65	64	21	.13	118	.75	65
60–62	61	24	.15	97	.61	62
57–59	58	16	.10	73	.46	59
54–56	55	23	.15	57	.36	56
51–53	52	15	.09	34	.22	53
48–50	49	7	.04	19	.12	50
45–47	46	3	.02	12	.08	47
42–44	43	4	.03	9	.06	44
39–41	40	1	.01	5	.03	41
36–38	37	3	.02	4	.03	38
33–35	34	1	.01	1	.01	35
Σ		158	1.00			

* Data from Levine (1950).

bution quite readily. The histogram or column chart of the distribution is shown in Figure 5.1.

In plotting a histogram, it is customary to represent the scores on the horizontal axis and the frequencies on the vertical axis. In graphic work, the horizontal axis is called the X axis or *abscissa*, and the vertical axis is called the Y axis or *ordinate*. The horizontal distance from the Y axis to a point on the graph is called the *abscissa* of the point. The vertical distance from the base line or X axis to a point on the graph is called the *ordinate* of the point. Two values, written in the order (X,Y), representing, respectively, the abscissa and ordinate of a point, are called the *coordinates* of a point. It is customary to write the X value first and the Y value second.

In general, people seem to find most pleasing a rectangular frame in which the vertical axis is somewhere between 60 and 75 per cent of the length of the horizontal axis. For this reason, tall, narrow graphs and wide, flat graphs may be avoided. Graph paper, ruled 10 to the inch, which can be obtained from most college book stores, will enable you to arrange a pleasing graph when plotting distributions.

It may be noted that on the horizontal axis of Figure 5.1 we have recorded the midpoints of the class intervals, 34, 37, · · · , and 73, rather than the limits of the intervals. The midpoints are the single scores that we may assume best represent all of the scores falling within a given interval.

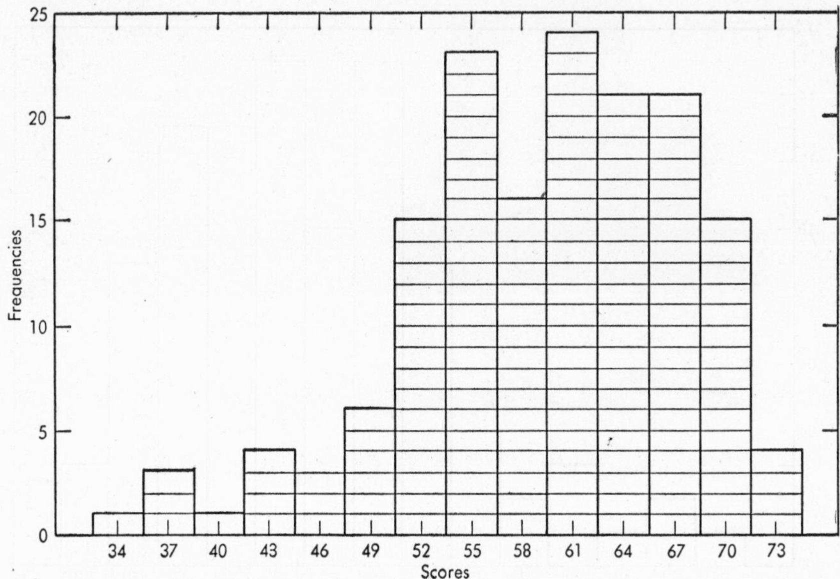

Fig. 5.1—Histogram for the distribution of scores shown in Table 5.1 with frequencies corresponding to area.

For each midpoint we have a corresponding frequency, and the paired midpoints and frequencies are the coordinates of the set of points to be plotted. For example, the first three coordinates are (34,1), (37,3), and (40,1). These coordinates are plotted in Figure 5.1 along with the other coordinates obtained from columns (2) and (3) of Table 5.1. It is sometimes said that the Y values are plotted *against* those of X or that Y is plotted *on* X.

In the histogram, each column represents a frequency corresponding to the number of scores in a given interval. We may think of each column as being subdivided into small rectangles, equal in size, a single rectangle representing a single score. The columns of the histogram are built up by piling these rectangles one on top of the other. Thus each score in the distribution corresponds to an area given by the dimensions of the small rectangle. The total area under the histogram would simply be the sum of the areas of the individual rectangles. In the histogram of Figure 5.1 we actually show these rectangles for purposes of illustration. We would, however, have no reason for showing them when our interest is in merely the picture of the frequency distribution given by the histogram. For graphical purposes, the columns would either be shaded or left blank.

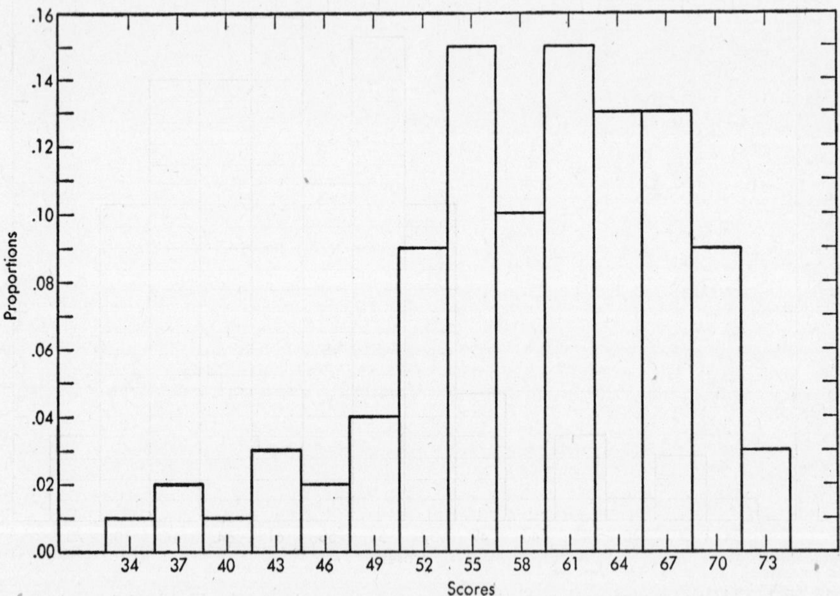

Fig. 5.2—Histogram for the distribution of scores of Table 5.1 with proportions corresponding to area.

Since we know that the total area of Figure 5.1 is made up of 158 little rectangles, one for each of the 158 scores, we could express the area in each column of the histogram as a proportion of the total area. We obtain these proportions by dividing each of the frequencies of the various class intervals by 158. The resulting proportions are shown in column (4) of Table 5.1. This procedure suggests that we could also plot a histogram with proportions rather than frequencies on the vertical axis. We have done this in Figure 5.2. Comparing Figure 5.2 with Figure 5.1, we see that no change has been made in the general form or shape of the histogram through the use of proportions rather than frequencies on the vertical axis.

When we sum the frequencies represented by the columns of the histogram of Figure 5.1, we obtain the total number of observations, 158.

If we summed the proportions represented by the columns of the histogram of Figure 5.2, we would obtain 1.00. The total area under this histogram has been set equal to unity. We shall see later that regarding a frequency distribution in terms of the area under the graph of the distribution is a very useful notion.

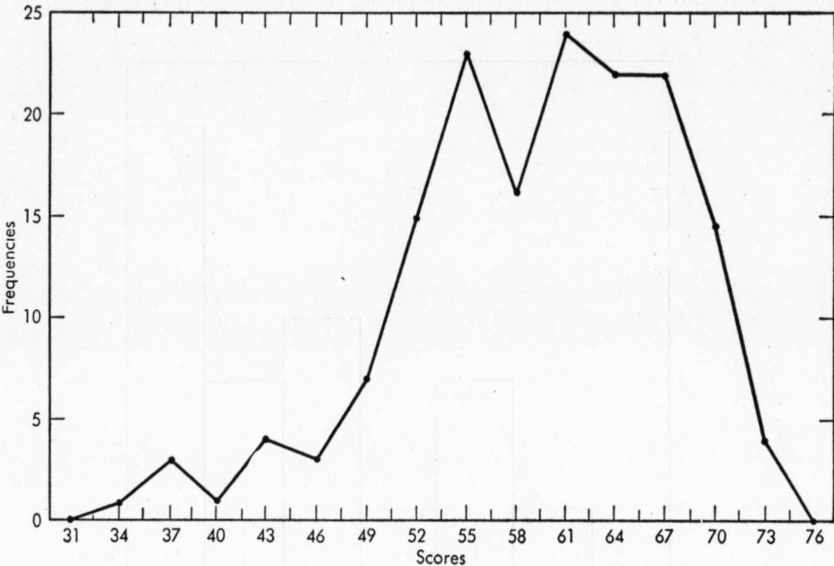

Fig. 5.3—Frequency polygon for the distribution of scores of Table 5.1.

The Frequency Polygon

We may also portray the frequency distribution of Table 5.1 by means of a *frequency polygon*. We again find the midpoints of the various class intervals and the frequencies corresponding to these midpoints. We then plot the frequencies against the corresponding midpoints. The plotted points are then connected by straight lines. It is customary to extend the distribution one class interval below and one class interval above those actually used in order to bring the ends of the frequency polygon down to the base line or horizontal axis. The frequency polygon for the data of Table 5.1 is shown in Figure 5.3.

You may observe that the area under the frequency polygon will be equal to the area under the histogram for the same distribution, if they are drawn on the same scale. We have taken a section, the first few intervals, of the histogram of Figure 5.1 and magnified it in Figure 5.4. Note that the shaded right triangles or areas are added by the frequency polygon and that these areas correspond to the unshaded right triangles or areas eliminated or cut off when we impose the frequency polygon on the histogram. Thus, for each section or area of the histogram cut off by the frequency polygon, an equal corresponding section or area is added. The area of the histogram and the corresponding frequency polygon are the same.

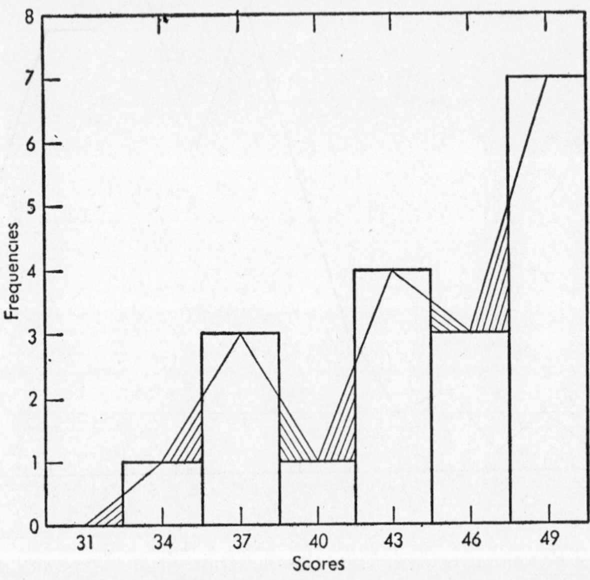

Fig. 5.4—Section of the histogram and frequency polygon for the distribution of scores of Table 5.1.

You should not get the false notion that it is possible to erect ordinates at any score on the base line of Figure 5.3 and then to read the frequency corresponding to this score at the point where the ordinate intersects the graph of the frequency polygon. We can, from the frequency polygon or histogram, tell only the frequency of scores within a given interval and not the frequencies corresponding to each individual score. Our base line representing the scores is essentially discontinuous. We have frequencies corresponding only to selected points on the X axis, namely, the midpoints of the class intervals.

■ Cumulative-Proportion Graph

Another useful way of depicting a frequency distribution is in terms of its *cumulative-proportion* or *percentage graph.* Note the entries in column (5) of Table 5.1. These are the cumulative frequencies, and they are obtained by adding to the frequency in each interval the sum of the frequencies falling below the interval. For example, the cumulative frequency corresponding to the interval 45–47 is 12. This entry is obtained by adding the frequencies falling below this interval, 1 + 3 + 1 + 4 = 9, to the frequency within the interval, 3, which gives us 12. The cumulative frequency for the highest class interval, 72–74, is 158, and represents the sum of all of the frequencies below this interval, 154, plus 4, the frequency within the interval.

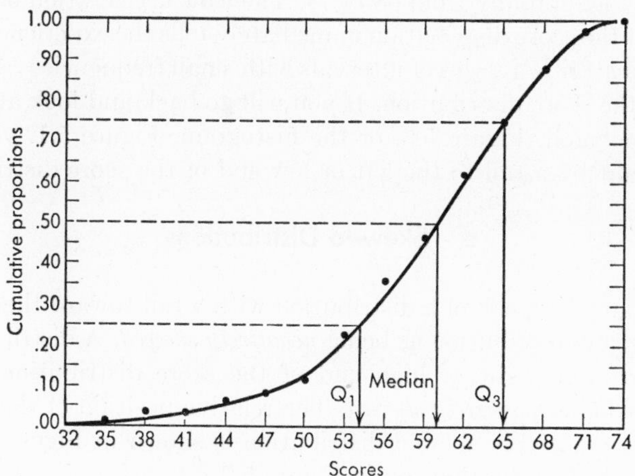

Fig. 5.5—Cumulative-proportion graph for the distribution of scores of Table 5.1.

If we divide each of the cumulative frequencies by 158, we shall have the cumulative proportions shown in column (6) of Table 5.1. Since multiplication is easier than long division, a simple way of obtaining the cumulative proportions is to find first the reciprocal of the total number of observations. For the data of Table 5.1, this is 1/158 = .00633. We can then multiply each of the cumulative frequencies by this reciprocal and obtain the cumulative proportions.[1] You should remember, from the discussion of the second chapter, that multiplication of one number by the reciprocal of another is the same as dividing the first by the second.

In plotting the histogram and frequency polygon, we found the midpoints of the class intervals and then plotted the frequencies against these values. For the cumulative distribution, we find the upper limits (the

[1] The cumulative proportions in column (6) of Table 5.1 were obtained in this way. You will note that if the proportions given in column (4) are added to obtain the cumulative proportions, some of these values will differ slightly from those shown in column (6) of the table as a result of rounding errors.

recorded instead of the theoretical upper limits will do) of the intervals and plot the cumulative frequencies or proportions against these values. The reason for this is that the cumulative frequency or proportion entered for a given interval represents the frequency or proportion of the total number of scores falling below the upper limit of the interval. The upper limits (recorded) of the intervals are shown in column (7) of Table 5.1.

We have plotted the cumulative-proportion distribution for the 158 scores on the Minnesota Psycho-Analogies Test in Figure 5.5. Note that the graph rises most rapidly toward the center of the score distribution and only slightly less rapidly from 68 to 74. The slow acceleration of the graph at the left of the score distribution immediately tells the experienced student that there is a tail—a series of intervals with small frequencies—toward the low end of the score distribution. If you will go back and look at either the frequency polygon, Figure 5.3, or the histogram, Figure 5.1, you will see what is meant by a tail to the left or low end of the score distribution.

■ Skewed Distributions

It is customary to speak of a distribution with a tail toward the left or low end of the score distribution as being *negatively skewed*. A distribution with a tail toward the right or high end of the score distribution would be described as being *positively skewed*. The relative position of the mean and median in a negatively skewed distribution is shown in Figure 5.6 and in a positively skewed distribution in Figure 5.7.

The mean, as you may recall, is influenced by the numerical size of the measurements, insofar as the sum of the deviations above the mean is equal to the sum of the deviations below the mean. One or two extremely high scores would have the effect of "pulling" the mean toward them and away from the center of the distribution. One or two extremely low scores would tend to pull the mean toward them or toward the low end of the distribution. The median, on the other hand, is not influenced by the numerical size of extreme scores. It is merely the point on each side of which there is an equal number of scores. Consequently, when a distribution is negatively skewed, the median will be larger than the mean, as in Figure 5.6, where values along the horizontal axis, as usual, increase from left to right. When a distribution is positively skewed, the median will be smaller in value than the mean, as in Figure 5.7.

Another term used to describe distributions is *kurtosis*, which refers to the relative peakedness or flatness of a distribution in the neighborhood of the mode. A distribution that is flatter than a normal distribution is called platykurtic, and a distribution that has a higher peak than a normal distribution is called leptokurtic. There are measures of the degree of skewness and kurtosis, but we shall have little need of them and they will not be discussed here. These measures are described in McNemar (1949), Hoel (1947), and Walker (1943).

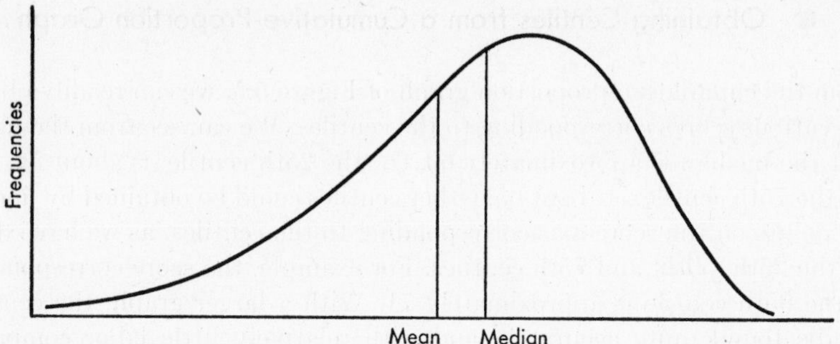

Fig. 5.6—Relative position of the mean and median in a negatively skewed distribution.

Can you imagine what the graph of a cumulative distribution that is positively skewed would look like? If your imagination, or reasoning, is not sufficient, turn your book upside down and look at Figure 5.5. A positively skewed distribution would show a rapid and then slow rise or acceleration

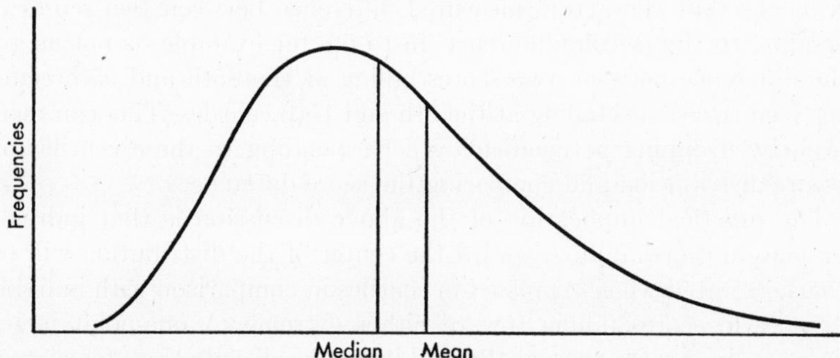

Fig. 5.7—Relative position of the mean and median in a positively skewed distribution.

toward the right or upper end of the score distribution, as Figure 5.5 would look when turned upside down.

Note that in the negatively skewed distribution of Figure 5.5, Q_1 is farther away from the median on the score distribution than Q_3. This will, in general, be true of negatively skewed distributions, but is not necessarily true of all such distributions. Similarly, for a positively skewed distribution

Q_3 will, in general, be farther away from the median on the score distribution than Q_1, but this statement also is not necessarily true for all such distributions.

■ Obtaining Centiles from a Cumulative-Proportion Graph

From the cumulative-proportion graph of Figure 5.5, we can readily obtain the various scores corresponding to the centiles. We can see from the figure that the median is approximately 60. Q_1, the 25th centile, is about 54, and Q_3, the 75th centile, is about 65. Other centiles could be obtained by finding the points on the score axis corresponding to the centiles, as we have done for the 25th, 50th, and 75th centiles. For example, the score corresponding to the 95th centile is approximately 71. With a larger graph, the centiles can be found quite accurately and with relatively little labor compared with their direct computation by means of a formula.

There is still an additional bit of information to be gained from a study of Figure 5.5. Note that the centile distances do not correspond to equal distances on the score continuum. Perpendiculars, corresponding to the centiles, dropped from the graph onto the score continuum would fall close together in the middle of the distribution, but would be farther apart toward both extremes of the score distribution. The centile distances, in other words, do not correspond to equal distances on the score continuum. This means that the actual measured difference between two scores corresponding to the centile difference 45 to 55, for example, is not as great as the difference between two scores falling at the 85th and 95th centiles or between two scores falling at the 5th and 15th centiles. This can readily be seen by dropping perpendiculars corresponding to these centiles onto the score distribution and comparing the score differences.

The practical implication of the above discussion is that individual differences in scores falling toward the center of the distribution will tend to be exaggerated when expressed in centiles in comparison with individual differences in scores falling toward either extreme. A one-point increase or decrease in a score toward the middle of the distribution, for example, may result in a rather large centile change as compared with a one-point increase or decrease in a score falling toward either extreme of the distribution. The typical distributions obtained with educational and psychological tests are characterized by a single mode and some degree of negative or positive skewness. For all such distributions the statements made concerning the relationship between centile distances and score distances will be true.

Consider, however, a distribution of scores in which each class interval has exactly the same frequency. The histogram for this distribution would be a series of columns equal in height. If the cumulative proportion graph were constructed for such a distribution, the result would be a straight line. In this instance, the centile distances would have to correspond to equal distances on the score axis. The score distance between the 95th and 96th centiles would be exactly equal to the score distance between any other two adjacent centiles. A rectangular distribution of scores is the only type of distribution in which the centiles will be equally spaced along the score continuum.

The Normal Distribution

The true normal distribution is represented by a bell-shaped, symmetrical *frequency curve.* This theoretical distribution curve has some important properties with which you should be familiar. Since the normal distribution curve is symmetrical, the mean and median will coincide, have exactly the same value. Fifty per cent of the total area under the curve will therefore fall on each side of the mean. We know also that for any normal distribution, .3413 of the total area will fall between an ordinate at the mean and an ordinate at a distance 1 standard deviation above the mean. This means that the 84th centile will correspond to that point in the score distribution that is approximately 1 standard deviation above the mean. Similarly, .3413 of the total area will fall between an ordinate at the mean and an ordinate 1 standard deviation below the mean. Since .3413 + .5000 of the total area will fall above this point, a score that is 1 standard deviation below the mean will correspond approximately to the 16th centile.

Above the ordinate that is 1 standard deviation above the mean will fall .1587 of the area under the curve, and, similarly, .1587 of the total area will fall to the left of the ordinate located at 1 standard deviation below the mean. When we go out 1.65 standard deviations from the mean, in each direction, we find that approximately .0500 of the total area will fall to the right of the ordinate located at 1.65 standard deviations above the mean and also that .0500 of the area will fall to the left of the ordinate located at 1.65 standard deviations below the mean. A distance 1.96 standard deviations above the mean will leave .0250 of the area falling to the right of the ordinate at this point. Similarly, .0250 of the total area will fall below or to the left of the ordinate that is 1.96 standard deviations below the mean. Finally, .0050 of the area will fall above the point set by an ordinate which is 2.58 standard deviations above the mean and .0050 of the area will fall below the point that is 2.58 standard deviations below the mean.

The important relations concerning the area of the normal curve and ordinates at points 1.00, 1.65, 1.96, and 2.58 standard deviations above and below the mean are illustrated in Figure 5.8. For this normal curve, the mean has been made equal to 5.5, and the standard deviation has been made equal to 1.5.

In Table 5.2 we give a frequency distribution that is reasonably normal in form. This distribution also has a mean of 5.5 and a standard deviation of 1.5. The mean and standard deviation of this distribution

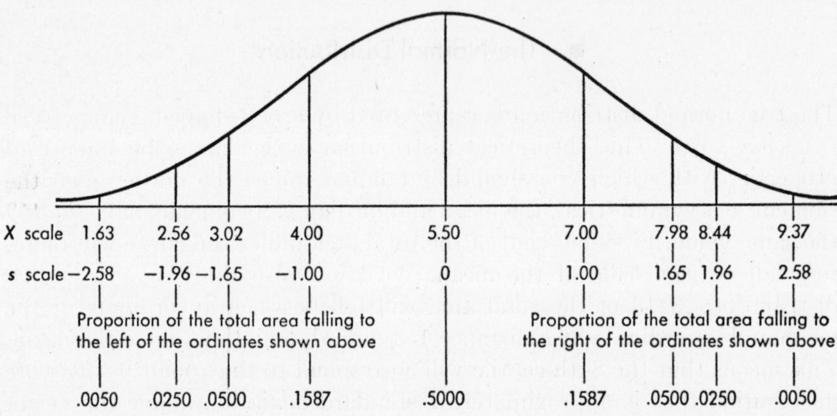

Fig. 5.8—Normal distribution curve with mean equal to 5.5 and standard deviation equal to 1.5.

thus correspond exactly to the mean and standard deviation of the normal curve shown in Figure 5.8. If the distribution of Table 5.2 is reasonably normal in form, then the relationships shown in Figure 5.8 should hold reasonably true for the data of the table.

We have said that in a normal distribution, the 16th centile will fall at a distance approximately 1 standard deviation below the mean. Since the mean of the distribution in Table 5.2 is 5.5 and the standard deviation is 1.5, the 16th centile should fall at the point $5.5 - 1.5 = 4.0$ on the score continuum. Similarly, we have said that the 84th centile should fall approximately 1 standard deviation above the mean and this would correspond to a point $5.5 + 1.5 = 7.0$ on the score continuum.

In each tail of the distribution, 1.65 standard deviations above the mean and 1.65 standard deviations below the mean, we should have approximately 5 per cent of the cases. On the score continuum, these two points would be $5.5 + (1.65)(1.5) = 7.98$ and $5.5 - (1.65)(1.5) = 3.02$, respectively. In the same manner, we may expect $5.5 + (1.96)(1.5) = 8.44$ and $5.5 - (1.96)(1.5) = 2.56$ to represent points on the score continuum above which and below which, respectively, 2.5 per cent of the cases fall.

Using the formula for centiles, which we have given in an earlier chapter, we could calculate the centiles for the data of Table 5.2 and compare them with the corresponding values for a normal distribution. But we can accomplish the same objective more readily by plotting the cumulative-proportion graph for the distribution. Column (4) of Table 5.2 shows the cumulative proportions, and these have been graphed in Figure 5.9.

Table 5.2—Frequency of Scores in an Approximately Normal Distribution with Mean Equal to 5.5 and Standard Deviation Equal to 1.5

(1) X	(2) f	(3) cf	(4) cp	(5) *Upper Limits of Intervals*
10	1	512	1.00	10.5
9	9	511	.998	9.5
8	36	502	.98	8.5
7	84	466	.91	7.5
6	126	382	.75	6.5
5	126	256	.50	5.5
4	84	130	.25	4.5
3	36	46	.09	3.5
2	9	10	.02	2.5
1	1	1	.002	1.5

From Figure 5.9 we can observe that the 16th and 84th centiles correspond approximately to the score values of 4.0 and 7.0, respectively. The 5th and 95th centiles appear to be close to the values 3.02 and 7.98, respectively. We cannot judge too accurately from the graph the points on the score continuum above which and below which exactly 2.5 per cent of the cases will fall. But columns (4) and (5) of Table 5.2 show that 2 per cent will fall below the point 2.5 and that 2 per cent will fall above 8.5 on the score continuum. It seems reasonably accurate to guess, therefore, that the exact values would not be too far away from the values of 2.56 and 8.44 of the theoretical normal curve.[2]

Note also in Figure 5.9 that if we take two centiles that are the same distance from the mean, but in opposite directions, say the 40th and 60th centiles, the scores corresponding to these centiles will also be equally

[2] By means of formula (3.11) we find that 2.5 per cent of the cases fall below 2.58 on the score continuum and that 2.5 per cent of the cases fall above 8.42. Our guess, in other words, was pretty good.

distant from the mean, but in opposite directions. Any distribution for which this is true is said to be *symmetrical.*

Imagine the graph in Figure 5.9 as being plotted on a rubber sheet which can be stretched. We now pull the sheet at the top and bottom in such a way as to stretch out the distances between centiles on the Y axis at the two extremes of the distribution, until the graph becomes a straight

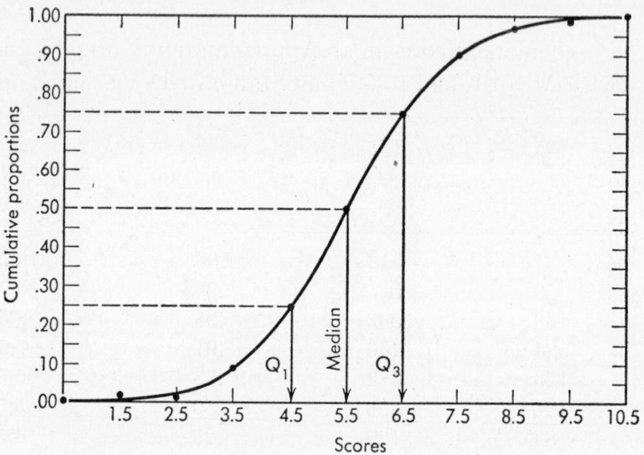

Fig. 5.9—Cumulative-proportion graph for the distribution of scores of Table 5.2.

line instead of S-shaped. If we plot a cumulative-proportion distribution on a special kind of paper, called *normal-probability paper*, the effect is much like plotting the distribution on a rubber sheet that has been pulled in the manner described. The resulting graph will be a straight line, if the distribution is normal. Plotting a cumulative-proportion graph on normal-probability paper is an extremely simple and useful way of seeing how closely a given distribution approximates the ideal normal distribution.

In Figure 5.10 we show the cumulative distribution of Table 5.2 plotted on normal-probability paper. It can readily be observed that the plotted points, in general, fall along a straight line. Only a slight departure from linearity is present at the two extremes.

■ Comparing Different Distributions Graphically

In a study undertaken by Thurstone for the Quartermaster Corps, one of the factors investigated was the food preferences of enlisted men. The details of the study need not concern us, but in Table 5.3 we show the

Table 5.3—Frequency Distributions of Ratings of Two Desserts on a Ten-Point Scale Ranging from Dislike to Like*

	Vanilla Ice Cream (n = 140)				*Roquefort Cheese* (n = 257)			
(1) X	(2) f	(3) p	(4) cf	(5) cp	(6) f	(7) p	(8) cf	(9) cp
10	3	.02	140	1.00	3	.01	257	1.00
9	10	.07	137	.98	16	.06	254	.99
8	25	.18	127	.91	36	.14	238	.93
7	50	.36	102	.73	43	.17	202	.79
6	30	.21	52	.37	54	.21	159	.62
5	14	.10	22	.16	26	.10	105	.41
4	4	.03	8	.06	26	.10	79	.31
3	2	.01	4	.03	16	.06	53	.21
2	1	.01	2	.01	20	.08	37	.14
1	1	.01	1	.01	17	.07	17	.07

* Data modified from Edwards and Thurstone (1952).

distributions of ratings for two desserts, "vanilla ice cream" and "Roquefort cheese." A high rating indicates that the dessert was liked and a low rating that it was disliked. For purposes of illustration, we have intentionally reduced the total number of ratings made for Roquefort cheese but without distorting greatly the relative frequencies of the original data.[3]

If we wished to compare these distributions of ratings graphically, it would not do to plot the frequency polygons or histograms for the frequencies as given. The reason for this is that we have a difference in the total number of judgments for the two desserts. The areas under the frequency polygons or histograms would therefore not be equal, and the graphs would not be directly comparable. We can, however, express the frequencies as proportions of the total number of judgments for each distribution separately. We have done this for each distribution, and the proportions are shown in columns (3) and (7) of Table 5.3.

If we now plot the frequency polygons (or histograms) for the two distributions, we know from our earlier discussion that the area under each will be equal to unity and the two graphs may be compared directly. These frequency polygons are shown in Figure 5.11. This method of

[3] The original data are given in Edwards and Thurstone (1952).

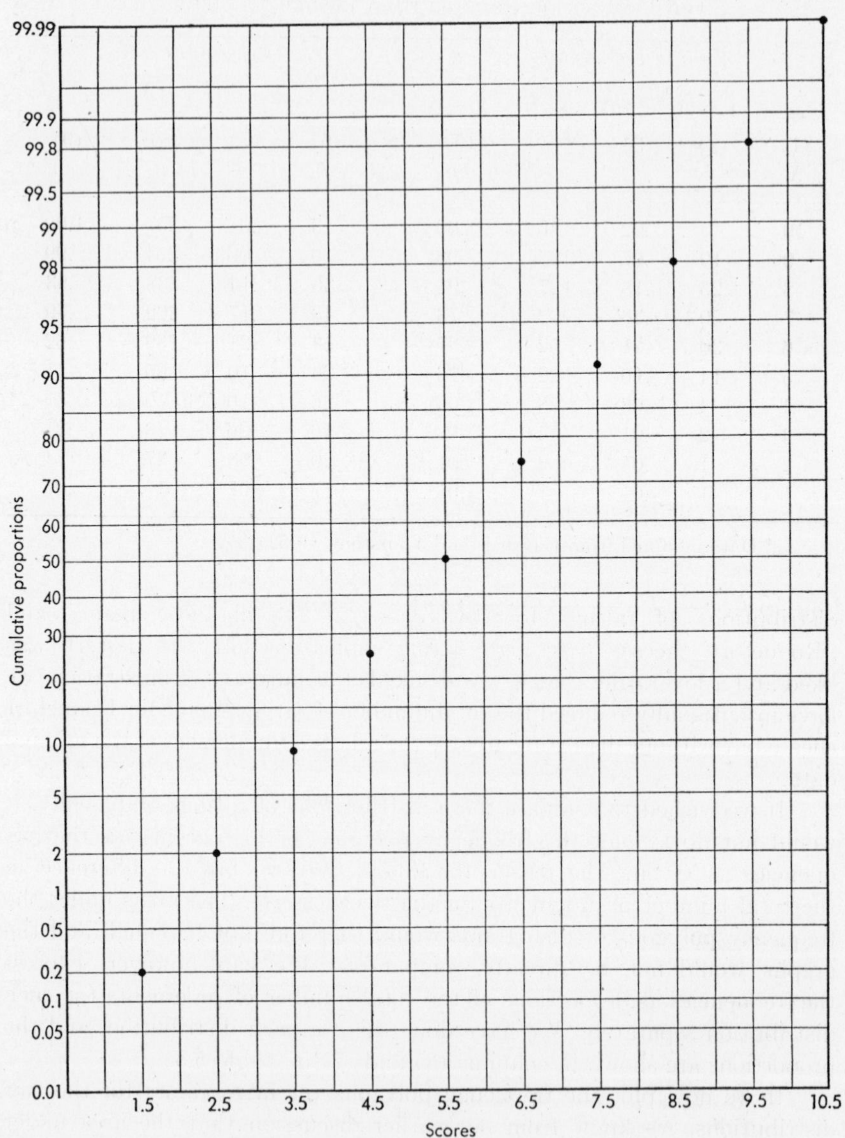

Fig. 5.10—Cumulative-proportion graph for the distribution of scores of Table 5.2 plotted on normal-probability paper.

comparing two frequency distributions, when they are based upon an unequal number of observations or measurements, is also an extremely useful graphical device. We might, for example, wish to compare graphically the distributions of scores on some test for grades or classes with differing numbers of students. By expressing the frequencies as proportions of the total number of scores for each class separately and then plotting the frequency polygons, we may show the extent to which the various

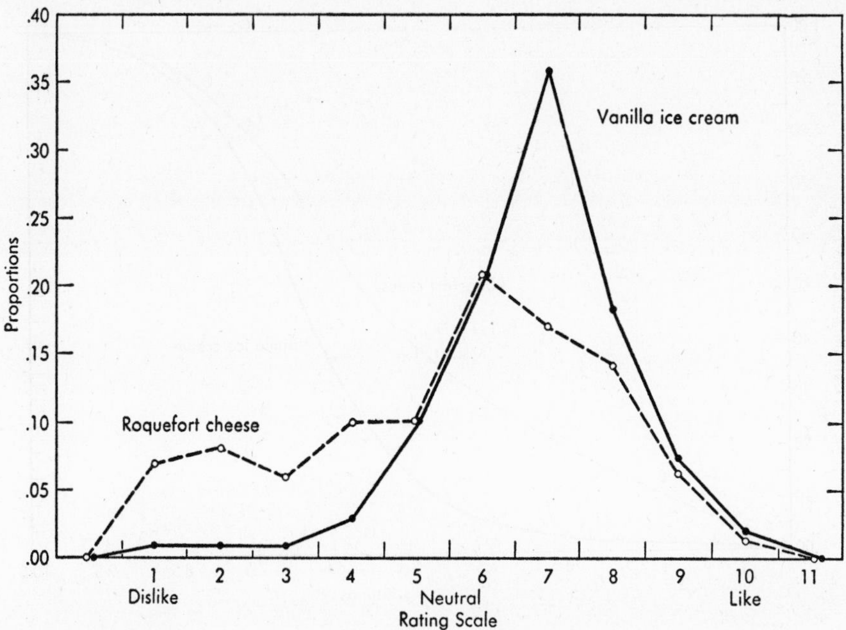

Fig. 5.11—Frequency polygons for the distributions of ratings of Table 5.3.

distributions overlap, which is most variable, and which has the higher central tendency.

It is perfectly obvious, for example that the median rating for vanilla ice cream in Figure 5.11 falls higher on the scale than the median rating for Roquefort cheese. Furthermore, it is apparent that the distribution of ratings for vanilla ice cream is much more symmetrical about the median or mode than is the case for the distribution of ratings for Roquefort cheese. The distribution of ratings for Roquefort cheese is almost rectangular for the first few intervals on the rating scale.

Another method of comparing two or more distributions based upon unequal numbers of observations is shown in Figure 5.12. There we have plotted the cumulative-proportion distributions for each of the desserts.[4] If we apply the information gained earlier in this chapter, then this graph also tells us that the median rating for vanilla ice cream is higher than the median rating for Roquefort cheese. Furthermore, the much steeper rise of the graph for vanilla ice cream, compared with the rise in the graph for Roquefort cheese, tells us that the variability of the ratings for vanilla

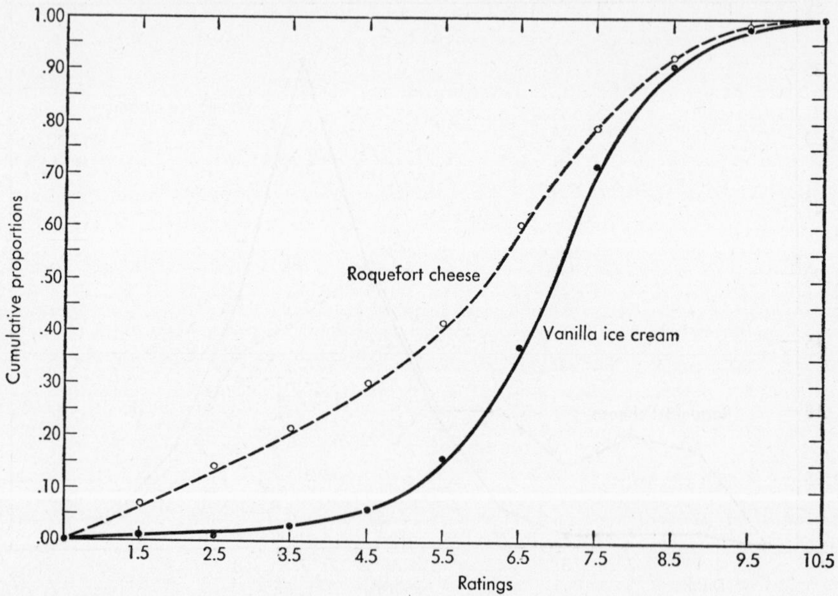

Fig. 5.12—Cumulative-proportion graphs for the distributions of ratings of Table 5.3.

ice cream is less than the variability of the ratings for Roquefort cheese. The more nearly S-shaped graph for vanilla ice cream, as compared with the graph for Roquefort cheese, also indicates the greater symmetry of the distribution of ice-cream ratings. The negative skewness of both

[4] The cumulative proportions given in columns (5) and (9) of Table 5.3 were obtained by multiplying the cumulative frequencies in columns (4) and (8) by the reciprocals of the n's of the two distributions, that is, by 1/140 and 1/257, respectively. If the proportions given in columns (3) and (7) are added to obtain the cumulative proportions, some of these values will differ slightly from those shown in columns (5) and (9) as a result of rounding errors.

distributions is clearly shown by the relatively long tails and less rapid acceleration of the graphs at the low end of the scale.

■ EXAMPLES

5.1—Sketch the following graphs:

(*a*) A cumulative-proportion graph for a negatively skewed distribution.
(*b*) A cumulative-proportion graph for a positively skewed distribution.
(*c*) A cumulative-proportion graph for a rectangular distribution.

5.2—(*a*) Sketch the cumulative-proportion graph for a normal distribution with mean equal to 50 and standard deviation equal to 10. (*b*) On the same figure, show the cumulative-proportion graph for a normal distribution with mean equal to 50 and standard deviation equal to 4.

5.3—Given a normal distribution with mean equal to 40 and standard deviation equal to 10,

(*a*) What score will correspond, approximately, to the 84th centile?
(*b*) What score will correspond, approximately, to the 16th centile?
(*c*) What score will correspond, approximately, to the 95th centile?

5.4—Draw a histogram for the following distribution of scores and on the same figure draw the frequency polygon.

Scores	*f*
55–59	1
50–54	2
45–49	7
40–44	12
35–39	16
30–34	23
25–29	15
20–24	12
15–19	7
10–14	3
5–9	2

5.5—The distributions of scores for two categories of Veterans Administration trainees in clinical psychology on the Miller Analogies Test are given below. Compare the cumulative-proportion graphs for the two groups. Data are from Kelly and Fiske (1950).

Scores	*Ph.D. Granted*	*Dismissals*
	f	*f*
95–99	1	
90–94	1	1
85–89	6	0
80–84	11	2
75–79	6	4
70–74	9	6
65–69	3	8
60–64	2	3
55–59	1	2
50–54		6
45–49		2
40–44		3
35–39		1
30–34		1

5.6—The following scores were obtained from 301 new employees in an industrial concern on the Junior Calculating Test. Draw a histogram for the distribution and on the same graph draw the frequency polygon. Data are from Selover and Vogel (1948).

Scores	*f*
9	11
8	20
7	38
6	46
5	72
4	44
3	36
2	22
1	12

5.7—Using the distribution of scores of Example 5.4, plot the cumulative-proportion graph.

■ CHAPTER SIX

Standard Scores and Normalizing Distributions

We shall now define a particular kind of score that plays a very important role in statistical analysis. This score is called a *standard score* or *relative deviate* and is symbolized by z. We define a standard score as

$$z = \frac{X - \bar{X}}{s} = \frac{x}{s} \tag{6.1}$$

where X = an original measurement
$\bar{X}$ = the mean of the distribution
s = the standard deviation of the distribution

In order to translate a set of measures into standard scores, we first express each value as a deviation from the mean of the distribution and then divide each resulting deviation by the standard deviation of the distribution. Some of the z scores will, of course, be negative in sign, since some of the scores or measures will be smaller than the mean. In general, if n is large a distribution of z scores will range in size from about -3.00 to 3.00. When n is small, the range of z scores will not be as great as that observed for distributions based upon larger n's. Table 6.1 shows the approximate range in standard scores to be expected for varying values of n, when samples have been drawn from distributions that are normal in form.

For the distribution of scores in Table 5.2 in the last chapter, we had an n equal to 512. The mean of this distribution was 5.5, and the standard deviation was 1.5. The highest observed value was 10, and the lowest score in the distribution was 1. The standard score corresponding to the highest value in the distribution would therefore be

$$z = \frac{10.0 - 5.5}{1.5} = 3.0$$

and similarly the standard score for the lowest value in the distribution would be

$$z = \frac{1.0 - 5.5}{1.5} = -3.0$$

Our observed range of standard scores is thus from -3.0 to 3.0 or 6.0, and this range corresponds very well with the expected range of 6.1 for samples based upon an n of 500 cases as given in Table 6.1.

Table 6.1—Average Range of Standard Scores in Samples of Varying Size Drawn from a Normally Distributed Population*

n	R	n	R
5	2.3	65	4.7
6	2.5	85	4.9
7	2.7	100	5.0
8	2.8	125	5.2
9	3.0	150	5.3
10	3.1	175	5.4
15	3.5	200	5.5
20	3.7	250	5.6
25	3.9	300	5.8
30	4.1	400	5.9
40	4.3	500	6.1
50	4.5	1,000	6.5

* Reproduced from L. H. C. Tippett. On the extreme individuals and the range of a sample from a normal population. *Biometrika*, **17** (1925), 386, by permission of *Biometrika* and the author.

Any set of measures transformed to standard scores will have the following properties: (1) the mean of the transformed distribution, that is, of the standard scores, will be equal to zero, and (2) the variance will be equal to 1.00. Since the standard deviation is the square root of the variance, the standard deviation of a set of standard scores will also be equal to 1.00.

That the mean of a distribution of standard scores will be equal to zero can be established very easily, since by definition the mean of a set of scores is the sum of the scores divided by n. Thus

$$\begin{aligned}\bar{z} &= \frac{\sum z}{n} \\ &= \frac{\sum \frac{x}{s}}{n} \\ &= \frac{\frac{\sum x}{s}}{n} \\ &= 0 \qquad \textbf{(6.2)}\end{aligned}$$

Since the mean of a set of standard scores is zero, as shown above, the variance will simply be the sum of the squared z scores, divided by $n - 1$. Then[1]

$$\begin{aligned}s_z^{\,2} &= \frac{\sum z^2}{n-1} \\ &= \frac{\sum \frac{x^2}{s^2}}{n-1} \\ &= \frac{\frac{\sum x^2}{s^2}}{n-1} \\ &= \frac{\sum x^2}{(n-1)s^2} \\ &= \frac{\sum x^2}{\sum x^2} \\ &= 1.00 \qquad \textbf{(6.3)}\end{aligned}$$

[1] Let us again emphasize that if the algebra is not perfectly clear, you should go back and study the rules of summation in Chapter 2. Nothing is involved but the application of these rules and the definitions given by the formulas.

The fact that the mean of any distribution of standard scores will always be equal to zero and the fact that the standard deviation (or variance) will always be equal to 1.00 have some very useful applications in statistical analysis. Standard scores, for example, derived from one distribution may be compared directly with standard scores of another distribution of comparable form.

■ Combining Scores from Different Tests

Let us suppose that we wish to find an average of an individual's scores on a history test and on an English test. The history test is scored in terms of the number of right answers and shows a spread of scores from 10 to 190 with a mean of 95. The English test, however, is scored in terms of the number of right answers minus the number of wrong, and the range of scores is from 50 to 70 with a mean of 59. Obviously, we cannot compare directly the standing of our subject on one test with his standing on the other. We could not find his average standing on both tests by adding his score on the history test and his score on the English examination and dividing by 2. This average would have no meaning, for we would be combining different units from different scales. It is as though we added together an individual's height, measured in inches, and his weight, measured in pounds, and divided the sum by 2 to get an average. Suppose we were foolish enough to do so and found that this average was 110—but 110 what? Inches? Pounds? Surely not either of these, nor would such an average have any other meaning.

If we wish to compare measurements from various distributions of comparable form, we must first reduce the measurements of each distribution to a common scale. By translating the original measures into standard scores for each distribution, we accomplish this end. The standard scores thus obtained are in comparable units.

There may be occasions when it seems legitimate to average original measures from several distributions without first transforming the measures into standard scores or in other ways obtaining a common scale. Suppose, for example, an instructor has given 5 examinations during the course of a quarter and each examination is scored in terms of the number of correct responses. You may feel that it is permissible to average the scores from the separate examinations. It should be emphasized, however, that if the distributions of scores on the various examinations have different standard deviations, an average score based upon all the examinations will not give equal weight to each examination.

In general, the scores obtained from the distributions with large standard deviations will have more influence upon the average than scores obtained from distributions with small standard deviations. Only in the exceptional case in which all distributions have comparable standard deviations will the separate scores be weighted equally in determining an average score. If we want each examination to be weighted equally with the others, and if the standard deviations are different, we can accomplish this by first translating the scores from each distribution into standard scores and then averaging the standard scores.

We may illustrate the point made above with the data of Table 6.2.

Table 6.2—*X* Scores and *z* Scores of Two Individuals on Five Examinations

(1) *Exami-nation*	(2) $\bar{X}$	(3) s	(4) *David's* X	(5) *Steven's* X	(6) *David's* z	(7) *Steven's* z
1	120	20	140	160	1.00	2.00
2	80	10	75	60	−.50	−2.00
3	42	8	66	44	3.00	.25
4	68	12	86	71	1.50	.25
5	200	50	150	300	−1.00	2.00
Σ			517	635	4.00	2.50

We see that the total number of points on 5 examinations is 517 for David and is 635 for Steven. If we depended upon the raw scores only, Steven would receive a higher grade in the course than David. Now let us express the scores on the examinations in the form of standard scores. These are obtained by subtracting the means of the examinations from the scores in columns (4) and (5), and dividing the resulting deviations by the standard deviations. The means and standard deviations are given in columns (2) and (3), and the resulting standard scores are shown in columns (6) and (7).

If we sum the standard scores, we see that David's total is 4.00 and Steven's is 2.50. Since the standard scores reduce the scores from each examination to a common scale, the sum of the standard scores gives each examination equal weight. When this is done, David has a higher standing than Steven on the 5 examinations. If we simply sum the original scores, Steven has a higher standing than David, primarily because Steven's best scores are on the examinations with the larger standard deviations (examinations 1 and 5), and these scores are weighted more heavily in determining the sum of the original scores. David's best work, however, is on the examinations with the smaller standard deviations (examinations 3 and 4), and in summing the original scores these examinations contribute less than the examinations with the larger standard deviations.

If we desire to do so, we can, of course, now weight the standard scores of the different examinations so that some of the examinations contribute more to the total than others. Suppose, for example, that the last examination is a final examination and that the instructor feels that this examination should carry more weight than any of the other examinations. This examination can be given additional weight by simply multiplying the standard scores on it with the desired weight. If the instructor wants the examination to count twice as much as any one of the other examinations, then the total score for each student would be given by

$$z_1 + z_2 + z_3 + z_4 + (2)(z_5) = \text{total score}$$

If the scores are to be averaged, then the divisor would be 6 instead of 5. However, since the divisor would be a constant for all students, the relative standings of the students given by the total scores would be the same as the relative standings given by the averages, and this additional computation would not be necessary for grading purposes.

The advantage of the procedure described is that the instructor would at least know what weights are being assigned to the examinations. By averaging the original scores, the unwary instructor may, in his ignorance, be assigning undue weights to minor examinations. With standard scores he can either weight the examinations equally or weight the individual examinations in terms of the judged importance of the material covered by each examination.

■ Transformed Standard Scores

Since standard scores, as defined by formula (6.1), take negative as well as positive values, it may sometimes be judged desirable to shift the origin of the distribution in such a way as to make all scores positive in sign. As we have seen in an earlier chapter, adding a constant to each score will have no effect upon the standard deviation of a distribution, but will merely have the result of increasing the mean by the amount of the constant that is added to each score. Thus, if 50 points are added to each of the standard scores obtained by means of formula (6.1), the mean of this new distribution will be 50 instead of zero, but the standard deviation will still be equal to 1.00. If we wish to increase the standard deviation by any given amount, we multiply the standard scores obtained by formula (6.1) by an appropriate constant.

We may define a new score with mean equal to a and standard deviation equal to b as

$$Z = a + b\left(\frac{X - \bar{X}}{s}\right) \tag{6.4}$$

where b = an arbitrary constant by which $z = (X - \bar{X})/s$ is multiplied
a = an arbitrary constant to be added to the product

In formula (6.1), b is equal to 1.00 and a is equal to zero, and the distribution of such a set of standard scores, as we already know, has a standard deviation of 1.00 and a mean of zero.

Suppose we now let a equal 50 and b equal 15, so that formula (6.4) becomes

$$Z = 50 + 15\left(\frac{X - \bar{X}}{s}\right)$$

This distribution of scores will have a mean equal to a or 50 and a standard deviation equal to b or 15. For a large number of observations, we may expect this transformation to give us a range of scores from approximately −3.00 to 3.00 standard deviations. Since the standard deviation is 15, our expected range will be from 5 to 95. The transformed scores thus have a convenient scale from approximately 0 to 100 with a mean equal to 50.

No matter what values we substitute for a and b in formula (6.4), the resulting mean and standard deviation of the transformed distribution will be equal to a and b, respectively. The proof of these statements is given in answer to one of the examples at the end of the chapter.

Normalizing a Distribution of Scores

It may be emphasized that changing a set of scores to standard scores does nothing to alter the shape of the original distribution. The only change is to shift the mean to zero and the standard deviation to unity. The form of the distribution remains exactly the same. Students sometimes get the mistaken notion that when scores are changed to standard scores, the distribution of scores is therefore somehow normalized, that is, changed to a normal distribution. This is not the case. If the original score distribution is normal in form, the standard score distribution will also be normal. But if the original distribution is skewed, the standard score distribution will also be skewed.

In Table 6.3 we repeat the distribution of scores on the Minnesota Psycho-Analogies Test for 158 students. The mean of the original distribution, as we mentioned earlier, is 59.3, and the standard deviation is 8.1. In column (3) we give the midpoints of each class interval. You may recall that our assumption is that all of the scores within a given interval can be represented by the midpoint of the interval. Thus the 4 scores within the class interval 72–74 are all assumed to be represented by 73. In column (4) we show the standard scores, obtained by formula (6.1),

Table 6.3—Transforming the Scores of Table 5.1 to Standard Scores, Normalized Standard Scores, and *T* Scores*

(1) *X*	(2) *f*	(3) *Midpoints of Intervals*	(4) *Observed z*	(5) *Upper Limit cf*	(6) *Midpoint cf*	(7) *Midpoint cp*	(8) *Normal z*	(9) *T Scores*
72–74	4	73	1.69	158	156.0	.987	2.23	72.3
69–71	15	70	1.32	154	146.5	.927	1.45	64.5
66–68	21	67	.95	139	128.5	.813	.89	58.9
63–65	21	64	.58	118	107.5	.680	.47	54.7
60–62	24	61	.21	97	85.0	.538	.10	51.0
57–59	16	58	−.16	73	65.0	.411	−.22	47.8
54–56	23	55	−.53	57	45.5	.288	−.56	44.4
51–53	15	52	−.90	34	26.5	.168	−.96	40.4
48–50	7	49	−1.27	19	15.5	.098	−1.29	37.1
45–47	3	46	−1.64	12	10.5	.066	−1.51	34.9
42–44	4	43	−2.01	9	7.0	.044	−1.71	32.9
39–41	1	40	−2.38	5	4.5	.028	−1.91	30.9
36–38	3	37	−2.75	4	2.5	.016	−2.14	28.6
33–35	1	34	−3.12	1	.5	.003	−2.75	22.5
Σ	158							

* Data from Levine (1950).

corresponding to the midpoints of the intervals. For example, the standard score corresponding to the midpoint of the class interval 72–74 was obtained by

$$z = \frac{73.0 - 59.3}{8.1} = 1.69$$

Direct calculation verifies that the mean of this distribution of z scores is equal to zero and that the standard deviation is equal to 1.00, within errors of rounding. The form of the distribution remains unchanged by this transformation.

Let us suppose, however, that we wish to alter the scale of scores in such a way that the transformed distribution will be normal in form. A simple method of doing this is shown in Table 6.3. We first find the cumulative frequencies as shown in column (5). These cumulative frequencies correspond to the upper limits of the class intervals. For our purpose, however, we need the cumulative frequencies up to the midpoints of the class intervals. If we assume that the frequencies within each interval are uniformly distributed throughout the interval, then the cumulative frequency to a given midpoint will be equal to the sum of all of the frequencies below that midpoint plus one half the frequency within the interval in which the midpoint is located. For example, the cumulative frequency falling below the midpoint 49, of the class interval 48–50, is found by adding 12, the sum of the frequencies falling below the interval 48–50, and one half of 7, the frequency within the interval 48–50. We thus have $12 + \frac{7}{2} = 15.5$ for the desired cumulative frequency up to the midpoint of the interval. The cumulative frequencies up to the midpoints of each of the other intervals are found in the same manner. These values are entered in column (6) of Table 6.3.

In column (7) the cumulative frequencies of column (6) are expressed as proportions by dividing each one by 158, the total number of observations. We again use the reciprocal of 158 or $1/158 = .00633$ to multiply the cumulative frequencies rather than the equivalent operation of dividing them by 158 in finding the proportions entered in column (7).

Table of the Normal Curve

We shall not discuss the equation of the normal curve at this time. For the present our need will be met if we know how to use the table of the unit normal curve. The unit normal curve is a theoretical normal distribution with mean equal to zero and standard deviation equal to 1.00 and in which the area under the curve has been set equal to unity. Table III, in the Appendix, is a table of the unit normal curve.

The first column of Table III is headed z and gives the distance from the mean along the abscissa in terms of standard deviation units or standard scores. For example, if you run down the first column of the table until you come to 1.00, this value represents a distance that is 1 standard deviation above the mean. The second column gives the proportion of the total area falling between an ordinate at the mean and an ordinate at the corresponding point given by the value in the first column. For example, from column (2) opposite the entry 1.00 in column (1) you will find .3413 tabled. This tells you that .3413 of the total area falls between the mean and a distance 1 standard deviation above the mean of the distribution.

The third column of the table gives the area of the curve falling below the value of z given in the first column or the area in the larger portion of the curve as it is sectioned by the ordinate at z. For example, opposite the z value of 1.00 in the first column, you will find the entry .8413 in the third column.

The fourth column of the table gives the area of the curve above z or in the smaller portion of the curve as sectioned by the ordinate at z. The entry in the fourth column opposite the z value of 1.00 in the first column, for example, is .1587. This is as it must be, since the area in the smaller portion of the curve, .1587, plus the area in the larger portion of the curve, .8413, must equal unity, the total area under the curve.

Since the normal curve is symmetrical, the tabled values are given for only one half of the curve, that is, only for positive values of z. Negative values of z would have exactly the same entries tabled as those for positive values of z. Hence the table may be entered with negative as well as with positive values of z. For a z of -1.00, column (2) tells us that the area between the ordinates corresponding to this z and the mean is .3413. Column (3) tells us that .8413 of the area will fall above a z of -1.00, and column (4) tells us that .1587 of the area will fall below the ordinate at z equal to -1.00.

The table of the unit normal curve is used a great deal in psychological and educational statistics, and it is important that you know how to use the table. You might go back and study Figure 5.8 at this time. You can check the relations shown there against the entries in the table of the curve. The entries in column (5) of the table give the value of the ordinate y erected at the point z for the unit normal curve. We shall have more to say about these ordinates later.

Normalized Standard Scores

We can now complete the project we started, namely, normalizing the distribution of scores in Table 6.3. The entries in column (7), you may recall, show the proportion of the total number of cases falling below the midpoints of the class intervals. For example, .003 of the total of 158 cases fall below the midpoint of the first interval 34. We have already shown, in column (4), that the z or standard-score value corresponding to this midpoint for our *observed distribution* of scores is -3.12. What we want to know now, however, is the z or standard-score value corresponding to this midpoint in a *theoretical normal distribution.* We can find this value from Table III.

We look in Table III to find the value of z below which .003 of the area will fall. Since .500 of the total area in a normal distribution will fall below a z equal to zero, or the mean of the distribution, any point below which less than .500 of the total area falls must correspond to a negative value of z. If we find the value of z such that .003 of the area of the curve falls to the left of the ordinate at z and such that .997 of the area falls to the right, this will be the value we want. We look in column (4) headed "Area in Smaller Portion" to find .003. We then read the corresponding z value from column (1) and find it to be 2.75. We attach a negative sign to this value (the z is below the mean) and enter -2.75 in column (8) of Table 6.3.

Let us find one more entry in column (8) to make sure that the procedure described is clear. We see that in our observed distribution .538 of the cases fall below the midpoint 61 of the class interval 60–62. We want to find the z value in a normal distribution below which .538 of the total area will fall. Since this proportion is greater than .500, the z value must be to the right of the mean or positive in sign. We now look in Table III, column (3), headed "Area in Larger Portion" to find .538. Our closest approximation to this value is given by .5398; consequently we take the z value corresponding to this entry. It is .10 and this is the value we have entered in column (8) opposite .538 in Table 6.3. You should check several of the other entries in column (8).

The standard scores we have just obtained are normalized standard scores. You would find upon calculation that the mean of this distribution of scores is zero and that the standard deviation is equal to 1.00.[2] But the distribution will no longer have the same form as the original distribution. We have stretched the score scale in such a way as to normalize the distribution. If, for example, you plot the cumulative proportions against the normalized standard scores in column (8) of Table 3.6 on normal-probability paper, you will find that the graph is a straight line. This will not be true of the original distribution.

T Scores

In column (9) of Table 6.3 we give a particular kind of normalized score that has come to be known as a T score. T scores are frequently

---

[2] Minor deviations from these values may be present as a result of rounding and grouping errors and errors introduced by using approximate values of z from Table III.

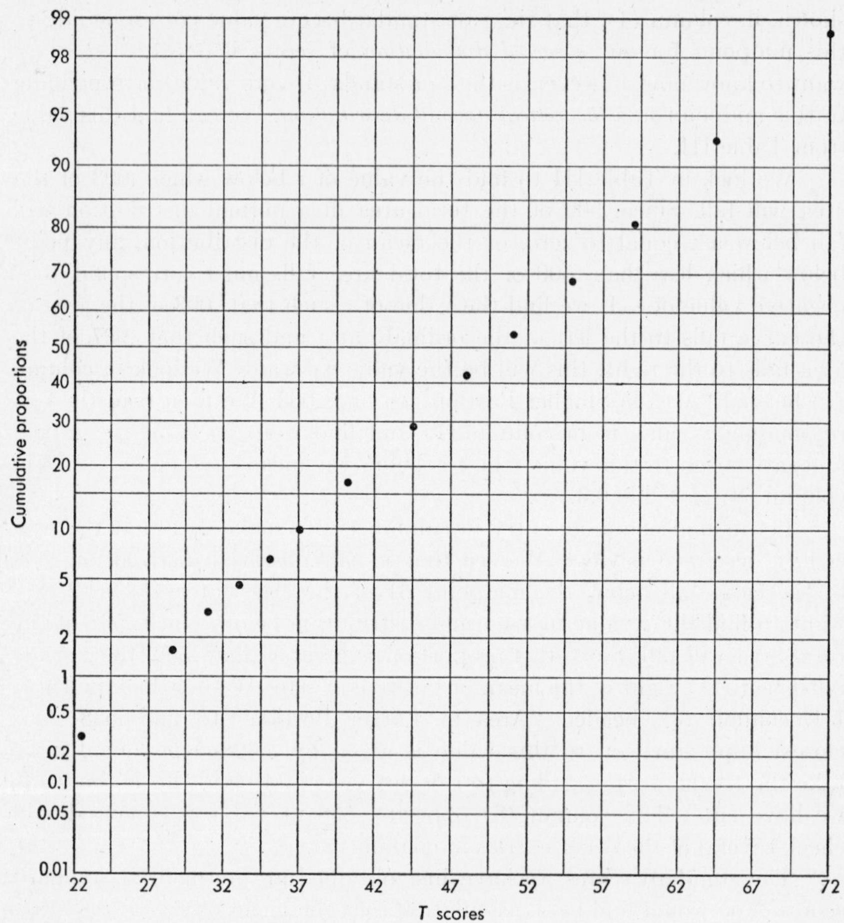

Fig. 6.1—Cumulative-proportion graph for the distribution of T scores of Table 6.3 plotted on normal-probability paper.

used in constructing norms for standardized psychological and educational tests. The values of the T scores are obtained directly from the normalized standard scores of column (8). We have simply multiplied each entry in column (8) by 10 and added 50 to the product. For example, the normalized standard score of 2.23 becomes $(10)(2.23) + 50 = 72.3$ when translated into a T score. The figure after the decimal place is usually dropped, and the T score is rounded to two digits.

The two constants, 50 and 10, correspond to the a and b constants of formula (6.4). You should know, therefore, that the mean of a distribution of T scores will be 50 and that the standard deviation will be equal to 10. Furthermore, the distribution of T scores will be normal in form. That this is true is shown in Figure 6.1 where we have plotted on normal-probability paper the cumulative proportions against the corresponding T scores. It is apparent that the graph is linear.

T scores are obtained directly from normalized standard scores, and these in turn refer to the proportion of the total frequency below a given score plus 1/2 the frequency of that score in a normal distribution. We may thus table, once and for all, the T scores corresponding to these proportions. This has been done in Table XI, in the Appendix. If we enter Table XI with the proportions of column (7) of Table 6.3, we can obtain the corresponding T scores without further computations. Table XI may be used to transform the scores in any distribution to T scores. We simply find the proportion of the total frequency below a given score plus 1/2 the frequency of that score. We then enter Table XI with these proportions to find the corresponding T scores.

■ Normalizing Ranked Data

In some cases it may not be possible for us to measure the variable in which we are interested, but it may be possible for us to obtain judgments of the degree to which each person or object possesses the variable. A convenient technique for obtaining such judgments is the *method of rank order*. A subject, for example, might be asked to arrange a series of pictures from the one most liked to the one least liked. After the task is completed, the pictures will be arranged in serial order, and we assign the number 1 to the picture liked most, the number 2 to the next most-liked picture, and so on. Individuals or objects arranged in this way are said to be ranked. The rank itself refers to the relative position of an object or individual in a group of objects or individuals.

It is important in dealing with ranks that we know the total number of objects ranked. A rank of 8, for example, would mean something quite different in a set of 20 ranks than it would if the set of ranks consisted of only 8 objects. In the first instance the rank of 8 is above the mean of the set of ranks, and in the second instance it is the last rank in the series. Furthermore, we should note that ranks do not tell us anything about the relative distances between the objects, with respect to the variable ranked, in the way in which measurements do. For example, we might rank a group of individuals with respect to their heights and we might also have available measurements of the heights of each individual. The measurements would tell us *how much* taller or shorter one individual was compared with another, whereas the ranks would only tell us whether one individual was taller or shorter than another.

Having obtained a set of ranks, we may make the assumption that the variable that was ranked is normally distributed. We could then use the procedures previously described for normalizing a distribution of observations to normalize the set of ranks. We could thus transform the ranks into T scores or any other form of normalized scores.

Table XII, in the Appendix, enables us to obtain directly the T scores for any set of ranks from 5 to 45. As indicated in the table, the mean of these transformed scores will be 50 and the standard deviation will be 10.

■ EXAMPLES

6.1—Prove that the mean of a set of standard scores is equal to zero.

6.2—Prove that the variance and standard deviation of a set of standard scores is equal to 1.00.

6.3—Prove that, if we multiply each value in a set of standard scores by a constant b and then add a constant a to the product, the mean of this new distribution will be equal to a and the variance will be equal to b^2.

6.4—If we have a normal distribution, then the centiles corresponding to various standard scores may be obtained from the table of the normal curve. Find the centiles for the following standard scores from Table III, in the Appendix.

(*a*) $z = .00$ (*e*) $z = -1.00$
(*b*) $z = .74$ (*f*) $z = 1.04$
(*c*) $z = -.67$ (*g*) $z = 1.23$
(*d*) $z = -.44$ (*h*) $z = 2.33$

6.5—Table XII in the Appendix gives the T scores for sets of ranks from 5 to 45. Verify these T scores for the ranks 1 to 10, using the method for normalizing a distribution described in the chapter.

6.6—Plot the cumulative-proportion graph for the T scores of Example 6.5 on normal-probability paper.

6.7—Given a normal distribution of scores with mean equal to 50, standard deviation equal to 10, and n equal to 500:

(*a*) What is the estimated range of scores?
(*b*) What score will correspond to Q_1?
(*c*) What proportion of the scores will fall between 40 and 60?
(*d*) What score will correspond to the median?

6.8—Using Table XI, in the Appendix, find the T scores for the midpoints of the following distribution of scores.

Scores	*f*
55–59	1
50–54	2
45–49	7
40–44	12
35–39	16
30–34	23
25–29	15
20–24	12
15–19	7
10–14	3
5– 9	2

Linear Regression

Many psychological research problems are concerned with the relationship between two or more variables. In this chapter we shall discuss methods of determining an equation that will relate values of an observed *dependent* variable Y to values of a second *independent* variable X. We shall assume that the values of the independent variable have been *selected* by the experimenter. These X values may represent measures of time, number of trials, varying levels of illumination, varying amounts of practice, varying dosages of a drug, intensities of electric shock, or any other variable of experimental interest.

For each X value, the experimenter subsequently obtains a corresponding observation of the dependent variable Y. We wish to determine whether these Y values are related to the X values. We shall be concerned primarily with the case of *linear relationships*. By a linear relationship, we mean that if the Y values are plotted against the X values in a graph, the resulting trend of the plotted points can be represented by a straight line. Our problem is to determine an equation for the straight line which represents the trend. We may regard this empirical equation as a rule that relates values of Y to those of X.

■ Equation of a Straight Line

Consider the values of X and Y in Table 7.1. What is the rule that relates Y to X? Examination of the pairs of values will show that each value of Y is exactly .5 of the corresponding value of X. We may express this rule in the following way

$$Y = bX \tag{7.1}$$

where $b = .5$ is a constant which multiplies each value of X. If each value of Y in Table 7.1 was exactly equal to the corresponding value of X, then the

Table 7.1—Values of $Y = .5X$ for Given Values of X

X	Y
8	4.0
5	2.5
6	3.0
2	1.0
10	5.0
12	6.0
7	3.5
4	2.0
3	1.5

value of b would have to be equal to 1.00. If each value of Y was numerically equal to X, but opposite in sign, then the value of b would be equal to -1.00.

Now examine the values of X and Y in Table 7.2. The rule or equation

Table 7.2—Values of $Y = 4 + .5X$ for Given Values of X

X	Y
4	6.0
9	8.5
14	11.0
6	7.0
16	12.0
5	6.5
8	8.0
7	7.5
11	9.5
10	9.0

relating values of Y to X may not be quite so obvious here. Its general form is as follows

$$Y = a + bX \tag{7.2}$$

where b is again a constant that multiplies each value of X, and a is a constant that is added to each of the products. For the data of Table 7.2 the value of b is .5 and the value of a is 4. Thus when $X = 6$, $Y = 4 + (.5)(6) = 7$.

Formula (7.1) and formula (7.2) are both equations for a straight line. For example, we could take any arbitrary constants for a and b. Then for any given set of X values we could substitute in formula (7.2) and obtain a set of Y values. If these obtained values of Y were plotted against the corresponding X values, the set of plotted points would fall on a straight line.

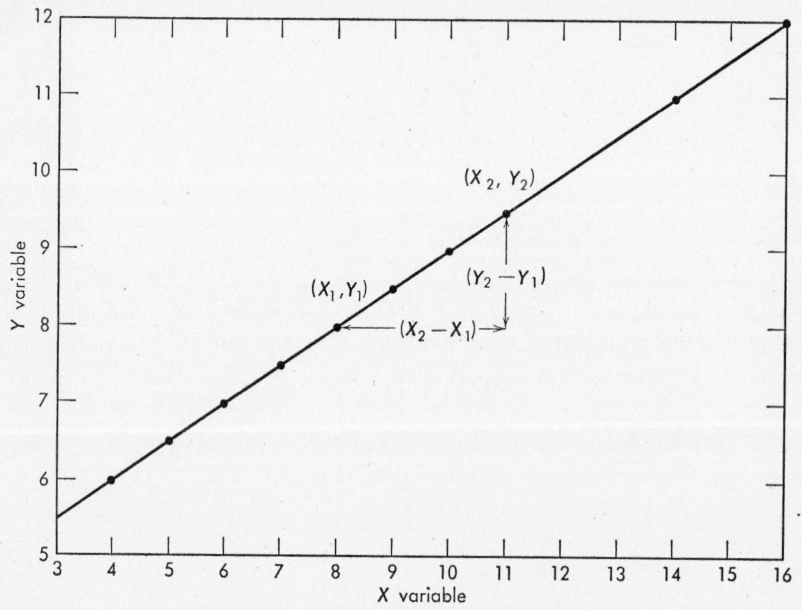

Fig. 7.1—Plot of the X, Y values of Table 7.2.

The Graph of $Y = a + bX$

Let us plot the values of Y given in Table 7.2 against the corresponding values of X. The graph will give us some additional insight into the nature of the constant b that multiplies each X and also the constant a that is added to the product. In making the graph, we set up two axes at right angles to each other. It is customary to let the horizontal axis represent the independent or X variable and the vertical axis the dependent or Y variable. We need not begin our scale on the X and Y axes at zero. We may begin with any convenient values that permit us to plot the lowest values of X and Y. In Figure 7.1, for example, we begin the X scale with 3 and the Y scale with 5. Nor is it necessary that the X and Y scales be expressed in the same units. You will note in Figure 7.1, for example, that a 1-point increase in X is represented by a distance on the X axis that is only 3/4 the distance corresponding to a 1-point increase on the Y axis.

You will recall that a pair of values (X,Y) represent the coordinates of a point.[1] To find the point on the graph corresponding to (11, 9.5) we go out the X axis to 11 and *imagine* a line perpendicular to the X axis erected at this point. We now go up the Y axis to 9.5 and *imagine* another line perpendicular to the Y axis erected at this point. The intersection of the two perpendiculars will be the point (11, 9.5) on the graph. It is obviously not necessary to draw the perpendiculars in order to plot a set of points.

The Slope and Intercept of the Line

It is clear that the points plotted in Figure 7.1 fall along a straight line. We already know that the equation of this line as given by formula (7.2) is

$$Y = 4 + .5X$$

What is the nature of the multiplying constant $b = .5$? Note, for example, that as we move from 10 to 11 on the X scale, the corresponding increase on the Y scale is from 9 to 9.5. An increase of 1 unit in X, in other words, results in only .5 of a unit increase in Y. Similarly, if we move from 10 to 15 on the X scale, a distance of 5 units, the corresponding increase on the Y scale is from 9 to 11.5, a distance of 2.5 units. It seems apparent that, b gives the *rate* at which Y changes with change in X.

The value of b can be determined directly from the graph in Figure 7.1. For example, if we take any two points on the line, with coordinates (X_1, Y_1) and (X_2, Y_2), then

$$b = \frac{Y_2 - Y_1}{X_2 - X_1} \tag{7.3}$$

Substituting in the above formula with the coordinates (8, 8.0) and (11, 9.5), we have

$$b = \frac{9.5 - 8.0}{11 - 8} = \frac{1.5}{3} = .5$$

In geometry, formula (7.3) is known as a particular form of the equation of a straight line, and the value of b is called the *slope* of the straight line.

---

[1] See p. 82.

The nature of the additive constant a in formula (7.2) can be readily determined by setting X equal to zero. The value of a must then be the value of Y when X is equal to zero. If the X and Y axes were extended downward in Figure 7.1, we would see that the graph of the straight line would intersect the Y axis at the point $(0, a)$. The number a is called the *Y-intercept* of the line. We already know that a is equal to 4. If the line passed through the point (0, 0), then a would be equal to zero, and the equation of the line would be $Y = bX$ as given in formula (7.1).

Positive and Negative Relationships

We may conclude that if the relationship between two variables is linear, then the values of a and b can be determined by plotting the values and finding the Y-intercept and the slope of the line, respectively. A single equation may then be written which will express the nature of the relationship. When the value of b is positive in sign, the relationship is also described as positive, that is, an increase in X is accompanied by an increase in Y and a decrease in X is accompanied by a decrease in Y. When the value of b is negative, the relationship is also described as negative. A negative relationship means that an increase in X is accompanied by a decrease in Y, and a decrease in X is accompanied by an increase in Y. When two variables are positively related, the line representing this relationship will extend from the lower left of the graph to the upper right, and the slope of the line is said to be positive. When the relationship is negative, the line will extend from the upper left of the graph to the lower right, and the slope of the line is said to be negative.

When a set of plotted points corresponding to values of an X variable and a Y variable fall precisely on a straight line such that no single point deviates from the line, the relationship between the two variables is said to be perfect. This means that every *observed* value of Y will be given exactly by $Y = a + bX$. With empirical data we do not expect to find perfect relationships. Errors of measurement may be involved along with other sources of variation. The trend of the plotted points may be linear, but the plotted points will not fall precisely on any line that we might draw.

Finding a Line of Best Fit

Our problem with empirical data is to find the *line of best fit* that relates Y to X. This line is called the *regression line of Y on X*, and the equation for the line is called a *regression equation*. The value of b in the regression equation is called a *regression coefficient*.

The notion of a best-fitting line will require some discussion. What does "best fit" mean? A set of empirical values may assist us in under-

Table 7.3—Finding the Line of Best Fit for $\tilde{Y} = a + bX$

	(1) X	(2) Y	(3) X^2	(4) Y^2	(5) XY	(6) $\tilde{Y}$	(7) $(Y - \tilde{Y})$	(8) $(Y - \tilde{Y})^2$
	6	6	36	36	36	5.84	.16	.0256
	5	4	25	16	20	4.73	− .73	.5329
	4	5	16	25	20	3.62	1.38	1.9044
	3	3	9	9	9	2.51	.49	.2401
	2	1	4	1	2	1.40	− .40	.1600
	1	−1	1	1	−1	.29	−1.29	1.6641
	−1	−2	1	4	2	−1.93	− .07	.0049
	−2	−4	4	16	8	−3.04	− .96	.9216
	−3	−3	9	9	9	−4.15	1.15	1.3225
	−4	−5	16	25	20	−5.26	.26	.0676
Σ	11	4	121	142	125	4.01	− .01	6.8437

standing this concept. Examine the data in Table 7.3 and the corresponding plotted points in Figure 7.2. It is obvious that the trend of the points can be described by a straight line. If we desire to represent the relationship by means of a single straight line, how shall we draw the line, and what will be the resulting values of a and b in the equation for the line?

The line might be drawn by inspection, and sometimes this will prove to be a satisfactory procedure. But if we have a large number of plotted points, drawing the line by inspection will be more difficult. If several different individuals draw what they believe is the line representing the trend, we may have several different lines, with corresponding differences in the values of a and b. How shall we select a single line from among the several possible? Which will give the best fit?

Inspectional procedures can never be as satisfactory as those involving analytical methods. If we can determine the line by algebraic operations upon the data, in terms of a criterion of best fit, we may expect agreement among different observers. Furthermore, we shall have a uniquely determined line to represent the trend.

Since we are no longer dealing with a perfect relationship between X and Y, let us make a slight change in notation and write

$$\tilde{Y} = a + bX \qquad (7.4)$$

where $\tilde{Y}$ indicates a value falling on the line given by the regression equation. $\tilde{Y}$ as given by formula (7.4) will no longer necessarily be equal to the observed value of Y corresponding to the observed value of X. We may regard the values of $\tilde{Y}$ as the predicted values for the observed values of Y. Then an error of prediction will be given by

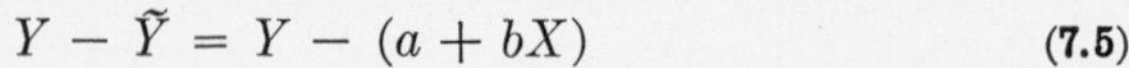

$$Y - \tilde{Y} = Y - (a + bX) \tag{7.5}$$

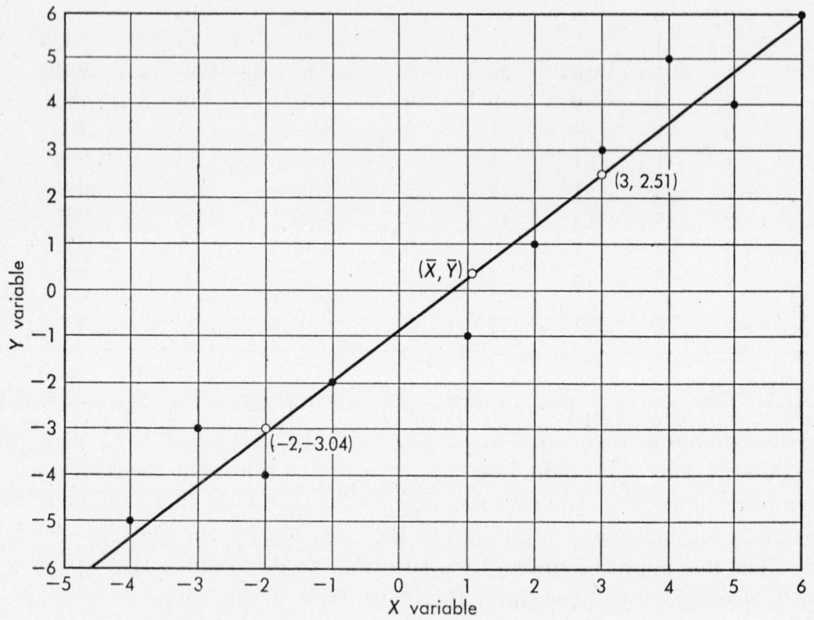

Fig. 7.2—Plot of the X, Y values of Table 7.3 and the line of best fit.

Method of Least Squares

We shall find the line of best fit by the *method of least squares*. This criterion of best fit demands that the values of a and b be determined in such a way that

$$\sum(Y - \tilde{Y})^2 = \sum[Y - (a + bX)]^2 \tag{7.6}$$

will be a minimum, that is, that the sum of squares of our errors of prediction will be less than it would be for any other values of a and b that might be selected. It can be shown that the values of a and b that will make the residual sum of squares $\sum(Y - \tilde{Y})^2$ a minimum must satisfy the following equations[2]

$$\sum Y = na + b\sum X \tag{7.7}$$

[2] The solution is obtained by expanding the right-hand side of formula (7.6). This expression is then differentiated with respect to a and then with respect to b. Setting these derivatives equal to zero gives the desired equations.

and
$$\sum XY = a\sum X + b\sum X^2 \tag{7.8}$$

If we divide both sides of (7.7) through by n and solve for a, we have

$$a = \bar{Y} - b\bar{X} \tag{7.9}$$

If we now substitute $\bar{Y} - b\bar{X}$ for a in (7.8), and solve for b, we have

$$b = \frac{\sum XY - \dfrac{(\sum X)(\sum Y)}{n}}{\sum X^2 - \dfrac{(\sum X)^2}{n}} \tag{7.10}$$

The necessary values for computing b are given in Table 7.3. Substituting these values in formula (7.10), we have

$$b = \frac{125 - \dfrac{(11)(4)}{10}}{121 - \dfrac{(11)^2}{10}} = \frac{120.6}{108.9} = 1.11$$

Since $\bar{X} = 11/10 = 1.10$ and $\bar{Y} = 4/10 = .40$, and we have just found that $b = 1.11$, we may substitute in formula (7.9) and find

$$\begin{aligned} a &= .40 - (1.11)(1.10) \\ &= -\ .82 \end{aligned}$$

The regression equation, formula (7.4), then becomes

$$\tilde{Y} = -.82 + 1.11X$$

Note now that if we predict a value of Y corresponding to the mean of the X distribution, we obtain

$$\begin{aligned} \tilde{Y} &= -.82 + (1.11)(1.10) \\ &= -.82 + 1.22 \\ &= .40 \end{aligned}$$

which is equal to the mean of the Y distribution. The regression line will therefore pass through the point established by the means of the X and Y distributions or, in other words, the point with coordinates $(\bar{X}, \bar{Y})$. This will always be true of any linear regression line fitted by the method of least squares.

The predicted value of Y when X is equal to 3 will be

$$\tilde{Y} = -.82 + (1.11)(3)$$

$$= 2.51$$

and when X is equal to -2, the predicted value of Y will be

$$\tilde{Y} = -.82 + (1.11)(-2)$$

$$= -3.04$$

The regression line will therefore pass through the points with coordinates (3, 2.51) and (−2, −3.04). These points are shown in Figure 7.2. If we draw a line through them, this will be the regression line of Y on X.

The Sum of Products

The denominator of formula (7.10) we recognize as the sum of squared deviations of X from the mean $\bar{X}$. This expression is identical with that given earlier in formula (4.1) for $\sum x^2$. The numerator of formula (7.10) is shown, in answer to one of the examples at the end of the chapter, to be equal to the sum of the products of the deviations of X and Y from their respective means. Thus, we have

$$\sum xy = \sum(X - \bar{X})(Y - \bar{Y}) = \sum XY - \frac{(\sum X)(\sum Y)}{n} \quad \textbf{(7.11)}$$

and formula (7.10) will be identical with

$$b = \frac{\sum xy}{\sum x^2} \quad \textbf{(7.12)}$$

The *sum of products*, $\sum xy$, is a basic quantity in statistical analysis, and we shall have occasion to refer to it again. You may recall that the sum of squares, $\sum x^2$ or $\sum y^2$, when divided by $n - 1$, gives a quantity we have called the variance. The sum of products, when divided by $n - 1$, gives a similar measure that is called the *covariance* of X and Y. If the numerator and denominator of formula (7.12) were both divided by $n - 1$, it would be clear that the regression coefficient b is the ratio of the covariance of the two variables to the variance of the independent variable.

If we have coded values of X and Y by division, as described in Chapter 4, and done our calculations with the coded values, then the formula for the sum of products of deviation measures becomes

$$\Sigma xy = \left[\Sigma x'y' - \frac{(\Sigma x')(\Sigma y')}{n}\right] i_x i_y \tag{7.13}$$

where $x' = X/i_x$

$y' = Y/i_y$

i_x = a constant by which each X has been divided

i_y = a constant by which each Y has been divided

Other formulas for the sum of products may be developed, corresponding to those given on page 67 for the sum of squares, when measures have been coded in various ways. All that we need to remember is that the sum of products will be influenced by coding operations in the same way in which the sum of squares is influenced. For example, if only the Y values are divided by a constant i_y and we use the original values of X, formula (7.13) would become

$$\Sigma xy = \left[\Sigma Xy' - \frac{(\Sigma X)(\Sigma y')}{n}\right] i_y \tag{7.14}$$

■ The Residual Sum of Squares

The residual sum of squares or errors of prediction as given by formula (7.6) is a measure of the variation of the Y values about the regression line. Let us see if we can gain some additional insight into the nature of this sum of squares.

By definition $\tilde{Y} = a + bX$

Substituting an identity for a from formula (7.9) $\tilde{Y} = \bar{Y} - b\bar{X} + bX$

Summing $\Sigma\tilde{Y} = n\bar{Y} - bn\bar{X} + b\Sigma X$

Since the last two terms on the right cancel, we have

$$\Sigma\tilde{Y} = \Sigma Y \tag{7.15}$$

The sum of the predicted values $\sum \tilde{Y}$ is thus equal to the sum of the observed values $\sum Y$, and the mean of the predicted values must therefore be equal to the mean of the observed values. We see that this is true, within rounding errors, for the data of Table 7.3, where $\sum \tilde{Y} = 4.01$ and $\sum Y = 4.00$. It also follows that the algebraic sum of the deviations of the observed values from the predicted values must equal zero. Thus

$$\sum(Y - \tilde{Y}) = \sum Y - \sum \tilde{Y} = 0 \tag{7.16}$$

since we have just shown that $\sum \tilde{Y}$ equals $\sum Y$.

In the development above we showed that a predicted value $\tilde{Y}$ could be written $\tilde{Y} = \bar{Y} - b\bar{X} + bX$. Rearranging the last two terms, we have

$$\begin{aligned} \tilde{Y} &= \bar{Y} + bX - b\bar{X} \\ &= \bar{Y} + b(X - \bar{X}) \\ &= \bar{Y} + bx \end{aligned}$$

and subtracting $\bar{Y}$ from both sides we obtain

$$\tilde{Y} - \bar{Y} = bx$$

If we let $\tilde{y} = \tilde{Y} - \bar{Y}$, then we may write

$$\tilde{y} = bx \tag{7.17}$$

where $\tilde{y}$ = a predicted value of Y expressed in terms of its deviation from the mean of the Y distribution
x = a deviation of X from the mean of the X distribution
b = the regression coefficient

An error of prediction will now be given by the discrepancy between the true deviation $y = Y - \bar{Y}$ and the predicted deviation $\tilde{y} = \tilde{Y} - \bar{Y}$.

Thus $$y - \tilde{y} = y - bx$$

Squaring $$(y - \tilde{y})^2 = y^2 - 2bxy + b^2x^2$$

Summating $$\sum(y - \tilde{y})^2 = \sum y^2 - 2b\sum xy + b^2\sum x^2$$

Substituting an identity for b from formula (7.12) $$\sum(y - \tilde{y})^2 = \sum y^2 - 2\frac{\sum xy}{\sum x^2}\sum xy + \frac{(\sum xy)^2}{(\sum x^2)^2}\sum x^2$$

Simplifying and combining terms, we arrive at

$$\sum(y - \tilde{y})^2 = \sum y^2 - \frac{(\sum xy)^2}{\sum x^2} \tag{7.18}$$

Table 7.3 gives the necessary values for finding $\sum y^2$ by means of formula (4.1). Thus

$$\sum y^2 = 142 - \frac{(4)^2}{10} = 140.4$$

Then, since we have already found that $\sum xy = 120.6$ and that $\sum x^2 = 108.9$, we find that the residual sum of squares, given by formula (7.18), will be

$$\sum(y - \tilde{y})^2 = 140.4 - \frac{(120.6)^2}{108.9} = 6.84$$

The value just obtained should check, and does within rounding errors, with the value of $\sum(Y - \tilde{Y})^2 = 6.8437$ shown in Table 7.3. We know that $\sum(y - \tilde{y})^2$ will equal $\sum(Y - \tilde{Y})^2$ since $\tilde{y} = \tilde{Y} - \bar{Y}$ and $y = Y - \bar{Y}$. Thus $y - \tilde{y} = (Y - \bar{Y}) - (\tilde{Y} - \bar{Y}) = Y - \tilde{Y}$.

Now, since $\sum y^2$ measures the total variation of the values of Y about the mean of the Y distribution, it is obvious that only if the regression coefficient was zero could the residual sum of squares $\sum(y - \tilde{y})^2$ be equal to $\sum y^2$. In that case we would know that there is no tendency for Y to change with change in X or, in other words, that the two variables are unrelated. Saying the same thing in a slightly different way, if the sum of products is zero, the variables are unrelated.

On the other hand, if a relationship between X and Y does exist, regardless of whether it is positive or negative, the value of $\sum(y - \tilde{y})^2$ will be smaller than $\sum y^2$. When the relationship is negative, as we have pointed out earlier, the sum of products, and consequently the regression coefficient, will be negative in sign. But since the product sum is squared in formula (7.18), the numerator of the last term will always be positive in sign, and the denominator, the sum of squares is, of course, always positive. Consequently, a negative relationship will also serve to reduce the residual sum of squares.

When the relationship between two variables is perfect, either positive or negative, the residual sum of squares will be equal to zero, and there will be no errors of prediction. If there is no relationship at all between X and Y, the residual sum of squares will be exactly equal to the sum of squares of the Y values from the mean of the Y distribution. In this instance, the best prediction that we could make for each Y value would be the mean of the Y distribution, for this would minimize the sum of squares of our errors of prediction. We have already shown, for example, that the sum of squared deviations from the mean is less than it would be from any single value not equal to the mean.[3]

By taking into account the relationship between Y and X, when one exists, we reduce the total variation of Y by an amount equal to $(\sum xy)^2/\sum x^2$. The residual sum of squares measures the remaining variation in Y that cannot be accounted for by the relationship. Instead of measuring the variation of the Y values in terms of their deviations from the mean of the Y distribution, the residual sum of squares measures the variation of each Y value from its corresponding predicted value given by the regression equation, formula (7.4).

The Residual Variance and Standard Error of Estimate

If we divide the residual sum of squares by $n - 2$, we obtain a measure known as the residual variance. Thus

$$s_{y \cdot x}^2 = \frac{\sum(y - \tilde{y})^2}{n - 2} \tag{7.19}$$

and for the data of Table 7.3, we have

$$s_{y \cdot x}^2 = \frac{6.84}{10 - 2} = .855$$

The residual variance is, as we have pointed out before, a measure of the variation of the Y measures about the line of regression. The "dot" separating the y and x subscripts serves to indicate that the regression line involved is that of Y on X, that is, that we are predicting Y values from corresponding X values.

The square root of the residual variance is called the *standard error of estimate*. Thus

$$s_{y \cdot x} = \sqrt{\frac{\sum(y - \tilde{y})^2}{n - 2}} \tag{7.20}$$

---

[3] See Example 4.14, page 80.

and for the data of Table 7.3, we have

$$s_{y \cdot x} = \sqrt{\frac{6.84}{10 - 2}}$$

$$= \sqrt{.855}$$

$$= .92$$

The residual variance and its square root, the standard error of estimate, are both important in correlation analysis which we shall take up in detail in Chapter 8.

The Power Curve

So far we have considered only relations that are linear. In other cases the plot of the Y values against the X values may indicate that the trend cannot be represented adequately by a straight line, that is, the relationship may be *curvilinear*. We again would like to find the equation of the curve representing the trend.

It is sometimes the case that a transformation of the X scale, the Y scale, or both the X and Y scales into a logarithmic scale will result in a linear relationship between X and Y. For example, a plot of the observed Y values against the X values may result in a curve for which the general equation is

$$Y = aX^b \tag{7.21}$$

Formula (7.21) is the equation of a curve in which the Y values are related to some power of the X values, and the curve is called a *power curve*. If b is negative, the curve will extend downward from upper left to lower right. If b is positive, the curve will extend upward from the lower left to the upper right. In one of the examples at the end of the chapter, we let b take various values from -2 to 2. If you plot the values of Y obtained against the given X values, in this example, you will gain an understanding of the form of the curve when b is integral or fractional and positive or negative.

If we take logarithms of both sides of formula (7.21), we obtain[4]

$$\log Y = \log a + b \log X \tag{7.22}$$

[4] Unless otherwise specified all logarithms are *common logarithms* for which the base is 10.

which is a linear relationship in log Y and log X. This will be apparent if formula (7.22) is compared with formula (7.2) which we have already shown is the equation of a straight line. Consequently, we may expect the plot of the log Y values against the log X values to be a straight line with slope equal to b and Y intercept equal to log a.

It is not actually necessary to find the logarithms of the Y and X values and to make the plot of these logarithms to determine whether the trend seems to be linear. Instead, we may plot the original values of Y and X on *logarithmic paper*. This paper is ruled in such a way that both the X and Y axes are logarithmic scales. Plotting the original Y and X values on logarithmic paper will be the same as if we found the logarithms of Y and X and plotted the logarithms on ordinary graph paper.

In Table 7.4 we have a set of X values recorded in column (1) and the

Table 7.4—Finding the Line of Best Fit for $\log \tilde{Y} = \log a + bX$

	(1) X	(2) Y	(3) $\log X$	(4) $\log Y$	(5) $(\log X)^2$	(6) $(\log X)(\log Y)$
	80.0	29.0	1.9031	1.4624	3.6218	2.7831
	50.0	20.0	1.6990	1.3010	2.8866	2.2104
	25.0	15.0	1.3979	1.1761	1.9541	1.6441
	20.0	12.0	1.3010	1.0792	1.6926	1.4040
	10.0	8.0	1.0000	.9031	1.0000	.9031
	7.0	6.0	.8451	.7782	.7142	.6577
	4.0	5.0	.6021	.6990	.3625	.4209
	2.5	3.2	.3979	.5051	.1583	.2010
	1.6	2.8	.2041	.4472	.0417	.0913
	1.2	2.1	.0792	.3222	.0063	.0255
Σ			9.4294	8.6735	12.4381	10.3411

corresponding values of Y in column (2). The plot of the Y values against the X values on ordinary graph paper is shown in Figure 7.3. We now plot the Y values against the X values on logarithmic paper, and this plot is shown in Figure 7.4. It seems apparent from this graph that log Y is linearly related to log X.

We may now, if we so desire, find the values of log a and the slope of the line b for the line of best fit relating the logarithmic values. Applying the method of least squares to the logarithms of Y and X will give us the line of best fit for the logarithmic relation of formula (7.22). In column (3) of Table 7.4 we give the values of log X, and in column (4) the values of log Y. Column (5) gives the values of $(\log X)^2$, and column (6) the values

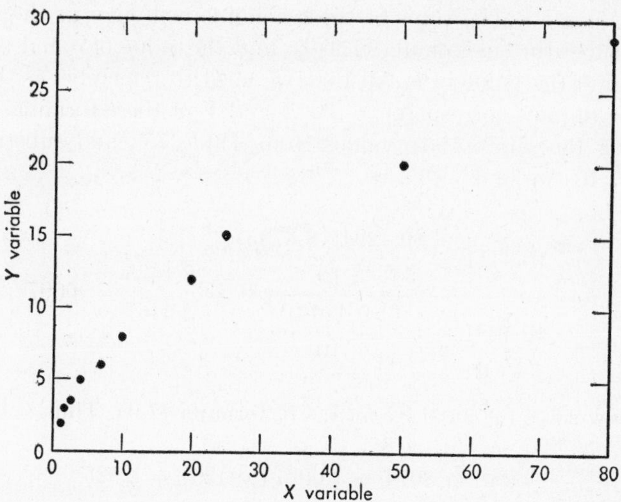

Fig. 7.3—Plot of the X, Y values of Table 7.4 on ordinary coordinate paper.

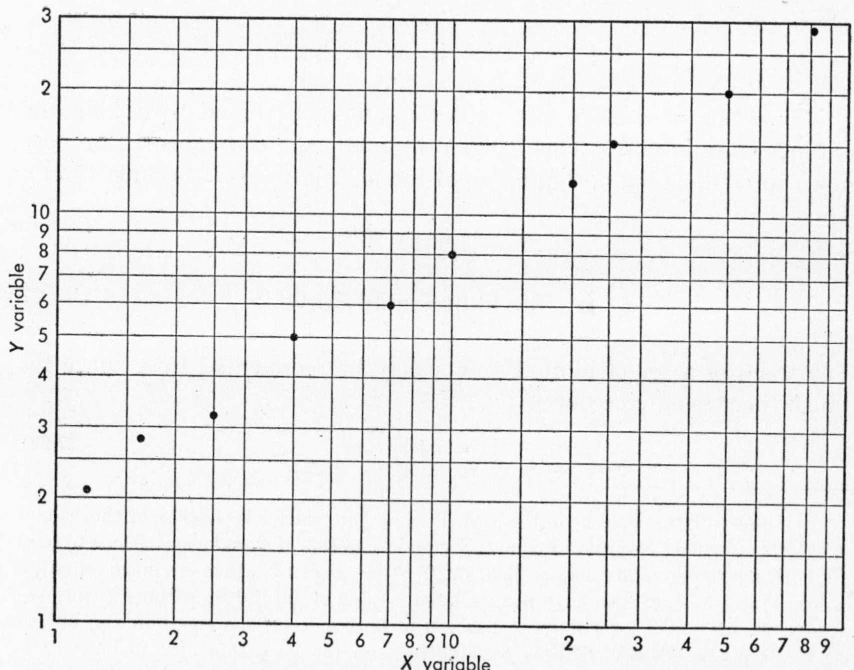

Fig. 7.4—Plot of the X, Y values of Table 7.4 on logarithmic paper.

of (log X) (log Y). The sums of these columns will give us the necessary values to substitute in formula (7.9) to find the value of a and in formula (7.10) to find the value of b. All that we need to remember is that log X and log Y will now correspond to the X and Y of these formulas.

Taking the appropriate values from Table 7.4, and substituting in formula (7.10) we find

$$b = \frac{10.3411 - \dfrac{(9.4294)(8.6735)}{10}}{12.4381 - \dfrac{(9.4294)^2}{10}} = \frac{2.1625}{3.5467} = .6097$$

We can now solve for log a by means of formula (7.9). Thus

$$\log a = .8674 - (.6097)(.9429) = .2925$$

The values of a and b determined above will minimize the sum of squared deviations of the observed log Y values from the predicted log Y values of formula (7.22). We may write the equation for the predicted log Y values as

$$\log \tilde{Y} = .2925 + (.6097)(\log X)$$

Since log a = .2925, the value of a may be found by taking the antilogarithm of .2925. This is equal to 1.961, and consequently we may now express the relationship between Y and X in terms of formula (7.21). Thus

$$\tilde{Y} = 1.961X^{.6097}$$

The Exponential Curve

The trend of a set of plotted points may be represented by a curve for which the general equation is [5]

$$Y = a10^{bX} \qquad \textbf{(7.23)}$$

---

[5] The equation may be in the form $Y = ae^{bX}$ in which e is the base of the system of *natural logarithms* and is approximately equal to 2.7183. If we take logarithms to base e of both sides of this equation, we have $\log_e Y = \log_e a + bX$, which is a linear equation in $\log_e Y$ and X. Since we have not included a table of natural logarithms in the Appendix, we may take logarithms to base 10 of both sides of the equation and obtain $\log Y = \log a + .4343bX$. This is possible because the logarithm of e to base 10 is approximately .4343. Whenever logarithms are written without a subscript, we are referring to common logarithms.

In formula (7.23) the independent variable appears as an exponent and the resulting curve is called an *exponential curve.* If we take logarithms of both sides of formula (7.23) we have

$$\log Y = \log a + bX \tag{7.24}$$

which is a linear equation in log Y and the original values of X.

It is easy to determine whether or not the trend of a set of plotted points can be represented by a curve of the kind given by formula (7.23). If we plot the logarithms of Y against the values of X on ordinary rectangular graph paper, we should obtain a straight line. It is simpler, however, to plot the original values of X and Y on *semilogarithmic paper.* This paper has the usual linear scale on one axis, but a logarithmic scale on the other axis. Thus, if the data can be represented by an exponential curve, plotting the original X values on the linear scale and the Y values on the logarithmic scale should result in a straight line. This procedure is much simpler than plotting X and log Y on ordinary coordinate paper.

In Table 7.5, we give values of X in column (1) and values of Y in

Table 7.5—Finding the Line of Best Fit for $\log \tilde{Y} = \log a + bX$

	(1) X	(2) Y	(3) $\log Y$	(4) X^2	(5) $(X)(\log Y)$
	7.5	1.2	.0792	56.25	.5940
	7.0	1.5	.1761	49.00	1.2327
	5.8	2.0	.3010	33.64	1.7458
	5.0	2.8	.4472	25.00	2.2360
	4.5	3.5	.5441	20.25	2.4484
	3.5	4.2	.6232	12.25	2.1812
	3.0	5.0	.6990	9.00	2.0970
	2.0	7.2	.8573	4.00	1.7146
	1.5	8.8	.9445	2.25	1.4168
	1.1	9.5	.9777	1.21	1.0755
Σ	40.9	45.7	5.6493	212.85	16.7420

column (2). The plot of these values on ordinary coordinate paper is shown in Figure 7.5. Figure 7.6 gives the plot of the same values on semilogarithmic paper and it is apparent that the trend is linear. We may obtain the line of best fit by the method of least squares. This will be the line of best fit relating the logarithms of Y to the original values of X.

In column (3) of Table 7.5 we give the log Y values. Column (4)

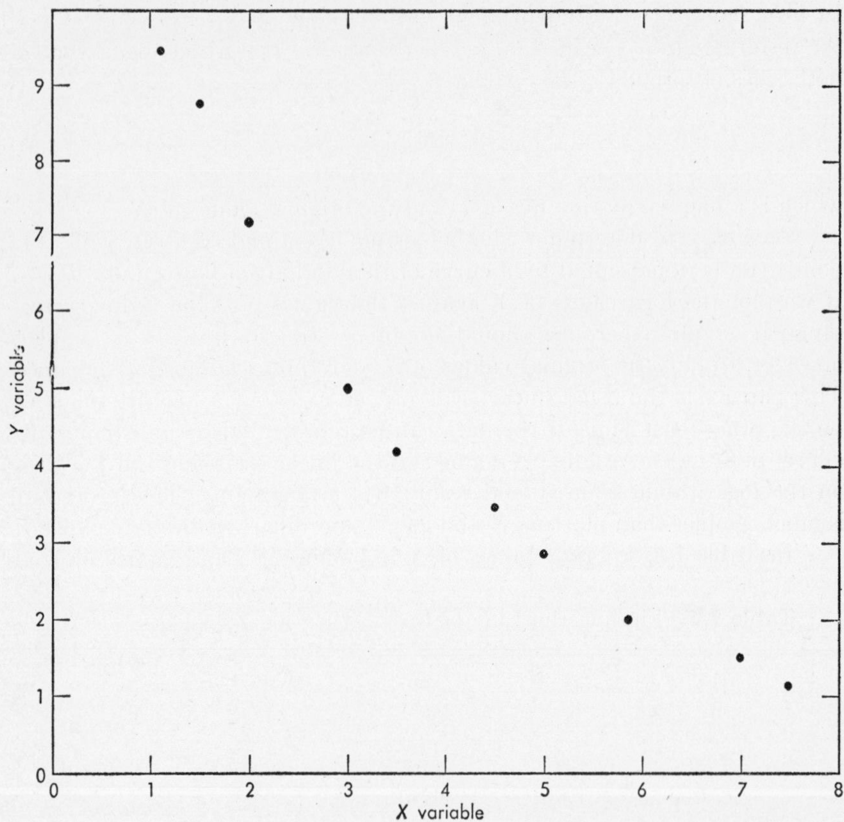

Fig. 7.5—Plot of the X, Y values of Table 7.5 on ordinary coordinate paper.

gives the values of X^2 and in column (5) we give the values of (X) $(\log Y)$. The sums of the columns in the table enable us to solve for b by means of formula (7.10). All that we need to remember is that now $\log Y$ will correspond to Y in the formula. Substituting the appropriate values from Table 7.5 in formula (7.10), we obtain

$$b = \frac{16.7420 - \dfrac{(40.9)(5.6493)}{10}}{212.85 - \dfrac{(40.9)^2}{10}} = -\ .1396$$

The value of b is negative in sign. This is to be expected if we look at Figure 7.6 in which the trend of the points is downward from upper left to lower right in the figure. The line, in other words, has a negative slope.

Substituting in formula (7.9) we obtain the value of log a, the Y intercept. Thus

$$\log a = .5649 - (-.1396)(4.09) = 1.1359$$

Then we may write our prediction equation, formula (7.24), as

$$\log \tilde{Y} = 1.1359 + (-.1396)X$$

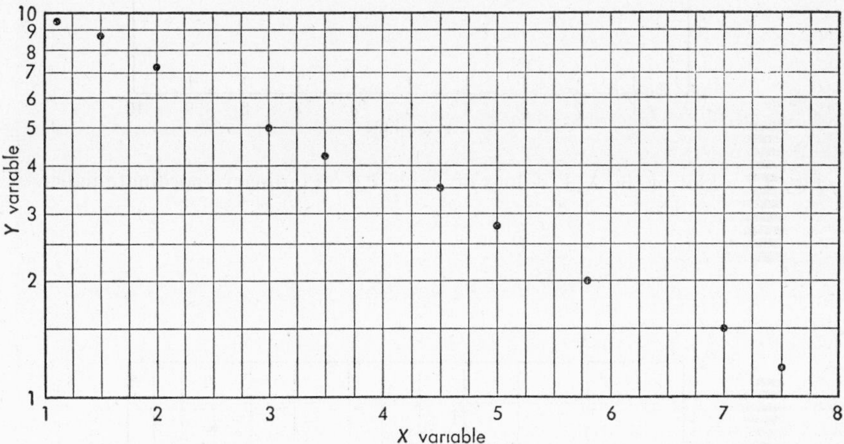

Fig. 7.6—Plot of the X, Y values of Table 7.5 on semilogarithmic paper.

and since the antilogarithm of 1.1359 is 13.67, we may write formula (7.23) as

$$\tilde{Y} = (13.67)(10)^{-.1396X}$$

■ The Logarithmic Curve

We may consider one further case, one in which the dependent variable Y may appear as an exponent. For example X may be related to Y in such a way that

$$Y = a + b \log X \tag{7.25}$$

which is a linear equation in Y and log X. Consequently, if this relation holds and we plot Y against log X on ordinary coordinate paper the graph should be a straight line. It is again simpler, however, to plot the original

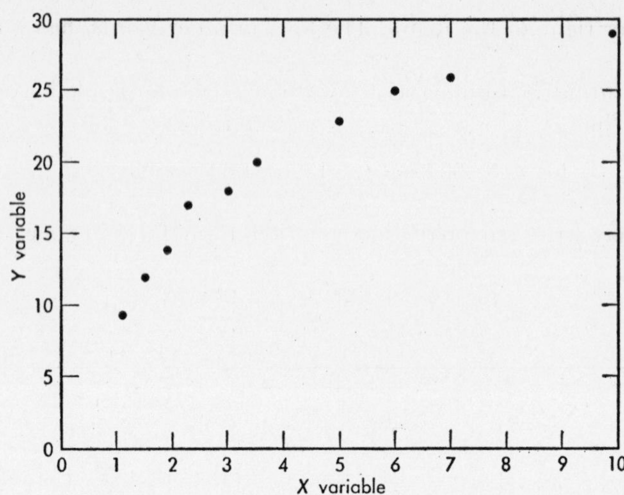

Fig. 7.7—Plot of the X, Y values of Table 7.6 on ordinary coordinate paper.

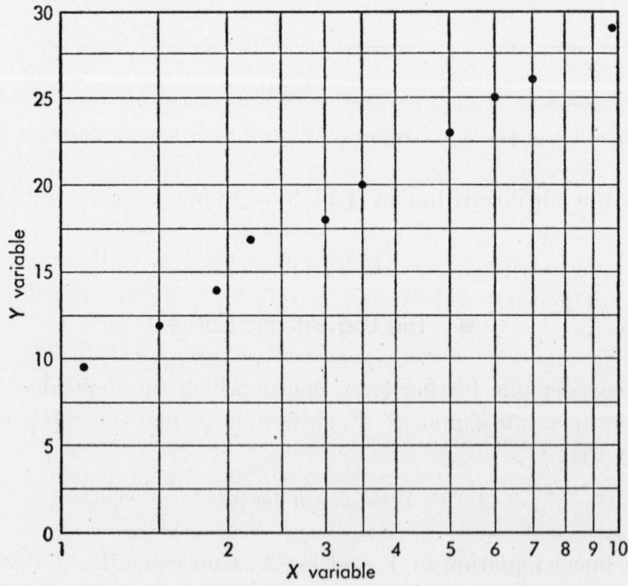

Fig. 7.8—Plot of the X, Y values of Table 7.6 on semilogarithmic paper.

values of X and Y on semilogarithmic paper. In this case, we use the logarithmic scale for the X axis and the linear scale for the Y axis.

In Table 7.6 we give values of X in column (1) and in column (2)

Table 7.6—Finding the Line of Best Fit for $\tilde{Y} = a + b \log X$

	(1) X	(2) Y	(3) $\log X$	(4) $(\log X)^2$	(5) $(\log X)(Y)$
	1.1	9	.0414	.0017	.3726
	1.5	12	.1761	.0310	2.1132
	1.9	14	.2788	.0777	3.9032
	2.2	17	.3424	.1172	5.8208
	3.0	18	.4771	.2276	8.5878
	3.5	20	.5441	.2960	10.8820
	5.0	23	.6990	.4886	16.0770
	6.0	25	.7782	.6056	19.4550
	7.0	26	.8451	.7142	21.9726
	9.9	29	.9956	.9912	28.8724
Σ	41.1	193	5.1778	3.5508	118.0566

values of Y. The plot of Y against X on ordinary graph paper is shown in Figure 7.7. The plot of Y against X on semilogarithmic paper is shown in Figure 7.8. The trend can apparently be represented by a straight line, and we may assume that Y values are linearly related to the logarithms of X.

The line of best fit may be found by the method of least squares. This will be the line of best fit relating the values of Y to the logarithms of X, and the intercept of this line will be a and the slope will be b. In column (3) of Table 7.6 we give the values of $\log X$ and in column (4) the values of $(\log X)^2$. Column (5) gives the values of $(\log X)(Y)$. From the sums of the columns of Table 7.6 we obtain the necessary values to substitute in formula (7.10) to find the value of b. All that we need to remember is that $\log X$ will now correspond to X in the formula. Thus

$$b = \frac{118.0566 - \dfrac{(5.1778)(193)}{10}}{3.5508 - \dfrac{(5.1778)^2}{10}} = 20.8382$$

Then substituting in formula (7.9) we obtain

$$a = 19.3 - (20.8382)(.5178) = 8.51$$

and our prediction equation then becomes

$$\tilde{Y} = 8.51 + 20.84 \log X$$

■ EXAMPLES

7.1—Prove that $\sum xy = \sum(X-\bar{X})(Y-\bar{Y}) = \sum XY - \dfrac{(\sum X)(\sum Y)}{n}$

7.2—Solve for a, if $\sum Y = na + b\sum X$

7.3—Substitute the value of a found in Example 7.2 in the following expression and solve for b. $\sum XY = a\sum X + b\sum X^2$

7.4—If $\tilde{Y} = a + bX$, and $a = \bar{Y} - b\bar{X}$, then show that $\sum\tilde{Y} = \sum Y$.

7.5—If $\tilde{y} = bx$, and $b = \sum xy/\sum x^2$, then show that

$$\sum(y - \tilde{y})^2 = \sum y^2 - \frac{(\sum xy)^2}{\sum x^2}$$

7.6—Find the value of a and b for the equation $Y = a + bX$ for the following data.

X	Y
20	0
16	2
10	5
6	7
0	10

7.7—Using the method of least squares, find the value of a and b for the equation $\tilde{Y} = a + bX$ for the data given below. Plot the points on coordinate paper and show the point with coordinates $(\bar{X}, \bar{Y})$. Draw the regression line of Y on X.

X	Y	X	Y
2	3	8	5
2	6	8	8
4	2	8	10
4	4	10	8
4	8	10	12
6	5	12	5
6	7	12	9
6	10	12	11

7.8—Six colors were scaled for their affectivity. Taking all possible pairs gives 15 pairs for which the distance between the pairs is known on the affectivity scale. The reaction time of subjects was measured in choosing a member of each pair. The reaction times have been converted to a percentage of the mean reaction time. It can be hypothesized that reaction time will be faster for pairs separated by greater affective distances than for pairs separated by shorter affective distances. Plot the points and see whether the relationship between Y and X appears to be linear. Data are from Shipley, Coffin, and Hadsell (1945).

X *Scale Distance*	Y *Mean Reaction Time*
2.31	83
1.75	91
1.69	91
1.36	87
1.29	93
1.13	93
1.02	96
.95	107
.74	100
.73	104
.62	97
.56	118
.40	113
.39	122
.34	107
.00	116

7.9—Assume that $Y = aX^b$, where $a = 2$ and $b = 2$.

(*a*) For the values of X given below find the values of Y.
(*b*) Plot the Y values against the X values on ordinary coordinate paper.
(*c*) Plot the points on semilogarithmic paper.

X
1.0
1.2
1.4
1.6
1.8
2.0

7.10—Assume that $Y = aX^b$, where $a = 2$ and $b = -.5$.

(*a*) For the values of X given below find the values of Y.
(*b*) Plot the Y values against the X values on ordinary coordinate paper.
(*c*) Plot the points on semilogarithmic paper.

X
1
4
9
16
25
36

7.11—Assume that $Y = aX^b$, where $a = 2$ and $b = .5$.

(*a*) For the values of X given below find the values of Y.
(*b*) Plot the Y values against the X values on ordinary coordinate paper.
(*c*) Plot the points on semilogarithmic paper.

X
1
4
9
16
25
36

7.12—Assume that $Y = aX^b$, where $a = 2$ and $b = -2$.

(*a*) For the values of X given below find the values of Y.
(*b*) Plot the Y values against the X values on ordinary coordinate paper.
(*c*) Plot the points on semilogarithmic paper.

X
1.0
1.2
1.4
1.6
1.8
2.0

7.13—See if a curve of the form $Y = a10^{bX}$ will fit the following data.

X	Y
1.0	2.5
1.3	2.8
1.5	3.0
1.8	3.7
2.1	4.1
2.3	4.9
2.5	5.0
2.8	6.5
3.1	7.8
3.4	9.2

7.14—See if a curve of the form $Y = aX^b$ will fit the following data.

X	Y
1.5	7.0
2.5	6.0
4.0	4.1
6.0	3.8
15.0	2.6
30.0	2.0
50.0	1.5
70.0	1.4

7.15—See if a curve of the form $Y = a + b \log X$ will fit the following data.

X	Y
1.2	2.2
1.5	2.4
1.7	2.6
2.0	2.6
3.0	3.2
4.4	3.6
7.0	4.2
10.0	4.4

■ CHAPTER EIGHT

The Product-Moment Correlation Coefficient

In the discussion of linear regression, in the last chapter, it was assumed that we had some basis for designating one of the two variables investigated as the dependent variable Y and the other as the independent variable X. For example, if we had measures of vocabulary at various age levels, it would seem logical to designate the vocabulary measures as the dependent variable and the age levels as the independent variable. Vocabulary may depend upon age, but it is rather difficult to imagine age as depending upon vocabulary. Or suppose that one of our variables is the number of trials in a learning experiment and the other variable is the amount learned per trial. Again it seems more reasonable to regard the amount learned as depending upon the number of trials rather than the number of trials as depending upon the amount learned. If one of our variables is amount remembered and the other is time elapsed, it would seem more logical to regard the amount remembered as depending upon the passage of time rather than the other way around. In problems of the kind just described, the experimenter would select certain values of the independent variable X for investigation and then subsequently observe the values of the dependent variable Y. His interest would then be in relating the values of the dependent variable Y to those of the independent variable X.

In many problems, however, involving the relationship between two variables, there is no clear-cut basis for designating one of the variables as the independent variable and the other as the dependent variable.

If we have measured the heights of husbands and also of their wives, which set of measurements shall we designate as the dependent variable? If we have scores on a test of submissiveness and also on a test of aggressiveness, shall we consider the measure of submissiveness or the measure of aggressiveness as the dependent variable?

In problems of the kind described above, it is a more or less arbitrary matter which variable we choose to designate as the dependent variable and which we choose to call the independent variable. If we arbitrarily designate one of the variables as Y and the other as X, then we may consider not only the prediction of Y values from X values, but also the prediction of X values from Y values. In other words, we may reverse the roles of our variables, considering first Y as a dependent variable with X as the independent variable and then considering X as a dependent variable with Y as the independent variable.

In the problems discussed in this chapter, therefore, we shall assume that we are dealing with a population of *paired* (X, Y) *values* and that we have a sample from this population. There is no question here of observing Y values for only certain selected values of X, as in our previous discussion of regression. Under these circumstances we shall have, ordinarily, not one but two regression lines. One will be for the regression of Y on X and the other for the regression of X on Y. We shall thus have two regression equations, one for each line, and also two regression coefficients. Furthermore, we shall have two residual variances and two standard errors of estimate. There is, however, one statistic involving both variables for which we shall have but a single value. That statistic is the *product-moment correlation coefficient.*

The Correlation Coefficient

In discussing the correlation coefficient, we shall again restrict ourselves to the case of linear relationships. For convenience, we shall assume that one of our variables, Y, is a dependent variable and that the other variable, X, is an independent variable, so that we shall be concerned with the regression of Y on X. Then later we may reverse the roles of our variables, taking X as the dependent variable and Y as the independent variable.

In the case of variables that are linearly related, the correlation coefficient is a measure of the degree of relationship present. Consider first the case of a perfect positive relationship between two variables as shown in Figure 8.1. In this instance, the correlation coefficient will be equal to 1.00. If we have a perfect negative relationship, as shown in Figure 8.2, the correlation coefficient will be equal to -1.00. In Figure 8.3 we have a positive relationship between X and Y, but it is not perfect, and the correlation coefficient for these measures is .74. Figure 8.4 shows the plot of a set of X and Y values for which the correlation coefficient is $-.73$. In Figure 8.5, the correlation coefficient is $-.12$.

Examination of these figures should indicate that the numerical value of the correlation coefficient is related to the scatter of the plotted points about the line representing their trend. The points in Figure 8.5, for example, would show the greatest scatter about the line representing

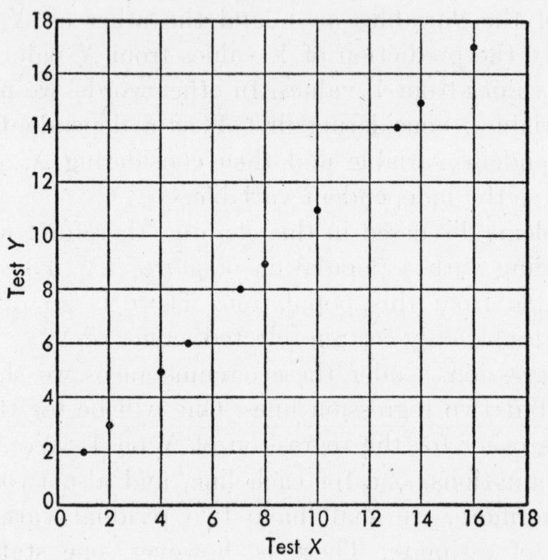

Fig. 8.1—Plot of X and Y values for which the correlation coefficient is equal to 1.00.

their trend and, in this instance, the correlation coefficient is $-.12$. When the plotted points fall precisely on a straight line, as in Figure 8.1 and Figure 8.2, the correlation coefficient is equal to 1.00 and -1.00, respectively. We have, in the last chapter, discussed a measure of the scatter of a set of plotted points about the regression line which we called the residual variance. You may suspect, therefore, that the numerical value of the correlation coefficient is somehow related to the amount of scatter about the regression line, and that is true. We shall show the nature of this relationship later.

The sign of the correlation coefficient is apparently related to the slope of the regression line, for in those instances in which the slope is negative, that is, downward from upper left to lower right, the correlation coefficient is negative in sign. When the trend of the plotted points is upward from lower left to upper right, so that the slope of the line is positive, the correlation coefficient is also positive in sign.

The correlation coefficient may range in value from -1.00 to 1.00. A correlation coefficient of 1.00 indicates a perfect positive relationship between two variables; a correlation of 0 indicates no relationship whatsoever between the two variables; and a correlation coefficient of -1.00 indicates a perfect negative relationship. Values between 0 and 1.00 or -1.00 indicate varying degrees of relationship. It is very seldom, if at all, that perfect relationships are found in the biological and social sciences,

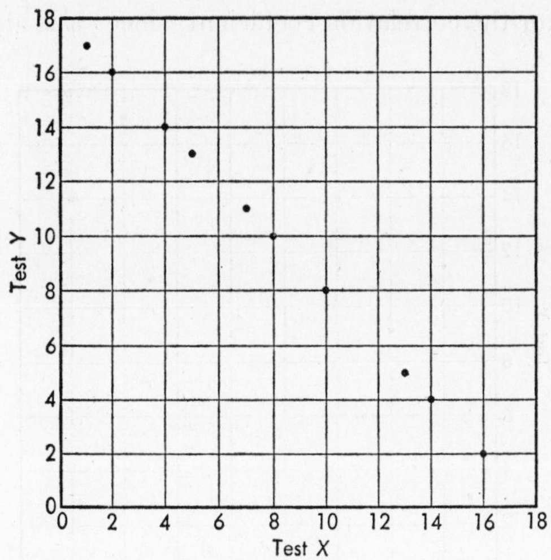

Fig. 8.2—Plot of X and Y values for which the correlation coefficient is equal to -1.00.

in part because of the limitations of our measuring instruments and also because of the difficulties of controlling all possible factors that may influence the two variables being studied. Correlation coefficients representing the relationship between performance on an academic-aptitude test and grades earned in college, for example, typically range from .40 to .60. The correlation coefficient between measures of intelligence on identical twins is substantially higher, being about .90. An examination of the research literature in a given field will reveal the typical values found for the correlation coefficient when various variables are considered.

Formulas for the Correlation Coefficient

The correlation coefficient may be defined as the ratio between the covariance and the geometric mean of the variances. The geometric mean of two numbers, you may recall from earlier disc ssion, is the square root of their product. Thus

$$r = \frac{\dfrac{\sum xy}{n-1}}{\sqrt{\left(\dfrac{\sum x^2}{n-1}\right)\left(\dfrac{\sum y^2}{n-1}\right)}} \tag{8.1}$$

where r = the correlation coefficient between X and Y. We do not need any subscripts for the correlation coefficient, since r_{xy} is identical with r_{yx}.

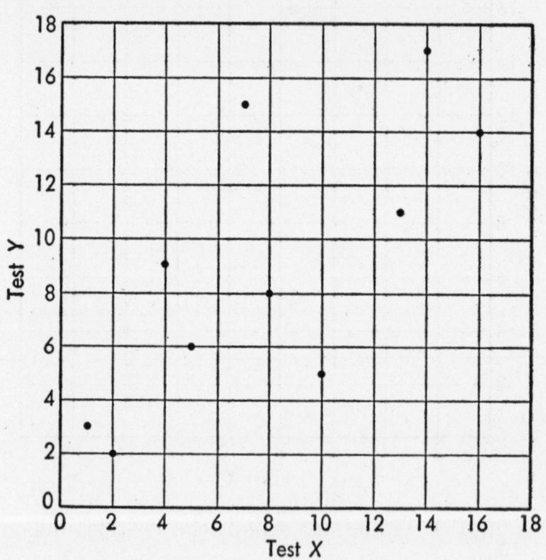

Fig. 8.3—Plot of X and Y values for which the correlation coefficient is equal to .74.

If we multiply both the numerator and denominator of formula (8.1) by $n - 1$, we obtain another commonly used expression for the correlation coefficient. Thus

$$r = \frac{\sum xy}{\sqrt{\sum x^2 \sum y^2}} \tag{8.2}$$

Formula (8.2) provides us with an important identity which we shall use later. Multiplying both sides by $\sqrt{\sum x^2 \sum y^2}$, we have

$$r\sqrt{\sum x^2 \sum y^2} = \sum xy \tag{8.3}$$

Thus for the product sum $\sum xy$ we have the identity $r\sqrt{\sum x^2 \sum y^2}$.

We have already developed methods for calculating the numerator and denominator of formula (8.2) when we deal in terms of the original values of X and Y rather than in terms of deviation measures. We can therefore calculate the correlation coefficient without first expressing values as

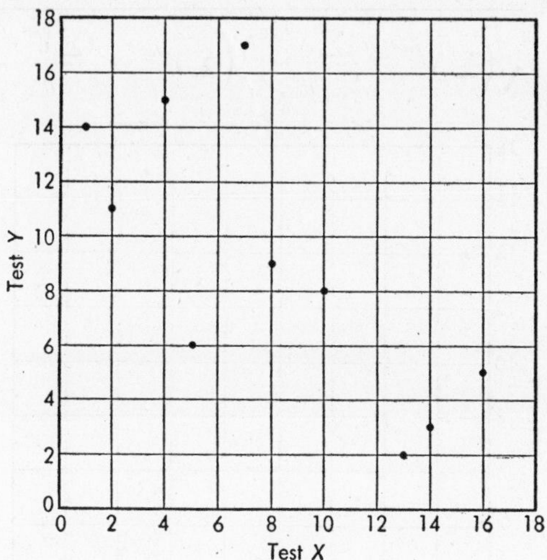

Fig. 8.4—Plot of X and Y values for which the correlation coefficient is equal to $-.73$.

deviations from the means of the X and Y distributions. Using formula (7.11) for the numerator and formula (4.1) for the denominator, we obtain

$$r = \frac{\Sigma XY - \dfrac{(\Sigma X)(\Sigma Y)}{n}}{\sqrt{\left(\Sigma X^2 - \dfrac{(\Sigma X)^2}{n}\right)\left(\Sigma Y^2 - \dfrac{(\Sigma Y)^2}{n}\right)}} \tag{8.4}$$

If measures have been coded by the subtraction of a constant, this will not influence the correlation coefficient and we could rewrite formula (8.4) substituting X' and Y' for X and Y. Nor will coding the X and Y values by division influence the correlation coefficient. In this instance we would rewrite formula (8.4) substituting x' for X and y' for Y. The coding constants, i_x and i_y, would appear in the numerator. In the denominator we would have $\sqrt{i_x^2}$ and $\sqrt{i_y^2}$. Since the coding constants appearing in the numerator would cancel those in the denominator, we need not bother to decode the sum of products and the two sums of squares in finding the value of the correlation coefficient. We may thus also write the following two formulas for the correlation coefficient.

$$r = \frac{\sum X'Y' - \frac{(\sum X')(\sum Y')}{n}}{\sqrt{\left(\sum X'^2 - \frac{(\sum X')^2}{n}\right)\left(\sum Y'^2 - \frac{(\sum Y')^2}{n}\right)}} \tag{8.5}$$

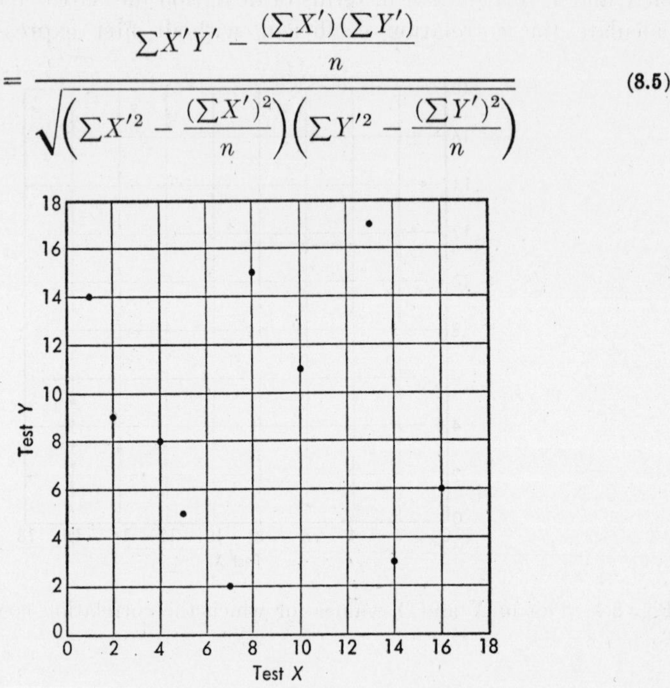

Fig. 8.5—Plot of X and Y values for which the correlation coefficient is equal to $-.12$.

where $X' = X - M_x'$ and $Y' = Y - M_y'$, and

$$r = \frac{\sum x'y' - \frac{(\sum x')(\sum y')}{n}}{\sqrt{\left(\sum x'^2 - \frac{(\sum x')^2}{n}\right)\left(\sum y'^2 - \frac{(\sum y')^2}{n}\right)}} \tag{8.6}$$

where $x' = X'/i_x$ and $y' = Y'/i_y$, or $x' = (X - M_x')/i_x$ and $y' = (Y - M_y')/i_y$.

The Correlation Table

When we have a fairly large number of values of X and Y it is often convenient to calculate the correlation coefficient from a scatter diagram.

We shall illustrate the steps involved with data published by Curtis (1943) relating measures on the Stanford-Binet Intelligence Test to measures on a hypnosis-susceptibility scale. We shall take the hypnosis-susceptibility scores as the Y variable and the Stanford-Binet scores as the X variable. These scores are given in Table 8.1. Although the n is small and the correlation coefficient might be found more easily by means of formula (8.4), the data will serve our purpose of illustrating the procedure of computing a correlation coefficient from a scatter diagram.

Table 8.1—Scores on a Measure of Susceptibility to Hypnosis and on a Measure of Intelligence for 32 Subjects*

Subject	*Hyp. Sus. Scale*	*Stanford-Binet*	*Subject*	*Hyp. Sus. Scale*	*Stanford-Binet*
MJ	22	136	TF	0	101
DJR	6	106	AEH	22	128
HIR	20	116	RR	16	122
SRB	8	139	JM	13	111
IC	0	103	SN	7	129
JDC	17	126	WP	10	117
MC	21	131	FW	6	116
JLF	13	137	SR	16	129
BHH	14	144	HF	13	109
MEG	5	130	CEF	0	103
DC	6	133	MM	0	104
SS	4	123	HMD	0	111
GG	9	134	JMD	12	131
FES	8	132	GA	4	112
MNS	6	117	GH	12	134
MLC	0	128	TF	0	101

* Data from Curtis (1943).

Our first step is to make a *scatter diagram*, which is, in fact, a simple two-way frequency distribution or double-entry table. On the left in Table 8.2 we group the scores on the hypnotic scale (Y variable) in terms of an interval of 2. In columns (1) and (2) at the right of the table, we give the frequencies and coded y' values for these intervals. At the top of the table we give the class intervals of 3 which we have used for grouping the measures of intelligence (X variable). At the bottom of the table in rows (1) and (2), we give the frequencies and coded x' values for these intervals.

For each subject in Table 8.1 we have two measurements, the score on the hypnotic scale and the score on the intelligence test. We make a tally mark in the proper cell of Table 8.2 for each subject, taking both measurements into consideration. For example, the first subject, MJ, has a score of 22 on the hypnotic scale and a score of 136 on the intelligence test. We want to find the cell in which to place the tally corresponding to this pair of scores, $X = 136$ and $Y = 22$. We find at the top of the table that $X = 136$ will fall in the class interval 135–137. From the class intervals at the left of the table, we see that $Y = 22$ will fall in the class interval 22–23. Consequently, we place a tally in the cell of the table corresponding to these two class intervals. You will find only one tally in this cell, which is the twelfth cell from the bottom and the thirteenth cell from the left. That is because we have only one pair of values falling in the class intervals 135–137 and 22–23. In the bottom left-hand corner cell you will find two tallies. That is because we have two subjects who have hypnotic scores of 0 to 1 and intelligence-test scores of 99 to 101.

In the manner just described we make a tally for each pair of scores. When we have finished, we could enter numbers in each cell to take the place of the individual tallies. In this form the table is often called a *correlation chart.* We have not entered the numbers in our table because of the small number of cells with more than one tally.

Let us look now at the various entries in the columns at the right of Table 8.2. The first four columns numbered (1), (2), (3), and (4) are already familiar. Column (1) is the sum of the tallies for each interval in the Y distribution. It is the f column we used when we worked with a single-frequency distribution to find the mean and standard deviation. Column (2) gives the coded y' values for each of the intervals. Column (3) gives the product fy'. Since all of the scores in a given interval have exactly the same y' value, this product gives the sum of the y' scores for the interval. The entries in column (4) are obtained by multiplying the entries in column (2) and those in column (3) to give $y'fy' = fy'^2$. Again, since all of the entries in a given interval have exactly the same y' value, if we square y' and multiply by f, we shall have the sum of squared y' values for that interval. Column (4) thus gives us the sum of these squared y' values for the various intervals. All of these values we have encountered before in our work with single-frequency distributions. The first four rows at the bottom of the table are the similar entries for the X variable. We could easily find the mean and sum of squared deviations from the mean for the Y distribution from the sums of columns (3) and (4) by means of formulas (4.9) and (4.10). And we could find the mean and sum of squared deviations from the mean for the X distribution from the sums at the end of rows (3) and (4) by means of the same formulas.

Columns (5) and (6) and rows (5) and (6) are new. They are used to

Table 8.2—Calculation of the Product-Moment Correlation Coefficient from a Correlation Table

X = Scores on Stanford-Binet (columns); *Y = Scores on Hypnotic-Susceptibility Scale* (rows)

		99–101	102–104	105–107	108–110	111–113	114–116	117–119	120–122	123–125	126–128	129–131	132–134	135–137	138–140	141–143	144–146	(1) f	(2) y'	(3) fy'	(4) fy'^2	(5) $\Sigma x' \cdot y'$	(6) $y'\Sigma x' \cdot y'$
	22–23										/			/				2	11	22	242	21	231
	20–21						/					/						2	10	20	200	15	150
	18–19																	0	9	0	0	0	0
	16–17								/		/	/						3	8	24	192	26	208
	14–15																/	1	7	7	49	15	105
	12–13				/	/						/	/	/				5	6	30	180	40	240
	10–11							/										1	5	5	25	6	30
	8–9												//		/			3	4	12	48	35	140
	6–7			/			/	/				/	/					5	3	15	45	34	102
	4–5					/				/		/						3	2	6	12	22	44
	2–3																	0	1	0	0	0	0
	0–1	//	///			/					/							7	0	0	0	16	0
(1)	f	2	3	1	1	3	2	2	1	1	3	5	4	2	1	0	1	32		141	993	230	1250
(2)	x'	0	1	2	3	4	5	6	7	8	9	10	11	12	13	14	15			$\Sigma y'$	$\Sigma y'^2$	↑	$\Sigma x'y'$
(3)	fx'	0	3	2	3	12	10	12	7	8	27	50	44	24	13	0	15	230	$\Sigma x'$				
(4)	fx'^2	0	3	4	9	48	50	72	49	64	243	500	484	288	169	0	225	2208	$\Sigma x'^2$				
(5)	$\Sigma y' \cdot x'$	0	0	3	6	8	13	8	8	2	19	29	17	17	4	0	7	141					
(6)	$x'\Sigma y' \cdot x'$	0	0	6	18	32	65	48	50	16	171	290	187	204	52	0	105	1250	$\Sigma x'y'$				

find the sum of products $\sum xy$ needed in the calculation of the correlation coefficient. Let us see how we get these entries. Column (5) is the sum of x' values for all individuals with the same y' value. For example, there are three subjects with a y' value of 8. From the table we see that one of these has an x' value of 7, another an x' value of 9, and the third has an x' value of 10. The sum of these x' values is 26, and that sum is recorded opposite the y' value of 8 in the column headed $\sum x'_{\cdot y'}$. *The "dot" means that we have summed x' for a constant value of y'.*

To take another case: there are seven individuals with y' values of 0. What is the sum of their x' values? Looking at the table, we see that two of these individuals have an x' value of 0, three have an x' value of 1, one has an x' value of 4, and another has an x' value of 9. Summing these x' values gives us $0 + 0 + 1 + 1 + 1 + 4 + 9 = 16$, and that value is recorded opposite the coded y' value of 0. The other entries are found in similar fashion.

The entries in row (5) at the bottom of the table give us the sum of y' values for all individuals with the same x' value. For example, we find that three individuals have an x' value of 4. What is the sum of their y' values? We find from the table that one of these individuals has a y' value of 6, another has a y' value of 2, and the third has a y' value of 0. The sum of these y' values is 8, and that figure is recorded in the $\sum y'_{\cdot x'}$ row below the x' value of 4. *The "dot" means that we are summing y' for a constant value of x'.*

The entries in column (6) are simply the products of the entries in column (2) and column (5), or $y'\sum x'_{\cdot y'}$. Since all the subjects in a given interval have exactly the same y' value, the sum of their x' values multiplied by y' will give us the product sum for these particular values of x' and y'.[1] The entries in row (6) at the bottom of the table are obtained by multiplying the entries in row (5) by those in row (2), or $x'\sum y'_{\cdot x'}$. For the same reasons just given these entries will give us the product sum for particular values of x'. The sum of row (6) should be exactly equal to the sum of column (6) and provides a check upon your calculations. Note also that other checks are provided. Arrows have been drawn to indicate the values that should be precisely the same if computations have been correctly made.

From the row and column sums of Table 8.2, we have all of the values needed to solve for the correlation coefficient by means of formula (8.6). The sum of row (6) or column (6) gives us $\sum x'y'$. The sum of row (3) gives us $\sum x'$, and the sum of column (3) gives us $\sum y'$. The sum of row

[1] Remember that the summation of a variable times a constant is equal to the constant times the sum of the variable. Thus $y'\sum x'_{\cdot y'} = \sum x'y'$ for a given value of y'.

(4) gives $\sum x'^2$, and the sum of column (4) gives $\sum y'^2$. Then, substituting the appropriate values from Table 8.2 in formula (8.6), we have

$$r = \frac{1{,}250 - \dfrac{(230)(141)}{32}}{\sqrt{\left(2{,}208 - \dfrac{(230)^2}{32}\right)\left(993 - \dfrac{(141)^2}{32}\right)}}$$

$$= \frac{236.56}{\sqrt{(554.88)(371.72)}}$$

$$= .52$$

You will note that if we had decoded $\sum x'y'$ and $\sum x'^2$ and $\sum y'^2$ to obtain $\sum xy$, $\sum x^2$, and $\sum y^2$, these values would be

$$\sum xy = \left(\sum x'y' - \frac{(\sum x')(\sum y')}{n}\right) i_x i_y = (236.56)(3)(2) = 1{,}419.36$$

$$\sum x^2 = \left(\sum x'^2 - \frac{(\sum x')^2}{n}\right) i_x{}^2 = (554.88)(9) = 4{,}993.92$$

$$\sum y^2 = \left(\sum y'^2 - \frac{(\sum y')^2}{n}\right) i_y{}^2 = (371.72)(4) = 1{,}486.88$$

and by means of formula (8.2) we would have

$$r = \frac{1{,}419.36}{\sqrt{(4{,}993.92)(1{,}486.88)}} = .52$$

as before. As we have pointed out, there is no need to decode the x' and y' measures in order to obtain the correlation coefficient.

■ The Difference Formula for *r*

Suppose we have given a test X and a test Y to a group of subjects and that scores on the two tests are expressed in terms of deviations from the respective means. Then we may define a difference score as

$$d = x - y \tag{8.7}$$

The variance of the distribution of measures defined by formula (8.7) will be of interest in later discussions, and this variance is also related to the correlation coefficient between X and Y. Let us see why this is so.

By definition $$d = x - y$$

Squaring both sides and summating $$\sum d^2 = \sum x^2 + \sum y^2 - 2\sum xy$$

But $\sum xy$ is a product sum and is equal to $r\sqrt{\sum x^2 \sum y^2}$. Thus $$\sum d^2 = \sum x^2 + \sum y^2 - 2r\sqrt{\sum x^2 \sum y^2}$$

Dividing both sides by $n - 1$ $$\frac{\sum d^2}{n-1} = \frac{\sum x^2}{n-1} + \frac{\sum y^2}{n-1} - 2r\sqrt{\left(\frac{\sum x^2}{n-1}\right)\left(\frac{\sum y^2}{n-1}\right)}$$

Substituting variance notation, we obtain

$$s_d^2 = s_x^2 + s_y^2 - 2rs_xs_y \tag{8.8}$$

If X and Y are uncorrelated, then formula (8.8) tells us that the variance of the differences will be equal to the variance of X plus the variance of Y. On the other hand, if the correlation between X and Y is positive, the variance of the differences will be less than the corresponding variance for the same measures with zero correlation. If the correlation is negative, then the variance of the differences will be greater than the corresponding variance for uncorrelated measures.

From formula (8.8) we may also obtain an expression for the correlation coefficient in terms of the variance of X, the variance of Y, and the variance of the differences. Thus, solving for r in the formula, we have

$$r = \frac{s_x^2 + s_y^2 - s_d^2}{2s_xs_y} \tag{8.9}$$

The formula for the rank correlation coefficient, discussed in a later chapter, is based upon the above development.

■ Summary of Methods for Finding *r*

You now have at your disposal a number of different methods for finding the correlation coefficient. Which method you will want to use depends upon the type of problem you may be called upon to work and upon whether or not you have available a calculating machine. A major advantage of using a scatter diagram is that you can get a picture of the trend of the paired values. This provides a visual indication of whether or not the relationship is linear—and therefore whether or not the correlation coefficient is an appropriate measure of the degree of association. If the relationship is not linear, the correlation coefficient will not give an adequate description of the extent to which the variables are related.[2]

There are opportunities for errors to occur in making the entries in the scatter diagram, and there is no check upon this part of the process except to tally the scores a second time.[3] Even then, if you find a discrepancy, you have no way of knowing whether an error was made in the first or second plotting or both. As an aid in preventing such errors, it is sometimes convenient to enter the X and Y values for each subject on a separate card. These cards can be sorted into piles according to the class intervals of one of the variables, say the Y variable. The cards in each pile or class interval can then be arranged in order according to their values on the X variable. It is then possible to make the tallies in the cells in the table one row at a time. This method is very convenient when n is large, say greater than 100.

The Regression of Y on X

We have previously defined the regression coefficient as the ratio of the covariance of two variables to the variance of the independent variable. Thus, when Y was considered to be the dependent variable and X the independent variable, we had

$$b_{yx} = \frac{\dfrac{\Sigma xy}{n-1}}{\dfrac{\Sigma x^2}{n-1}} = \frac{\Sigma xy}{\Sigma x^2}$$

where we have used the subscripts yx, in that order, to indicate that the regression coefficient is for Y on X. In our previous discussion of regression we were concerned only with the regression of Y on X, and the subscripts were not necessary.

[2] We shall take up in the next chapter a measure of association for relationships that are not linear. Later we shall also discuss tests that can be used to determine whether or not a relationship can be assumed to be linear.

[3] It should also be pointed out that the formula for r is based upon measurements taken by pairs. The calculation of r from a correlation table results in a slight loss in precision. This, however, is negligible if there are 12 or more class intervals and if n is approximately 50 or greater.

We have already found $\sum xy$ to be equal to 1,419.36 and $\sum x^2$ to be equal to 4,993.92 for the data of Table 8.2. The regression coefficient will therefore be

$$b_{yx} = \frac{1{,}419.36}{4{,}993.92} = .284$$

For the same data, the mean of the Y distribution as given by formula (4.9) is

$$\bar{Y} = .5 + \left(\frac{141}{32}\right) 2 = 9.32$$

and by the same formula, the mean of the X distribution is

$$\bar{X} = 100 + \left(\frac{230}{32}\right) 3 = 121.57$$

The regression equation for predicting Y values from X values will therefore be

$$\tilde{Y} = a + .284X$$

where
$$a = \bar{Y} - b_{yx}\bar{X}$$

$$= 9.31 - (.284)(121.57)$$

$$= -25.22$$

The residual sum of squares, as given by formula (7.18), will be

$$\sum (y - \tilde{y})^2 = 1{,}486.88 - \frac{(1{,}419.36)^2}{4{,}993.92}$$

$$= 1{,}083.47$$

and dividing by $n - 2$, we obtain the residual variance

$$s_{y \cdot x}{}^2 = \frac{1{,}083.47}{32 - 2} = 36.12$$

If we now take the square root of the residual variance, we obtain the standard error of estimate. Thus

$$s_{y \cdot x} = \sqrt{36.12} = 6.01$$

The standard error of estimate, as we have pointed out previously, is a measure of the variability of the Y values about the regression line of Y on X. The standard deviation of the Y distribution, on the other hand, is a measure of the variation of the Y values about the mean of the Y distribution. In the present problem, the standard deviation is

$$s_y = \sqrt{\frac{1{,}486.88}{32 - 1}} = 6.93$$

In the absence of any knowledge concerning the relationship between X and Y, our best prediction for any given value of X would, of course, be the mean of the Y distribution, and the extent of our errors of prediction would be the standard deviation of the Y distribution. If you look for a moment at Figure 8.6, where we have drawn the regression line of Y on X, you may be able to see more clearly just what influence correlation will have in reducing our errors of prediction.

If we draw a horizontal line through the mean of the Y distribution, then the vertical deviation of each plotted point from this line would represent the deviation $Y - \bar{Y}$, and the sum of these squared deviations would be $\sum(Y - \bar{Y})^2$. If the horizontal line through the mean of the Y distribution is now rotated counterclockwise about the point A, where the mean of the X and the mean of the Y distribution fall, then the sum of squared deviations from the line becomes smaller and smaller until the line coincides with the regression line—line AB in Figure 8.6. The sum of squared deviations from this line would now be $\sum(Y - \tilde{Y})^2$, and $\sum(Y - \tilde{Y})^2$ will be smaller than $\sum(Y - \bar{Y})^2$, if there is any relationship between X and Y.

It is the second variable, X, which makes the regression line and $\sum(Y - \tilde{Y})^2$ meaningful. As long as the Y measures are considered alone, the best predicted value of Y for any single X measure would be the horizontal line, or mean of the Y distribution. But when there is regression of Y on X, we find that different values of Y are associated with different values of X. These associated values become our predictions when we have knowledge of the relationship between the two variables.

Let us assume that the Y values for any fixed X value are normally distributed about their mean with a variance that is the same for each fixed X value. If Y is related to X and we take a sample of paired (X,Y) values, holding X constant, then it should be clear that the mean Y value

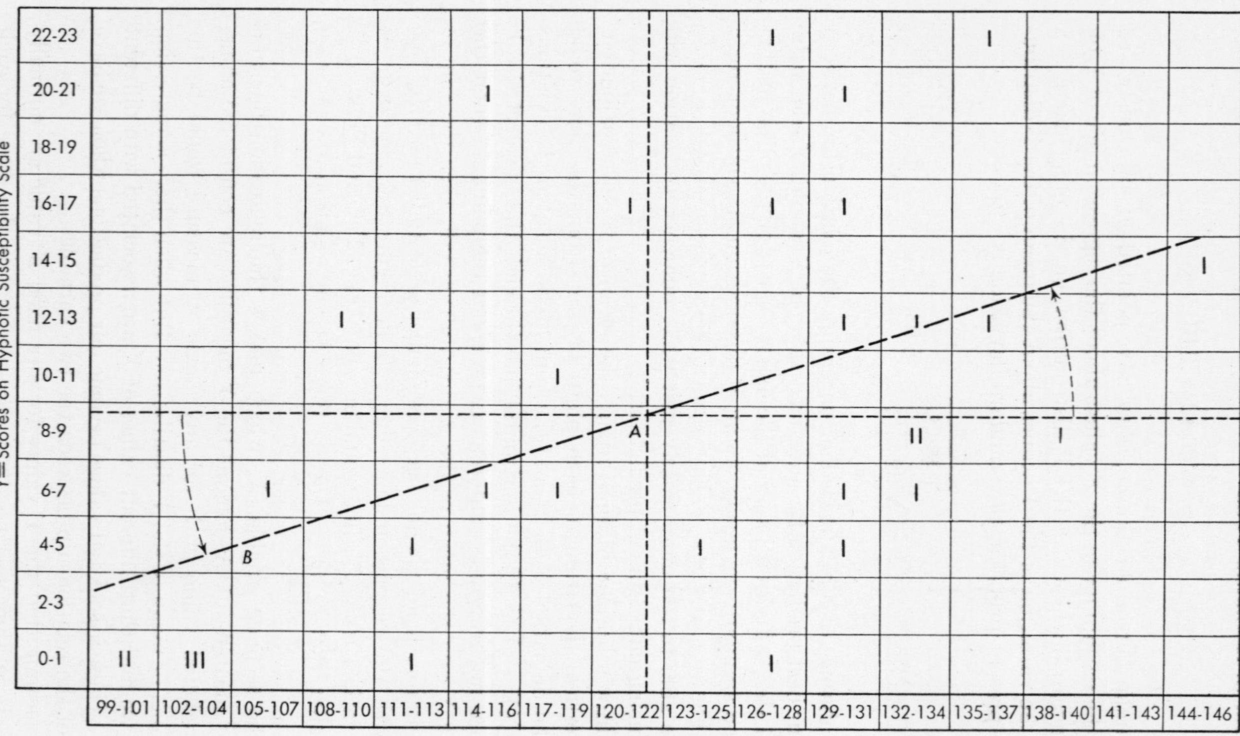

Fig. 8.6—A scatter diagram of scores on a hypnotic-susceptibility scale and scores on the Stanford-Binet Intelligence Test. Dotted lines have been drawn through the means of X and Y. The regression line of Y on X is represented by the line AB.

for such a sample will depend upon the particular value of X selected and held constant. It should also be clear that the Y values for such a sample will not vary as much as the Y values we would obtain if no restriction were placed upon X and if the X values were also allowed to vary. Then, as our estimate of the variance of these Y values for a constant value of X, we may use the residual variance $s_{y \cdot x}{}^2$. This estimate will be useful in later discussions.

■ The Regression of X on Y

If we now consider X as the dependent variable and Y as the independent variable, we will have

$$b_{xy} = \frac{\dfrac{\sum xy}{n-1}}{\dfrac{\sum y^2}{n-1}} = \frac{\sum xy}{\sum y^2} \tag{8.10}$$

where the subscripts xy, in that order, indicate that we are now concerned with the regression of X on Y.

The regression equation for predicting X values from Y values will thus be

$$\tilde{X} = a + b_{xy}Y \tag{8.11}$$

where

$$a = \bar{X} - b_{xy}\bar{Y} \tag{8.12}$$

The residual sum of squares $\sum(x - \tilde{x})^2 = \sum(X - \tilde{X})^2$ in predicting X from Y will be

$$\sum(x - \tilde{x})^2 = \sum x^2 - \frac{(\sum xy)^2}{\sum y^2} \tag{8.13}$$

and the residual variance will be

$$s_{x \cdot y}{}^2 = \frac{\sum(x - \tilde{x})^2}{n-2} \tag{8.14}$$

The standard error of estimate will be the square root of formula (8.14) or

$$s_{x \cdot y} = \sqrt{\frac{\sum(x - \tilde{x})^2}{n-2}} \tag{8.15}$$

Correlation and Regression Coefficients

We thus see that if we consider the regression of X on Y, instead of the regression of Y on X, we shall have corresponding formulas for the regression coefficient, the regression line, the residual variance, and the standard error of estimate. Although these formulas correspond in appearance, we should not expect them to yield identical numerical values. The only way in which these formulas could all yield identical pairs of values would be if the means and standard deviations of both the X and Y distributions were identical. Let us see why this is so.

Consider the value of the regression coefficient for Y on X as given by formula (7.12).

By definition
$$b_{yx} = \frac{\sum xy}{\sum x^2}$$

Multiplying both numerator and denominator of the right-hand side by the same value
$$b_{yx} = \left(\frac{\sum xy}{\sum x^2}\right)\left(\frac{\sqrt{\sum x^2 \sum y^2}}{\sqrt{\sum x^2 \sum y^2}}\right)$$

Rearranging terms
$$b_{yx} = \left(\frac{\sum xy}{\sqrt{\sum x^2 \sum y^2}}\right)\left(\frac{\sqrt{\sum x^2 \sum y^2}}{\sum x^2}\right)$$

Substituting an identity from formula (8.2)
$$b_{yx} = r\,\frac{\sqrt{\sum x^2 \sum y^2}}{\sum x^2}$$

Dividing both numerator and denominator by $n - 1$ and substituting identities
$$b_{yx} = r\,\frac{s_x s_y}{s_x{}^2}$$

We thus have another commonly used expression for the regression coefficient.

$$b_{yx} = r\,\frac{s_y}{s_x} \qquad \textbf{(8.16)}$$

And the corresponding expression for the regression coefficient of X on Y would be

$$b_{xy} = r\,\frac{s_x}{s_y} \qquad \textbf{(8.17)}$$

It is now readily apparent that if the standard deviation of the Y distribution was exactly equal to the standard deviation of the X distribution, then the two regression coefficients would also be identical and equal to the value of the correlation coefficient.[4] For example, both the X and Y values might be expressed in the form of standard scores with $z_x = (X - \bar{X})/s_x$ and $z_y = (Y - \bar{Y})/s_y$. Then, since we know that the standard deviation of a set of standard scores is equal to 1.00, for these two sets of standard scores the two regression coefficients would be equal and identical with the correlation coefficient.

If we multiply the regression coefficients of formula (8.16) and formula (8.17), we obtain

$$\left(r\frac{s_y}{s_x}\right)\left(r\frac{s_x}{s_y}\right) = (b_{yx})(b_{xy})$$

$$r^2 = (b_{yx})(b_{xy})$$

$$\pm\sqrt{r^2} = \pm\sqrt{(b_{yx})(b_{xy})} \tag{8.18}$$

and we see that the correlation coefficient is the geometric mean of the regression coefficients. Since r may be either plus or minus in sign, we say that $\sqrt{r^2} = r$ if the b's are positive in sign, but $\sqrt{r^2} = -r$ if the b's are negative in sign.[5]

The Residual Sum of Squares

In the chapter on regression we showed that $\sum(y - \tilde{y})^2 = \sum y^2 - \frac{(\sum xy)^2}{\sum x^2}$ where $y - \tilde{y}$ was an error of prediction resulting from the discrepancy between y and $\tilde{y}$ as predicted by the regression equation.[6] If we multiply both $(\sum xy)^2$ and $\sum x^2$ by $\sum y^2$, we obtain

$$\sum(y - \tilde{y})^2 = \sum y^2 - \frac{(\sum xy)^2 \sum y^2}{\sum x^2 \sum y^2}$$

From formula (8.2) we see that

---

[4] Formulas (8.16) and (8.17) also show that if r is positive, then both regression coefficients will be positive in sign, whereas if r is negative, both regression coefficients will be negative in sign.

[5] See page 19.

[6] See formula (7.18), page 127.

$$r^2 = \frac{(\sum xy)^2}{\sum x^2 \sum y^2}$$

and substituting this identity in the above equation, we get

$$\sum (y - \tilde{y})^2 = \sum y^2 - r^2 \sum y^2 \tag{8.19}$$

Then, solving for r^2, in formula (8.19), we obtain

$$r^2 = \frac{\sum y^2 - \sum (y - \tilde{y})^2}{\sum y^2} \tag{8.20}$$

or

$$r^2 = 1 - \frac{\sum (y - \tilde{y})^2}{\sum y^2} \tag{8.21}$$

We shall have occasion to refer to formula (8.21) in later discussions.

Formula (8.19) tells us that we may express the residual sum of squares in terms of $\sum y^2$ and the correlation coefficient. Thus

$$\sum (y - \tilde{y})^2 = \sum y^2 (1 - r^2) \tag{8.22}$$

The residual variance can be easily obtained from formula (8.22) by dividing both sides by $n - 2$. Then

$$s_{y \cdot x}{}^2 = \frac{\sum y^2 (1 - r^2)}{n - 2} \tag{8.23}$$

and the square root of formula (8.23) will give the standard error of estimate. Similar expressions for $\sum (x - \tilde{x})^2$ and $s_{x \cdot y}{}^2$ can be obtained by substituting $\sum x^2$ for $\sum y^2$ in formulas (8.22) and (8.23). Thus

$$\sum (x - \tilde{x})^2 = \sum x^2 (1 - r^2) \tag{8.24}$$

and

$$s_{x \cdot y}{}^2 = \frac{\sum x^2 (1 - r^2)}{n - 2} \tag{8.25}$$

Coefficients of Determination and Nondetermination

In formula (8.19) for the residual sum of squares, we showed that $\sum (y - \tilde{y})^2 = \sum y^2 - r^2 \sum y^2$. Rearranging these terms, we have

$$\sum y^2 = \sum (y - \tilde{y})^2 + r^2 \sum y^2$$

and substituting an identity from formula (8.22) for $\sum (y - \tilde{y})^2$, we obtain

$$\sum y^2 = \sum y^2(1 - r^2) + r^2 \sum y^2 \tag{8.26}$$

We may now divide both sides of the above expression by $\sum y^2$. In this way we shall express the two terms on the right-hand side as proportions of the sum of squares. Thus

$$1.00 = (1 - r^2) + r^2 \tag{8.27}$$

and we see that the sum of squared deviations about the mean of the Y distribution can be expressed as the sum of two proportions. The proportion given by $(1 - r^2)$ represents the variation, as we know, about the regression line. Apparently, then, this is the proportion of the variation in Y that is independent of the variation in X. The value $(1 - r^2)$ is called the *coefficient of nondetermination* and indicates the proportion of $\sum y^2$ that is independent of the regression of Y on X. The second term of formula (8.27), represented by r^2, is called the *coefficient of determination.* This coefficient represents the proportion of $\sum y^2$ that is associated with variation in X.

When r is equal to 1.00, then the coefficient of determination is equal to 1.00, and we can account for all of the variation represented by $\sum y^2$ in terms of the regression of Y on X. When r is equal to .80, we can account for .64 of the variation represented by $\sum y^2$ in terms of the regression of Y on X. This leaves $1.00 - r^2 = .36$ as the proportion of $\sum y^2$ that is independent of the variation in X.

We may prefer to think of r^2 and $(1 - r^2)$ in terms of the variance $s_y{}^2$ of the Y distribution rather than in terms of the sum of squares $\sum y^2$. We can do this by dividing both sides of formula (8.26) by $n - 1$, to obtain

$$\frac{\sum y^2}{n - 1} = (1 - r^2)\frac{\sum y^2}{n - 1} + r^2 \frac{\sum y^2}{n - 1}$$

and then

$$s_y{}^2 = (1 - r^2)s_y{}^2 + r^2 s_y{}^2 \tag{8.28}$$

From formula (8.28) we see that the proportion of the total variance $s_y{}^2$ associated with variation in X is equal to r^2 and that the proportion of the total variance that is independent of variation in X is $(1 - r^2)$. Do not, however, make the mistake of regarding $(1 - r^2)s_y{}^2$ as equal to the residual variance $s_{y \cdot x}{}^2$. In formula (8.28), for example, $(1 - r^2)\sum y^2$

has been divided by $n - 1$ and not by $n - 2$ as required by formula (7.19) or formula (8.23) for the residual variance.

It can be shown, for example, that $s_{y \cdot x}^2$ as defined by formula (7.19) or formula (8.23) is an unbiased estimate of the population value $\sigma_{y \cdot x}^2$, whereas $(1 - r^2)s_y^2$ is a biased estimate of this parameter. The nature of the bias may be indicated if we multiply both the numerator and denominator of the right-hand side of formula (8.23) by $n - 1$. Then

$$s_{y \cdot x}^2 = \frac{n-1}{n-2} s_y^2(1 - r^2)$$

It is apparent, therefore, that s_y^2 $(1 - r^2)$ will, in general, underestimate $\sigma_{y \cdot x}^2$ and that this bias is most pronounced when n is small. As n becomes very large, the fraction $(n - 1)/(n - 2)$ will approach 1.00 as a limit, and the bias of $s_y^2(1 - r^2)$ as an estimate of $\sigma_{y \cdot x}^2$ becomes less serious.[7]

■ EXAMPLES

8.1—Subtract 24 from each of the X values given below and 14 from each of the Y values. Find the correlation coefficient, using formula (8.5).

X	Y
36	26
34	27
33	23
32	21
31	22
30	19
28	17
27	14
25	16
24	15

[7] In some texts you will find that any and all sums of squares and products are divided by n. No distinction is made, in other words, between division by n, $n - 1$, or $n - 2$, as the case may be. When n is very large, it will, of course, make little difference in the values obtained whether we divide by n, $n - 1$, or $n - 2$, but this will not be true when n is small.

In the history of statistical methods, large-sample theory (with n very large) was developed before small-sample theory (with n small). Many current texts are still written in the tradition of large-sample theory without regard to sample size or, more

8.2—Compute the correlation coefficient for the data below.

Y Scores	*X Scores* 0–2	3–5	6–8	9–11	12–14	15–17	18–20
95–99						1	1
90–94				1		2	
85–89			1	2	1	1	
80–84		2	3	2	4		
75–79		1	3				
70–74	1	1	1	1			
65–69			1				

8.3—The following table shows the relationship between reported weekly wages and verified weekly wages for 61 female workers on jobs held from 0 to 12 months prior to the time of the interviews. The interviews were made in 1940–1942 with unemployed persons in St. Paul, Minnesota. Find the correlation coefficient. Data are from Keating, Paterson, and Stone (1950).

Reported Weekly Wage	*Verified Weekly Wage* 0–4	5–9	10–14	15–19	20–24	25–29
25–29						2
20–24					3	
15–19			4	19		
10–14			24	3		
5–9		3	1			
0–4	2					

8.4—Find the correlation coefficient for Example 7.8, page 139, in which mean reaction times were plotted against affective distances for various colors.

8.5—Find the correlation coefficient for the following data, using formula (8.4).

---

appropriately, the notion of degrees of freedom and unbiased estimates of population parameters. This reflects a limited interest in the sample at hand rather than in the population from which the sample was drawn. The latter is of much more general interest and concern to the research worker.

X	Y
12	12
10	13
9	9
8	8
7	5
6	6
4	0
2	2
1	1
0	3

8.6—Plot the data of Example 8.5 on coordinate paper. Show the point with coordinates $(\bar{X},\bar{Y})$. Draw the regression line of Y on X and the regression line of X on Y.

8.7—Twenty-five items in an attitude test were rated on a 9-point scale ranging from extremely unfavorable to extremely favorable. The ratings were made independently by two groups of subjects. The scale values of the items were found for each group of subjects. The correlation between the two sets of scale values may be taken as an indication of the reliability of the scale values. Find the value of the correlation coefficient.

Scale Values Group 1	*Scale Values Group* 2
8.2	8.9
7.7	8.6
7.3	7.5
7.0	7.3
6.7	7.4
2.7	1.9
2.0	1.2
3.1	3.1
1.8	1.6
1.0	1.0
3.7	3.0
8.4	8.9
4.8	4.5
4.6	4.0
3.2	2.8
6.2	6.3
6.0	6.2
5.1	5.5
4.1	3.4
6.4	6.9

8.8—A class in applied psychology was given Shaffer's (1936) S-scale and C-scale. Shaffer states that there is little relationship between scores on these two scales. Find the value of the correlation coefficient without grouping the scores. On the basis of the correlation coefficient obtained would you agree with Shaffer's conclusion?

C	S	C	S	C	S	C	S	C	S
5	10	15	7	14	10	9	10	18	9
19	9	11	6	13	7	6	19	14	14
17	10	18	11	19	8	8	8	13	6
14	6	13	11	11	11	18	9	18	8
13	10	14	4	18	8	16	6	18	7
7	12	13	8	5	6	5	7	8	4
13	14	13	6	18	13	14	8	19	12
8	10	4	7	17	6	15	7	22	17
6	17	8	9	23	18	18	12		

8.9—The data below are scores on two tests given to an introductory class in general psychology. One test was designed to measure the student's general understanding of the subject matter of the course. We shall call this variable X. The Y variable consists of scores on a vocabulary test of psychological terms. Construct a correlation table, letting $i = 5$ on both variables, and find the correlation coefficient. Begin the first class intervals with a multiple of the size of the interval.

X	Y	X	Y	X	Y	X	Y	X	Y	X	Y	X	Y	X	Y	X	Y	X	Y
55	71	50	57	49	53	58	65	76	65	74	65	74	75	72	71	57	63	96	80
60	59	67	64	53	46	67	67	58	55	68	71	55	65	59	66	63	75	74	76
56	48	69	70	61	65	59	51	53	61	87	78	68	72	74	61	79	71	91	95
56	60	59	68	60	62	63	66	60	59	61	56	55	61	59	52	49	51	82	66
57	67	59	70	45	54	58	61	65	67	66	70	61	63	60	62	58	71	63	74
55	53	56	67	71	61	73	61	74	63	58	72	48	58	73	78	82	80	96	85
61	60	66	58	71	63	48	62	73	73	58	55	69	58	57	62	97	84	90	89
54	63	49	47	67	57	50	68	67	64	45	55	77	63	71	66	82	75	86	75
57	61	60	61	52	52	55	59	55	60	76	68	78	78	74	81	79	76	82	85
58	68	45	57	60	60	61	40	48	66	50	63	86	82	55	62	90	73	97	86

8.10—For the data of Example 8.9, find the regression coefficient b_{yx}. Using the regression equation $\tilde{Y} = a + bX$, find the predicted score on Y for the following scores on X.

(*a*) If $X = 48$, then $\tilde{Y} =$
(*b*) If $X = 55$, then $\tilde{Y} =$
(*c*) If $X = 73$, then $\tilde{Y} =$
(*d*) If $X = 82$, then $\tilde{Y} =$
(*e*) If $X = 90$, then $\tilde{Y} =$

8.11—For the data of Example 8.9, find the regression coefficient b_{xy}. Using the regression equation $\tilde{X} = a + bY$, find the predicted score on X for the following scores on Y.

(*a*) If $Y = 58$, then $\tilde{X} =$
(*b*) If $Y = 71$, then $\tilde{X} =$
(*c*) If $Y = 76$, then $\tilde{X} =$
(*d*) If $Y = 80$, then $\tilde{X} =$
(*e*) If $Y = 95$, then $\tilde{X} =$

8.12—Find the standard errors of estimate $s_{y \cdot x}$ and $s_{x \cdot y}$ for the data of Example 8.9.

8.13—Show that if $d = x - y$, then $s_d{}^2 = s_x{}^2 + s_y{}^2 - 2rs_xs_y$

8.14—Show that $b_{yx} = r \dfrac{s_y}{s_x}$

8.15—Show that $r^2 = 1 - \dfrac{\sum(y - \tilde{y})^2}{\sum y^2}$

8.16—Show that $\sum y^2 = \sum y^2(1 - r^2) + r^2 \sum y^2$

8.17—Make a correlation table for the following pairs of X and Y values and find the correlation coefficient. Let $i_x = 3$ and let $i_y = 5$. Begin the first intervals with a multiple of the size of the intervals.

X	Y	X	Y	X	Y	X	Y	X	Y
4	77	25	53	20	67	14	61	31	49
18	37	9	46	27	38	21	52	16	57
24	38	20	52	11	66	29	58	23	62
6	55	25	53	21	37	14	71	31	54
18	42	9	51	27	43	22	52	16	57
24	38	20	57	11	71	29	58	23	67
6	60	25	58	21	42	14	71	33	39
19	42	10	51	27	43	22	52	16	57
24	43	20	57	12	46	29	63	23	67
7	65	25	58	21	42	15	42	33	44

X	Y	X	Y	X	Y	X	Y	X	Y
19	47	10	56	27	48	22	52	16	62
24	48	20	57	12	56	30	39	23	72
7	65	26	63	21	42	15	47	34	44
19	47	10	62	28	53	22	57	17	62
24	48	20	62	13	56	30	44	34	49
7	70	26	63	21	47	16	47	17	67
19	47	11	62	28	53	22	57	36	34
24	53	20	62	13	56	31	44	17	67
8	75	26	73	21	47	16	52	36	39
19	52	11	66	28	53	23	62	17	77

CHAPTER NINE

Random Errors of Measurement

Every set of measurements is subject to errors of observation. If, for example, we had several hundred objects of varying lengths and we measured the length of each object twice, we would not expect all of the pairs of measurements to be precisely the same. Slight errors of observation are apt to be present, despite efforts to reduce these to a minimum. Sometimes the second reading might be slightly less than the first, sometimes it might be slightly more, and in other cases we might have exactly the same recorded value for both readings.

We may distinguish between *systematic* and *random* errors of observation or measurement. Systematic errors are errors that tend to result in a consistent over- or under-estimation of the true measurement. For example, suppose that we have several hundred objects whose true weights are known. These objects are now weighed on a scale, and the resulting scale values are recorded. If we now subtract the true value for each weight from the corresponding observed value, we may call the resulting discrepancy an error of measurement.

If, in general, the errors of measurement tended to be consistently positive or consistently negative in sign, we would regard them as systematic errors. If, on the other hand, we found that the positive and negative errors occurred with approximately the same frequency and that the sum of the negative errors was approximately equal to the sum of the positive errors, we would regard them as random or chance errors. It should be clear that if the sum of the positive errors is equal to the sum of the negative errors, then the average error would be equal to zero.

A good research worker or experimenter makes every effort to free his measurements from systematic errors and to reduce his random errors to a minimum. Random errors of measurement can perhaps never be eliminated completely, and the notion of a true score or measurement, at least in the social and biological sciences at the present time, must remain a theoretical concept. We can, however, work with the notion of a true score even though we recognize the difficulties involved in actually obtaining such a score.

Assume, for example, that we have given to a large group of subjects a test designed to measure some aspect of arithmetic ability. We have available the scores of each subject on the test. These scores do not necessarily correspond to the true scores of the subjects, and we make the assumption that the error of measurement, which will be the difference between the observed score and the true score, is random rather than systematic. *We shall hold to this assumption throughout the rest of the discussion in this chapter.*

From the statements made above we may define a random error of measurement as

$$e = X - X_t \tag{9.1}$$

where e = a random error of measurement
X = the observed score or measurement
X_t = the true score or measurement

The problem we now wish to take up is the influence of random errors of measurement, as defined by formula (9.1), upon the sum of scores, the sum of squares, and the sum of products. Since the mean of a set of measurements depends upon the sum of scores, the variance upon the sum of squares, and the correlation coefficient upon the sum of products and the sum of squares, we shall thus see what influence random errors of measurement have upon these statistics.

Random Errors and the Mean

From formula (9.1) it follows that the observed score will be given by

$$X = X_t + e \tag{9.2}$$

If we sum both sides of formula (9.2) and if the errors of measurement are random in the sense we have previously described, then we may expect $\sum e$ to be equal to zero.[1] Consequently, we may conclude that the sum of

[1] This, of course, may not be true for any particular set of measures in which the sum of positive errors may differ slightly from the sum of negative errors. We are dealing here, however, with theoretical notions rather than with actualities, and in theory $\sum e$ will be equal to zero.

scores will not be influenced by random errors of measurement. If after summing we divide both sides of formula (9.2) by n, we will expect the observed mean to be equal to the true mean, since the mean of the errors will be zero.

■ Influence of Random Errors on the Sum of Squares

If the mean of the errors is equal to zero, then e of formula (9.2) is already in deviation form. And, since the observed mean is equal to the true mean, we may write formula (9.2) in deviation form so that

$$x = x_t + e \tag{9.3}$$

where x = a deviation from the observed mean
x_t = a deviation from the true mean
e = a random error of observation

If we now square both sides of (9.3) and sum, we obtain

$$\sum x^2 = \sum x_t^2 + \sum e^2 + 2\sum x_t e \tag{9.4}$$

From an identity, formula (8.3), in the previous chapter, we know that the product sum $\sum x_t e = r_{x_t e}\sqrt{\sum x_t^2 + \sum e^2}$. But, if the errors of measurement are random, there will be no relationship between x_t and e, and the correlation $r_{x_t e}$ will equal zero. Consequently, the product sum $\sum x_t e$ must also be zero. Thus we have

$$\sum x^2 = \sum x_t^2 + \sum e^2 \tag{9.5}$$

Formula (9.5) tells us that the observed sum of squares $\sum x^2$ must be greater than the true sum of squares $\sum x_t^2$, if random errors of measurement are present. Since the observed sum of squares, divided by $n - 1$, gives us the variance, we must conclude that the observed variance will be greater than the true variance, if random errors of measurement are present.

If we subtract $\sum e^2$ from both sides of formula (9.5) we may note that

$$\sum x_t^2 = \sum x^2 - \sum e^2 \tag{9.6}$$

and this is an expression that we shall want to use later.

■ Random Errors and the Product Sum

Let us now see what influence random errors of measurement will have upon the product sum. Suppose that we have a second set of measurements

Y and that these measurements are also subject to random errors. These Y measurements, in other words, will have exactly the same properties as those we have just established for the set of X measurements. If we now correlate the X and Y measurements, what influence will the random errors, present in both sets of observations, have upon the correlation coefficient?

Expressing both the X and Y measures in the form given by formula (9.3), the numerator of the correlation coefficient will be given by

$$\sum xy = \sum(x_t + e_1)(y_t + e_2) \tag{9.7}$$

where x and y = deviations from the observed means
x_t and y_t = deviations from the true means
e_1 and e_2 = random errors present in the X and Y measures, respectively.

Expanding the right side of formula (9.7), and then summating, we obtain

$$\sum xy = \sum x_t y_t + \sum x_t e_2 + \sum y_t e_1 + \sum e_1 e_2 \tag{9.8}$$

Again we know, from formula (8.3), that the various product sums will involve the corresponding correlation coefficients. But we have previously stated, in connection with formula (9.4), that if the errors of measurement are random they will be uncorrelated with the true scores. Consequently, $\sum x_t e_2$ and $\sum y_t e_1$ must both be equal to zero. Furthermore, random errors of measurement will be uncorrelated with each other, and therefore $\sum e_1 e_2$ will also be zero. Thus we have

$$\sum xy = \sum x_t y_t \tag{9.9}$$

Influence of Random Errors on the Correlation Coefficient

Formula (9.9) tells us that the observed product sum $\sum xy$ will be equal to the true product sum $\sum x_t y_t$, despite the presence of random errors of measurement. But the denominator of the correlation coefficient will involve the sum of squares for X and also the sum of squares for Y. Thus

$$r = \frac{\sum xy}{\sqrt{\sum x^2 \sum y^2}}$$

We have just shown that $\sum xy = \sum x_t y_t$. Formula (9.5) gives us an identity for $\sum x^2$ and we have a similar expression for $\sum y^2$. Substituting these expressions in the formula for the correlation coefficient, we obtain

$$r = \frac{\sum xy}{\sqrt{(\sum x_t^2 + \sum e_1^2)(\sum y_t^2 + \sum e_2^2)}} \tag{9.10}$$

It is clear from formula (9.10) that if random errors of measurement are present in X and Y, the denominator of the correlation coefficient will be larger than would be the case for measurements free from such errors. We may therefore conclude that random errors of measurement will tend to reduce the value of the observed correlation coefficient in comparison with the value that would be obtained in the absence of such errors.

■ The Reliability Coefficient

Suppose that we have available two forms of the same psychological or educational test. We shall assume that if we gave both forms of the test to a group of subjects we would find approximately the same means and variances for the two sets of scores. The two scores for each subject, however, will not be identical, for the scores involve random errors of measurement. The correlation coefficient between the two sets of scores will take the form

$$r_{x_1x_2} = \frac{\sum x_1x_2}{\sqrt{\sum x_1^2 \sum x_2^2}}$$

where $r_{x_1x_2}$ = the correlation coefficient between the two forms of the same test
x_1 = a deviation score on one form of the test
x_2 = a deviation score on the second form of the test

The sum of products in the numerator of the correlation coefficient will be similar to that given by formula (9.7). Substituting this expression in the formula for the correlation coefficient, we obtain

$$r_{x_1x_2} = \frac{\sum (x_t + e_1)(x_t + e_2)}{\sqrt{\sum x_1^2 \sum x_2^2}}$$

Expanding the numerator of the right-hand side of the above expression we have

$$r_{x_1x_2} = \frac{\sum x_t^2 + \sum x_t e_2 + \sum x_t e_1 + \sum e_1 e_2}{\sqrt{\sum x_1^2 + \sum x_2^2}}$$

Since the random errors will be uncorrelated with the true scores and with each other, $\sum x_t e_2$, $\sum x_t e_1$, and $\sum e_1 e_2$ will be equal to zero. Therefore

$$r_{x_1 x_2} = \frac{\sum x_t^2}{\sqrt{\sum x_1^2 \sum x_2^2}}$$

Since we have assumed equal variances, it follows that $\sum x_1^2$ and $\sum x_2^2$ will be equal, and we may drop the subscript and take the square root of the denominator to obtain

$$r_{x_1 x_2} = \frac{\sum x_t^2}{\sum x^2} \tag{9.11}$$

Substituting an identity from formula (9.6) for the numerator in the above expression, we have

$$r_{x_1 x_2} = \frac{\sum x^2 - \sum e^2}{\sum x^2}$$

$$= 1 - \frac{\sum e^2}{\sum x^2} \tag{9.12}$$

Dividing both $\sum e^2$ and $\sum x^2$ by $n - 1$, we obtain the following expression

$$r_{x_1 x_2} = 1 - \frac{s_e^2}{s_x^2} \tag{9.13}$$

Formula (9.13) is a commonly used expression for the correlation coefficient $r_{x_1 x_2}$. This correlation coefficient is called a *reliability coefficient.* The ratio s_e^2/s_x^2 is the ratio between the error variance of one of the forms of the test to the observed variance of the test. Since we have assumed comparable tests so that $s_{e_1}^2 = s_{e_2}^2$ and $s_{x_1}^2 = s_{x_2}^2$, it does not matter which form of the test we are concerned with, and we have, therefore, dropped the subscripts.

It is apparent, from formula (9.13), that, if the error variance is as great as the observed variance, the reliability coefficient will be equal to zero. On the other hand, the smaller the error variance, in comparison with the observed variance of the test scores, the larger the reliability coefficient. In the limiting case, with no random errors of measurement, the reliability coefficient will be equal to 1.00.

Methods of Determining Reliability

If a psychological or educational test were developed so that two forms of the test were available, the reliability coefficient could be obtained by testing a large group of subjects with both forms and correlating the resulting scores. We assume, of course, that the two forms could be made comparable by the careful selection of items used in each form.

The construction of a single form of a test involves a great deal of work, and the construction of two comparable forms more than doubles the labor involved in constructing a single form. In many instances, therefore, a test is available in only a single form. When this is the case, the reliability coefficient for the scores on the test is often determined by dividing the items on the test in such a way as to yield two scores. If, for example, a score is obtained from the odd-numbered items and another score is obtained from the even-numbered items, these two scores may be correlated. The resulting correlation coefficient is called a *split-half reliability coefficient.*

It is shown in textbooks dealing with the theory of test construction that the reliability coefficient of a test is influenced by the number of items in the test.[2] In general, the larger the number of items, with other things being equal, the larger the value of the reliability coefficient. The split-half reliability coefficient gives us the correlation between the two halves of the test and consequently refers to the reliability of a test with one half the number of items that the test itself contains. What we desire to know is not the reliability of the scores obtained from the split-halves, but rather the reliability of the test in its original length, that is, of scores based upon all of the items.

The reliability of the scores on the total test can be estimated from the split-half reliability coefficient by means of the *Spearman-Brown Prophecy Formula.* For example, if we have a reliability coefficient based upon the correlation between two sets of n items, and we wish to estimate the reliability coefficient for a test based upon the correlation between two sets of k items, then

$$r_{kk} = \frac{mr_{nn}}{1 + (m - 1)r_{nn}} \tag{9.14}$$

where r_{kk} = the estimated reliability of the test with k items

$m = k/n$

r_{nn} = the observed reliability coefficient of the scores based upon n items each

Now, if we have divided a test into two halves, so that each half contains n items, the scores on the total test will be based upon $2n$ items. Then $m = k/n = 2n/n = 2$. Thus, for the estimated reliability coefficient

[2] See, for example, Gulliksen (1950).

of the complete test, we have

$$r_{kk} = \frac{2r_{nn}}{1 + r_{nn}} \tag{9.15}$$

Another method of estimating the reliability of scores on a test when only one form of the test is available is to test the same subjects twice with the single test. Certain difficulties are involved in this procedure in that if the interval separating the two administrations of the test is quite short, memory, practice effects, and other factors may influence the scores obtained from the second administration. If the time interval is quite long and if the variable that the test is designed to measure changes during the interval, the correlation coefficient will be influenced by these changes. The same difficulties would be involved in administering two comparable forms of the test, except that, if we have different items in the two forms, we might rule out memory as a contributing influence.

The relative advantages and disadvantages of the three methods we have described for estimating reliability are discussed in detail in books dealing with the theory of measurement and test construction. We have only touched upon the problems involved.[3]

Correction for Attenuation

We may now raise the question of the maximum correlation that we might obtain between two variables X and Y, if no random errors of measurement were present in either set of test scores. This correlation coefficient would be of the form

$$r_{x_t y_t} = \frac{\sum x_t y_t}{\sqrt{\sum x_t^2 \sum y_t^2}} \tag{9.16}$$

We have already shown, in formula (9.9), that $\sum xy = \sum x_t y_t$. We may observe also that if we multiply both sides of formula (9.11) by $\sum x^2$, we obtain

$$r_{x_1 x_2} \sum x^2 = \sum x_t^2 \tag{9.17}$$

and we would have a similar expression, $r_{y_1 y_2} \sum y^2 = \sum y_t^2$, for the true sum of squares for Y. Substituting these identities in formula (9.16) for the correlation coefficient, we have

$$r_{x_t y_t} = \frac{\sum xy}{\sqrt{(r_{x_1 x_2} \sum x^2)(r_{y_1 y_2} \sum y^2)}}$$

[3] Gulliksen's (1950) book provides a complete, but fairly technical, discussion. Other good references include Thurstone (1935), Goodenough (1949), and Cronbach (1949).

Rearranging these terms, we get

$$r_{x_t y_t} = \left(\frac{\sum xy}{\sqrt{\sum x^2 \sum y^2}}\right)\left(\frac{1}{\sqrt{r_{x_1x_2}r_{y_1y_2}}}\right)$$

in which the first expression on the right is the observed coefficient of correlation between X and Y. Therefore

$$r_{x_t y_t} = \frac{r_{xy}}{\sqrt{r_{x_1x_2}r_{y_1y_2}}} \tag{9.18}$$

Formula (9.18) is called the *correction for attenuation* for the correlation coefficient. The correction is of theoretical interest in that we obtain an estimate of the correlation that might be obtained between X and Y if we had "true" measures of our variables, free from random errors of measurement.

If we multiply both sides of formula (9.18) by the denominator of the right-hand side, we get

$$r_{xy} = r_{x_t y_t}\sqrt{r_{x_1x_2}r_{y_1y_2}} \tag{9.19}$$

We may observe from formula (9.19) that if we had perfectly reliable measures of X and Y, so that the resulting reliability coefficients would each be equal to 1.00, the observed correlation would be equal to the true correlation. If one of our variables is perfectly reliable and the correlation between the true scores is also perfect, then the observed correlation coefficient cannot be greater than the square root of the reliability coefficient of the second variable. If the reliability coefficient of the X variable is equal to the reliability coefficient of the Y variable, then the observed correlation coefficient cannot be greater than the common reliability coefficient, since $r_{x_t y_t}$ cannot be greater than 1.00. Finally, if the correlation between the true scores is perfect, but if random errors of measurement are present in both variables, the observed correlation coefficient cannot exceed the geometric mean of the reliability coefficients.

The Validity Coefficient

The correlation between scores on a test X and some independent measure Y of the thing the test is supposed to measure is called a *validity coefficient.* For example, we might design a test that is supposed to measure academic success of students in college. As an independent measure of academic success in college we might take the grade points earned by students in their college courses. If we correlate these two sets of variables, the resulting correlation coefficient would be called a validity coefficient. The higher the validity coefficient, the better we can predict success in college in terms of the regression equation. With perfect validity, for example, we should be able to predict precisely the grade point of each student from his score on the test. If the test fails to correlate with the grade-point average, we should say that the test is not valid for this purpose.

Any particular psychological test may, of course, have many different validities in terms of the degree of correlation it shows with different variables, and it is nonsense to talk about validity in the abstract. The validity of a test is always with reference to some particular variable and not variables in general. A test may have a specified degree of validity for predicting academic success and no validity whatsoever for predicting income or some other variable.

Validity, as measured by the correlation between a test X and some other criterion of what the test is supposed to measure Y, is closely related to the reliability coefficient of the test $r_{x_1x_2}$ and also to the reliability coefficient of the criterion $r_{y_1y_2}$. This follows from formula (9.19) where

$$r_{xy} = r_{x_ty_t}\sqrt{r_{x_1x_2}r_{y_1y_2}}$$

It is obvious, for example, that we can have maximum validity in terms of r_{xy} only when we have perfect reliability in terms of $r_{x_1x_2}$ and $r_{y_1y_2}$. If the reliability coefficient of our test and criterion are equal, but less than 1.00, then the observed validity coefficient r_{xy} cannot be greater than the common reliability coefficient, since the true validity coefficient $r_{x_ty_t}$ cannot be greater than 1.00. If our test was perfectly reliable and the true validity coefficient $r_{x_ty_t}$ was also equal to 1.00, the observed validity coefficient r_{xy} could not be greater than the square root of the reliability coefficient of the criterion.[4]

■ EXAMPLES

9.1—Show, algebraically, that the mean will not be influenced by random errors of measurement.

9.2—Show, algebraically, that the sum of squares will be increased by random errors of measurement.

[4] The interpretations of the validity coefficient in terms of formula (9.19) are the same as those we made earlier in discussing the correction for attenuation. See page 178.

9.3—Develop the formula $r_{x_1x_2} = 1 - \frac{s_e^2}{s_x^2}$

9.4—Develop the formula for the correction for attenuation.

9.5—If the split-half reliability of a test of 60 items is .80, then what is the estimated reliability of the complete test?

9.6—If $r_{x_1x_2} = .81$, $r_{y_1y_2} = .64$, and $r_{x_ty_t} = 1.00$, then what is the estimated maximum value of the observed correlation between X and Y?

9.7—If $r_{x_1x_2} = .81$, $r_{x_ty_t} = 1.00$, and $r_{xy} = .90$, then what is the value of $r_{y_1y_2}$?

9.8—If the split-half reliability of a test of 20 items is .60, then what is the estimated reliability of the complete test?

9.9—If the split-half reliability of a test of 20 items is .60, then how many items would the test have to have in order to obtain an estimated reliability coefficient of .90?

Point Coefficients and Other Measures of Association

There are times when an investigator is faced with this situation: he wants to find the relationship between two variables, but the data for one variable are expressed in terms of a dichotomy. By a dichotomy we mean that only two categories or classes of the variable are available. For example, the response of a subject to an item on a test may be scored "right" or "wrong," and we may arbitrarily assign a coded score of 1 to the right response and a coded score of 0 to the wrong response. If we consider the response to the item a variable, then the variable can take only the two values, 1 or 0. Can we find a measure of the extent to which this variable, response to the item, is related to another variable that is continuous?

Or suppose that we have a group of male subjects and we wish to determine whether there is any relationship between their marital status and scores on a personality test. Our subjects can be classified as "single" or "married," and we wish to see whether this classification is related to scores on the test. Again we have a case where one of our variables is dichotomous, has only two classes, and again we might arbitrarily assign a value of 1 to one of the classes and a value of 0 to the other.

Other examples of a dichotomous variable might be subjects who are employed and those who are unemployed; individuals who are Democrats and those who are Republicans; animals that survive and those that die after an injection of a drug; subjects who are males and those who are female; subjects who respond in a particular way in an experimental situation and those who respond in some other fashion. This list could be extended, but the examples cited should be sufficient to indicate the nature of a variable for which we may have but two classes or categories. We shall refer to such variables as *dichotomous variables.*

The Point Biserial Coefficient of Correlation: r_{pb}

The product-moment coefficient of correlation between a continuous variable and a dichotomous variable is called the *point biserial coefficient of correlation.* Let us see how we may obtain this coefficient.

Suppose that we have given an intelligence test to a group of subjects and that we also have available their response to an item on a vocabulary test. The subjects either make a correct response to the vocabulary item or they fail to make a correct response. If the subjects make the correct response they are given a score of 1, and if they make the incorrect response they are given a score of 0. We wish to relate the scores on this dichotomous variable, which we shall call the X variable, to the scores on the intelligence test, which we shall call the Y variable.

In Table 10.1 we have set up a correlation table in the manner described in the chapter on the correlation coefficient. Columns (1) to (6) and rows (1) to (6) have exactly the same meaning as they did in our earlier discussion of the correlation table. In calculating the correlation coefficient from a correlation table, we made use of the formula

$$r = \frac{\Sigma x'y' - \dfrac{(\Sigma x')(\Sigma y')}{n}}{\sqrt{\left(\Sigma x'^2 - \dfrac{(\Sigma x')^2}{n}\right)\left(\Sigma y'^2 - \dfrac{(\Sigma y')^2}{n}\right)}}$$

When one of our variables is dichotomous and the other is continuous, the coefficient obtained by the above formula is called the point biserial coefficient of correlation or r_{pb}. Thus, substituting the appropriate values from Table 10.1, we obtain

$$r_{pb} = \frac{208 - \dfrac{(42)(303)}{66}}{\sqrt{\left(42 - \dfrac{(42)^2}{66}\right)\left(1{,}639 - \dfrac{(303)^2}{66}\right)}}$$

$$= \frac{15.18}{\sqrt{(15.27)(247.95)}}$$

$$= .25$$

Let us designate the number of subjects who have 0 scores on the dichotomous variables as n_0 and the number of subjects who have a score of 1 on this variable as n_1. Then n will be equal to $n_0 + n_1$. For the data of

Table 10.1—Calculation of the Point Biserial Coefficient of Correlation

Y Intervals	X Categories f_0	f_1	(1) f	(2) y'	(3) fy'	(4) fy'^2	(5) $\sum x'._{y'}$	(6) $y'\sum x'._{y'}$
130–134	0	2	2	9	18	162	2	18
125–129	0	3	3	8	24	192	3	24
120–124	1	5	6	7	42	294	5	35
115–119	4	7	11	6	66	396	7	42
110–114	3	4	7	5	35	175	4	20
105–109	8	10	18	4	72	288	10	40
100–104	5	9	14	3	42	126	9	27
95– 99	0	1	1	2	2	4	1	2
90– 94	2	0	2	1	2	2	0	0
85– 89	1	1	2	0	0	0	1	0
(1) f	24	42	66		303	1,639	42	208
(2) x'	0	1			$\sum y'$	$\sum y'^2$		$\sum x'y'$
(3) fx'	0	42	42	$\sum x'$				
(4) fx'^2	0	42	42	$\sum x'^2$				
(5) $\sum y'._{x'}$	95	208	303					
(6) $x'\sum y'._{x'}$	0	208	208	$\sum x'y'$				

Table 10.1, $n_0 = 24$ and $n_1 = 42$. We may also designate the sum of coded scores on the Y variable for the n_1 subjects as $\sum y_1'$. The sum of coded scores for all n subjects will be written without a subscript as $\sum y'$.

Now, if you examine the row and column sums of Table 10.1, you will note the following:

$$\sum x'y' = \sum y_1'$$

$$\sum x' = n_1$$

$$\sum x'^2 = n_1$$

If we substitute these identities in the formula for the coefficient of correlation, we obtain

$$r_{pb} = \frac{\sum y_1' - \dfrac{n_1 \sum y'}{n}}{\sqrt{\left(n_1 - \dfrac{(n_1)^2}{n}\right)\left(\sum y'^2 - \dfrac{(\sum y')^2}{n}\right)}} \tag{10.1}$$

where r_{pb} = the point biserial coefficient of correlation
$\sum y_1'$ = the sum of coded y' scores for the subjects in category 1 on the dichotomous variable
$\sum y'$ = the sum of coded y' scores for all n subjects
n_1 = the number of subjects in category 1 on the dichotomous variable
n = the total number of subjects

In answer to one of the examples at the end of the chapter, we show that[1]

$$n_1 - \frac{(n_1)^2}{n} = \frac{n_0 n_1}{n}$$

and consequently we may also write formula (10.1) as

$$r_{pb} = \frac{\sum y_1' - \dfrac{n_1 \sum y'}{n}}{\sqrt{\left(\dfrac{n_0 n_1}{n}\right)\left(\sum y'^2 - \dfrac{(\sum y')^2}{n}\right)}} \tag{10.2}$$

Multiplying both the numerator and denominator of formula (10.2) by n, we obtain

$$r_{pb} = \frac{n \sum y_1' - n_1 \sum y'}{\sqrt{(n_0 n_1)[n \sum y'^2 - (\sum y')^2]}} \tag{10.3}$$

Substituting in formula (10.3) with the appropriate values from Table 10.1 we obtain

$$r_{pb} = \frac{(66)(208) - (42)(303)}{\sqrt{(24)(42)[(66)(1{,}639) - (303)^2]}}$$

---

[1] See Example 10.17.

$$= \frac{1{,}002}{\sqrt{(1{,}008)(16{,}365)}}$$

$$= .25$$

which is the same value we obtained before.

Formula (10.3) is extremely easy to use and involves a minimum amount of calculation in finding the point biserial coefficient of correlation. A variety of other formulas, based upon formula (10.1) could be developed, but they all involve additional calculations.[2] Formula (10.3) may also be used with Y values that have not been grouped into classes. In this instance, we would merely substitute Y for y' and Y_1 for y_1'. Thus

$$r_{pb} = \frac{n\sum Y_1 - n_1\sum Y}{\sqrt{(n_0n_1)[n\sum Y^2 - (\sum Y)^2]}} \qquad \textbf{(10.4)}$$

The sign of the point biserial coefficient of correlation will depend upon whether the mean score on the Y variable is larger or smaller for the n_1 subjects than it is for the n_0 subjects. For the data of Table 10.1 there was a logical basis for assigning a 1 value to the subjects making the correct response on the dichotomous variable. Thus the fact that the point biserial correlation coefficient was, in this instance, positive in sign, means that the subjects making the correct response to the vocabulary item have a higher mean score on the intelligence test than the subjects making the incorrect response.

In many cases, however, we shall have no logical basis for assigning the 0 and 1 values for the dichotomous variables. For example, if our dichotomous variable was sex, should we give the males or the females a score of 1? If our dichotomous variable consists of Democrats and Republicans, shall we give the Democrats or the Republicans the score of 1? It should be clear that in such cases the sign of the point biserial coefficient of correlation will be an arbitrary matter, and the direction of the relationship must be interpreted from the arrangement of the X variable in the correlation table.

The Phi Coefficient: r_ϕ

Suppose that both of our variables are dichotomous. We can again arrange our data in the form of a correlation table. If we obtain the product-moment

[2] See the answer to Example 10.18 at the end of the chapter.

correlation coefficient for two dichotomous variables, the resulting coefficient is called the *fourfold point coefficient* or the *phi coefficient* or r_ϕ.

In Table 10.2 we show the data for two dichotomous variables. The

Table 10.2—Calculation of the Phi Coefficient

Y *Item* 2	*X* *Item* 1 *Incorrect*	*X* *Item* 1 *Correct*	(1) f	(2) y'	(3) fy'	(4) fy'^2	(5) $\sum x'._{y'}$	(6) $y'\sum x'._{y'}$
Correct	^{a} 45	^{b} 45	90	1	90	90	45	45
Incorrect	^{c} 80	^{d} 30	110	0	0	0	30	0
(1) f	125	75	200		90	90	75	45
(2) x'	0	1			$\sum y'$	$\sum y'^2$		$\sum x'y'$
(3) fx'	0	75	75	$\sum x'$				
(4) fx'^2	0	75	75	$\sum x'^2$				
(5) $\sum y'._{x'}$	45	45	90					
(6) $x'\sum y'._{x'}$	0	45	45	$\sum x'y'$				

two dichotomous variables are responses to two items in a vocabulary test. We have assigned the 1 score to the correct responses and the 0 score to the incorrect responses to each item. Columns (1) to (6) and rows (1) to (6) have exactly the same meaning as in the correlation table for two continuous variables. If we substitute the appropriate values from Table 10.2 in the formula for the correlation coefficient, we obtain

$$r_\phi = \frac{45 - \dfrac{(75)(90)}{200}}{\sqrt{\left(75 - \dfrac{(75)^2}{200}\right)\left(90 - \dfrac{(90)^2}{200}\right)}}$$

$$= \frac{45 - 33.75}{\sqrt{(75 - 28.125)(90 - 40.5)}}$$

$$= .23$$

You will note that in Table 10.2 we have assigned the letters a, b, c, and d to the four cells of the table. If we let these letters stand for the corresponding cell entries, then we may observe the following identities:

$$\Sigma x'y' = b$$

$$\Sigma x' = b + d$$

$$\Sigma x'^2 = b + d$$

$$\Sigma y' = a + b$$

$$\Sigma y'^2 = a + b$$

$$n = a + b + c + d$$

Substituting identities from the above equations in the formula for the correlation coefficient, we obtain

$$r_\phi = \frac{b - \dfrac{(b+d)(a+b)}{n}}{\sqrt{\left[(b+d) - \dfrac{(b+d)^2}{n}\right]\left[(a+b) - \dfrac{(a+b)^2}{n}\right]}} \tag{10.5}$$

Expanding the terms in the numerator and the denominator and substituting $a + b + c + d$ for n, we obtain the following simplified expression for the phi coefficient

$$r_\phi = \frac{bc - ad}{\sqrt{(a+c)(b+d)(a+b)(c+d)}} \tag{10.6}$$

where r_ϕ = the fourfold point coefficient or phi coefficient
bc = the product of the entries in cells b and c
ad = the product of the entries in cells a and d
and the terms in the denominator are the marginal sums of the 2×2 table.

Substituting the appropriate values from Table 10.2 in formula (10.6) we have

$$r_\phi = \frac{(45)(80) - (45)(30)}{\sqrt{(125)(75)(90)(110)}} = .23$$

which is equal to the value we obtained before.

As in the case of the point biserial coefficient of correlation, the sign of the phi coefficient depends upon the arrangement of the dichotomous variables in the 2×2 table. In the example of Table 10.2 we had some basis for assigning the 1 score to the correct response to the two items and the 0 score to the incorrect response. In many cases, however, assigning the scores of 0 and 1 will be an arbitrary matter. The direction of the relationship must, in these cases, be determined from inspection of the arrangement of the dichotomous variables in the table.

■ The Biserial Coefficient of Correlation: r_b

The formula for the point biserial coefficient of correlation measures the degree of linear relationship between a dichotomous variable and a continuous variable. Under some circumstances, we may make the assumption that the dichotomous variable is essentially continuous and normally distributed. The coefficient used to measure the relationship when this assumption can be made is the *biserial coefficient of correlation* r_b rather than the point-biserial coefficient.

The assumption that the dichotomous variable is essentially continuous and normally distributed is most likely to be valid when we have artificially dichotomized a continuous variable. For example, we may arbitrarily divide the scores on a test or some other variable into those that are above the mean and those that are below the mean, or into those that are above the median and those that are below the median. In this instance, we would know that the dichotomous variable is continuous, and we might further assume that it is normally distributed. Consequently, we would use the biserial coefficient of correlation to measure the relationship between the dichotomous variable and the continuous variable.

A convenient formula for the biserial coefficient of correlation may be obtained by multiplying formula (10.3) by $\sqrt{p_1 q}/y_p$. Then

$$r_b = \frac{n\sum y_1' - n_1\sum y'}{\sqrt{(n_0 n_1)[n\sum y'^2 - (\sum y')^2]}}\left(\frac{\sqrt{p_1 q}}{y_p}\right) \qquad \textbf{(10.7)}$$

where p_1 is the proportion of the total number of subjects in the 1 category of the dichotomous variable, that is, $p_1 = n_1/n$, and q is the proportion of the total number of subjects in the 0 category, that is, $q = n_0/n = 1 - p_1$. We use y_p to represent the ordinate of the normal curve at the point of division of the two groups on the dichotomous variable. We find the value of y_p from Table III, in the Appendix. We enter Table III with $p_1 = n_1/n$ and look down column (3) or column (4) of the table until we find the value most closely approximating p_1. We then read the corresponding value of y_p from the last column of the table. For example, if p_1 is .488, the value of y_p would be equal to .3988. If p_1 is equal to .591, then we find that y_p would be equal to .3885.

We may simplify the computation involved in formula (10.7) by substituting n_1/n for p_1 and n_0/n for q. Then

$$r_b = \frac{n\sum y_1' - n_1\sum y'}{\sqrt{(n_0 n_1)[n\sum y'^2 - (\sum y')^2]}}\left(\frac{\sqrt{\dfrac{n_0 n_1}{n^2}}}{y_p}\right)$$

$$= \frac{(n\sum y_1' - n_1\sum y')/n}{y_p\sqrt{n\sum y'^2 - (\sum y')^2}}$$

$$= \frac{\sum y_1' - p_1\sum y'}{y_p\sqrt{n\sum y'^2 - (\sum y')^2}} \tag{10.8}$$

We may also write formula (10.8) in terms of Y values that have not been grouped into classes. In this case, we have

$$r_b = \frac{\sum Y_1 - p_1\sum Y}{y_p\sqrt{n\sum Y^2 - (\sum Y)^2}} \tag{10.9}$$

We now obtain the biserial coefficient of correlation for the data shown in Table 10.3. In the table we have calculated the values to be substituted in formula (10.8). From Table III we find that $y_p = .394$ for the value of p_1 equal to .5625. Substituting in formula (10.8), we get

$$r_b = \frac{172 - (.5625)(281)}{.394\sqrt{(80)(1{,}209) - (281)^2}}$$

$$= \frac{172 - 158.06}{.394\sqrt{17{,}759}}$$

$$= \frac{13.94}{52.51}$$

$$= .27$$

Another condition must be met before we can legitimately compute the biserial coefficient of correlation. Our dichotomous variable must not

Table 10.3—Calculation of the Biserial Coefficient of Correlation

Y *Intervals*	(1) f_0	(2) f_1	(3) f	(4) y'	(5) f_1y'	(6) fy'	(7) fy'^2
85–89	0	2	2	8	16	16	128
80–84	1	2	3	7	14	21	147
75–79	2	3	5	6	18	30	180
70–74	3	7	10	5	35	50	250
65–69	4	11	15	4	44	60	240
60–64	12	8	20	3	24	60	180
55–59	10	10	20	2	20	40	80
50–54	3	1	4	1	1	4	4
45–49	0	1	1	0	0	0	0
Σ	35	45	80		172	281	1,209
					$\Sigma y_1'$	$\Sigma y'$	$\Sigma y'^2$

constitute merely the two extremes of a larger group but must include the entire group. We could not, for example, give a test to a large group and then select only the bottom 25 per cent and the top 25 per cent as the members of our dichotomy. If we attempted to compute the biserial coefficient of correlation with only these two extreme groups, the assumption concerning continuity and normality of the dichotomous variable would indeed be difficult to justify.

If we have dichotomized a variable that is continuous and normally distributed and then found the biserial coefficient of correlation for this dichotomous variable and another variable, the resulting coefficient is an estimate of the corresponding product-moment coefficient for the two continuous variables. This estimate will be best when we have a large n and when the point of division on the continuous variable that is reduced to a dichotomy is made near the median. This will mean that we shall have approximately the same number of subjects in each of the two categories. We assume, also, of course, that the scores or measures on the dichotomized variable are normally distributed. This assumption is involved when we enter the table of the unit normal curve to obtain the value of the ordinate y_p for the corresponding value of p_1.

The Tetrachoric Correlation Coefficient: r_t

In the case of two dichotomized variables where we have used the phi coefficient to measure the degree of relationship present, we may also, under certain circumstances, assume that both variables are essentially continuous and normally distributed. If we can make this assumption about both of the dichotomized variables, then the coefficient that we should use to measure the relationship is the *tetrachoric coefficient of correlation* r_t, rather than the phi coefficient.

The tetrachoric coefficient of correlation could properly be applied, for example, if we have artificially dichotomized two continuous variables that are normally distributed. We may, for example, divide the scores on a test into those that are above the median and those that are below the median. We may make a similar division for a second test or variable. If we now assign a score of 1 to those subjects who are above the median and a score of 0 to those who are below, we have the following possible pairs of scores on the two tests:

Interpretation of Pairs of Scores	*Test 1* X	*Test 2* Y
Above the median on both tests	1	1
Above median on Test 1, below on Test 2	1	0
Below median on Test 1, above on Test 2	0	1
Below the median on both tests	0	0

We may make a 2 × 2 correlation table for these pairs of scores as we did in the case of the phi coefficient. Such a table is shown in Table 10.4,

Table 10.4—Relationship between Success as a Salesman and Social Adjustment*

		Unsuccessful Salesmen		*Successful Salesmen*	*Totals*
Socially Adjusted	a	25	b	35	60
Socially Maladjusted	c	30	d	10	40
Totals		55		45	100

* Data from Garrett (1937).

where we have also assigned letters to represent the corresponding cell entries. We could now develop an approximation formula for tetrachoric r which would involve the solution of a quadratic equation. We shall instead give a much easier method for estimating tetrachoric r.

We now calculate the products ad and bc corresponding to the products of the cell entries in Table 10.4. We then find the ratio $k = bc/ad$ or its reciprocal, whichever is the larger. Thus, if *bc* is greater than *ad*, we find

$$k = \frac{bc}{ad} \tag{10.10}$$

and, if *ad* is greater than *bc*, we find

$$\frac{1}{k} = \frac{1}{\frac{bc}{ad}} = \frac{ad}{bc} \tag{10.11}$$

In essence, then, we put either *bc* or *ad*, whichever is the larger, in the numerator and divide by the other product.

We then enter Table X, in the Appendix, with this ratio and read the corresponding value of the tetrachoric coefficient of correlation in the column headed r_t. The values of r_t in Table X are based upon one of the formulas developed by Pearson (1901) to estimate the tetrachoric coefficient of correlation.[3]

In Table 10.4 we report data for which the tetrachoric r as obtained by direct calculation from one of the formulas for the coefficient is .53. We illustrate the use of Table X for the same data. Thus

$$ad = (25)(10) = 250$$

$$bc = (35)(30) = 1{,}050$$

Putting *bc* in the numerator, since it is larger than *ad*, we obtain

$$\frac{bc}{ad} = \frac{1\,050}{250} = 4.2$$

Entering Table X with 4.2 we find that the corresponding estimate of the tetrachoric r is .51. The ease by which this estimate is obtained more than

[3] Computing diagrams for the tetrachoric coefficient of correlation have also been prepared by Cheshire, Saffir, and Thurstone (1933). To use these diagrams, the points of division on the variables must be taken into consideration. Table X, prepared by Davidoff and Goheen (1953), does not involve the points of division on the two variables and therefore is extremely convenient to use.

It should be emphasized, however, that Table X provides estimates of r_t that are most accurate when the points of division on the two variables are close to the medians. A table similar to Table X but with correction graphs for nonmedian dichotomization has been prepared by Perry, Kettner, Hertzka, and Bouvier (1953).

justifies the slight discrepancy between its value and that obtained by direct calculation.[4] In general, the estimates of tetrachoric r obtained from Table X will agree quite well with estimates obtained from other methods of determining the coefficient.

The Rank Correlation Coefficient: r′

If we have a set of objects or individuals arranged in order according to the degree of some characteristic which they possess, the individuals or objects are said to be *ranked*. After the individuals are arranged in order, we may then assign the number 1 to the first individual, 2 to the second, 3 to the third, and so on, with the number n corresponding to the nth or last individual. We thus have a series or set of ranks in which $X_1, X_2, X_3, \cdots, X_n = 1, 2, 3, \cdots, n$. It can be shown that the sum of the n terms in this series will be given by

$$\Sigma X = \frac{n(n+1)}{2} \tag{10.12}$$

and that the sum of the squares of the n terms in the series will be given by[5]

$$\Sigma X^2 = \frac{n(n+1)(2n+1)}{6} \tag{10.13}$$

We have previously shown, formula (4.1), that the sum of squared deviations from the mean will be given by

$$\Sigma x^2 = \Sigma X^2 - \frac{(\Sigma X)^2}{n}$$

Then, substituting from formula (10.12) and formula (10.13) in the above expression, we obtain for the set of ranks

$$\Sigma x^2 = \frac{n(n+1)(2n+1)}{6} - \frac{\left(\frac{n(n+1)}{2}\right)^2}{n}$$

[4] It should be pointed out that the formulas usually quoted and actually used in calculating tetrachoric r's are themselves approximations in which the terms involving powers of r greater than the second are customarily ignored.

[5] Methods for proving formula (10.12) and formula (10.13) are usually given in college algebra texts in the sections dealing with sequences and series. See, for example, Reagan, Ott, and Sigley (1948).

$$= \frac{n(n+1)(2n+1)}{6} - \frac{n(n+1)^2}{4}$$

$$= \frac{n^3 - n}{12} \tag{10.14}$$

The mean of the set of ranks may be obtained by dividing both sides of formula (10.12) by n. Thus

$$\bar{X} = \frac{n+1}{2} \tag{10.15}$$

When we have available two sets of ranks for the same objects or individuals, we may then wish to determine the degree of relationship between the two sets of ranks. The product-moment correlation coefficient obtained from two sets of ranks is called a *rank correlation coefficient*, and we shall designate this coefficient by r'.[6]

We have shown earlier[7] that if we let $d = x - y$, then

$$\sum d^2 = \sum x^2 + \sum y^2 - 2r\sqrt{\sum x^2 \sum y^2}$$

We can then express the correlation coefficient as

$$r = \frac{\sum x^2 + \sum y^2 - \sum d^2}{2\sqrt{\sum x^2 \sum y^2}} \tag{10.16}$$

But, if X and Y consist of two sets of n ranks each, $\sum x^2$ will be given by formula (10.14) as will also $\sum y^2$. Thus, using r' to indicate the rank correlation coefficient and substituting from formula (10.14) in formula (10.16), we obtain

$$r' = \frac{\dfrac{n^3 - n}{12} + \dfrac{n^3 - n}{12} - \sum d^2}{2\sqrt{\left(\dfrac{n^3 - n}{12}\right)\left(\dfrac{n^3 - n}{12}\right)}}$$

---

6 The symbol ρ is used in some texts to designate the rank correlation coefficient.

7 See page 154.

$$= \frac{2\left(\frac{n^3 - n}{12}\right) - \sum d^2}{2\left(\frac{n^3 - n}{12}\right)}$$

$$= 1 - \frac{\sum d^2}{2\left(\frac{n^3 - n}{12}\right)}$$

$$= 1 - \frac{6\sum d^2}{n^3 - n} \tag{10.17}$$

Formula (10.17) involves calculating $\sum d^2 = \sum (x - y)^2$, and we now show that $\sum d^2 = \sum (X - Y)^2$. Thus, if we let $d = x - y$ and $D = X - Y$, then

$$\begin{aligned} d &= x - y \\ &= (X - \bar{X}) - (Y - \bar{Y}) \\ &= X - \bar{X} - Y + \bar{Y} \end{aligned}$$

But, if X and Y are two sets of n ranks each, then $\bar{X}$ will be equal to $\bar{Y}$, and consequently

$$d = X - Y = D \tag{10.18}$$

Then, substituting D for d in formula (10.17), the rank correlation coefficient may be computed by means of the following formula

$$r' = 1 - \frac{6\sum D^2}{n(n^2 - 1)} \tag{10.19}$$

where r' = the rank correlation coefficient
D = the difference between a pair of ranks
n = the number of pairs of ranks

In Table 10.5 we give the ranks assigned to 8 morale items by a group of employers and a group of employees. Substituting the appropriate values from the table in formula (10.19) we obtain

$$r' = 1 - \frac{6(92)}{8(8^2 - 1)}$$

$$= 1 - 1.095$$

$$= -.10$$

which indicates that there is a very slight tendency for the ranks assigned by the two groups to the 8 morale items to be negatively related.

Table 10.5—Ranks Assigned to Various Morale Items by Employers and Employees*

Item	*Employer Ranking*	*Employee Ranking*	*Difference*	*Difference Squared*
1. Credit for work done	1	7	−6	36
2. Interesting work	2	3	−1	1
3. Fair pay	3	1	2	4
4. Understanding and appreciation	4	5	−1	1
5. Counsel on personal problems	5	8	−3	9
6. Promotion on merit	6	4	2	4
7. Good physical working conditions	7	6	1	1
8. Job security	8	2	6	36
				92

* Data from Fosdick (1939).

If you apply any of the formulas previously given for the product-moment coefficient of correlation to the ranks of Table 10.5, you will find that the value obtained is identical with that given by formula (10.19). The rank correlation coefficient, in other words, is the product-moment correlation coefficient applied to two sets of integral ranks. The value obtained by formula (10.19) and by any of the other formulas for the product-moment correlation coefficient must, therefore, give identical results.

Sometimes, however, in obtaining sets of ranks it may be difficult to distinguish between two of the individuals or objects being ranked. What happens, for example, if two objects seem to be tied for the same rank? If judgments of equality are to be permitted, we might assign an average rank to those objects that are judged equal. For example, if no choice can be made between two objects when we come to, let us say, the assignment of rank 4, then we might assign the average of ranks 4 and 5, or

4.5, to each of these objects. If no choice can be made between three objects, then we might assign the average of ranks 4, 5, and 6, or 5 to each of these objects. In other words, when apparent ties for a given rank are present, we give each of the tied objects the average of the ranks they would ordinarily occupy.

If judgments of equality are permitted so that we have tied ranks, the rank correlation coefficient as given by formula (10.19) will no longer be identical with the value obtained by applying to the same data one of the other formulas for the correlation coefficient. Formula (10.19) is equivalent to the product-moment coefficient only when the ranks for each variable are integral. Formula (10.19) may still be used, however, to determine the relationship between two sets of ranks, even though tied ranks are present in the data, provided the number of ties is not large. If the number of ties is large, however, then formula (10.19) should not be used. Instead a correction factor, described in Chapter 19, should be used in connection with formula (10.16) to find the rank correlation coefficient.

The Correlation Ratio: η

All of the methods of measuring the association or relationship between two variables described so far in this chapter give the *degree of linear relationship* between the variables. This is not to say that the product-moment correlation coefficient involves the *assumption* that the variables are linearly related. There is nothing in the derivation of the formula for the correlation coefficient or in the calculation of the coefficient that requires us to make this assumption. In fact, a product-moment correlation coefficient can be computed for any set of paired X, Y values. It is true, however, that if the relationship departs from linearity in any way, the correlation coefficient will underestimate the degree of relationship present. Consequently, we might say that the correlation coefficient is an *adequate* measure of relationship only when the variables are linearly related. We now consider a measure of relationship that may be used when the relationship between two variables is not linear.

Think for a moment of a correlation table in which the means of each Y column are the same. A line drawn through these means, from left to right, would be a straight line across the correlation table at the level of the mean of the entire Y distribution. Hence there would be no change in Y with change in X; the average Y score for all individuals with a given *high* average X score would be the same as the average Y score for individuals with a given *low* average value of X. The relationship between X and Y would be zero. On the other hand, if the means of the Y columns increased by a constant amount from left to right, then the relationship between X and Y would be positive, and the relationship could be represented by the line drawn through the means of the columns. If the column Y means decreased by a constant amount from left to right,

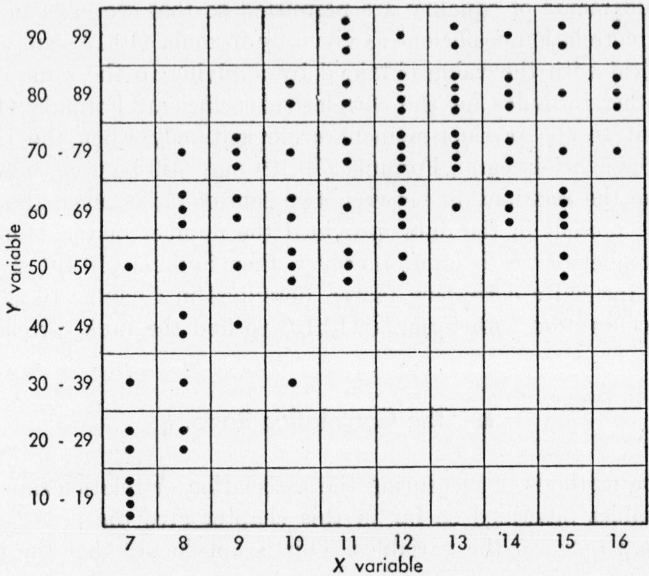

Fig. 10.1 — Correlation chart for X and Y in which the relationship between X and Y cannot be adequately represented by the equation for a straight line.

the relationship between X and Y would be negative, and again this relationship could be represented by a straight line drawn through the means of the columns.

Let us suppose, however, that the means of the Y columns at first increase with increases in X and then begin to level off with values of X beyond a certain point. This situation is represented in Figure 10.1. Obviously, the trend of the plotted points cannot very well be represented by any straight line, and the correlation coefficient computed for these values would greatly underestimate the relationship that is present.

The *correlation ratio* is the appropriate measure of relationship between two variables when the relationship is not linear. The method of calculating the correlation ratio will be illustrated with the data of Table 10.6. Table 10.6 is a correlation table in which the Y variable consists of Q values obtained for 129 items in an attitude scale. A group of judges rated the 129 items in terms of the degree of "favorableness" or "un-

Table 10.6—Calculation of the Correlation Ratio of Y on X

Q Values (Y)	Scale Values (X) 0	1	2	3	4	5	6	7	8	f	y'	fy'	fy'^2
4.0–4.4			1	1	1	2				5	8	40	320
3.5–3.9		1	1	1	4	5	4	2		18	7	126	882
3.0–3.4		4	3	1	6	3	2	6	2	27	6	162	972
2.5–2.9		3	2		2	2	1	3		13	5	65	325
2.0–2.4	4	3	2					3	3	15	4	60	240
1.5–1.9	8	6			1				5	20	3	60	180
1.0–1.4	6								9	15	2	30	60
.5– .9	3								11	14	1	14	14
.0– .4	1								1	2	0	0	0
n_i	22	17	9	3	14	12	7	14	31	129		557	2,993
x'	0	1	2	3	4	5	6	7	8			$\sum y'$	$\sum y'^2$
$\sum y_i'$	55	76	51	21	85	79	45	77	68	557			

Col.	n_i	$\sum y_i'$	$(\sum y_i')^2$	$\frac{(\sum y_i')^2}{n_i}$
0	22	55	3,025	137.50
1	17	76	5,776	339.76
2	9	51	2,601	289.00
3	3	21	441	147.00
4	14	85	7,225	516.07
5	12	79	6,241	520.08
6	7	45	2,025	289.29
7	14	77	5,929	423.50
8	31	68	4,624	149.16
$\sum_{1}^{k} \frac{\left(\sum_{1}^{n_i} y_i'\right)^2}{n_i}$	......	......	....	2,811.36

favorableness" expressed by each item toward a social institution. The ratings were done on a 9-point scale, and for each item we have the scale value S and the Q value. The scale value S is the median of the ratings and is a measure of the relative degree of favorableness or unfavorableness of the item. The Q value is a measure of the variability of the ratings given to an item.[8] From the correlation table, it seems clear that items with low scale values tend to have low Q values as do items with high scale values. Items with average scale values tend to have higher Q values than items at the two extremes of the scale continuum. We wish to determine the degree of relationship between the Q values and the scale values, as measured by the correlation ratio.

Let the mean of the Y values in any particular column of the correlation table be $\bar{Y}_i$ and let n_i be the corresponding number of observations in the column. Let k equal the number of columns in the correlation table. We shall as usual let $\bar{Y}$ be the mean of all of the Y values and n the total number of observations. Then

$$\sum_1^n (Y - \bar{Y})^2 = \sum_1^k n_i(\bar{Y}_i - \bar{Y})^2 + \sum_1^k \sum_1^{n_i} (Y - \bar{Y}_i)^2 \tag{10.20}$$

Formula (10.20) is fundamental in statistical analysis, and we shall have occasion to refer to it in one form or another frequently in later discussions. The term on the left is the sum of squared deviations of the Y values from the mean of the entire Y distribution. This is often called the *total sum of squares*. The two terms on the right tell us that this total sum of squares has been analyzed into two component parts. The first term on the right is a sum of squares based upon the deviations of the means of the columns from the mean of the entire distribution. These deviations are squared and then multiplied by the corresponding value of n_i. The summation sign indicates that we sum these values over the k columns of the table. This sum of squares may be called the *sum of squares between columns*. The last term on the right is based upon the deviations of the individual Y values in each column from the mean of the column. The double summation sign indicates that we sum these squared deviations within the various columns and then sum over all columns. This sum of squares may be called the *sum of squares within columns*. As a matter of convenience, we indicate these sums of squares as follows:

$$\text{Total} \quad = \sum_1^n (Y - \bar{Y})^2 \quad = \sum y_t^2 \tag{10.21}$$

$$\text{Between} = \sum_1^k n_i(\bar{Y}_i - \bar{Y})^2 = \sum y_b^2 \tag{10.22}$$

$$\text{Within} \quad = \sum_1^k \sum_1^{n_i} (Y - \bar{Y}_i)^2 = \sum y_w^2 \tag{10.23}$$

[8] Q as a measure of variability was discussed in Chapter 3, page 47.

The correlation ratio squared may now be defined as

$$\eta_{yx}{}^2 = \frac{\sum y_b{}^2}{\sum y_t{}^2} \tag{10.24}$$

where $\eta_{yx}{}^2$ = the square of the correlation ratio of Y on X
$\sum y_b{}^2$ = the sum of squares between columns for the Y variable
$\sum y_t{}^2$ = the total sum of squares for the Y variable

If we take the square root of formula (10.24), we have the correlation ratio of Y on X. Thus

$$\eta_{yx} = \sqrt{\frac{\sum y_b{}^2}{\sum y_t{}^2}} \tag{10.25}$$

Formula (10.24) gives the correlation ratio squared in terms of the decoded sums of squares. In working from a correlation table, however, we need not decode the resulting sums of squares, since the same coding constant will appear in the numerator and in the denominator. If we let the coded sum of squares between groups be represented by $\sum y_b{}'^2$ and the coded total sum of squares be represented by $\sum y_t{}'^2$, then

$$\eta_{yx}{}^2 = \frac{\sum y_b{}'^2}{\sum y_t{}'^2} \tag{10.26}$$

will be identical with the value obtained from formula (10.24).

The calculation of $\sum y_b{}'^2$ from the correlation table is accomplished very conveniently by means of the following formula

$$\sum y_b{}'^2 = \sum_1^k \frac{\left(\sum_1^{n_i} y_i{}'\right)^2}{n_i} - \frac{\left(\sum_1^n y'\right)^2}{n} \tag{10.27}$$

where we find the sum of y' values in each column of the table, square these sums, divide the squares by the corresponding values of n_i, and sum over all k columns. We then subtract the correction term for origin $\left(\sum_1^n y'\right)^2/n$.

The coded total sum of squares will be given by

$$\sum y_t{}'^2 = \sum y'^2 - \frac{(\sum y')^2}{n} \tag{10.28}$$

The calculation of the coded sum of squares between columns and of the coded total sum of squares is shown in Table 10.6. Substituting these values in formula (10.26) we obtain

$$\eta_{yx}{}^2 = \frac{2{,}811.36 - \dfrac{(557)^2}{129}}{2{,}993.00 - \dfrac{(557)^2}{129}}$$

$$= \frac{406.33}{587.97}$$

$$= .6911$$

Then the correlation ratio will be

$$\eta_{yx} = \sqrt{.6911}$$

$$= .83$$

Properties of the Correlation Ratio

We can determine some of the properties of the correlation ratio if we express it in a somewhat different form. From formula (10.20), we see that the sum of squares between columns will be equal to the total sum of squares minus the sum of squares within columns. Thus

$$\sum y_b{}^2 = \sum y_t{}^2 - \sum y_w{}^2 \qquad \textbf{(10.29)}$$

Then the correlation ratio squared of formula (10.24) may be written[9]

$$\eta_{yx}{}^2 = \frac{\sum y_t{}^2 - \sum y_w{}^2}{\sum y_t{}^2}$$

$$= 1 - \frac{\sum y_w{}^2}{\sum y_t{}^2} \qquad \textbf{(10.30)}$$

Now $\sum y_w{}^2$ can be equal to $\sum y_t{}^2$ only in the case that $\sum y_b{}^2$ is equal to zero. In this instance the correlation ratio would also be equal to zero. But in order that $\sum y_b{}^2$ be equal to zero, each column mean would have to equal the mean of the entire Y distribution, as formula (10.20) will show.

[9] The similarity of this expression to formula (8.21) should be noted.

In other words, the correlation ratio will be zero only when each column mean is equal to the mean of the entire Y distribution. Under this condition there will be no change in the average Y values with change in X, and we say that Y is unrelated to X.

The correlation ratio can be equal to 1 only when the variation within columns as measured by $\sum y_w^2$ is zero. In this instance, each individual observation in a given column would correspond exactly to the mean of the column, and the variation in the means of the columns, as measured by $\sum y_b^2$, would be as great as the total variation measured by $\sum y_t^2$.

Standard Error of Estimate

The sum of squares within columns, in a very real sense, represents the errors made in predicting Y values from X values. If the means of the columns differ, then our best prediction of the Y values in a given column is the mean of the column. An error of prediction will be given by $Y - \bar{Y}_i$, and these errors squared and summed over all columns are equal to $\sum y_w^2$. If the means of the columns do not vary from the mean of the entire Y distribution, then our best prediction for each Y value will be $\bar{Y}$, regardless of the particular column in which it falls, and the sum of squares of our errors of prediction will be given by $\sum_1^n (Y - \bar{Y})^2 = \sum y_t^2$.

A measure of the errors of prediction, corresponding to the standard error of estimate for linear relations, may be obtained by finding

$$s_w^2 = \frac{\sum y_w^2}{n - k} \tag{10.31}$$

where s_w^2 = the variance within columns
$\sum y_w^2$ = the sum of squares within columns
n = the total number of observations
k = the number of columns in the correlation table

Then the square root of formula (10.31) will be

$$s_w = \sqrt{\frac{\sum y_w^2}{n - k}} \tag{10.32}$$

and s_w may be regarded as the standard error of estimate when predictions of Y values for given values of X are made in terms of the column means.

■ The Correlation Ratio and Correlation Coefficient

If the correlation ratio and the correlation coefficient are both computed for the same set of data, then, in general, the correlation ratio will be larger than the correlation coefficient. This may be made clear by a comparison of formula (8.21) for the correlation coefficient squared with formula (10.30) for the correlation ratio squared. Thus

$$r^2 = 1 - \frac{\sum (y - \tilde{y})^2}{\sum y^2}$$

and

$$\eta_{yx}{}^2 = 1 - \frac{\sum y_w{}^2}{\sum y_t{}^2}$$

where $\sum y_t{}^2 = \sum y^2$

In the formula for the product-moment correlation coefficient, the errors of prediction are measured from the linear regression line of Y on X. Only in the case that the means of the columns fall precisely on this line will $\sum (y - \tilde{y})^2$ be equal to $\sum y_w{}^2$. If the means of the columns deviate at all from the linear regression line, then $\sum (y - \tilde{y})^2$ will be greater than $\sum y_w{}^2$, and, consequently, the correlation ratio will be larger than the correlation coefficient, since $\sum y_t{}^2 = \sum y^2$. If the column means fall precisely on the linear regression line, then the correlation coefficient will be equal to the correlation ratio.[10] In the formula for the correlation ratio, we no longer place the restriction upon the data that the column means must be fitted by a *straight line*.

It should be pointed out that the correlation ratio is extremely sensitive to small numbers of observations in the columns of the correlation table. Obviously, if only a single observation were present in each column, $\sum y_b{}^2$ would be equal to $\sum y_t{}^2$ and the correlation ratio would be equal to 1. Therefore, in computing a correlation ratio we should make sure that we have a sufficient number of observations in each of the columns of the correlation table. In some cases this may mean that we shall have to use fairly wide intervals on the X axis. Further, the correlation ratio must be obtained from *sets* of measurements for each value or interval on the X axis. We cannot, in other words, compute the correlation ratio for pairs of X, Y values in the same way in which we compute the correlation coefficient.

---

[10] The sum of squared deviations of a set of n observations is at a minimum when the deviations are taken from the mean of the set, as we have previously shown. Thus the sum of squared deviations, $\sum_1^k \sum_1^{n_i} (Y - \bar{Y}_i)^2 = \sum y_w{}^2$, being based upon the deviations within each column from the column mean, will be less than the corresponding sum of squared deviations $\sum (y - \tilde{y})^2$ from the linear regression line—if the regression line does not pass through the means.

We may also emphasize that in the case of the correlation coefficient $r_{xy} = r_{yx}$, and consequently we dropped the subscripts. But it should be clear from formula (10.24), or any of the other formulas for the correlation ratio, that η_{yx} will not, in general, be equal to η_{xy}. The subscripts, therefore, are important in that they let us know whether we are concerned with the relation of Y to X as measured by η_{yx} or the relation of X to Y measured by η_{xy}.

If we desire to find η_{xy}, it is only necessary to remember that we are dealing with *rows* instead of columns in the correlation table. Any of the formulas presented for η_{yx} may be used to find η_{xy} by replacing the sums of squares for the Y variable by the corresponding sums of squares for the X variable and substituting the word *rows* for columns in the formulas. For example, we may rewrite formula (10.24) and obtain

$$\eta_{xy}^2 = \frac{\sum x_b^2}{\sum x_t^2} \tag{10.33}$$

where η_{xy}^2 = the square of the correlation ratio of X on Y
$\sum x_b^2$ = the sum of squares between rows for the X variable
$\sum x_t^2$ = the total sum of squares for the X variable

Similarly, formula (10.25) becomes

$$\eta_{xy} = \sqrt{\frac{\sum x_b^2}{\sum x_t^2}} \tag{10.34}$$

formula (10.26) becomes

$$\eta_{xy}^2 = \frac{\sum x_b'^2}{\sum x_t'^2} \tag{10.35}$$

formula (10.27) becomes

$$\sum x_b'^2 = \sum_1^k \frac{\left(\sum_1^{n_i} x_i'\right)^2}{n_i} - \frac{\left(\sum_1^n x'\right)^2}{n} \tag{10.36}$$

formula (10.28) becomes

$$\sum x_t'^2 = \sum x'^2 - \frac{(\sum x')^2}{n} \tag{10.37}$$

formula (10.29) becomes

$$\sum x_b^2 = \sum x_t^2 - \sum x_w^2 \tag{10.38}$$

formula (10.30) becomes

$$\eta_{xy}^2 = 1 - \frac{\sum x_w^2}{\sum x_t^2} \tag{10.39}$$

formula (10.31) becomes

$$s_w^2 = \frac{\sum x_w^2}{n - k} \tag{10.40}$$

and formula (10.32) becomes

$$s_w = \sqrt{\frac{\sum x_w^2}{n - k}} \tag{10.41}$$

where, in all of the above formulas, k now corresponds to the number of *rows* in the correlation table.

EXAMPLES

10.1—The data given below show the scores on a test of 40 subjects who were below average on Test X and 30 subjects who were above average in their performance. The distribution of scores of these two groups on a second test Y are given below. Compute the biserial coefficient of correlation.

Scores	*Below Average*	*Above Average*
27–29	3	2
24–26	4	4
21–23	5	8
18–20	6	12
15–17	11	2
12–14	6	1
9–11	2	1
6–8	2	0
3–5	1	0

10.2—Two judges each ranked a set of pictures from the most liked to the least liked. Find the rank correlation coefficient for the two sets of ranks.

Pictures	*Judge 1*	*Judge 2*
A	1	6
B	3	5
C	2	2
D	6	1
E	4	8
F	5	3
G	9	4
H	8	7
I	7	9

10.3—Find the phi coefficient for the 2 × 2 table given below.

Response to Item	*Sex*	
	Women	*Men*
Pass	10	30
Fail	40	20

10.4—A group of employees who had been rated as above average in the performance of their jobs and a group of employees who had been rated as below average were given a test. There were 121 employees in the above-average group and 79 employees in the below-average group. The value of $\sqrt{\sum y^2/n}$ on the test for the combined groups was 11.00. The mean score on the test for the combined groups was 82.05. For the above-average group, the mean score was 81.45. Assume that the distribution of ratings was approximately normal and that the dichotomous classification has been imposed upon the data. Find the biserial coefficient of correlation.

10.5—Mangus (1936) had 581 women describe the interests of their fathers and of their ideal husbands in science and religion. Find the phi coefficient for the data reported below.

Father	*Ideal Husband*	
	More interested in religion than in science	*More interested in science than in religion*
More interested in science than in religion	63	326
More interested in religion than in science	68	134

10.6—Find the correlation ratio, η_{yx}, for the data given below.

Y Distribution	*X Distribution* 3	4	5	6	7	8
4	2	2				
3	2	3	3	1	2	1
2	1	2	3	2	1	1
1		2	1	1		

10.7—Compute the correlation ratio of Y on X for the following data.

Vocabulary Test Scores	*Chronological Age* 15	16	17	18	19	20	21	22	23
150–159					3	1	2	1	2
140–149				2	2	4	4	3	1
130–139			3	1	2	5	5	2	1
120–129		1	2	2	1	4	1	3	4
110–119		3	1	3	3	2			2
100–109	1	1	1						
90– 99		2		1					
80– 89	1								
70– 79	2	2							
60– 69	4								

10.8—Peters and Van Voorhis (1940) report a tetrachoric r of .57 for the data given below. What is the value of tetrachoric r as estimated

Number of Hours of Pedagogy	*Teacher Classification* *Unsuccessful Teachers*	*Successful Teachers*
Six hours or more	20	80
Less than 6 hours	70	55

by the method described in the chapter? Do these data meet the assumptions required by tetrachoric r? Would it be better to use the phi coefficient in this instance?

10.9—Lindquist (1940) reports a tetrachoric r of .35 for the following data on responses of 150 students to two test items. What is the value of tetrachoric r as estimated by the method described in the chapter? Can you justify the calculation of tetrachoric r for these data? Would the phi coefficient be a more appropriate measure of association?

Response to Item 2	*Response to Item 1*	
	Wrong	*Right*
Right	24	56
Wrong	36	34

10.10—Assign ranks to the scores listed below and find the rank correlation coefficient.

Subject	*X*	*Y*
1	8	4
2	13	14
3	13	6
4	18	13
5	14	8
6	19	12
7	8	10
8	4	7
9	17	6
10	15	7
11	22	17
12	6	17
13	18	9
14	8	9
15	12	4

10.11—A group of men and women were polled to determine whether they liked or disliked a particular radio commentator. The results are shown below. Find the value of the phi coefficient.

	Like	*Dislike*
Men	55	45
Women	10	60

10.12—Kelly and Fiske (1950) give the following distributions of scores on the Miller Analogies Test for two categories of Veterans Administration trainees in clinical psychology. Find the value of the point biserial coefficient.

	VA Trainees	
Scores	*Dismissals*	*Ph.D. Granted*
95–99		1
90–94	1	1
85–89	0	6
80–84	2	11
75–79	4	6
70–74	6	9
65–69	8	3
60–64	3	2
55–59	2	1
50–54	6	
45–49	2	
40–44	3	
35–39	1	
30–34	1	

10.13—The following data were obtained from a class in social psychology on a final examination. Find the value of the point biserial coefficient of correlation.

	Response to Item 22	
Total Scores	*Incorrect*	*Correct*
80–84		2
75–79		3
70–74	1	5
65–69	4	7
60–64	3	4
55–59	8	10
50–54	5	9
45–49		1
40–44	2	
35–39	1	1

10.14—Kellar (1934) reports the following data concerning Q and S values of items in an attitude scale. Find the value of η_{yx}.

Y: Q Values	X: Scale Values of Items									
	1	2	3	4	5	6	7	8	9	10
2.1–2.3		5	9	6	4		5	3		
1.8–2.0		3	3	2	1	2	5	2	7	
1.5–1.7	1			2	1	2		1	4	
1.2–1.4	3								1	8
.9–1.1						1				1
.6– .8	4									3
.3– .5						1				

10.15—A study of 100 women who thought their marriage was successful and 100 women who thought their marriage was unsuccessful revealed a differential in response to the question: Did you have a happy childhood? Find the value of the phi coefficient.

Childhood Status	*Marital Status*	
	Unsuccessful Marriage	*Successful Marriage*
Happy	40	70
Unhappy	60	30

10.16—Dorcus (1944) had an industrial concern select two extreme groups of workers, a "satisfactory group" and an "unsatisfactory group." Each member of both groups was then given the Humm-Wadsworth Scale, and on the basis of the scores on the scale predictions were made of the group in which the individual belonged. Find the value of the phi coefficient.

Humm-Wadsworth Scale	*Company Ratings*	
	Unsatisfactory	*Satisfactory*
Satisfactory	6	18
Unsatisfactory	16	8

10.17—Show that if $p_1 = n_1/n$, and $q = 1 - p_1$, or n_0/n, then

$$n_1 - \frac{(n_1)^2}{n} = \frac{n_0 n_1}{n}$$

10.18—Given the definitions of p_1 and q in example 10.17, show that formula (10.4) may also be written as

$$r_{pb} = \left(\frac{\overline{Y}_1 - \overline{Y}}{\sqrt{\frac{\sum y^2}{n}}} \right) \frac{\sqrt{p_1}}{\sqrt{q}}$$

and that r_b will then be given by

$$r_b = \left(\frac{\overline{Y}_1 - \overline{Y}}{\sqrt{\frac{\sum y^2}{n}}} \right) \frac{p_1}{y_p}$$

CHAPTER ELEVEN

Probability and the Binomial Distribution

We have already observed how individual members of a group differ from one another in terms of almost any measurement we might care to make of the members of the group. We also know how to measure the variation in a given set of observations by calculating the standard deviation or variance. Individuals, however, not only vary with respect to each other; they also differ from themselves if measured at different times. Height, for example, is said to be different in the morning upon arising and at night before retiring. One's weight increases with a heavy meal. Individuals tend to perform better on achievement tests when not fatigued, and so on. Now, since measurements on the same individual made at different times may vary, and since measurements of different individuals at the same time may vary, we may expect statistics derived from samples of individual measurements to vary also.

The mean achievement score of a group of college freshmen tested in the morning may not be precisely the same mean score that would have been obtained if the same group had been tested in the afternoon. Nor would we necessarily expect another sample of college freshmen, drawn from the same larger group or population as the first sample and in the same manner, to have precisely the same mean score as the first sample.

If we found the mean intelligence-test score of a group of freshmen at a given college to be 115, we might expect the mean intelligence-test score of another sample of freshmen to differ from this value. If the difference was only 1 point, we might be inclined to say that it was just a "chance" difference. But would we also be willing to attribute to chance a difference of 3 points between the two means? If so, then what about a difference as great as 10 points? How much would the two means have to differ, in other words, before we would be willing to give up the hypothesis that the difference is due to chance?

To take another example: suppose that we assume that the chance that a rat will turn to the right at a choice-point in a maze is equal to the chance that he will turn to the left. If we had no scruples against betting and, equally important, if we had a dollar to bet, we would be willing to bet our dollar against another dollar that the rat would turn to the right. And we would be just as willing to bet one dollar against another dollar that the rat would turn to the left.

If the chance of a right turn is equal to the chance of a left turn and if we watched the behavior of 30 rats at the choice-point, what would we expect? We should expect close to 15 of the rats to turn left and the rest to turn right, but we would not be too surprised if 16 went one way and 14 the other. What if 20 went to the left and only 10 to the right? How far would our sample have to depart from the 50-50 division in order for us to suspect that their behavior was not the result of chance?

These questions bring us to our next problem in statistical methods: the problem of how much confidence we can place in means, proportions, correlation coefficients, and other statistics derived from samples. The statistical methods used in investigating this problem are known as *tests of significance*, and they enable us to determine, among other things, whether observed differences in sample statistics may be assumed to be the result of chance factors or whether we may reject this hypothesis. But in order to understand the use of these statistical techniques we shall have to consider first something of the general nature of probability and chance and some of the properties of the distributions that enable us to make tests of significance.

■ Meaning of Probability

By probability we shall mean theoretical relative frequency. If the theoretical expected frequency of occurrence of an event is a times in n trials, the probability of the event occurring may be expressed as $p = a/n$. If an unbiased coin is tossed into the air an indefinitely large number of times, we may expect the frequency of heads occurring to be equal to the frequency of tails. We may thus say that the probability of obtaining a head is 1/2, since this is the theoretical relative frequency with which we expect heads to occur.[1]

The probability of an event occurring plus the probability that it will not occur equals 1.00, if we assume a dichotomy of "occur" *vs.* "not occur." The probability that a tossed coin will show a head is 1/2, and the probability that it will not is 1/2. The sum of these two probabilities is equal to 1.00. It is customary to let p equal the probability that an event will occur, and $1 - p$, which is represented by q, the probability that the event will not occur.

If we assume that the probability of obtaining a head in the toss of a single coin is 1/2, then what is the probability of getting two heads when the coin is tossed twice? The possible outcomes are HH, HT, TH, and TT, and we may expect each of these outcomes to occur equally often. Then HH may be expected to occur with a theoretical relative frequency of 1/4, and the probability of HH, we say, is 1/4.

We may expect to obtain H on the first toss and T on the second toss with a theoretical relative frequency of 1/4. We may also expect to obtain a T first and H second with a theoretical relative frequency of 1/4. If we are not interested in the particular order of these outcomes, then the theoretical relative frequency or probability of obtaining one H and one T is 2/4 or 1/2. The sum of the probabilities for all of the possible outcomes is equal to 1.00.

This simple illustration also provides us with a general rule or principle: *the probability that all of a set of independent events will occur is the product of the separate probabilities of each event.* When a single coin is tossed twice, the probability of getting a head on the first toss is 1/2, and the probability of getting a head on the second toss is also 1/2. The probability of getting two heads—the two tosses are independent in the sense that regardless of how the first toss comes out it will not influence the second toss—is therefore $(1/2)(1/2) = 1/4$. In similar fashion we could determine that the probability of getting three heads from tossing a single coin three times would be $(1/2)(1/2)(1/2) = 1/8$.

We have also another rule from the illustrative example of coin tossing: *the probability that any one of a set of mutually exclusive events will occur is the sum of the probabilities of the separate events.* By mutually exclusive events is meant that if one event occurs, then none of the others can occur. In the coin-tossing example, the events HT and TH were

[1] There are a number of possible ways of stating the probability just described. We sometimes say that the chances of getting a head on a single toss are even; that the chances are 50-50 of getting a head; that the proportion of heads expected if ten coins were tossed is .5; or that 50 per cent of the coins are expected to be heads.

mutually exclusive. The probability of HT was 1/4, and the probability of TH was also 1/4. The probability, therefore, of getting one of these two outcomes was $1/4 + 1/4 = 2/4$. All four of the outcomes of the two coin tosses were mutually exclusive, and the probability that any one of them would occur is, therefore, $1/4 + 1/4 + 1/4 + 1/4 = 1.00$.

Suppose we have the hypothesis that a student taking a true-false test will respond to each item by tossing a coin, as students sometimes do in answering true-false questions. If we assume that 50 per cent of the time the coin toss will result in the student making the correct response, we may say that the probability of a correct response to the item is 1/2. If this test consisted of 10 items, and if the student answered each item by flipping a coin, then what is the probability that he will get a score of 10 correct? Since each response is an independent event, the chance of getting all 10 items correct would be given by the product of the separate probabilities of each event, according to the rule described above. Thus $(1/2)^{10}$ would give the probability of this happening. What is the probability that he will get all 10 items wrong? Since, again, on the basis of our hypothesis, the probability of a wrong response on each individual item is 1/2, the probability of getting a score of zero would also be $(1/2)^{10}$.

Combinations

The cases just described are simple enough. But suppose that we asked what the probability was of the student getting precisely 7 correct answers and therefore 3 wrong ones? Note that we are not here specifying which particular 7 answers need to be correct, but only that 7 be correct. This is similar to the question of the probability of getting exactly one head and one tail when a coin is tossed twice and when we were not concerned with whether the head appeared on the first toss and the tail on the second toss, or the other way around. In that example, we found that there were two *ways* in which the event could happen, HT and TH, and that the desired probability was the *sum* of these ways divided by the total number of possible outcomes. Similarly, in the present example, we need to know the number of ways in which we can have 7 items correct and 3 wrong in the set of 10. This can be determined by the formula for combinations of independent events. Thus

$$ {}_nC_r = \frac{n!}{(n-r)!(r)!} \tag{11.1} $$

where ${}_nC_r$ = the number of combinations of n things taken r at a time
$n!$ = factorial n or the product of all the integers from n to 1

$(n - r)! =$ the product of all the integers from $(n - r)$ to 1
$(r)! =$ the product of all the integers from r to 1

In the present problem, n stands for the total number of items, r stands for the number of correct items, and $n - r$ for the number of wrong items. Substituting in the formula, we find that

$$
\begin{aligned}
{}_{10}C_7 &= \frac{10!}{(10 - 7)!(7)!} \\
&= \frac{10 \times 9 \times 8 \times 7 \times 6 \times 5 \times 4 \times 3 \times 2 \times 1}{(3 \times 2 \times 1)(7 \times 6 \times 5 \times 4 \times 3 \times 2 \times 1)} \\
&= \frac{10 \times 9 \times 8}{3 \times 2 \times 1} \\
&= 120
\end{aligned}
$$

Thus we find that there are 120 different ways in which a student might get precisely 7 items correct and 3 incorrect on a 10-item test, but we still do not know how frequently these particular combinations will turn up. Our complete formula for the probability of getting 7 items correct and 3 incorrect on the test should read

$$
{}_nC_r p^r q^{n-r} = \frac{n!}{(n - r)!(r)!} p^r q^{n-r} \qquad \textbf{(11.2)}
$$

In this formula, p is the probability of getting a correct answer to a single item on the test, and the exponent of p indicates that the total number of correct items we are interested in is r. The value of q is $1 - p$, and the exponent of q indicates the number of incorrect items. Substituting in the formula we get

$$
\begin{aligned}
{}_{10}C_7 (\tfrac{1}{2})^7 (\tfrac{1}{2})^{10-7} &= \frac{10!}{(10 - 7)!(7)!} \left(\frac{1}{2}\right)^7 \left(\frac{1}{2}\right)^3 \\
&= \frac{120}{1{,}024} \\
&= .117
\end{aligned}
$$

Similarly, we could use formula (11.2) to determine the probability of the student getting any particular score ranging from 10 to 0 correct responses.[2]

[2] It is customary to let $0! = 1$.

The Binomial Expansion

If you have studied algebra, you may have noticed that the value of ${}_nC_r$ gives the coefficient of the $(n - r + 1)$ term in the binomial expansion of $(p + q)^n$; that is, ${}_{10}C_7$, for example, gives the coefficient of the $(10 - 7 + 1)$ or the fourth term of $(p + q)^{10}$. Expanding, we would get

$$(p + q)^{10} = p^{10} + 10p^9q + 45p^8q^2 + 120p^7q^3 + 210p^6q^4 + 252p^5q^5 + 210p^4q^6 + 120p^3q^7 + 45p^2q^8 + 10pq^9 + q^{10}$$

and the fourth term is $120p^7q^3$, the coefficient being the number 120. The exponent of p in each of the terms of the binomial expansion, as in formula (11.2), indicates the number of items correct (successes) and that of q indicates the number of items incorrect (failures), and the coefficients represent the number of ways in which each of the combinations of successes and failures may occur.

The rules for expanding the binomial $(p + q)^n$ are summarized below:

1. Each term in the binomial consists of the product of a numerical coefficient and a power of p and a power of q.
2. The first term always has a numerical coefficient of 1 which is understood and therefore is not written; the power of p in the first term is always n, and the power of q is zero, and q therefore does not appear; thus the first term is always p^n.
3. In each succeeding term, the power of p decreases by 1 in regular order, while the power of q increases by 1 in regular order, until the final term, q^n, is reached.
4. The product of the numerical coefficient and the power of p in any given term, divided by 1 plus the power of q in that term, will give the numerical coefficient of the term that follows. For example, the numerical coefficient 120, of the fourth term, is obtained by multiplying the coefficient of the third term by its power of p and then dividing by one more than the power of q. Thus

$$\frac{(45)(8)}{2 + 1} = \frac{360}{3} = 120$$

If you have difficulty in remembering the rules for the binomial expansion, you will find the coefficients for n up to 10 given in Table 11.1. Note that any entry in a given row consists of the sum of the coefficients to the right and left of the entry in the row directly above. Thus the entries for $n = 11$ could be obtained from the entries for $n = 10$. They would be

1, 11, 55, 165, 330, 462, 462, 330, 165, 55, 11, and 1. In this way you can extend Table 11.1 to obtain the binomial coefficients for values of n greater than those given in the table.

Table 11.1—The Binomial Coefficients of $(p + q)^n$

n	*Binomial Coefficients*
1	1 1
2	1 2 1
3	1 3 3 1
4	1 4 6 4 1
5	1 5 10 10 5 1
6	1 6 15 20 15 6 1
7	1 7 21 35 35 21 7 1
8	1 8 28 56 70 56 28 8 1
9	1 9 36 84 126 126 84 36 9 1
10	1 10 45 120 210 252 210 120 45 10 1

■ Probabilities from the Binomial Expansion

To interpret the binomial expansion in terms of the true-false test on which we have assumed that each of the 10 answers is determined by chance, we see that the probability of getting a score of 10 correct is $p^{10} = 1/1{,}024 = .001$; the probability of getting a score of precisely 9 correct and 1 wrong is $10p^9q = 10/1{,}024 = .010$; the probability of getting a score of precisely 8 correct and 2 wrong is $45p^8q^2 = 45/1{,}024 = .044$; and so forth. The advantage of the binomial expansion is that from it we can readily determine the probability of obtaining a score as large as or larger than any given score. For example, the probability of getting a score of 7 *or more* items correct is the sum of the probabilities for the scores 7, 8, 9, and 10, or $\frac{120 + 45 + 10 + 1}{1{,}024}$, which is equal to $176/1{,}024 = .172$. Thus about 17 times in 100 we would expect a score of 7 or more correct items to occur by chance alone, under the hypothesis assumed.[3]

We may now ask another question about our student. How many items must he answer correctly before we would begin to question the hypothesis that his answers are determined by chance alone? A score of 8

[3] The question we ask refers to the probability of a score of 7, 8, 9, or 10 occurring. Since these are mutually exclusive events in the sense that if the student gets a score of 7 he cannot get any of the other scores, we use the rule previously stated for the probability of any one of a set of mutually exclusive events occurring.

or above would occur by chance just slightly more than 5 per cent of the time ($p = .055$), and a score of 9 or more correct items would occur by chance just slightly more than 1 per cent of the time ($p = .011$). Although the limits are arbitrary, it is customary in much statistical work to refer to the occurrence of an event that would happen by chance alone 5 per cent of the time as representing a *significant* departure from chance expectations, and the occurrence of an event that would happen by chance alone 1 per cent of the time is regarded as representing a *very significant* departure. If we accept these standards, we would regard a score of 9 or above as one that deviates significantly from chance expectations. We would, in other words, have doubts concerning the hypothesis that the answers to the items were merely a chance affair.

If the answers are a matter of chance, a score of 9 or greater is one that would occur only about 1 time in 100. If our hypothesis is true, then a very unusual, that is, improbable, event has occurred. You have your choice: you can retain your hypothesis and believe that the event just happens to be that 1 in 100 expected by the hypothesis, or you can reject the hypothesis. The decision you make will be determined by a number of considerations, and we shall come back to this point in a later discussion of testing hypotheses.

If we tested N students with our true-false test, and if we still assume that each student answered each item by flipping a coin, that is, by chance, then we may readily determine the number of students expected to obtain each possible score. We would thus have

$$N(p+q)^n = Np^n + N(np^{n-1}q) + N\left(\frac{n(n-1)}{(1)(2)}\,p^{n-2}q^2\right) + N\left(\frac{n(n-1)(n-2)}{(1)(2)(3)}\,p^{n-3}q^3\right) + \cdots + Nq^n \qquad \textbf{(11.3)}$$

where N = the number of students tested
n = the number of items in the test
p = the probability of a correct response to a single item
$q = 1 - p$

For simplicity we shall take N equal to 1,024. Then, multiplying each term in the binomial expansion of $(p+q)^{10}$ by 1,024, we obtain the expected number of students getting each of the possible scores. These expected numbers are shown in column (4) of Table 11.2.

We should not be surprised now if in the 1,024 students tested we found one who made a score of 10 correct, for that is the expected frequency for this score under our hypothesis. Nor should we be surprised to find one

Table 11.2—The Binomial Distribution $(p + q)^n$ and $N(p + q)^n$ with $p = .5$, $n = 10$, and $N = 1{,}024$

(1) *Score Number Correct*	(2) *Score Proportion Correct*	(3) *Probability* f	(4) *Expected Number of Students* f
10	1.0	.001	1
9	.9	.010	10
8	.8	.044	45
7	.7	.117	120
6	.6	.205	210
5	.5	.246	252
4	.4	.205	210
3	.3	.117	120
2	.2	.044	45
1	.1	.010	10
0	.0	.001	1
Σ		1.000	1,024

student with a score of 0, for this also is the expected frequency for this score under our hypothesis. What would our attitude be if we found 5 scores of 10 correct instead of 1, 15 scores of 9 correct instead of 10, and various other departures from chance expectancy? We cannot answer this question now, but later we shall see that it is possible to determine whether a set of observed frequencies is in accord with the frequencies to be expected under some hypothesis. In other words, we shall be able to determine whether our observed frequencies obtained from actually testing a group of students may be assumed to follow the binomial distribution.[4]

Mean and Standard Deviation of the Binomial Distribution

In column (1) of Table 11.2 we show the possible scores on the 10-item true-false test in terms of the number or frequency of correct responses. In column (2) of the table we express these frequencies as proportions of the total number of responses made. Column (3) gives the theoretical relative frequency or probability of each possible score as obtained from the binomial expansion $(p + q)^n$. If we test $N = 1{,}024$ students, then $N(p + q)^n$ will give us the expected number of students making each of the possible scores. These values are shown in column (4) of the table.

[4] See Chapter 18.

The mean and standard deviation of the scores shown in column (1) of Table 11.2 could be obtained by regarding either the probabilities of column (3) or the number of students of column (4) as frequencies.[5] If we actually made the calculations, we would find that the mean number of correct responses is 5.0 and that the standard deviation is 1.58. It is not necessary, however, to make these calculations, since the mean of the binomial distribution may be readily obtained from the following formula:

$$m = np \tag{11.4}$$

where m = the mean number of correct responses of the binomial $(p + q)^n$
n = the exponent of $(p + q)$

You will note, first of all, that we have used m instead of $\bar{X}$ for the mean of the binomial distribution. The reason for this is that given any specified value of p and the exponent n, *the mean is not an estimate of the population value but is the actual value of the binomial distribution.* We shall represent the mean of a population by the symbol m in order to distinguish this parameter from an estimate of a population mean for which we use the symbol $\bar{X}$.[6] If we substitute in formula (11.4) we obtain

$$m = (10)(.5) = 5.0$$

and we would find that this is also the value obtained by direct calculation.

The variance of the binomial distribution can also be easily obtained. Thus

$$\sigma^2 = npq \tag{11.5}$$

where σ^2 = the variance of the binomial distribution $(p + q)^n$
n = the exponent of $(p + q)$

The standard deviation of the binomial distribution will be equal to the square root of formula (11.5) or

$$\sigma = \sqrt{npq} \tag{11.6}$$

---

[5] If we use the frequencies of column (4), division of the sum of squares would be by 1,024. Similarly, if we use the frequencies or probabilities of column (3), division of the sum of squares would be by 1. We are dealing with parameters and not estimates of parameters, and this accounts for the discrepancy between our procedure here and that described earlier in terms of formula (3.8). This point is discussed in greater detail on page 246.

[6] Some texts use the symbol μ for the population mean.

If we substitute in formula (11.6) we get

$$\sigma = \sqrt{(10)(.5)(.5)} = \sqrt{2.5} = 1.58$$

You will note that in formula (11.5) and formula (11.6) we have used σ^2 and σ instead of s^2 and s to represent the variance and standard deviation, respectively. The reason for this is that given any specified value of n and p, the variance or standard deviation of the binomial distribution is known exactly and is not estimated from a sample of observations. The variance and standard deviation of the binomial distribution are thus parameters rather than estimates of the parameters. We shall use the symbol σ^2 to represent a population variance and σ to represent a population standard deviation and reserve s^2 and s for the corresponding estimates of the parameters based upon a sample of observations.

Formula (11.4) and formula (11.6) give the mean and standard deviation of the binomial distribution in terms of the *frequency* of correct responses—or in terms of the scores of column (1) in Table 11.2. We may also express the mean and standard deviation in terms of the *proportion* of correct responses, or the scores of column (2). The proportion of correct responses corresponding to any given frequency of correct responses will simply be the frequency divided by n, the total number of responses made. The mean and standard deviation of this distribution will therefore be $1/n$th the values given by formula (11.4) and formula (11.6), respectively. Thus, in terms of the proportion of correct responses, we have

$$m = p \tag{11.7}$$

and

$$\sigma = \sqrt{\frac{pq}{n}} \tag{11.8}$$

Approximation of the Binomial Probabilities

It is useful to know that if np (or nq, if q is smaller than p) is equal to or greater than 5, the binomial distribution $(p + q)^n$ may be taken as an approximation of a normal distribution. For the 10-item true-false test, where we have assumed p to be equal to .5, we have $np = (10)(.5) = 5$. We might, therefore, assume that this distribution is approximately normal with mean equal to 5 and standard deviation equal to 1.58. Then any specified frequency X of correct responses might be expressed as a relative deviate or standard score by finding

$$z = \frac{X - m}{\sigma} \tag{11.9}$$

where z = a relative deviate or standard score
X = a specified frequency or number of correct responses
$m = np$, the mean of the binomial distribution
$\sigma = \sqrt{npq}$, the standard deviation of the binomial distribution

Substituting in formula (11.9) with $X = 7$, $m = 5$, and $\sigma = 1.58$, we have

$$z = \frac{7 - 5}{1.58} = 1.27$$

From the table of the normal curve we find that the proportion of the total area falling to the right of an ordinate that is 1.27 standard deviations above the mean is .102, and this would correspond to a probability of .102 for a frequency of 7 or more correct responses on the test. We have previously found, in terms of the binomial expansion, that the probability of 7 or more correct responses is .172. Apparently something is wrong, for if our assumption that this binomial distribution is approximately normal is correct, then we should obtain a value close to .172 from the normal curve also. Instead, we find a probability of .102.

The major basis of the discrepancy between the two probabilities is that whereas the binomial distribution is discrete, the normal distribution is continuous. If we are to evaluate a discrete frequency in terms of a continuous distribution, we may obtain a better approximation of the desired probability by making a *correction for continuity*. We regard the frequency X of formula (11.9) as occupying an interval, the lower limit of which is .5 a unit below the specified frequency. If we desire to find the probability corresponding to 7 or more correct responses, we should find the area in the normal curve falling to the right of the *lower limit* of this frequency or, in other words, to the right of the ordinate located at 6.5 on the continuum. If we now substitute in formula (11.9) with the lower limit of the interval, we find

$$z = \frac{6.5 - 5.0}{1.58} = .95$$

From the table of the normal curve we find that the proportion of the total area falling to the right of the ordinate at z equal to .95 is .171. This probability is in much closer correspondence with the probability of .172 as obtained previously from the binomial expansion.

We may take one other example. Suppose we wished to determine the probability of obtaining exactly 5 correct responses by chance on the 10-item test. The binomial expansion showed that this probability was

252/1,024 = .246. Let us see what probability we obtain, assuming the binomial distribution to be approximately normal.

We wish to find the area between the lower and upper limit of 5, or between 4.5 and 5.5, in a normal distribution with mean equal to 5 and standard deviation equal to 1.58. Then, in terms of formula (11.9), we have

$$\frac{5.5 - 5.0}{1.58} = .32 \qquad \text{and} \qquad \frac{4.5 - 5.0}{1.58} = -.32$$

From the table of the normal curve, we find that .1255 of the total area will fall between the mean and an ordinate that is .32 standard deviations above the mean. Since the curve is symmetrical, it is also true that .1255 of the area will fall between the mean and an ordinate located at −.32 standard deviations. Thus the area falling between 4.5 and 5.5 will be .1255 + .1255 = .2510, and this would be the probability of obtaining exactly 5 correct responses. We thus see that the probability of .251 as obtained from the normal curve is a fairly good approximation of the probability of .246 as obtained from the binomial expansion.

Variance of the Binomial $(p + q)$

In the discussion of the point-biserial coefficient of correlation, we had n_0 subjects in one category of a dichotomy and n_1 in the other category. The total number of subjects was $n = n_0 + n_1$. If you go back and look at formula (10.1), you will see that one of the terms in the denominator is[7]

$$n_1 - \frac{(n_1)^2}{n}$$

and, as you may have guessed, this was the sum of squares for the dichotomized variable. If we divide this sum of squares by $n = n_0 + n_1$, we will have the variance of the binomial $(p + q)$ for the special case where the exponent is equal to 1. If the exponent of the binomial is 1, formula (11.5) tells us that the variance will also be equal to the product pq. We should, therefore, have

$$\sigma^2 = pq = \frac{n_1 - \dfrac{(n_1)^2}{n}}{n} \tag{11.10}$$

[7] See page 184.

For the data of Table 10.1, we have n_0 equal to 24, n_1 equal to 42, and n, therefore, equal to 66. We may express n_1 as a proportion by dividing by n. Thus $p = n_1/n = 42/66$. Expressing n_0 also as a proportion, we would have $n_0/n = 24/66$, and this must be equal to $1 - p = q$. Then, substituting in the above expression, we get

$$\sigma^2 = pq = p(1 - p)$$

$$= p - p^2$$

$$= \frac{n_1}{n} - \frac{(n_1)^2}{n^2}$$

$$= \frac{n_1 - \dfrac{(n_1)^2}{n}}{n}$$

In terms of the numerical values from Table 10.1, we see that formula (11.10) gives us

$$\sigma^2 = \left(\frac{42}{66}\right)\left(\frac{24}{66}\right) = \frac{42 - \dfrac{(42)^2}{66}}{66}$$

$$= \frac{1\,008}{4{,}356} = \frac{15.27}{66}$$

$$= .2314 = .2314$$

Formula (11.10) is used frequently in the statistical analysis of test data where we need to know the variance of responses to items. In dealing with the items of a test, we may have two categories such as "pass-fail," "right-wrong," "yes-no," or some other dichotomy. Since we then have the special case of the binomial expansion $(p + q)$, the variance of the responses to the dichotomous variable will be given by formula (11.10).

■ EXAMPLES

11.1—A student claims that he can detect a taste difference between two brands of a popular drink. This claim is put to test by presenting him with two cups, one cup containing Brand A, the other Brand B. The student is asked to tell which of the two cups contains Brand A. Care is taken to control various factors other than taste that might influence his choice. Let us assume that the student will make his choice upon the basis of chance. The student is given 12 trials. Using the binomial expansion, find:

(*a*) the probability that he will make 12 correct choices,
(*b*) the probability that he will make exactly 9 correct choices,
(*c*) the probability that he will make 9 or more correct choices.

11.2—Since we have $np > 5$ in Example 11.1, we may assume that we can use the table of the normal curve in arriving at the desired probabilities. Using formula (11.9), with the correction for continuity, find:

(*a*) the probability of 12 correct choices,
(*b*) the probability of exactly 9 correct choices,
(*c*) the probability of 9 or more correct choices.

Compare these probabilities with those obtained in Example 11.1.

11.3—In a taste test, oleomargarine and butter are presented in pairs to a subject, and he is asked to detect which member of each pair is butter. Care is taken to control factors other than taste that might influence his choice. If the subject is given 16 trials, what is the probability that he will make 12 or more correct choices by chance? Use formula (11.9) with the correction for continuity.

11.4—In an experiment, similar to the one described in Example 11.3, a subject is presented with frozen orange juice, fresh orange juice, and canned orange juice. The subject is asked to judge which of the three is the fresh juice. We shall assume that factors other than taste are controlled and that the subject's choice is determined by chance.

(*a*) What is the minimum number of trials that can be given, if formula (11.9) is to be used in evaluating the outcome of the experiment?
(*b*) If 18 trials are given, what is the probability that the subject will make 10 or more correct choices?
(*c*) In how many ways can he make 16 correct choices?

11.5—Five coins are tossed.

(*a*) What is the probability that at least 2 (there may be more than 2) of the coins will show heads?
(*b*) What is the probability that exactly 2 of them will show heads?

11.6—A student takes a multiple-choice test of 6 items. Each item has 4 alternatives.

(*a*) What is the probability that he will get a score of 6 by chance alone?
(*b*) What is the probability that he will get a score of 5 or higher by chance alone?

11.7—Suppose that a student is taking a true-false test consisting of 8 items and answers each question by flipping a coin, that is, by chance.

(*a*) What is the probability of his getting a score of 8 correct?
(*b*) What is the probability of his getting a score of 6 or higher?

11.8—Six men and 3 women have volunteered to serve in an experiment.

(*a*) In how many ways can a group of 3 be chosen from the group of 9?
(*b*) In how many ways can a group of 3 be chosen from the group of 6 men?
(*c*) What is the probability that, if 3 are selected at random from the group of 9, the 3 will all be men?

11.9—We have a set of 5 pictures of children who are superior in intelligence and a set of 5 pictures of children who are feeble-minded. The children are all males and of the same age.

(*a*) In how many ways can a set of 5 pictures be selected from the group of 10?
(*b*) What is the probability that a judge would select the 5 pictures of the feeble-minded children by chance alone from the set of 10?

11.10—What is the value of the mean and standard deviation of the binomial distribution $(p + q)^n$, if $p = .5$ and $n = 100$?

11.11—Three different cola drinks were presented to each of 105 subjects. The subjects were asked to choose Brand A from the 3 presented. The complete study is described by Pronko and Herman (1950). If we assume that each subject can do no better than chance, then the probability of a correct identification will be 1/3.

(*a*) How many subjects would we expect to make correct identification by chance alone?
(*b*) Assuming a binomial distribution, find the standard deviation.
(*c*) It was found that 57 subjects correctly identified Brand A. Is this a significantly greater number than chance would indicate? Use formula (11.9) with the correction for continuity.

11.12—Locke and Grimm (1949) gave 69 subjects perfumers' blotters saturated with a standard strength of perfume solution. Some of the perfumes tested were expensive and others were inexpensive. The subjects were asked to judge whether the blotters were saturated with an expensive or inexpensive brand. In one of the tests an expensive brand was classified correctly by 43 subjects and incorrectly by 26. Assume that the probability of a correct identification is .5.

(*a*) For the group tested, what is the expected number of correct identifications by chance alone?
(*b*) What is the standard deviation of the binomial distribution?
(*c*) What is the probability of 43 or more subjects making a correct identification by chance alone? Use formula (11.9) with the correction for continuity.

11.13—In the text, page 214, we raised the question what our attitude would be if 20 rats turned to the left and 10 rats turned to the right at a choice-point in a maze. If we assume that the probability of each rat making a left turn is 1/2, what is the probability of 20 or more rats making a left turn by chance alone? Use formula (11.9) with the correction for continuity.

11.14—Calculate the mean and standard deviation of the scores of column (1) of Table 11.2, using the frequencies of column (3).

CHAPTER TWELVE

The Normal Distribution

Assume that we have a 10-item true-false test in which the probability of a correct response to a single item is 1/2. Then $(\frac{1}{2} + \frac{1}{2})^{10}$ will give us the binomial distribution of the scores on the test. In Figure 12.1 we show the histogram of this theoretical distribution. We have let the base line correspond to the proportion of items answered correctly. The only possible values that p can take for the 10-item test are those shown in the figure.

We may regard each column of the histogram as being made up of small rectangles, the area of each rectangle being equal to 1/1,024 or approximately .001. The first column of the histogram, corresponding to 0 correct responses, would have one such rectangle. The second column of the histogram, corresponding to 1 correct response or $p = .1$, would have 10 such rectangles, and the total area in this column would be .010. Similarly, for $p = .5$, corresponding to 5 correct responses, the column of the histogram would have 246 rectangles, each with area equal to .001, or a total area of .246. We already know, from the discussion in the last chapter, that, if we sum the areas for all columns of the histogram, the total area under the histogram would be equal to 1.00.

Note the symmetry of the binomial distribution of Figure 12.1 and observe that the distribution begins to approximate the bell-shaped, normal distribution to which we have had occasion to refer before. Suppose now that we increase the number of items in the test to 100 and that we again assume that the probability of a correct response to each item will be 1/2. Then $(\frac{1}{2} + \frac{1}{2})^{100}$ will give the binomial distribution of scores on this test. The possible scores, in terms of the proportion of items answered correctly, range from .00 to 1.00 in steps of .01, instead of steps of .10 as was true for the

10-item test. Consequently, we shall now have 101 columns in the histogram for the 100 item test, instead of the 11 columns we had for the 10-item test. For each of the possible 101 proportions, we shall also have a theoretical relative frequency or probability that we can again represent by the area in the columns of the histogram. We know also that, if we sum the areas in each column of the histogram, the total area will be equal to 1.00.

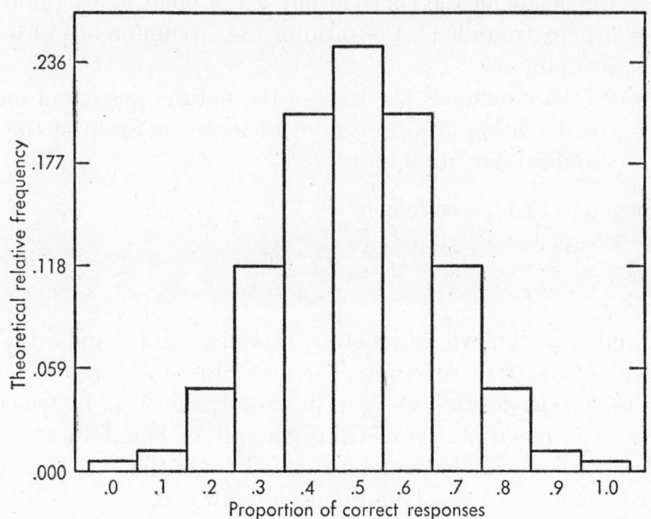

Fig. 12.1—Histogram of the binomial distribution $(p + q)^n$ with p equal to .5 and n equal to 10.

If we impose the histogram for the 100-item test over that for the 10-item test shown in Figure 12.1, each would have the same area and base line. But, since, the 100-item test would have 101 columns instead of the 11 columns that the 10-item test has, the columns of the 100-item test would thus have to be drawn narrower than those of the 10-item test. If we let n become larger, say 1,000, we could, following the same procedure, impose this histogram on Figure 12.1. The columns of this histogram would be even narrower than those of the 100-item test. As n increases indefinitely, the columns of the histogram would become narrower and narrower, so that the steps from one column to the next would in turn be so small that we might regard the resulting graph as a continuous curve, normal in form.

Even when n is small, as long as np (or nq, if q is smaller than p) is equal to or greater than 5, the binomial distribution may be taken as an *approximation* of a normal distribution—as we pointed out in the last chapter.

Equation of the Normal Curve

The equation for the unit normal curve is

$$y = \frac{1}{\sqrt{2\pi}} e^{-(1/2)z^2} \tag{12.1}$$

where y = the height of the curve at any given point along the base line.
π = 3.1416 (rounded), the ratio of the circumference of a circle to its diameter
e = 2.7183 (rounded) the base of the natural system of logarithms
z = the deviation of a measurement from the mean of the series in standard deviation units

In formula (12.1), z is defined as

$$z = \frac{X - m}{\sigma}$$

where m and σ are known parameters, the mean and standard deviation, respectively, of the X distribution. The distribution of z, as defined above, will have the properties that we have previously shown to be true of standard scores. The mean of the distribution will be equal to zero and the standard deviation will be equal to one. In addition, if X is normally distributed, then z will also be normally distributed.

You will recall that in an earlier chapter we pointed out that it was useful to set the area under a curve equal to unity or 1.00. That has been done in the case of the *unit normal curve*, where the area under the curve is equal to 1.00. For the unit normal curve, the standard deviation has been set equal to 1.00 by expressing the measurements or distances along the base line in terms of standard deviation units. These are the values of $z = (X - m)/\sigma$ which are squared in formula (12.1).

Let us solve the equation of the normal curve for the value of y, the ordinate of the curve, when $z = (X - m)/\sigma = 0$. This will be the ordinate at the mean of the distribution. If we set z equal to 0, then the exponent of e will be equal to 0, and we know that any number raised to the zero power is equal to 1.[1] Thus, if we let y_0 equal the ordinate when z equals 0, we have

$$y_0 = \frac{1}{\sqrt{2\pi}}$$

$$= \frac{1}{\sqrt{(2)(3.1416)}}$$

[1] See page 22.

$$= \frac{1}{\sqrt{6.2832}}$$

$$= \frac{1}{2.5066}$$

$$= .3989$$

Now, if you will look in the table of the unit normal curve—Table III, in the Appendix—to find the value of y tabled there when z is equal to 0, you will find that this value is .3989, the value we obtained above. The other entries in the y column of this table may be obtained in exactly the same way from the equation for the unit normal curve.

Suppose we see what the value of y will be when z is equal to 1.00. This will correspond to a measure that is 1 standard deviation above the mean. We know that a number raised to the $-\frac{1}{2}$ power is equal to the reciprocal of the square root of the number.[2] Thus, if we let y_1 be the ordinate corresponding to $z = 1.00$, we have

$$y_1 = \frac{1}{\sqrt{2\pi}} e^{-1/2}$$

$$= \frac{1}{\sqrt{e}\sqrt{2\pi}}$$

$$= \frac{1}{\sqrt{(2.7183)(2)(3.1416)}}$$

$$= \frac{1}{\sqrt{17.0796}}$$

$$= \frac{1}{4.1328}$$

$$= .2420$$

Again, if we enter the table of the normal curve with z equal to 1.00, we find .2420 tabled in the y column opposite this value. The value .2420 is

---

[2] See page 23.

the ordinate of the unit normal curve at a distance 1 standard deviation unit above the mean. From the equation of the curve, it is obvious that, since z is squared, we shall also obtain a value of y equal to .2420 when z is equal to -1.00. The curve, as we now can see, must be symmetrical, for the ordinate of any given negative value of z will be exactly equal to the ordinate for the corresponding positive value of z.

The value of a table of the unit normal curve is that it can be used for *any* normal distribution, regardless of the particular mean, standard deviation, and number of observations. All that is necessary is that we express the measures in any given distribution in terms of standard scores. If the distribution is normal, then, from the table of the curve, we can determine the proportion of the total area falling between the mean and an ordinate at any given distance from the mean. We can also find the proportion of the total area falling above any given ordinate, below any given ordinate, and between any two given ordinates.

Suppose, for example, we had a normal distribution of measures with mean equal to 60 and standard deviation equal to 10. Let us now write the value of each measure on a disc, place the discs in a box, and mix them thoroughly. We then draw out one disc at a time, record the value appearing on it, and put it back into the box. We do this n times. Between what limits may we expect 95 per cent of our values to fall? These limits will be established by the ordinates that cut off 2.5 per cent of the area of the curve in each tail. From column (4) of the table of the normal curve, we find that an ordinate at z equal to 1.96 will cut off 2.5 per cent in the tail of the curve, and this will be true also for z equal to -1.96.

Then, letting m and σ stand for the known parameters of this distribution, we may solve for the lower score limit X_1 and the upper score limit X_2 as follows:

$$\frac{X_1 - m}{\sigma} = -1.96 \qquad \text{and} \qquad \frac{X_2 - m}{\sigma} = 1.96$$

and

$$X_1 = m - (1.96)(\sigma) \tag{12.2}$$

and

$$X_2 = m + (1.96)(\sigma) \tag{12.3}$$

Solving formulas (12.2) and (12.3) for the distribution with mean equal to 60 and standard deviation equal to 10, we have

$$X_1 = 60 - (1.96)(10) = 40.4$$

and

$$X_2 = 60 + (1.96)(10) = 79.6$$

We should thus expect 2.5 per cent of the observations to fall below 40.4 and 2.5 per cent to fall above 79.6. These per cents are theoretical relative frequencies, and we may regard them as probabilities. We can say that the probability of obtaining a value above 79.6 is .025 and the probability of obtaining a value below 40.4 is also .025. Since these outcomes represent mutually exclusive events, the probability of obtaining either a value above 79.6 or a value below 40.4 will be $.025 + .025 = .05$.

We see from the discussion above that, if we have a large normal distribution with a given mean and standard deviation, we can easily determine the proportion of scores to be expected at given distances above or below the mean, if we draw these scores at random from the distribution. That is to say, if we put each score on a disc, mix the discs in a box, and draw them one at a time, we can make a probability statement concerning the frequency with which we expect to obtain scores at or above a given point, or between two given points.

Sampling Distribution of the Mean

Let us assume that the distribution of scores shown in Table 12.1 was obtained by giving an objective examination to a psychology class of 100 students. We shall regard this distribution of scores as a population. In the present instance it is possible for us to calculate the mean, variance, standard deviation, and any other parameter of interest, for the population as defined. This is not the case in actual research where we have available only samples drawn from a population and not the population itself. We can calculate an estimate of a population parameter, such as the mean, from a sample, but the population value remains unknown to us.

Samples, however, are not often studied for themselves but in order to generalize beyond the samples to the populations from which they were drawn. Let us see what inferences we might make about the mean of the population of scores in Table 12.1 on the basis of a random sample drawn from the population.

Suppose that we place each of the numbers in Table 12.1 on a disc and mix them up in a box and draw samples of 1 case each from the box, replacing the disc after each drawing. The mean of each sample would be equal to $\sum X/n$, and, since we have but a single X with n equal to 1, the mean of the sample would be equal to the value of the score itself. If we drew a large number of such samples from the box, we could plot the means of these samples in a frequency distribution. If we then found the mean of the means, we would find that this value is approximately equal to the population mean of the 100 scores of Table 12.1. Furthermore, if we found the standard deviation of this distribution, it would be approximately equal to the population standard deviation of the scores of Table 12.1. The reason for this is simply that each sample mean would deviate from the population mean in the same way that each score deviates from the population mean. Our sample means, being based upon single scores, would show as much variability or dispersion about the population mean as would the scores themselves.

Table 12.1—Hypothetical Distribution of Scores of 100 Students on an Objective Type of Examination

87	76	73	70	67	66	64	63	61	60
85	75	72	69	67	65	64	62	61	60
82	74	71	69	67	65	63	62	61	60
78	74	71	68	66	65	63	62	61	60
77	74	70	68	66	64	63	62	61	60
60	59	58	57	56	54	52	50	46	43
60	59	58	57	55	54	52	49	46	42
60	59	58	57	55	53	51	49	46	38
60	59	58	56	55	53	51	48	45	35
60	59	57	56	54	53	50	47	44	33

The frequency distribution of statistics calculated from random samples of size n drawn from some defined population is called a *sampling distribution*. The distribution of means just described would be the sampling distribution of means based upon samples of 1 case each. We have just shown that the expected variation of the means of samples of 1 case is equal to the standard deviation of the single measures. The standard deviation of the statistics in a sampling distribution is called a *standard error*. The standard error of the means of samples of 1 each, therefore, may be expected to be equal to the standard deviation of the single measures.

The variance of the means of random samples of size n drawn from a population with known variance equal to σ^2 is given by the following formula:

$$\sigma_{\bar{x}}^2 = \frac{\sigma^2}{n} \qquad \textbf{(12.4)}$$

where $\sigma_{\bar{x}}^2$ = the variance of the mean
σ^2 = the known population variance of the individual measures
n = the number of observations upon which the mean is based

The square root of formula (12.4) gives

$$\sigma_{\bar{x}} = \frac{\sigma}{\sqrt{n}} \tag{12.5}$$

where $\sigma_{\bar{x}}$ = the standard error of the mean
σ = the known population standard deviation of the individual measures
n = the number of observations upon which the mean is based

Formulas (12.4) and (12.5) support the statements made concerning the variation of the means of samples based upon a single case. In this instance the variance of the means may be expected to be equal to the variance of the individual measures, and the standard error of the mean may be expected to be equal to the standard deviation of the individual measures, since n in formula (12.4) and formula (12.5) would be equal to 1.

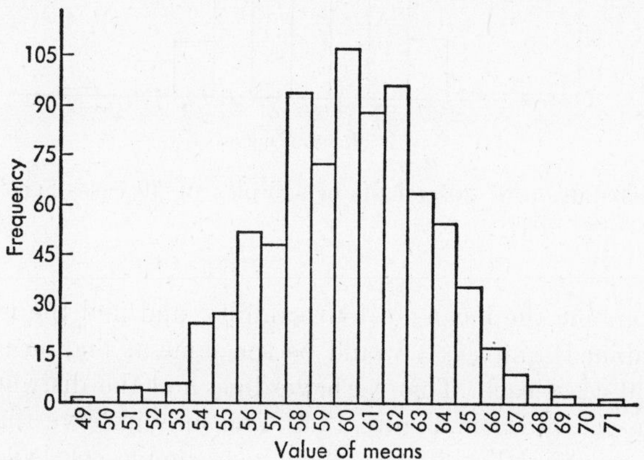

Fig. 12.2—Distribution of 820 means of samples of 10 cases each drawn from the scores of Table 12.1.

Suppose we now increase the size of our samples to 10 cases each and draw a large number of such samples at random from the scores of Table 12.1. Formulas (12.4) and (12.5) now tell us that we may expect the means of these samples to show less variation than the means of samples of 1 case each.

The relationship between the variation of the sample means and the size of the sample is illustrated by an actual sampling experiment. Figure 12.2 is a distribution of means of 820 samples of 10 cases each. These samples were drawn by students in statistics classes at the University of Maryland and the University of Washington. Note that the lowest mean is 49 and that the highest mean is 71, the range being 22. Observe also the concentration of the sample means about the mean of the means and the approximately normal shape of the distribution.

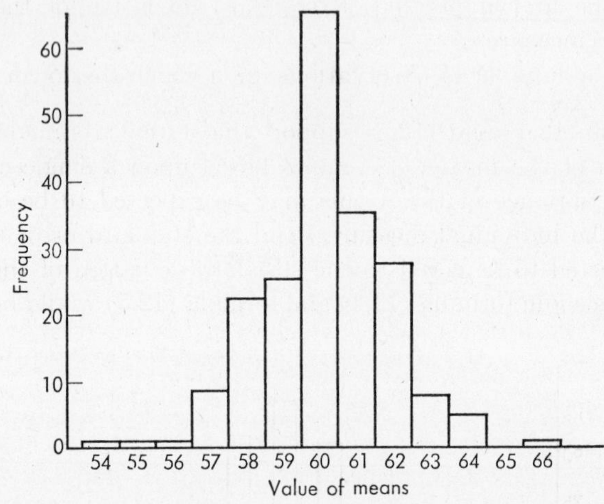

Fig. 12.3—Distribution of 205 means of samples of 40 cases each drawn from the scores of Table 12.1.

If we combine the means of four samples, and find the mean of each of these combined samples, it would be the same as finding the means of samples of 40 cases each. This we have done and the distribution of 205 sample means is shown in Figure 12.3. You may observe that the range of means is now less than it was when each sample consisted of only 10 cases. The lowest mean is now 54 and the highest mean is 66. The range, 12, is only about half that for the samples of 10 cases each.

Formulas (12.4) and (12.5) and Figures 12.2 and 12.3 should make it clear that the variance and standard error of a distribution of sample means are related to the size of the samples. As more observations are included in the sample, the less the means will vary. The variance of the means is also related to the variance of the individual measures. The greater the variation of the individual measures, the greater the expected variation in the means of samples drawn from the population of individual measures. This is clearly shown in formula (12.4) and formula (12.5) where the numerator is a measure of the variation of the individual observations.

Testing Hypotheses about the Population Mean

Suppose that we have drawn a random sample, in the manner previously described, of 1,000 observations from the population of scores given in Table 12.1. We find that the mean of this sample is 60.42. Then, since we know that the population standard deviation is 10, the standard error of the mean, as given by formula (12.5), will be

$$\sigma_{\bar{x}} = \frac{10.00}{\sqrt{1{,}000}} = \frac{10.00}{31.62} = .316$$

Our interest is not so much in the mean of the sample, but in the mean of the population from which the sample was drawn. We may ask how reliable an estimate of the population mean our obtained sample mean of 60.42 is. We might even wish to ask what the probability is that the population mean is the same as that derived from our sample.[3] Unfortunately, if we insisted on asking the question in this way, we would be courting disappointment; for the manner in which the question is phrased precludes any possibility of an answer.

But, you may ask, did we not say before that the statistic derived from a sample is an estimate of the population parameter? Are we not justified, therefore, in saying that the best estimate of the population mean is 60.42? True enough, but note that this is but another way of stating that the best *hypothesis* we can make about the value of the population mean with the data at hand is 60.42. Another sample of 1,000 cases drawn from the same population might have a mean of 60.43; a third sample might have a mean of 59.90. Without actually drawing a second or third sample, we might state, *as a hypothesis*, that the population mean is 60.43 or 59.90 or any other specified value, and that our observed mean of 60.42 simply represents a chance deviation from this value. Obviously, whether we care to accept or reject the various hypotheses that might be made concerning the value of the population mean will depend upon the theoretical relative frequency with which observed sample means, based upon 1,000 cases, would deviate from these assumed or hypothetical values as a result of sampling variation.

Recall that in a normal distribution we may find the ratio $(X - m)/\sigma = z$ and that we may then enter the table of the normal curve with any given value of z in order to determine the relative frequency with which deviations as large as or larger than the given $X - m$ occur. Now, since

[3] We *can* make the following statement: *if* the population mean is equal to 60.42, then the probability of obtaining a sample value greater than 60.42 is equal to the probability of obtaining a sample value less than 60.42.

the distribution of means of random samples is also normal,[4] and since these means will cluster around the population mean at the center of the distribution, it is also possible to write

$$z = \frac{\bar{X} - m}{\sigma_{\bar{x}}} \tag{12.6}$$

Thus formula (12.6) tells us that we may assume some hypothetical value of the population mean m, find the extent to which our sample mean deviates from this hypothetical value in terms of $\sigma_{\bar{x}}$, and then, by reference to the table of the normal curve, determine how frequently such deviations or larger ones may be expected to occur by chance *if the hypothesis is true.* If deviations as large as or larger than the one we have obtained would occur quite frequently as a result of sampling variation, then we would have very little confidence in rejecting the hypothesis that the population mean is the value we have assumed. On the other hand, if a deviation from the hypothetical value of the population mean as large as or larger than the one we have obtained would occur quite infrequently as a result of sampling variation, then we might reject the assumed value with a greater degree of confidence.

Let us test the hypothesis that the population mean is 60.41, assuming that our sample mean of 60.42 represents a deviation from this value. Substituting in formula (12.6) we get

$$z = \frac{60.42 - 60.41}{.316} = .03$$

Entering the table of the normal curve, we find that 48.18 per cent of the cases in a normal distribution may be expected to deviate from the mean by plus .03 standard deviation units or more. On the assumption, then, of random sampling from a population with mean of 60.41, sample means of 60.42 or larger, based upon 1,000 cases, would occur in the long run 48.18 per cent of the time. We must admit that if this is the case we would have very little confidence in rejecting the hypothesis that the population mean is as low as 60.41.

In a similar manner we could test the hypothesis that the population mean is 59.50. The deviation of our observed mean in terms of standard deviation units would be $(60.42 - 59.50)/.316 = 2.91$, and we would find from the table of the normal curve that z values of plus 2.91 or larger

[4] This is true even when the population from which the samples were drawn departs considerably from normality.

may be expected to occur by chance 18 times in 10,000. Consequently, if the population mean is 59.50, then sample means of 60.42 or larger, based upon 1,000 cases, could be expected to occur by chance only 18 times in 10,000. In this instance we would have a great deal of confidence in rejecting the hypothesis that the population mean is as low as 59.50.

From these two examples you may see that the degree of confidence we may have in rejecting or accepting a given hypothesis about the population mean depends, as we have said before, upon the relative frequency with which deviations as great as our sample mean or greater might be expected to occur from the hypothetical value as a result of sampling variation. In other words, assuming a given hypothesis to be true, we test it by finding the relative frequency with which deviations from it as large as or larger than our sample deviation might be expected to occur by chance. If such deviations would occur very frequently by chance, then we cannot reject the hypothesis about the population mean with much confidence. On the other hand, if such deviations would occur very infrequently by chance, then we may reject the hypothesis with a high degree of confidence.

Note that in both of the examples cited, we have *not* made the assumption that our sample mean is at the center of the distribution of sample means. It is m that is assumed to be at the center of this distribution and $\bar{X}$ that is assumed to represent a *deviation* from m

■ Fiducial Limits

The discussion of the previous section, let us hope, has provided a basis for understanding the method now to be described. Instead of testing one hypothesis after another, as we might possibly do, it is more convenient to determine the *interval* within which any hypothesis might be considered tenable and outside which any hypothesis might be considered untenable. This interval is known as a *fiducial interval*, and the limits defining it are called *fiducial limits*. Statements of probability made in terms of fiducial limits are called statements of *fiducial probability*.

It may be observed from the table of the normal curve that absolute values of z equal to 1.96 or greater will occur, by chance, 5 per cent of the time. It may also be observed that absolute values of z of 2.58 or greater will occur, by chance, 1 per cent of the time. Statistical workers generally agree to reject a hypothesis about the population mean if the value of z obtained would occur by chance only 5 times or less in 100, when the hypothesis is true. For example, if we assumed a value for the population mean and found that our sample mean deviated from this hypothetical value to the extent that we obtained an absolute value of

z equal to 1.96, we would say that we reject this hypothesis at the *5 per cent level of confidence*. Similarly, if we obtained an absolute value of z equal to 2.58, we would say that the hypothesis is rejected at the *1 per cent level of confidence*. If we agree upon these standards, then we may determine for a given sample the line dividing hypotheses that would be acceptable from those that would be rejected at these levels of confidence. Let us do this for the problem we discussed earlier where the sample mean was 60.42 and the standard error of the mean was .316.

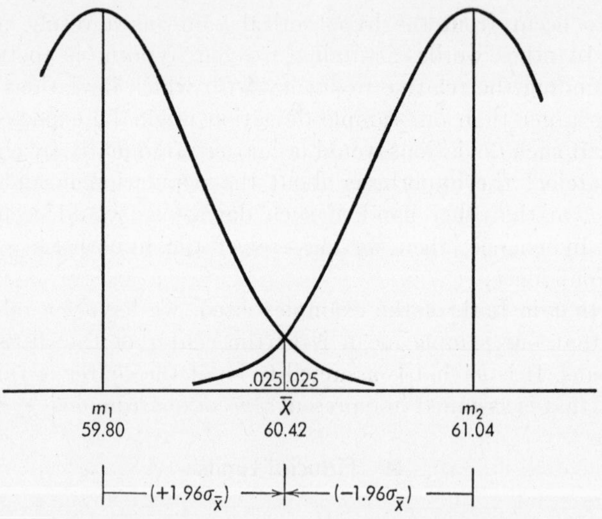

Fig. 12.4—The fiducial limits at the 5 per cent level as determined from the table of the normal probability curve.

The fiducial limits at the 5 per cent level of confidence are illustrated in Figure 12.4. For the lower fiducial limit m_1 of the parameter we have

$$\frac{\bar{X} - m_1}{\sigma_{\bar{x}}} = 1.96$$

and for the upper fiducial limit m_2 we have

$$\frac{\bar{X} - m_2}{\sigma_{\bar{x}}} = -1.96$$

and solving for m_1 and m_2 we obtain

$$m_1 = \bar{X} - (1.96)(\sigma_{\bar{x}}) \tag{12.7}$$

and $$m_2 = \bar{X} + (1.96)(\sigma_{\bar{x}}) \quad \textbf{(12.8)}$$

Substituting in formula (12.7) and formula (12.8) with the values of $\sigma_{\bar{x}}$ and $\bar{X}$, we obtain

$$m_1 = 60.42 - (1.96)(.316) = 59.80$$

and $$m_2 = 60.42 + (1.96)(.316) = 61.04$$

The interpretation of the fiducial limits is as illustrated in Figure 12.4. If the population mean is as low as $m_1 = 59.80$, then our observed mean deviates from this value to an extent that we obtain a *plus* z of 1.96. Such values would occur by chance only 2.5 per cent of the time in random sampling. Similarly, if the population mean is as high as m_2, our observed mean deviates from this value to the extent that we obtain a *minus* z of 1.96. Such values would also occur by chance only 2.5 per cent of the time in random sampling. Putting these two figures together, we may observe that absolute values of z equal to 1.96 or greater would arise by chance 5 per cent of the time.

Hence, any hypothesis that the population mean is as low as 59.80 or lower or as high as 61.04 or higher, will, in terms of the sample mean we have obtained, yield a value of z which would occur 5 per cent of the time or less by chance. The sample mean would be said to differ significantly from either of these two hypothetical values (or any values outside of these two), and any such hypothesis concerning the population mean would be rejected according to the standards agreed upon. We also know that any hypothesis that the population mean is greater than 59.80 but less than 61.04 will be in accord with the value of the sample mean we have obtained, that is, the sample mean will not differ significantly from any of these hypothetical values.

The limits set by the interval described above have been termed by Fisher (1942) the fiducial limits of the parameter at the 5 per cent level. Just as we saw that the fiducial probability that the population mean was 61.04 or greater was 2.5 per cent and that the fiducial probability that the population mean was 59.80 or less was 2.5 per cent, so also we may say that the fiducial probability that the population mean lies within these fiducial limits is 95 per cent (Fisher, 1942, pp. 190–191). That is to say, in the long run we shall be correct 95 times in 100 in *inferring* that a population mean lies within the 5 per cent fiducial limits.

The kind of inference we may make in terms of the fiducial limits is illustrated in Figure 12.5. We may think of the population mean as having a fixed value equal to m. This value is represented by the horizontal line in the figure. We draw a random sample from the population and calculate the fiducial limits at, say, the 5 per cent level. The fiducial limits established by successive random samples are indicated by the vertical lines in the figure. The end points of these vertical lines represent the lower fiducial limit m_1 and the upper fiducial limit m_2, as established by the data of each of the successive random samples. We may note that the majority of the end points contain the value m, that is, the population mean is within the fiducial limits. If we had a large number of such samples, each

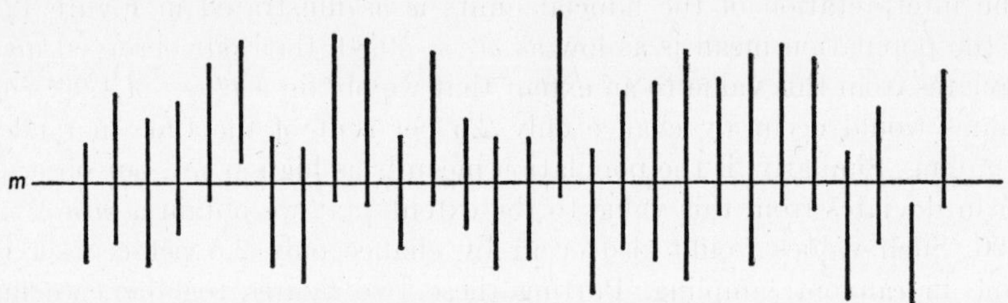

Fig. 12.5—Illustration of the fiducial limits at the 5 per cent level. The horizontal line represents the fixed value of the population mean m. Varying values of the lower fiducial limit m_1 and the upper fiducial limit m_2, in successive random samples, are represented by the lower and upper end points, respectively, of the vertical lines. It is assumed that, in the long run, 95 per cent of the vertical lines will contain the parameter m.

with its own fiducial limits at the 5 per cent level, then our expectation is that about 95 per cent of these limits would contain m and about 5 per cent would not. For any given sample, therefore, we might say that if we infer that the population mean falls within the fiducial limits, the probability of this inference being correct is .95.

If we desire a higher degree of confidence before rejecting a hypothesis concerning the population mean, then we would of course work with the fiducial limits of the parameter at the 1 per cent level. Since an absolute value of z equal to 2.58 will cut off 1 per cent of the total area in the two tails of a normal distribution, we could substitute 2.58 for 1.96 in formula (12.7) and formula (12.8) and obtain the fiducial limits at the 1 per cent level. We would thus obtain 59.60 for the value of m_1 and 61.24 for the value of m_2. In this case the fiducial probability that the population mean is 61.24 or greater is .005, and the fiducial probability that the population mean is 59.60 or lower is .005. The fiducial probability, therefore, that the population mean lies within these limits is 99 per cent.

■ EXAMPLES

12.1—Place the scores of Table 12.1 on discs or beans. Assume that the 100 scores make up a population with known parameters. From this population each member of the class will draw 10 samples of 10 cases each. The technique to be used in drawing the samples is this: place the numbered discs in a box with a hole cut in one end; shake the box and draw out one disc; record the number and put the disc back into the box; shake it, draw out another disc, and so on until 10 numbers have been recorded. These numbers will make up the first sample. Repeat the process until you have drawn 10 samples.

(*a*) Find the mean of each of your 10 samples. Do not worry about the decimal place; round the number.
(*b*) To get some idea of the sampling distribution of means, make a frequency distribution of all of the sample means drawn by the members of your class.
(*c*) What would you expect to happen to the range of means if the sample size had been larger than 10? Why?

12.2—Using the equation for the normal curve, find the value of the ordinate y when z is equal to 2.00. Check this value against that given in the table of the normal curve—Table III, in the Appendix.

12.3—If σ^2 is equal to 100, what is the estimated variance of means of random samples of (*a*) 10 cases each; (*b*) 25 cases each; (*c*) 50 cases each?

12.4—Let σ^2 equal 100. Sketch the curve relating $\sigma_{\bar{x}}{}^2$ to n, as n increases from 1 to 100.

12.5—If the standard error of a mean based upon 10 cases is 4.0, what is the estimated value of n required, if the standard error of the mean is to be reduced from 4.0 to 2.0, assuming that the second sample is drawn from the same population as the first?

12.6—Using the data given in Example 12.5, what is the estimated value of n required, if the standard error is to be reduced from 4.0 to 1.0?

CHAPTER THIRTEEN

The t *Test for the Means of Independent Samples*

In testing hypotheses about the population mean in the last chapter, you will note that we assumed that we had a sample drawn from a population with a known population variance σ^2. Ordinarily, however, the experimental worker does not deal with samples from populations with known variances, but must estimate these parameters from his sample data. Thus, instead of having available the value of σ^2, we shall have an estimate of this parameter. This estimate is s^2 which we have previously defined as

$$s^2 = \frac{\sum(X - \bar{X})^2}{n - 1}$$

The variance of the means of random samples of size n drawn from a population with estimated variance equal to s^2 will be given by

$$s_{\bar{x}}^2 = \frac{s^2}{n} \tag{13.1}$$

and the standard error of the mean will be the square root of formula (13.1) or

$$s_{\bar{x}} = \frac{s}{\sqrt{n}} \tag{13.2}$$

We may then define t as

$$t = \frac{\bar{X} - m}{s_{\bar{x}}} \tag{13.3}$$

where m is the population mean.

With large samples of 500 or more observations the ratio $(\bar{X} - m)/s_{\bar{x}}$ may be assumed to be approximately normally distributed, but this is not the case as n becomes smaller. If we wish to test hypotheses about the population mean with small samples, we shall have to make use of the t distribution rather than the normal distribution.

The *t* Distribution

In the limiting case, with n indefinitely large, the t distribution and the normal distribution are the same. With a very large n, say of 1,000 cases, the two distributions are approximately the same. Beyond a certain point, however, depending upon the value of n, the t curve does not approach the base line as rapidly as does the normal curve. For the normal distribution, we found that if we moved out 1.96 standard-deviation units on each side of the mean, the ordinates erected at these points would cut off 2.5 per cent of the total area under the curve in each tail. If we have, however, only 10 cases in our sample, the ordinates cutting off 2.5 per cent of the total area in each tail of the curve for the t distribution will be located at a distance of 2.262 standard-deviation units on each side of the mean.

Our procedure in testing hypotheses will be the same as before. The only difference is that instead of entering the table of the normal curve we shall enter the t table, Table V, in the Appendix, in order to evaluate the ratio $(\bar{X} - m)/s_{\bar{x}}$. To enter the t table, we must know the number of *degrees of freedom* available in our sample set of observations.

The number of degrees of freedom available in a set of n observations depends upon the number of restrictions placed upon the observations. In finding the value of s^2, which is needed for finding the value of the standard error of the mean, we first calculate the mean of the sample. We then take the deviations of the n observations from the sample mean. Since the sum of these deviations must equal zero, only $n - 1$ of them are free to vary, the last observation being fixed. We thus say that our estimate of the population variance is based upon $n - 1$ degrees of freedom. The degrees of freedom are clearly indicated by the denominator of s^2.

Division of the sum of squares by $n - 1$ gives us an unbiased estimate s^2 of the population variance σ^2. If we knew the population mean, we could compute $\sum(X - m)^2$ instead of $\sum(X - \bar{X})^2$. We have already shown that $\sum(X - \bar{X})^2$ is at a minimum, that is, less than it would be from any other value.[1] Only in the unusual case where the sample mean happened to be identical with the population mean would the sum of squares based upon deviations from the sample mean be as large as the sum of squared deviations from the population mean. Any variation at all, no matter how slight, of sample mean from the population mean would give us a smaller sum of squared deviations, if the deviations are taken from the sample mean, than would be found if the deviations were taken from the population mean. Division of the sum of squares by n would thus give us a biased estimate of the population variance, an estimate that is too small. It can be demonstrated algebraically that this bias can be corrected for, on the average, by dividing the sum of squares by $n - 1$ instead of by n.[2]

■ Fiducial Limits for the Mean

Suppose that we draw a random sample of 10 observations from the scores in Table 12.1. This sample is drawn in the way that we described in the last chapter. We find that the mean of the sample is 64.50 and that the standard error of the mean, as given by formula (13.2), is 3.22. You should not be surprised at the fact that our standard error of the mean is now much larger than it was when we had a sample of 1,000 cases. The variability of the mean, you will recall, is related to the size of the sample.

We now wish to establish fiducial limits for the population mean in the same way as in the last chapter. We want to find, in other words, the limits within which hypotheses about the population mean will be tenable and outside of which they will be rejected at the 5 per cent level. The particular mean that we have obtained may be a value that falls above the population mean or it may be a value that falls below the population mean. If we are to establish fiducial limits at the 5 per cent level, we must know the value of t which will cut off 2.5 per cent of the area in each tail of the t distribution, when n is equal to 10.

Since n is equal to 10, we have $n - 1 = 9$ degrees of freedom, and we enter the row of the t table—Table V, in the Appendix—with this value. The column headings of the t table show the per cent of the area cut off *in both tails* of the distribution. For example, for 9 degrees of freedom we find that the tabled entry under the column headed .05 is 2.262. This means that ordinates erected at plus *and* minus 2.262 standard-deviation units will cut off 2.5 per cent of the total area in *each* tail. The column

---

[1] See the proof given in answer to Example 4.14.

[2] A proof is given in Edwards (1950*a*).

heading .05 gives the sum of the areas, that is, the area in the left tail *plus* the area in the right tail.

For the lower fiducial limit m_1 of the parameter, we thus have

$$\frac{\bar{X} - m_1}{s_{\bar{x}}} = t$$

or
$$m_1 = \bar{X} - (t)(s_{\bar{x}}) \tag{13.4}$$

and for the upper fiducial limit m_2, we have

$$\frac{\bar{X} - m_2}{s_{\bar{x}}} = -t$$

or
$$m_2 = \bar{X} + (t)(s_{\bar{x}}) \tag{13.5}$$

Substituting our obtained values of $\bar{X}$, $s_{\bar{x}}$, and the value of t obtained from Table V, and solving for m_1 and m_2 we find

$$m_1 = 64.50 - (2.262)(3.22) = 57.22$$

and
$$m_2 = 64.50 + (2.262)(3.22) = 71.78$$

You will observe that we must now regard as tenable a much wider range of assumed values for the population mean than was the case when our sample was based upon 1,000 observations. Note also that our procedure was the same as when we used the table of the normal curve. The only difference is that the value of t used in solving for m_1 and m_2 will vary depending upon the number of degrees of freedom available.

The Difference between Two Means

In experimental and research work the determination of whether an observed difference is of such magnitude that it cannot be attributed to chance factors or sampling variation is often our major interest. We may find, for example, that a group of subjects tested under one set of experimental conditions has a higher mean than a comparable group tested under a different set of experimental conditions. Is the observed difference between the means one that might occur frequently by chance, that is, as a result of sampling variation? If not, then we might infer that the difference is a product of the experimental conditions.

Random Assignment of Subjects

Let us suppose that we are interested in the problem of whether attitudes toward working conditions are important determinants of output. We have 20 subjects and we divide them at random into two groups of 10 subjects each. We might do this by assigning each subject a number corresponding to the numbers from 0 to 19. We also place these numbers on discs. The numbered discs might be placed in a box and thoroughly mixed. The discs could then be drawn out of the box one at a time, the first disc being assigned to one group, the second disc to the second, the third to the first, the fourth to the second, and so on, until the discs in the box are exhausted. Then by flipping a coin we could designate one of the groups as Group 1 and the other as Group 2.

A still more efficient method of random assignment of the subjects, however, is to make use of a table of random numbers. These tables consist of numbers arranged at random in columns and rows. The tables can be used by entering at any point and by reading in any direction, down or up, right or left. Table I, in the Appendix, is a table of random numbers, and we can illustrate its use for the case at hand where we wish to divide our 20 subjects into two groups of 10 subjects each.

First we number our subjects. We may write down the names of the subjects in any arbitrary manner and then pick any name on the list and give it the number 00. From the remaining 19 names we may pick any one name and give it the number 01. The next name that we pick would be given the number 02, and so on, with the last name being given the number 19. If we have our subjects arranged in any order whatsoever, we could, of course, give the first subject the number 00, the next 01, and so on, with the last being given the number 19.

You will note that Table I consists of 5 blocks of 1,000 random numbers each. For each block the rows have been numbered from 00 to 24 and the columns from 00 to 39. Let us suppose that our point of entry into the table is the second block, row 02 and column 05. But since the numbers assigned to our subjects are two-digit numbers, we shall make use of two columns in the table, that is, columns 05 and 06. It makes no difference, once the point of entry has been determined, in which direction we read. Let us assume that we are going to read downward. We read down columns 05 and 06 until we have 10 unlike numbers between 00 and 19. We skip any number that is 20 or above and any number that is a repetition of a number previously read. Our first number is found in row 00, columns 05 and 06, of the third block of random numbers. It is 02. Our next number is 12, the next is 03, and the next is 01. We then find that 01 is followed by 02, and we skip this number, since the subject assigned 02 has already been selected. When we have reached the last row of the fifth block of numbers in the table, we may continue to read numbers by going up the adjoining columns, for example, columns 07 and 08. We continue in this way until we have 10 unlike numbers between 00 and 19.

The first 10 numbers below 20 that we have read from the table of random numbers would tell us which subjects to put in one of our groups, and the remaining 10 individuals would constitute the second group. In similar fashion we could divide a large number of subjects at random into any number of smaller groups. Tables of random numbers can also be used for selecting at random a single small group of subjects from a larger total, and for assigning groups at random to one of a number of experimental conditions.[3]

Having divided our subjects at random into two groups of 10 subjects each, we may designate one of the groups as Group 1 and the other as Group 2. The members of Group 1 are told that they are going to be subjects in an experiment on distraction which is to be a check on experiments previously done. It has been found, we add, that working under conditions of noise tends to facilitate the adding of numbers, that is, that most individuals find that they can add faster under conditions of noise than they can under quiet conditions. The members of Group 2 are also told that they are to be subjects in an experiment on distraction, but they are told that previous experiments have shown that working under conditions of noise tends to result in less rapid adding of numbers than working under conditions of quiet.

Each group is then put to work adding problems under noisy conditions, and performance is measured in terms of the number of problems

---

[3] We could make our selection of subjects more rapid by initially giving each subject a *set of numbers* rather than a single number. For example, the subject who was given the number 01 could be given the set of numbers 00 to 04. The subject who was given the number 02 could be given the set of numbers 05 to 09, and so on, with the last subject being given the set of numbers 95 to 99. In this way each subject would be assigned an equal set of 5 numbers. We would then enter the table of random numbers, in the manner described, in order to select 10 of the subjects from the group of 20. For example, if the first number in the table at our point of entry should be 07, the subject with the numbers 05 to 09 would be selected for one of the groups. If the next number in the table should be 13, the subject with the set of numbers 10 to 14 would be selected. If the next number should be 06, it would be skipped, for we have already selected the subject with the set of numbers 05 to 09. We would continue to read numbers in the table until we have selected a group of 10 subjects from the 20. Any number in the table of random numbers between 00 and 95 would now be used in the selection of our 10 subjects, whereas in the previous method only the numbers in the table between 00 and 19 would be used.

correctly added. The scores of Group 1 and Group 2 are given in Table 13.1.[4]

Table 13.1—Performance Scores of Two Groups of Subjects Working under Different Sets of Instructions

	Group 1		*Group 2*	
	X_1	X_1^2	X_2	X_2^2
	2	4	1	1
	3	9	3	9
	6	36	4	16
	4	16	2	4
	5	25	5	25
	2	4	5	25
	5	25	2	4
	4	16	4	16
	3	9	3	9
	6	36	1	1
Σ	40	180	30	110

Standard Error of the Difference between Two Means

Let us assume that the experiment is repeated an indefinitely large number of times and that for each repetition we subtract the mean for Group 2 from the mean for Group 1.[5] We could then plot the distribution of the differences between the means, and these differences would be normally distributed about the population mean difference.[6] If we let m_1 represent the population mean for subjects tested under Condition 1 and m_2 represent the population mean for subjects tested under Condition 2, then the population mean difference will be equal to $m_1 - m_2$. The distribution of the sample mean difference $\bar{X}_1 - \bar{X}_2$ about the population mean difference $m_1 - m_2$ would be the sampling distribution of the difference between the means, and the standard deviation of this distribution would be called the standard error of the difference between the means.

[4] The data are hypothetical for the sake of simplicity, but see the experiment by Baker (1937).

[5] We could, of course, subtract the mean for Group 1 from the mean for Group 2, in each of the repetitions, without modifying in any way the essential nature of the argument.

[6] If we have random samples from normal populations, the means of the samples will be normally distributed. The differences between the means of the samples will also be normally distributed.

The estimated standard error of the difference between the means will be given by

$$s_{\bar{x}_1-\bar{x}_2} = \sqrt{{s_{\bar{x}_1}}^2 + {s_{\bar{x}_2}}^2} \tag{13.6}$$

where ${s_{\bar{x}_1}}^2 = {s_1}^2/n_1$ and ${s_{\bar{x}_2}}^2 = {s_2}^2/n_2$. Substituting these identities in formula (13.6), we obtain the following formula for the standard error of the difference between the means.

$$s_{\bar{x}_1-\bar{x}_2} = \sqrt{\frac{{s_1}^2}{n_1} + \frac{{s_2}^2}{n_2}} \tag{13.7}$$

Assuming that the variances are the same, within the limits of random sampling, we may pool the sum of squares and degrees of freedom from our two samples to obtain an estimate of the common variance. Thus

$$s^2 = \frac{\sum {x_1}^2 + \sum {x_2}^2}{n_1 + n_2 + - 2} \tag{13.8}$$

where s^2 = the estimate of the common population variance
$\sum {x_1}^2$ = the sum of squares for the n_1 observations about the mean of Group 1, $\sum (X_1 - \bar{X}_1)^2$
$\sum {x_2}^2$ = the sum of squares for the n_2 observations about the mean of Group 2, $\sum (X_2 - \bar{X}_2)^2$

The degrees of freedom for the estimate of s^2 are clearly indicated by the denominator, $n_1 + n_2 - 2$.

Substituting the common estimate s^2 of formula (13.8) in formula (13.7), we get

$$s_{\bar{x}_1-\bar{x}_2} = \sqrt{\frac{\dfrac{\sum {x_1}^2 + \sum {x_2}^2}{n_1 + n_2 - 2}}{n_1} + \frac{\dfrac{\sum {x_1}^2 + \sum {x_2}^2}{n_1 + n_2 - 2}}{n_2}}$$

which may be written

$$s_{\bar{x}_1-\bar{x}_2} = \sqrt{\left(\frac{\sum {x_1}^2 + \sum {x_2}^2}{n_1 + n_2 - 2}\right)\left(\frac{1}{n_1} + \frac{1}{n_2}\right)} \tag{13.9}$$

For the data of Table 13.1, the sum of squares for Group 1 will be given by

$$\sum {x_1}^2 = \sum {X_1}^2 - \frac{(\sum X_1)^2}{n_1}$$

$$= 180 - \frac{(40)^2}{10}$$

$$= 20$$

and similarly, for the sum of squares for Group 2, we have

$$\Sigma x_2^2 = \Sigma X_2^2 - \frac{(\Sigma X_2)^2}{n_2}$$

$$= 110 - \frac{(30)^2}{10}$$

$$= 20$$

Then the standard error of the difference, obtained from formula (13.9), will be

$$s_{\bar{x}_1-\bar{x}_2} = \sqrt{\left(\frac{20 + 20}{10 + 10 - 2}\right)\left(\frac{1}{10} + \frac{1}{10}\right)}$$

$$= \sqrt{\left(\frac{40}{18}\right)\left(\frac{2}{10}\right)}$$

$$= \sqrt{.4444}$$

$$= .67$$

■ The Test of Significance

We may now define t in terms of the following formula

$$t = \frac{\bar{X}_1 - \bar{X}_2}{s_{\bar{x}_1-\bar{x}_2}} \qquad \textbf{(13.10)}$$

where t = the t ratio with $n_1 + n_2 - 2$ degrees of freedom
$\bar{X}_1$ = the mean of Group 1
$\bar{X}_2$ = the mean of Group 2
$s_{\bar{x}_1-\bar{x}_2}$ = the standard error of the difference obtained from formula (13.9)

For the data of Table 13.1, we find that $\bar{X}_1 = 40/10 = 4.0$ and that $\bar{X}_2 = 30/10 = 3.0$. Then from formula (13.10) we obtain

$$t = \frac{4.0 - 3.0}{.67} = 1.49$$

with $n_1 + n_2 - 2 = 18$ degrees of freedom.

The value of t obtained from formula (13.10) provides us with a test of significance of the hypothesis we make concerning the relationship between m_1 and m_2. It enables us to decide whether to reject or accept the hypothesis. By implication, if we reject the hypothesis we have tested, we shall accept some specified alternative hypothesis. But if we do not reject the hypothesis, this does not necessarily mean that we regard it as true.

The Null Hypothesis

A hypothesis that is set up with the possibility of its being rejected at some defined probability value is called a *null hypothesis*, the term "null" referring to our interest in the possible rejection of the hypothesis.[7] Under the assumption that the null hypothesis is true, the sampling distribution of the difference between the means may be used to determine the probability that random sampling from the population for which the hypothesis holds would yield differences deviating from the population mean difference as much as the sample one does.

Since the null hypothesis specifies the frequencies with which the different results of an experiment may occur, we may also divide these results into two classes, one of which shows a significant discrepancy or deviation from this hypothesis, and the other no significant discrepancy or deviation from the null hypothesis. "If these classes of results are chosen, such that the first will occur when the null hypothesis is true with a known degree of rarity in, for example, 5 per cent or 1 per cent of the trials, then we have a test by which to judge, at a known level of significance, whether or not the data contradict the hypothesis to be tested" (Fisher, 1942, p. 182).

Two Types of Error

Let us assume that the null hypothesis being tested is, in fact, true, but our test of significance erroneously results in the rejection of this hypothesis;

[7] Fisher (1942, p. 16) has emphasized that "every experiment may be said to exist only in order to give the facts a chance of disproving the null hypothesis."

then we have made what is known as a *Type I error*. On the other hand, if the null hypothesis is, in fact, false, but our test of significance yields a result such that we fail to reject the hypothesis, we have made what is known as a *Type II error*. We should like very much, in testing hypotheses, to reject as few true hypotheses as possible and, at the same time, to reject as many false hypotheses as possible.

The probability of rejecting a true hypothesis can be set by the experimenter. For example, having specified the null hypothesis to be tested, we can then choose a class of results that, if the null hypothesis is true, would occur with a theoretical relative frequency of 5 times in 100. If our particular result falls within this class, we shall reject the null hypothesis. Thus, in the long run, the frequency of Type I errors would be 5 in 100, and we may say that the probability of a Type I error is .05. By choosing a class of results that would occur less frequently than 5 per cent of the time, when the null hypothesis is true, and by rejecting the null hypothesis only if our particular result falls within this class, we can reduce the frequency of Type I errors. For example, if we demand, in order to reject the null hypothesis, that our particular result be such that it would occur not more than 1 per cent of the time, when the null hypothesis is true, the frequency of Type I errors would be 1 in 100. In this instance, the probability of a Type I error would be .01. If we refuse to reject the null hypothesis unless the result we have obtained is such that it would occur but 1 time in 1,000, when the null hypothesis is true, the probability of a Type I error would be .001. The unfortunate circumstance, however, is that at the same time we shall *increase* the frequency of Type II errors; that is, we shall increase the frequency with which we fail to reject the null hypothesis when it is, in fact, false.

As with any rule-of-thumb procedure, caution must be exercised in critical cases. Under certain circumstances a Type I error may be more serious than a Type II error, and under other circumstances a Type II error may have more serious consequences than a Type I error. By demanding a very small probability before rejecting the null hypothesis, the number of Type II errors will be increased; that is, we shall more often fail to reject the null hypothesis when it is, in fact, false. If we choose a less severe probability as a basis for rejecting the null hypothesis, we shall increase the number of Type I errors; that is, we shall more often reject the null hypothesis when it is, in fact, true. Setting the probability of a Type I error at .05 or .01 is a fairly common practice in research work, though it must be recognized that these are arbitrary values.[8]

---

[8] Type I and Type II errors are discussed in greater detail by Hoel (1947), Mood (1950), and Johnson (1949). Less technical discussions can be found in Tippett (1941), Cochran and Cox (1950), and Marks (1951).

■ Two-Tailed Tests of Significance

In any well-planned experiment, prior to the experiment itself a decision is made about the nature of the particular null hypothesis to be tested. We shall consider first the case of an experiment in which the experimenter has no more basis for believing that m_1 should be greater than m_2 than he has for believing that m_1 should be less than m_2. The experimenter, in this instance, is interested in any difference that is observed between the two means, regardless of the direction of the difference. The appropriate null hypothesis for this case is that $m_1 = m_2$. If a test of significance results in the rejection of this hypothesis, the experimenter will accept the alternative hypothesis that $m_1 \neq m_2$. If the experimenter accepts this alternative hypothesis, it, in turn, implies that *either* $m_1 > m_2$ *or* $m_1 < m_2$.

The experimenter usually also specifies the risk he wishes to take in making a Type I error. Let us assume, in the present instance, that the test of significance is to be made in such a way that the probability of a Type I error is to be .05. Under the null hypothesis being tested, $m_1 - m_2$ will be equal to 0. The expected or average value of t will also be 0, in a series of trials, if the null hypothesis is true. For any given sample, however, t will be positive if $\bar{X}_1$ is greater than $\bar{X}_2$ and negative if $\bar{X}_1$ is less than $\bar{X}_2$. We are prepared to reject the null hypothesis if the value of t we obtain from formula (13.10) is *either* positive *or* negative and falls within the class of those values that would occur 5 per cent of the time when the null hypothesis is true.

From the table of t—Table V, in the Appendix—we observe that with 18 degrees of freedom, $t = 2.101$ will cut off .025 of the total area in the right tail of the t distribution and $t = -2.101$ will cut off .025 of the total area in the left tail. Absolute values of t equal to or greater than 2.101 will, in other words, occur 5 per cent of the time, when we have 18 degrees of freedom and when the null hypothesis is true. If we reject the null hypothesis when the *absolute* value of our observed t is equal to or greater than 2.101, the probability that we shall make a Type I error will be .05.

For the data of Table 13.1, we obtained a t equal to 1.49, and we must consider the null hypothesis as tenable. Our sample data, in other words, do not indicate that the two means differ significantly. Our failure to reject the null hypothesis, however, does not mean that we regard it as true, but only that the data we have offer insufficient evidence for rejecting it.

The nature of the test we have made is illustrated in Figure 13.1. The shaded areas in the two tails of the t distribution together make up .05 of the total area under the curve. The null hypothesis that $m_1 = m_2$

is rejected if the observed value of t, as given by formula (13.10), falls in either of the shaded areas. Since our test of significance is based upon both tails of the distribution of t, we say that we have made a *two-tailed* test of significance. It will be convenient if we designate the probability

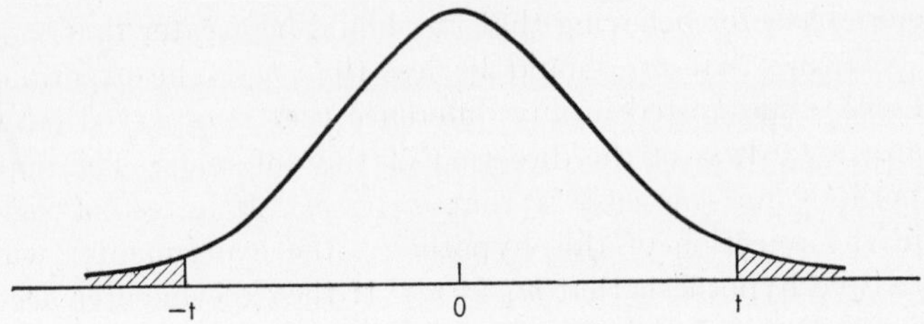

Fig. 13.1—The two-tailed test of significance for the null hypothesis $m_1 = m_2$. The null hypothesis is rejected if t falls in either of the two shaded areas.

obtained from a two-tailed test of significance, that is, the probability of obtaining either a positive or negative t, as a *level of significance.* If t is significant with a probability of .05 for a two-tailed test, we shall say that it is significant at the 5 per cent *level.*

■ One-Tailed Tests of Significance

In many cases the experimenter will have a theoretical basis for predicting, in advance of the experiment itself, that a particular one of the two means to be compared should be greater than the other. For example, if we have two groups, one of which is shown a motion picture designed to influence their attitudes favorably and the other is not shown the picture, we might expect that the group seeing the picture should have a *more* favorable attitude than the other group. We may predict that rats in learning a maze under 12 hours of food deprivation will learn in *fewer* trials than rats learning the maze under 6 hours of food deprivation. In the experiment described earlier in this chapter, if the different instructions given to the two groups of subjects operate in the way in which we might expect, then we should also expect the mean for Group 1 to exceed the mean for Group 2.

Consider the null hypothesis that $m_1 \leqq m_2$. If we reject this null hypothesis, we shall accept the alternative hypothesis that $m_1 > m_2$. We wish to make our test of significance in such a way that the probability of a Type I error does not exceed .05. In other words, if it is actually true that $m_1 \leqq m_2$, we want the probability of rejecting this hypothesis to be no greater than .05. Now, if $m_1 = m_2$, the expected or average value of t will be 0. If $m_1 < m_2$, the expected value of t will be negative. It is obvious that if our observed value of t, as obtained from formula (13.10), is 0 or negative, the null hypothesis will not be contradicted, that is, such a result will in no way provide evidence *against* the null hypothesis. Only if $\bar{X}_1$ is greater than $\bar{X}_2$, so that we obtain a positive value of t, will the data provide evidence against the null hypothesis. Hence, we need to find the class of *positive* values of t that may be expected 5 per cent of the time when the null hypothesis is true. If our observed t falls in this class we shall reject the null hypothesis.

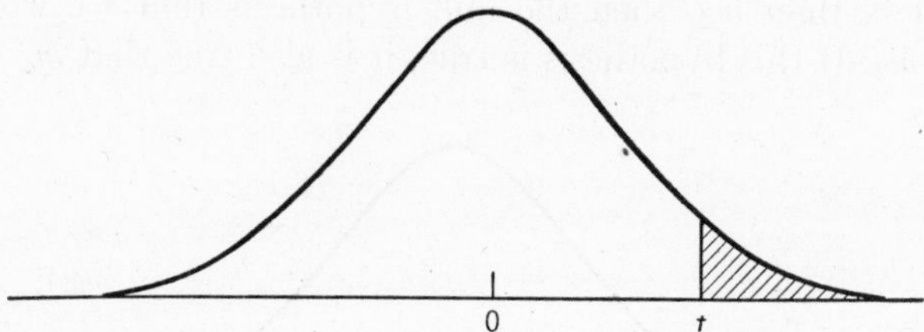

Fig. 13.2—The one-tailed test of significance for the null hypothesis $m_1 \leqq m_2$. The null hypothesis is rejected if t falls in the shaded area at the right.

From the table of t, we find that for 18 degrees of freedom a value of 1.734 will cut off .05 of the total area in the right tail of the t distribution when $m_1 = m_2$ or when $m_1 - m_2 = 0$.[9] If $m_1 < m_2$ so that $m_1 - m_2 < 0$, the probability of obtaining a positive value of t equal to or greater than 1.734 will be less than .05. Thus if we reject the null hypothesis only if we obtain a positive value of t equal to or greater than 1.734, the probability of a Type I error will not exceed .05. The worst that could happen to us, as far as a Type I error is concerned, would be if $m_1 = m_2$, in which case we shall erroneously reject the null hypothesis 5 per cent of the time. If m_1 is less than m_2, the probability of a Type I error will be less than .05.

The nature of the test of significance for the null hypothesis that $m_1 \leqq m_2$ is shown graphically in Figure 13.2. The shaded area in the right tail of the distribution represents .05 of the total area when the expected value of t is 0. In the present problem, we reject the null hypothesis only if t is positive and falls within the region represented by the shaded area. Any value of t to the left of the shaded area will be regarded as not contradicting the null hypothesis. If we reject the null

[9] We emphasize, once again, that the probabilities given in the table of t refer to the areas in the *two* tails of the distribution. Thus, for 18 degrees of freedom, $t = \pm 1.734$ will cut off 10 per cent of the area in the two tails of the distribution, with 5 per cent of the area falling to the right of 1.734 and 5 per cent falling to the left of -1.734.

hypothesis, we shall accept the alternative hypothesis that $m_1 - m_2 > 0$ or that $m_1 > m_2$. In making a one-tailed test of significance on the right tail of the t distribution, the probability of a Type I error will be equal to or less than .05.

We have already designated the probability obtained in a two-tailed test of significance as a level of significance. When we make a one-tailed test of significance, we shall refer to the probability obtained as a *point.* In other words, if we make a one-tailed test and find that t has a probability of .05, we shall say that it is significant at the 5 per cent *point.*

If we have reason to believe, in a particular experiment, that m_1 should be less than m_2, then the null hypothesis that we would test is that $m_1 \geqq m_2$. If this hypothesis is true, it is also true that $m_1 - m_2 \geqq 0$.

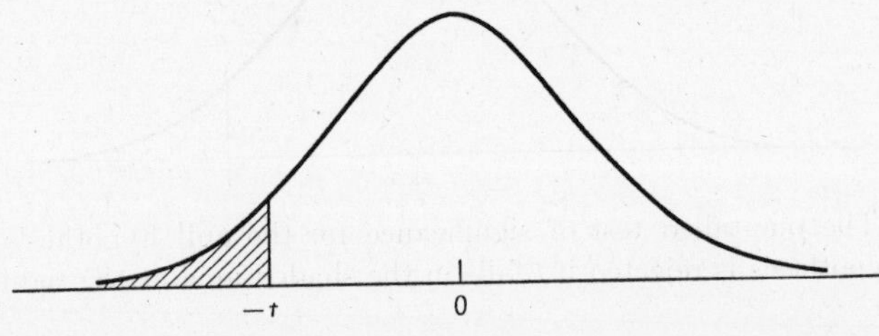

Fig. 13.3—The one-tailed test of significance for the null hypothesis $m_1 \geqq m_2$. The null hypothesis is rejected if t falls in the shaded area at the left.

If we reject this hypothesis, we shall accept the alternative hypothesis that $m_1 - m_2 < 0$ or that $m_1 < m_2$. Again we may specify that we wish to make the test of significance in such a way that the probability of a Type I error does not exceed .05.

If the null hypothesis is true, the expected or average value of t will be equal to or greater than 0. Consequently, if the observed value of t, as determined from formula (13.10), is 0 or positive, the null hypothesis will not be contradicted. Only negative values of t will provide evidence *against* the null hypothesis, that is, provide a basis for the rejection of the null hypothesis. If we wish the probability of a Type I error not to exceed .05, we find the class of *negative* values of t that will occur not more than 5 per cent of the time when the null hypothesis is true.

From the table of t, we find that a value of -1.734 will cut off .05 of the total area in the left tail of the t distribution, when the expected value of t is 0 and 18 degrees of freedom are available. The probability of obtaining a t in this area is therefore .05, if $m_1 = m_2$ or when $m_1 - m_2 = 0$. If $m_1 > m_2$ so that $m_1 - m_2 > 0$, the probability of obtaining a t to the left of -1.734 will be less than .05. Therefore, if we reject the hypothesis that $m_1 \geqq m_2$ only if t is equal to -1.734 or to the left of this value, the probability of a Type I error will be equal to or less than .05.

Figure 13.3 illustrates the test of the null hypothesis that $m_1 \geqq m_2$. The shaded area in the left tail of the t distribution represents .05 of the total area when the expected value of t is 0. We reject the null hypothesis only if t, as determined from formula (13.10) falls within this area. All values of t to the right of this area will be regarded as not contradicting the null hypothesis. If our observed value of t falls within the shaded area, we reject the null hypothesis that $m_1 \geqq m_2$ and accept the alternative that $m_1 < m_2$. In making the test on the left tail of the t distribution, the probability of a Type I error will be equal to or less than .05.[10]

■ The Power of a Test of Significance

In our discussion of one- and two-tailed tests of significance we have been primarily concerned with the probability of making a Type I error, that is, of rejecting the null hypothesis when it is true. We shall now give some attention to the probability of making a Type II error, that is, of failing to reject the null hypothesis when it is false.

As a matter of convenience and simplicity in presentation, we shall assume that we have two samples drawn from two normal populations with equal and known variances. We shall, therefore, not have to be concerned about degrees of freedom and the table of t, but instead we may use the table of the normal curve. The table of the normal curve is much more complete than the table of t we have included in the Appendix, and this will prove useful in our discussion. The argument presented, the procedure described, and the general conclusions we arrive at will, however, be exactly the same as if we had used the t distribution. The only difference is that we shall be using the areas or probabilities of the normal distribution rather than those of the t distribution.

Let us assume that we have two samples, each with two observations. We assume that the populations from which the samples were drawn are normally distributed and that the variances of the two populations are the same and known to be equal to 1.00. We do not, however, know anything about the two population means. The standard error of the difference between the means will be given by

$$\sigma_{\bar{x}_1-\bar{x}_2} = \sqrt{\frac{{\sigma_1}^2}{n_1} + \frac{{\sigma_2}^2}{n_2}}$$

[10] A more detailed discussion of the one- and two-tailed tests of significance in psychological research is given by Jones (1952). See also Marks (1951), Hick (1952), and Burke (1953).

$$= \sqrt{\frac{1}{2} + \frac{1}{2}}$$

$$= 1.00$$

Power of the Two-Tailed Test of $m_1 = m_2$

Suppose we wish to test the null hypothesis $m_1 = m_2$, with the probability of a Type I error being set at .05. Our test statistic will be the z ratio with

$$z = \frac{\bar{X}_1 - \bar{X}_2}{\sigma_{\bar{x}_1 - \bar{x}_2}}$$

As in the two-tailed t test, described earlier, we shall reject the null hypothesis if the absolute value of z is one that would occur but 5 per cent of the time when the null hypothesis is true. From the table of the normal curve, we find that $z = 1.96$ will cut off .025 of the total area in the right tail and $z = -1.96$ will cut off .025 of the total area in the left tail. For the two-tailed test, then, we would reject the null hypothesis if the obtained value of z was equal to or greater than 1.96 or equal to or less than -1.96. If the null hypothesis is true, for this test, the probability of a Type I error will be equal to .05.

We may note that since $\sigma_{\bar{x}_1 - \bar{x}_2} = 1.00$, we have

$$z = \bar{X}_1 - \bar{X}_2$$

and, for the conditions described, we may say that we would reject the null hypothesis if $\bar{X}_1 - \bar{X}_2 \geqq 1.96$ or if $\bar{X}_1 - \bar{X}_2 \leqq -1.96$. The frequency with which we shall obtain values of $\bar{X}_1 - \bar{X}_2 \geqq 1.96$ or of $\bar{X}_1 - \bar{X}_2 \leqq -1.96$ will depend upon the unknown true population mean difference $m_1 - m_2$.

Let us designate the null hypothesis $m_1 = m_2$ or, in other words, $m_1 - m_2 = 0$, as H_0. Then one general class of alternatives to the null hypothesis would be all possible values of $m_1 > m_2$ so that $m_1 - m_2 > 0$. Let us designate all members of this class as H_1. Another general class of alternatives, which we may designate as H_2, would be all possible values of $m_1 < m_2$ so that $m_1 - m_2 < 0$. From the class of H_1 and H_2 alternatives we may select various values of $m_1 - m_2$ and determine, if a particular alternative is true, how frequently we would obtain values of $\bar{X}_1 - \bar{X}_2 \geqq 1.96$ and $\bar{X}_1 - \bar{X}_2 \leqq -1.96$.

Suppose, for example, it is true that $m_1 - m_2 = 1.00$. Then the sampling distribution of $\bar{X}_1 - \bar{X}_2$ will be normally distributed about the population mean difference $m_1 - m_2 = 1.00$ and we would have

$$z = \frac{(\bar{X}_1 - \bar{X}_2) - (m_1 - m_2)}{\sigma_{\bar{x}_1 - \bar{x}_2}}$$

$$= \frac{(1.96) - (1.00)}{1.00}$$

$$= .96$$

and the expected frequency of $\bar{X}_1 - \bar{X}_2 \geqq 1.96$ would be the area to the right of $z = .96$ in the normal curve. This area is .168. We would also have

$$z = \frac{(-1.96) - (1.00)}{1.00}$$

$$= -2.96$$

and the expected frequency of $\bar{X}_1 - \bar{X}_2 \leqq -1.96$ would be the area to the left of $z = -2.96$ in the normal curve. This area is .002. Then, if we reject the null hypothesis $m_1 - m_2 = 0$ whenever $\bar{X}_1 - \bar{X}_2 \geqq 1.96$ or whenever $\bar{X}_1 - \bar{X}_2 \leqq -1.96$, we shall do so with a theoretical relative frequency of $.168 + .002 = .170$, if it is true that $m_1 - m_2 = 1.00$.

Following the procedure just described, we can determine how frequently the null hypothesis would be rejected when other alternatives of the class H_1 and H_2 are true. We have done this for the selected values of $m_1 - m_2$ shown in column (1) of Table 13.2. The probability of obtaining values of $\bar{X}_1 - \bar{X}_2 \geqq 1.96$ for each of these alternatives is shown in column (2) of the table. In column (3) we have the probability of obtaining values of $\bar{X}_1 - \bar{X}_2 \leqq -1.96$ for each alternative. The sums of these two probabilities are given in column (4), and these are the probabilities of rejecting the null hypothesis for each of the corresponding alternatives given in column (1).

The only way in which we can make a Type I error is if it is true that $m_1 - m_2 = 0$ and we reject the null hypothesis. This probability is .05, as column (4) shows. A Type II error will occur, however, whenever the null hypothesis $m_1 - m_2 = 0$ is false, but we fail to reject it. Since we know the probability of rejecting the null hypothesis for each of the alternatives given in column (1) of Table 13.2, the probability of not rejecting will be equal to one minus the probability of rejecting the null hypothesis. These probabilities are given in column (5) of Table 13.2.

Table 13.2—Probability of Rejecting and Failing to Reject the Null Hypothesis $m_1 - m_2 = 0$ When $\sigma_{\bar{x}_1-\bar{x}_2} = 1.00$ and the Various Values of $m_1 - m_2$ Shown in the Table Are True. The Hypothesis Is Rejected If $z = \bar{X}_1 - \bar{X}_2 \geqq 1.96$ or $z = \bar{X}_1 - \bar{X}_2 \leqq -1.96$.

(1) *Values of* $m_1 - m_2$	(2) *Probability of* $\bar{X}_1 - \bar{X}_2 \geqq 1.96$	(3) *Probability of* $\bar{X}_1 - \bar{X}_2 \leqq -1.96$	(4) *Probability of Rejecting* $m_1 - m_2 = 0$	(5) *Probability of Not Rejecting* $m_1 - m_2 = 0$
4.0	.979	.000	.979	.021
3.5	.938	.000	.938	.062
3.0	.851	.000	.851	.149
2.5	.705	.000	.705	.295
2.0	.516	.000	.516	.484
1.5	.323	.000	.323	.677
1.0	.168	.002	.170	.830
.5	.072	.007	.079	.921
.0	.025	.025	.050	.950
−.5	.007	.072	.079	.921
−1.0	.002	.168	.017	.983
−1.5	.000	.323	.323	.677
−2.0	.000	.516	.516	.484
−2.5	.000	.705	.705	.295
−3.0	.000	.851	.851	.149
−3.5	.000	.938	.938	.062
−4.0	.000	.979	.979	.021

Since it is obvious that we cannot make a Type II error if it is true that $m_1 - m_2 = 0$, all of the probabilities given in column (5) of the table except the one in the row $m_1 - m_2 = 0$ are the probabilities of making a Type II error for each of the alternatives given in column (1).

Statisticians refer to the *power of a statistical test* and they define the power of a test as

$$\textit{Power} = 1 - \textit{Probability of a Type II error}$$

In terms of this definition, the power of a test depends upon the probability of making a Type II error. If this probability is small for a given test of significance, the test has greater power than one for which the probability of a Type II error is larger, assuming that both tests have equal probabilities of making a Type I error.

An equivalent definition of the power of a test would be the probability of rejecting the null hypothesis when it is false. The graph of these probabilities for various alternatives to $m_1 - m_2 = 0$ is shown in Figure 13.4. This graph is called the power function of the test of significance. From Figure 13.4 it is obvious that the two-tailed test of significance has power against both groups of alternatives H_1 and H_2. Let us now see what happens when we make a one-tailed test of significance.

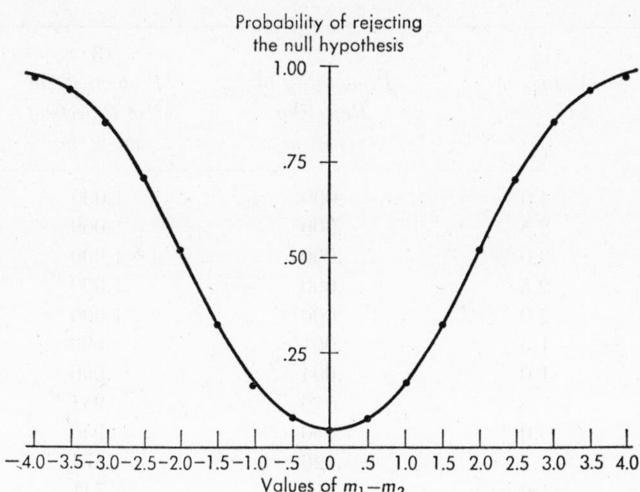

Fig. 13.4—Power function of the two-tailed test of the null hypothesis $m_1 - m_2 = 0$ when $\sigma_{\bar{x}_1 - \bar{x}_2} = 1.00$ and the probability of a Type I error is set at .05.

Power of the One-Tailed Test of $m_1 \geqq m_2$

If we test the null hypothesis $m_1 \geqq m_2$, we shall use the left tail of the normal curve, just as we used the left tail of the t distribution in testing this hypothesis. From the table of the normal curve we find that $z = -1.645$ will cut off .05 of the area in the left tail, and, if we reject the null hypothesis whenever z falls in this region, the probability of a Type I error will not exceed .05. We have only one general class of alternatives to this null hythesis, namely, H_2 or all possible values of $m_1 < m_2$ so that $m_1 - m_2 < 0$.

We may observe that since we have $\sigma_{\bar{x}_1 - \bar{x}_2} = 1.00$, we have $z = \bar{X}_1 - \bar{X}_2$, as before, and we will reject the null hypothesis if $\bar{X}_1 - \bar{X}_2 \leqq -1.645$. The frequency with which we will obtain values of $\bar{X}_1 - \bar{X}_2 \leqq -1.645$ will depend upon the unknown true population difference between the means $m_1 - m_2$. Suppose, for example, that it is true that $m_1 - m_2 = 1.00$.

This is consistent with the null hypothesis $m_1 - m_2 \geqq 0$, and we shall see that the probability of rejecting the null hypothesis, if this alternative is true, that is, the probability of making a Type I error, will be less than .05.

Table 13.3—Probability of Rejecting and Failing to Reject the Null Hypothesis $m_1 \geqq m_2$ When $\sigma_{\bar{x}_1-\bar{x}_2} = 1.00$ and the Various Values of $m_1 - m_2$ Are True. The Hypothesis Is Rejected If $z = \bar{X}_1 - \bar{X}_2 \leqq -1.645$.

(1) *Values of* $m_1 - m_2$	(2) *Probability of Rejecting* $m_1 \geqq m_2$	(3) *Probability of Not Rejecting* $m_1 \geqq m_2$
4.0	.000	1.000
3.5	.000	1.000
3.0	.000	1.000
2.5	.000	1.000
2.0	.000	1.000
1.5	.001	.999
1.0	.004	.996
.5	.016	.984
.0	.050	.950
− .5	.126	.874
−1.0	.259	.741
−1.5	.442	.558
−2.0	.639	.361
−2.5	.804	.196
−3.0	.912	.088
−3.5	.968	.032
−4.0	.991	.009

If it is true that $m_1 - m_2 = 1.00$, then $\bar{X}_1 - \bar{X}_2$ will be normally distributed about the population mean difference $m_1 - m_2 = 1.00$ and we have

$$z = \frac{(\bar{X}_1 - \bar{X}_2) - (m_1 - m_2)}{\sigma_{\bar{x}_1 - \bar{x}_2}}$$

$$= \frac{(-1.645) - (1.00)}{1.00}$$

$$= -2.645$$

and the expected frequency of $\bar{X}_1 - \bar{X}_2 \leqq -1.645$ will be given by the area of the normal distribution that falls to the left of $z = -2.645$. This area is .004 and corresponds to the probability of rejecting the null hypothesis $m_1 \geqq m_2$ when it is true that $m_1 > m_2$ and $m_1 - m_2 = 1.00$.

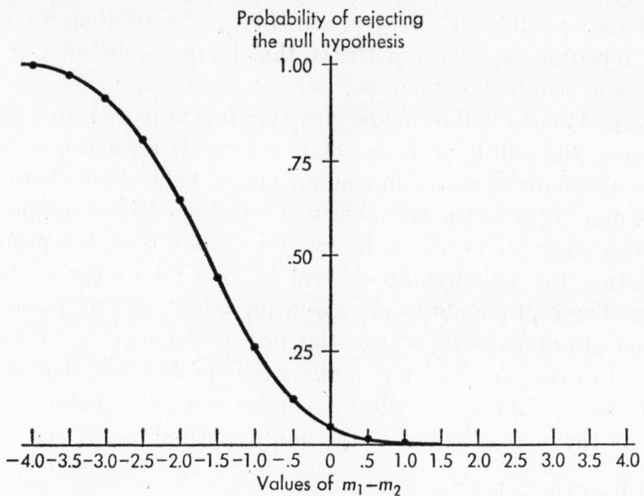

Fig. 13.5—Power function of the one-tailed test of the null hypothesis $m_1 - m_2 \geqq 0$ when $\sigma_{\bar{x}_1 - \bar{x}_2} = 1.00$ and the probability of a Type I error is not to exceed .05.

Suppose, however, that the alternative $m_1 - m_2 = -1.00$ is true and that we test the null hypothesis $m_1 \geqq m_2$ as before, using the left tail of the normal curve. Then

$$z = \frac{(\bar{X}_1 - \bar{X}_2) - (m_1 - m_2)}{\sigma_{\bar{x}_1} - {}_{\bar{x}_2}}$$

$$= \frac{(-1.645) - (-1.00)}{1.00}$$

$$= -.645$$

and the expected frequency of $\bar{X}_1 - \bar{X}_2 \leqq -1.645$ will be given by the area in the normal curve falling to the left of $z = -.645$. This area is .259 and corresponds to the probability of rejecting the null hypothesis $m_1 \geqq m_2$ when it is true that $m_1 < m_2$ and $m_1 - m_2 = -1.00$.

In the manner described above, we have determined the probability of rejecting the null hypothesis $m_1 \geqq m_2$ for the various other selected values of $m_1 - m_2$ shown in column (1) of Table 13.3. These probabilities are given in column (2) of the table. In testing the null hypothesis $m_1 \geqq m_2$, a Type I error will occur whenever this hypothesis is true, but our test of significance rejects the hypothesis. Thus a Type I error can occur only if one of the alternatives $m_1 \geqq m_2$ shown in column (1) of Table 13.3 is true and the null hypothesis is rejected. It can be seen in column (2) of the table that this probability will be .05, if $m_1 = m_2$. If m_1 is greater than m_2, the probability of rejecting the null hypothesis, that is, the probability of making a Type I error, will be less than .05.

A Type II error will be made whenever it is true that $m_1 < m_2$ and we fail to reject the null hypothesis. Thus a Type II error can only be made for those alternatives shown in column (1) of Table 13.3 where $m_1 < m_2$. Since column (2) gives the probability of rejecting the null hypothesis when the various alternatives shown in column (1) are true, the probability of not rejecting the null hypothesis will be one minus the probability of rejecting. These probabilities are given in column (3) of Table 13.3. For all of the alternatives $m_1 < m_2$, the probabilities given in column (3) correspond to the probability of making a Type II error, that is, of failing to reject the null hypothesis when it is false. Figure 13.5 shows the power function of the one-tailed test of the null hypothesis $m_1 \geqq m_2$.

Power of the One-Tailed Test of $m_1 \leqq m_2$

In Table 13.4 we have followed the procedures described above for the one-tailed test of the null hypothesis $m_1 \leqq m_2$. Column (1) of Table 13.4 gives selected values of $m_1 - m_2$. Column (2) gives the probability of rejecting the null hypothesis for each of the alternatives shown in column (1). For this one-tailed test, a Type I error can occur only if one of the alternatives $m_1 \leqq m_2$ is true and we reject the null hypothesis. Column (2) shows that the probability of a Type I error will be .05, if it is true that $m_1 = m_2$. If $m_1 < m_2$, the probability of a Type I error will be less than .05.

A Type II error will occur when it is true that $m_1 > m_2$, but our test fails to reject the null hypothesis. Again, since we know the probability of rejecting the null hypothesis for the various alternatives shown in column (1) of Table 13.4, we can find the probability of failing to reject the null hypothesis for these alternatives. The probability for any given alternative in column (1) will be one minus the corresponding probability of rejecting the null hypothesis. These probabilities are given in column (3) of Table 13.4. Figure 13.6 shows the power function for the one-tailed test of the null hypothesis $m_1 \leqq m_2$.

A Comparison of a One- and a Two-Tailed Test When $m_1 > m_2$

Consider only the one-tailed test of the null hypothesis $m_1 \leqq m_2$ and the two-tailed test of the null hypothesis $m_1 = m_2$, when one of the alterna-

Table 13.4—Probability of Rejecting and Failing to Reject the Null Hypothesis $m_1 \leqq m_2$ When $\sigma_{\bar{x}_1-\bar{x}_2} = 1.00$ and the Various Values of $m_1 - m_2$ Shown in the Table Are True. The Hypothesis Is Rejected If $z = \bar{X}_1 - \bar{X}_2 \geqq 1.645$.

(1) *Values of* $m_1 - m_2$	(2) *Probability of Rejecting* $m_1 \leqq m_2$	(3) *Probability of Not Rejecting* $m_1 \geqq m_2$
4.0	.991	.009
3.5	.968	.032
3.0	.912	.088
2.5	.804	.196
2.0	.639	.361
1.5	.442	.558
1.0	.259	.741
.5	.126	.874
.0	.050	.950
− .5	.016	.984
−1.0	.004	.996
−1.5	.001	.999
−2.0	.000	1.000
−2.5	.000	1.000
−3.0	.000	1.000
−3.5	.000	1.000
−4.0	.000	1.000

tives, $m_1 > m_2$, is true. In Figure 13.7 we have graphed the power functions of (a) the two-tailed test of the null hypothesis $m_1 = m_2$ and of (b) the one-tailed test of the null hypothesis $m_1 \leqq m_2$. It will be clear from an examination of Figure 13.7 that both tests have less power, that is, they are less likely to reject the null hypothesis when it is false—when $m_1 > m_2$, and $m_1 - m_2$ is close to 0. The power of both tests increases as m_1 becomes greater than m_2. The power of the one-tailed test is greater than that of the two-tailed test, but both approach maximum power of 1.00 as m_1 becomes greater than m_2.

The power of both the one- and two-tailed test can be increased by increasing the number of observations in the two samples. As n increases, the standard error of the difference between the means will decrease, and the power functions of the two tests will show a much more rapid rise than those shown in Figure 13.7. This means that the test of significance, whether one- or two-tailed, is much more likely to detect small positive values of $m_1 - m_2$ when n is large than it is when n is small.

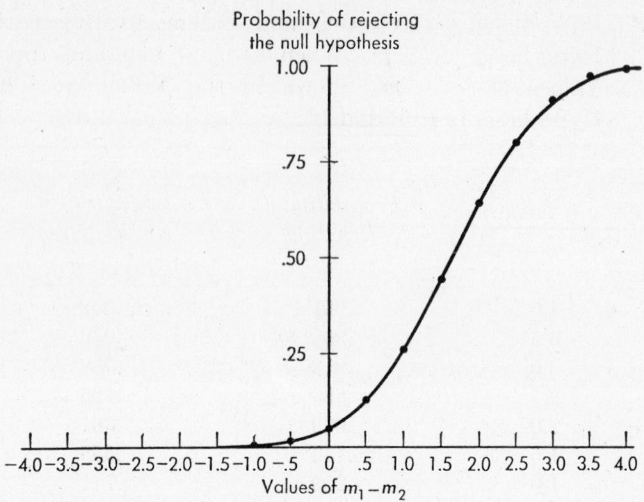

Fig. 13.6—Power function of the one-tailed test of the null hypothesis $m_1 - m_2 \leqq 0$ when $\sigma_{\bar{x}_1 - \bar{x}_2} = 1.00$ and the probability of a Type I error is not to exceed .05.

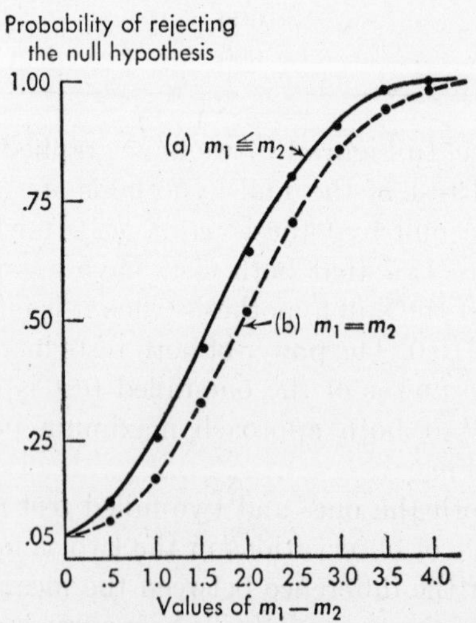

Fig. 13.7—A comparison of the power functions of the one-tailed test of the null hypothesis $m_1 \leqq m_2$ and of the two-tailed test of the null hypothesis $m_1 = m_2$ for the class of alternatives $m_1 > m_2$.

As a comparison of Figures 13.4 and 13.6 will show, the probability of making a Type II error will depend upon the true, but unknown, difference between m_1 and m_2, and whether we make a one-tailed or a two-tailed test of significance. In making a two-tailed test of the null hypothesis $m_1 = m_2$, the experimenter is expressing his interest in a difference between $\bar{X}_1$ and $\bar{X}_2$, regardless of the direction of this difference. The two-tailed test thus guards against both groups of alternatives H_1 and H_2, that is, $m_1 > m_2$ and $m_1 < m_2$. In making a one-tailed test of the null hypothesis $m_1 \geqq m_2$, the experimenter is saying that he is willing to accept all values of $\bar{X}_1 - \bar{X}_2 \geqq 0$ as compatible with the null hypothesis, regardless of their magnitude, and that he wishes to guard only against the alternatives H_2, that is, of making a Type II error when it is true that $m_1 < m_2$. Similarly, in making a one-tailed test of the null hypothesis $m_1 \leqq m_2$, the experimenter is saying that he is willing to regard all possible values of $\bar{X}_1 - \bar{X}_2 \leqq 0$ as compatible with the null hypothesis, regardless of their magnitude, and that he wishes only to guard against the alternatives H_1, that is, of making a Type II error when it is true that $m_1 > m_2$.

■ Failure to Reject a Given Null Hypothesis

In discussing tests of various null hypotheses, we have had occasion to point out the circumstances under which the value of t obtained from formula (13.10) would be regarded as not contradicting the null hypothesis tested. It is worth stressing that results or outcomes that do not contradict a given null hypothesis do not, in turn, prove the null hypothesis to be true. If the null hypothesis is not rejected, this means only that our data offer no significant evidence against it. For example, we tested the null hypothesis that $m_1 - m_2 = 0$ for the data of Table 13.1. Our test of significance failed to reject this hypothesis, and we regarded it as tenable, that is, as a hypothesis that might be defended insofar as the available data offered insufficient evidence against it. But this particular null hypothesis is only one of many possible hypotheses that would be regarded as tenable. We would find, in the example under discussion, that the hypothesis $m_1 - m_2 = .01$ is also tenable, as would be many other hypotheses that we might test. Failure to reject a given null hypothesis, in other words, means only that the hypothesis is tenable—along with a host of other hypotheses that might be formulated—and not that it is necessarily true.

■ Homogeneity of Two Variances

In the evaluation of the difference between two means by the t test, we have implicitly stated as part of the hypothesis being tested, that the population variances from which the samples are drawn are equal. In rejecting the null hypothesis tested, however, we imply that the way in which the two populations differ is with respect to their means rather than with respect to their variances. If it seems desirable to test the hypothesis that $\sigma_1^2 = \sigma_2^2$, this may be done without involving any hypothesis whatsoever about

Table 13.5—Means and Sums of Squares for Two Groups of Subjects

	Group 1	*Group 2*
$\bar{X}$	54.60	50.40
$\sum x^2$	243.36	165.04
n	10	30

the population means. For our two samples, we may obtain two independent estimates s_1^2 and s_2^2 of the assumed common population variance σ^2. For the data of Table 13.5 we have

$$s_1^2 = \frac{\sum x_1^2}{n_1 - 1} = \frac{243.36}{9} = 27.04$$

and

$$s_2^2 = \frac{\sum x_2^2}{n_2 - 1} = \frac{165.04}{29} = 5.69$$

If we put s_1^2 or s_2^2, whichever is the larger, into the numerator and the smaller value into the denominator, we may define

$$F = \frac{s_1^2}{s_2^2} \quad \text{or} \quad F = \frac{s_2^2}{s_1^2} \tag{13.11}$$

so that F will always be greater than 1.

The distribution of F is known and has been tabled in convenient form by Snedecor (1946). Table VIII, in the Appendix, is a table of the values of $F > 1$ which are significant at the 1 and 5 per cent *points* for varying degrees of freedom. We enter the column of the table with the degrees of freedom in the numerator of the F ratio and follow this column down to the row entry corresponding to the degrees of freedom in the denominator. The value given in lightface type is the value of F significant at the *5 per cent point*, and the value in boldface type is the value significant at the *1 per cent point*. The values tabled, therefore, are those that will cut off 5 and 1 per cent of the area in one tail only of the distribution.

We wish to test the hypothesis that $\sigma_1^2 - \sigma_2^2 = 0$ against the alternative hypothesis that $\sigma_1^2 - \sigma_2^2 \neq 0$. In other words, we do not have a directional hypothesis, and we want to make a two-tailed test of significance rather than a one-tailed test. Consequently, we must *double* the probability values given in the table of F.[11] Thus, for the test described by formula (13.11), the values given in the F table will correspond to the .02 and .10 levels of significance.

For the data of Table 13.5, we have $s_1^2 = 27.04$ and $s_2^2 = 5.69$. Then

$$F = \frac{27.04}{5.69} = 4.75$$

with $n_1 - 1 = 9$ degrees of freedom for the numerator and $n_2 - 1 = 29$ degrees of freedom for the denominator. From the table of F—Table VIII, in the Appendix—we find that a value of 2.22 will be significant at the 10 per cent level and a value of 3.08 will be significant at the 2 per cent level.[12] Since our observed value of 4.75 is greater than 3.08, we may conclude that the null hypothesis is untenable.

Significance of the Difference between Two Means When the Variances Differ Significantly

Since we have found that s_1^2 and s_2^2 do differ significantly, can we still determine whether the two means differ significantly, irrespective of the differences in variances?

If s_1^2 and s_2^2 differ significantly, and if n_1 is not equal to n_2, then calculate the standard error of the difference by means of formula (13.7). Do not, in other words, pool the sums of squares in order to arrive at a common estimate of the population variance, for the F test has already told us that this hypothesis of a common population variance is not tenable. Instead, use the estimates of the *two* population variances as given in formula (13.7). For the data of Table 13.5, we have

$$s_{\bar{x}_1 - \bar{x}_2} = \sqrt{\frac{27.04}{10} + \frac{5.69}{30}}$$

$$= \sqrt{2.704 + .190}$$

$$= 1.7$$

[11] An explanation of the reciprocal function $1/F$ which makes this procedure possible is given by Hoel (1947, p. 153).

[12] By approximate interpolation we find that a value of 2.54 will be significant at the 5 per cent level.

The value of t will be given by dividing the difference between the means by the standard error of the difference obtained by formula (13.7). Thus we have

$$t = \frac{54.60 - 50.40}{1.7} = 2.47$$

To determine whether this obtained t is significant, we make use of an approximation suggested by Cochran and Cox (1950). We have n_1 equal to 10 and n_2 equal to 30. Let us assume that we are making a two-tailed test of significance at the 5 per cent level. Then we enter the table of t with $n_1 - 1 = 9$ degrees of freedom and find that the value of t significant at the 5 per cent level is 2.262. Let us call this value t_1. Similarly, we find that for $n_2 - 1 = 29$ degrees of freedom, the value of t that is significant at the 5 per cent level is 2.045. Let us call this value t_2. Then the approximate value of t significant at the 5 per cent level may be determined from the following formula:

$$t_{.05} = \frac{(s_{\bar{x}_1}{}^2)(t_1) + (s_{\bar{x}_2}{}^2)(t_2)}{s_{\bar{x}_1}{}^2 + s_{\bar{x}_2}{}^2} \qquad \textbf{(13.12)}$$

$$= \frac{(2.704)(2.262) + (.190)(2.045)}{2.704 + .190}$$

$$= 2.248$$

Since our obtained value of 2.47 exceeds the value 2.248, we may conclude that the two means differ significantly.

If we find that $s_1{}^2$ and $s_2{}^2$ differ significantly, but if $n_1 = n_2$, it can be shown that the standard error of the difference as given by formula (13.7) will be equal to that obtained from formula (13.9). Thus it makes no difference which formula you use, in this instance. Since t_1 will also be equal to t_2 in formula (13.12), $t_{.05}$ simply becomes the tabled value of t for one half the number of degrees of freedom that would ordinarily be available. In other words, the t test may be made in the usual way, but the table of t should be entered with one half the usual number of degrees of freedom.

Significance of the Difference between the Means When the Measures Are Not Normally Distributed

The t test for the difference between two means involves the assumption that the measures upon which the means are based are normally distributed in the population. If samples are drawn from moderately skewed populations and a two-tailed test of significance of the difference between the means is made, there is reason to believe that the probability given in the table of t will not be seriously in error.[13] The one-tailed t test, on the other hand, is much more likely to be influenced by departures from normality, such as skewness, than the two-tailed t test. Thus, if we make a one-tailed t test, taking the probability as one half that of the tabled value for t, the probability given by the table may be greater or less than the true probability for the observed difference between the means, if the samples are from skewed populations.

There are often occasions when we have good reasons for believing that the assumption of normality of distribution is not warranted for the data under consideration. While, as we have pointed out above, the two-tailed t test for the difference between the means may not be seriously in error for samples drawn from skewed populations, the one-tailed test may. Under any circumstances, we may have more confidence in a test of significance that will enable us to compare our two samples without the necessity of making any assumption about how the measures are distributed in the population. Such tests are called *distribution-free* or *nonparametric tests*, and two such tests are described in the next chapter, where we deal with paired observations and equated groups. For the case of independent samples, as described in this chapter, distribution-free tests are discussed in Chapter 18 and Chapter 19.[14]

■ EXAMPLES

13.1—Two groups of rats were tested under different experimental conditions. The measures of performance consist of the speed in feet per second during critical test trials for each rat. Data are from Crespi (1942).

(*a*) Test the hypothesis that $\sigma_1^2 = \sigma_2^2$.
(*b*) Test the hypothesis that $m_1 = m_2$.

Group 1	*Group 2*
1.90	3.08
1.87	2.62
1.41	2.58
1.37	2.44
1.13	2.32
.64	1.84
.46	1.44

[13] See, for example, the discussion by Cochran (1947).
[14] See pp. 387–390 and pp. 417–422.

13.2—The Miller Analogies Test was given to VA trainees in clinical psychology. A group of 40 trainees was granted the Ph.D. degree and another group of 39 trainees was dismissed from the program. It is predicted that the group receiving the Ph.D. should have a mean score higher than that for the group dismissed from the program. Data are from Kelly and Fiske (1950).

(*a*) Test the null hypothesis that $\sigma_1^2 = \sigma_2^2$.
(*b*) Test the appropriate null hypothesis concerning the means.

	Ph.D. Granted	*Dismissed*
$\bar{X}$	77.6	62.4
s	8.4	13.7
n	40	39

13.3—A test of musical meaning was given to a group of eighth-grade and a group of tenth-grade students. We have reason to believe that the tenth-grade students should have the higher mean. Data are from Watson (1942).

(*a*) Test the hypothesis that $\sigma_1^2 = \sigma_2^2$.
(*b*) Test the appropriate null hypothesis concerning the means.

	Eighth Grade	*Tenth Grade*
$\bar{X}$	90.76	99.32
s	19.32	18.36
n	200	200

13.4—The performance of a control and an experimental group is to be compared. Performance scores of the subjects are given below. Test the hypothesis that $m_1 = m_2$.

Control	*Experimental*
10	7
5	3
6	5
7	7
10	8
6	4
7	5
8	6
6	3
5	2

13.5—Thirty subjects are divided at random into two groups. The experimental group is tested under conditions that it is believed will depress performance.

(*a*) Test the hypothesis that $\sigma_1^2 = \sigma_2^2$.
(*b*) Test the appropriate null hypothesis concerning the means.

	Control	*Experimental*
$\bar{X}$	29.66	26.14
$\sum x^2$	14.50	76.80
n	10	20

13.6—A random sample of 25 subjects yields a mean of 22.4. The estimate of the population standard deviation is 10.0.

(*a*) Find the fiducial limits for the mean at the 5 per cent level.
(*b*) Assume that the estimates of the parameters remain the same, but the sample size is increased to 100. What would the fiducial limits for the mean now be?

13.7—Forty subjects are divided at random into two groups of 20 subjects each. One group is then assigned to the experimental condition, and the other to the control condition.

(*a*) Test the hypothesis that $\sigma_1^2 = \sigma_2^2$.
(*b*) Test the hypothesis that $m_1 = m_2$.

Control		*Experimental*	
7	13	2	5
17	7	9	13
14	8	11	10
11	13	9	10
8	11	7	15
11	17	9	10
13	14	10	12
12	15	10	1
10	10	11	10
14	15	4	12

The Difference between the Means for Paired Observations and Equated Groups

Let us make a modification in the design of our experiment on the influence of two sets of instructions upon the adding of arithmetic problems. Suppose that we first gave all 20 subjects a series of practice trials in the addition of numbers and that we obtained a measure of initial level of performance based upon the practice trials. We may now arrange these measures in rank order, and, taking the two subjects with the highest measures, we may assign at random one of the subjects to Group 1 and the other to Group 2. We then take the next two subjects and do the same thing, and so on, until all of the subjects have been assigned. We shall now have two groups in which the subjects have been *paired* on the basis of initial performance.

■ Standard Error of the Difference for Paired Observations

Whenever we deal with observations based upon paired or matched subjects, we have to modify our formula for the standard error of the difference between the means in order to take into account the possible correlation between the paired observations. The formula for the standard error of the difference now becomes

$$s_{\bar{x}_1-\bar{x}_2} = \sqrt{s_{\bar{x}_1}{}^2 + s_{\bar{x}_2}{}^2 - 2rs_{\bar{x}_1}s_{\bar{x}_2}} \tag{14.1}$$

where $s_{\bar{x}1-\bar{x}2}$ = the standard error of the difference between the means of paired observations

$s_{\bar{x}_1}$ = the standard error of mean 1

$s_{\bar{x}_2}$ = the standard error of mean 2

r = the correlation coefficient between the pairs of observations

In the previous design the subjects were randomly assigned to the two groups without pairing. Since the observations were not paired in any way, there is no logical way to compute a correlation coefficient. We could, of course, consider the scores in Table 13.1 as paired and compute a correlation coefficient. But the particular arrangement of scores in the table is an entirely arbitrary matter, and some other arrangement would result in a different correlation coefficient. We have no legitimate basis for capitalizing upon any of the possible correlation coefficients that might be obtained by any of the arbitrary arrangements that might be made of the scores. Our assumption, then, is that, with subjects randomly assigned to the two groups without pairing, the correlation term should be zero or a matter of chance and is, therefore, to be ignored.

In the present design, however, we have paired our subjects before actually conducting the experiment, and we did so with the expectation that performance under the experimental conditions might be positively related to initial level of performance. We have a logical basis, in this instance, for taking advantage of any possible correlation in performance between our paired subjects under the experimental conditions. Thus formula (14.1) is the appropriate formula for computing the standard error of the difference.

Formula (14.1), however, is not as convenient in terms of actual calculations as its identity,

$$s_{\bar{x}_1 - \bar{x}_2} = \frac{s_d}{\sqrt{n}} \tag{14.2}$$

where $s_{\bar{x}_1 - \bar{x}_2}$ = the standard error of the difference between the means for paired observations

s_d = the estimate of the population standard deviation of the differences between paired observations

n = the number of pairs of observations

If we let D equal the difference $(X_1 - X_2)$ between any given pair of observations and d equal the deviation of D from the mean difference $\bar{D}$, then, by the usual formula for the sum of squares,

$$\sum d^2 = \sum D^2 - \frac{(\sum D)^2}{n} \tag{14.3}$$

where n is equal to the number of differences or pairs of observations.

The variance of the distribution of differences will be given by

$$s_d^2 = \frac{\sum d^2}{n - 1} \tag{14.4}$$

and the standard deviation of the distribution of differences will be the square root of formula (14.4). Thus

$$s_d = \sqrt{\frac{\sum d^2}{n - 1}} \tag{14.5}$$

The degrees of freedom available for s_d are indicated by the denominator of formula (14.5). We shall have $n - 1$ degrees of freedom, where n is the *number of pairs* of observations involved. We may substitute the value obtained from formula (14.5) in formula (14.2) to obtain the standard error of the difference between the means of the paired observations.

Table 14.1—Scores for Two Groups of Paired Individuals

	(1) *Group 1* X_1	(2) *Group 2* X_2	(3) $X_1 - X_2$ D	(4) $(X_1 - X_2)^2$ D^2
	2	1	1	1
	5	2	3	9
	2	4	−2	4
	3	3	0	0
	7	4	3	9
	3	2	1	1
	5	6	−1	1
	4	3	1	1
	5	4	1	1
	4	1	3	9
Σ	40	30	10	36

In Table 14.1, we show the scores obtained in an experiment where we assume that the observations are paired. For these data

$$\sum d^2 = 36 - \frac{(10)^2}{10}$$

$$= 26$$

and

$$s_d = \sqrt{\frac{26}{10 - 1}}$$

$$= \sqrt{2.8889}$$

$$= 1.70$$

The standard error of the difference for the paired observations will then be given by formula (14.2). Thus

$$s_{\bar{x}_1-\bar{x}_2} = \frac{1.70}{\sqrt{10}}$$

$$= .54$$

The value of t will be given by formula (13.10), and for the present problem we get

$$t = \frac{4.0 - 3.0}{.54}$$

$$= 1.85$$

The number of degrees of freedom available for evaluating t will be equal to the number of pairs of observations minus 1. For the data of Table 14.1 we have 10 pairs of observations, and the degrees of freedom will be equal to 9. From the table of t we find that a value of 2.262 will be required at the 5 per cent *level* for a two-tailed test of significance of the null hypothesis $m_1 = m_2$, and that a value of 1.833 will be required at the 5 per cent *point* for a one-tailed test of significance of the null hypothesis $m_1 \leqq m_2$. Since the value we obtained for t is 1.85, it will be regarded as significant, with a probability of less than .05, if we have made the one-tailed test of significance, but not if we have made a two-tailed test.

If we compute the correlation coefficient between the paired observations of Table 14.1, we will find that

$$r = \frac{129 - \frac{(40)(30)}{10}}{\sqrt{\left(182 - \frac{(40)^2}{10}\right)\left(112 - \frac{(30)^2}{10}\right)}}$$

$$= .41$$

The standard error of mean 1 is .4944, and that is also the value for mean 2. The variance of the mean will be $(.4944)^2$ which is equal to .2444. If we substitute these values in formula (14.1), we obtain

$$s_{\bar{x}_1-\bar{x}_2} = \sqrt{.2444 + .2444 - (2)(.41)(.4944)(.4944)}$$

$$= \sqrt{.2884}$$

$$= .54$$

which is the same value we obtained using formula (14.2)

There are many cases where formula (14.1), or its identity, formula (14.2), should be used. It obviously should be used in cases where subjects have been paired, as in the example described. It should also be used if we test the same group of subjects twice and wish to determine whether the mean obtained on the second testing and that obtained from the first testing differ significantly. In this case also we shall have paired observations.

In general, if we have paired observations and there is *positive* correlation between the pairs, the standard error of the difference will be smaller than it will be for unpaired observations. The amount of reduction will depend upon the value of the correlation coefficient. If there is any advantage to be gained from pairing observations, the correlation coefficient must be sufficiently high to offset the loss in degrees of freedom involved in using formula (14.2). With 20 unpaired observations, we have $n_1 + n_2 - 2 = 18$ degrees of freedom available, and a t of 2.101 will be significant at the 5 per cent level. If we had paired these observations we would only have 9 degrees of freedom available, and a t of 2.262 would be required for significance at the 5 per cent level. Thus, for a statistical advantage to result from pairing observations, the correlation must be positive and sufficiently high to offset the fact that a larger value of t will be required for significance at the 5 per cent level.

Standard Error of the Difference for Equated Groups

Consider a variable X that is positively correlated with a variable Y. Assume that we take successive random samples of n values each from the X population and that we find the mean of each of these samples. Because of the correlation between X and Y, we know that, in general, samples that have a high mean on X will also have a high mean on Y, and that samples that have a low mean on X will also tend to have low means on Y. There will be, in other words, correlation between the means of the samples as well as between the individual measures. This situation is illustrated in Figure 14.1.

Suppose that we take a group of n subjects and that we have available a measure of the X variable for each subject. Suppose also that we divide these subjects into two groups in such a way that the means and standard deviations for the two groups on the X variable are comparable. It is not necessary that we have the same number of subjects in each group, that is,

n_1 does not have to be equal to n_2. Let us assume that we now assign one of the groups to Experimental Condition 1 and the other group to Experimental Condition 2. The performance of the subjects on variable Y is measured under the experimental conditions, and we wish to determine whether the means $\bar{Y}_1$ and $\bar{Y}_2$ differ significantly.

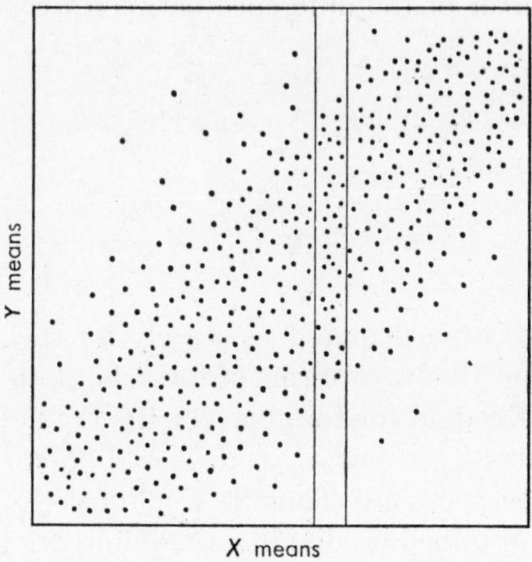

Fig. 14.1—Correlation table showing the relationship between $\bar{X}$ and $\bar{Y}$. The expected variation in Y means for samples with the same X mean is the variation within a single column of the correlation table.

Since our two groups of subjects have the same means on X, the random variation in the Y means may be expected to be represented by the variation within a single column of the correlation chart shown in Figure 14.1. In our previous discussion of correlation and regression,[1] we showed that the variation of the single measures of the Y variable for a constant value of X would be given by

$$s_{y \cdot x}^2 = \frac{\sum y^2 - \dfrac{(\sum xy)^2}{\sum x^2}}{n - 2} \tag{14.6}$$

Similarly, for a constant value of the mean of X, we may expect the variation in the Y means to be given by $1/n$th the variation of the individual measures. Thus the variance of the Y mean will be

$$s_{\bar{y} \cdot \bar{x}}^2 = \frac{s_{y \cdot x}^2}{n} \tag{14.7}$$

[1] See pages 127 and 157.

and the standard error of the Y mean will be the square root of formula (14.7) or

$$s_{\bar{y}\cdot\bar{x}} = \frac{s_{y\cdot x}}{\sqrt{n}} \tag{14.8}$$

The standard error of the difference between two Y means will then be given by

$$s_{(\bar{y}_1-\bar{y}_2)\cdot\bar{x}} = \sqrt{s_{\bar{y}_1\cdot\bar{x}}{}^2 + s_{\bar{y}_2\cdot\bar{x}}{}^2} \tag{14.9}$$

or

$$s_{(\bar{y}_1-\bar{y}_2)\cdot\bar{x}} = \sqrt{\frac{s_{y_1\cdot x}{}^2}{n_1} + \frac{s_{y_2\cdot x}{}^2}{n_2}} \tag{14.10}$$

where $s_{y_1\cdot x}{}^2$ and $s_{y_2\cdot x}{}^2$ are calculated separately for the two sets of n_1 and n_2 observations, respectively, in terms of formula (14.6).

The degrees of freedom for formula (14.10) are indicated by the fact that the two estimates $s_{y_1\cdot x}{}^2$ and $s_{y_2\cdot x}{}^2$ are based upon $n_1 - 2$ and $n_2 - 2$ degrees of freedom, respectively. Thus we would have $n_1 + n_2 - 4$ degrees of freedom for the t obtained by dividing the difference between the means $\bar{Y}_1$ and $\bar{Y}_2$ by the standard error of the difference given by formulas (14.9) or (14.10). The two additional degrees of freedom are lost because we have calculated two regression coefficients in determining the two residual sums of squares.

We may, however, assume that the regression of Y on X is the same for the two groups and that the two Y variances will not differ significantly. Thus we can pool the sums of squares for Y and use a single regression coefficient to obtain a residual sum of squares for Y. Let us denote this sum of squares by $\sum y._x{}^2$. Then

$$\sum y._x{}^2 = (\sum y_1{}^2 + \sum y_2{}^2) - \frac{(\sum xy)^2}{\sum x^2} \tag{14.11}$$

where $\sum y._x{}^2$ = the residual sum of squares
$\sum y_1{}^2$ = the sum of squares on the Y variable for Group 1
$\sum y_2{}^2$ = the sum of squares on the Y variable for Group 2
$\sum xy$ = the sum of products for the combined group of $n_1 + n_2$ subjects
$\sum x^2$ = the sum of squares on the X variable for the combined group of $n_1 + n_2$ subjects

Then the residual sum of squares, as defined by formula (14.11), will have $n_1 + n_2 - 3$ degrees of freedom. Dividing this sum of squares by the degrees of freedom, we obtain an estimate of the common residual variance. Thus

$$s_{y \cdot x}{}^2 = \frac{\sum y_{\cdot x}{}^2}{n_1 + n_2 - 3} \tag{14.12}$$

Substituting this common estimate for the two separate estimates of formula (14.10), we obtain for the standard error of the difference

$$s_{(\bar{y}_1 - \bar{y}_2) \cdot \bar{x}} = \sqrt{\frac{s_{y \cdot x}{}^2}{n_1} + \frac{s_{y \cdot x}{}^2}{n_2}} \tag{14.13}$$

where $s_{y \cdot x}{}^2$ is the estimate of the common residual variance. Formula (14.13) may be written directly in terms of the residual sum of squares defined by formula (14.11). Thus

$$s_{(\bar{y}_1 - \bar{y}_2) \cdot \bar{x}} = \sqrt{\left(\frac{\sum y_{\cdot x}{}^2}{n_1 + n_2 - 3}\right)\left(\frac{1}{n_1} + \frac{1}{n_2}\right)} \tag{14.14}$$

The development of formula (14.14) may seem quite complicated, but in terms of the actual calculations involved it is quite simple. For example, in Table 14.2 we show a group of 25 subjects who have been divided into Group 1 with 15 subjects and Group 2 with 10 subjects. Column (1) of the table shows the scores on the X variable used to equate the two groups. That the two groups are comparable on the X variable is indicated by the fact that $\bar{X}_1 = 4.20$ and $\bar{X}_2 = 4.20$. Calculations would also show that $s_x{}^2 = 100.4/14 = 7.17$ and that $s_{x_2}{}^2 = 67.6/9 = 7.51$.

In column (2) the scores of the two groups on the Y variable are given. We find that $\bar{Y}_1 = 110/15 = 7.33$ and that $\bar{Y}_2 = 51/10 = 5.10$. We wish to determine whether these two means differ significantly.

We first find

$$\sum y_1{}^2 = 934 - \frac{(110)^2}{15}$$

$$= 127.33$$

and

$$\sum y_2{}^2 = 329 - \frac{(51)^2}{10}$$

$$= 68.90$$

Table 14.2—Scores on an Equating Variable X and a Dependent Variable Y for a Group of 15 Subjects and a Group of 10 Subjects

	Group 1				
	(1) X_1	(2) Y_1	(3) X_1^2	(4) Y_1^2	(5) X_1Y_1
	6	10	36	100	60
	1	6	1	36	6
	1	3	1	9	3
	1	4	1	16	4
	6	9	36	81	54
	7	10	49	100	70
	2	3	4	9	6
	4	8	16	64	32
	8	11	64	121	88
	8	11	64	121	88
	1	6	1	36	6
	5	10	25	100	50
	7	10	49	100	70
	3	5	9	25	15
	3	4	9	16	12
$\sum$	63	110	365	934	564
	Group 2				
	X_2	Y_2	X_2^2	Y_2^2	X_2Y_2
	3	2	9	4	6
	1	4	1	16	4
	1	2	1	4	2
	7	7	49	49	49
	6	6	36	36	36
	3	2	9	4	6
	1	4	1	16	4
	5	6	25	36	30
	8	10	64	100	80
	7	8	49	64	56
$\sum$	42	51	244	329	273
$\sum$	105	161	609	1,263	837

For the combined groups, the product sum will be

$$\Sigma xy = 837 - \frac{(105)(161)}{25}$$

$$= 160.80$$

and the sum of squares for the X variable for the combined groups will be

$$\Sigma x^2 = 609 - \frac{(105)^2}{25}$$

$$= 168.00$$

It is of some importance to note at this time that if the two groups have exactly the same mean on the X variable, and we assume that this is the case when the groups have been equated on X, the sum of squares for the X variable, obtained above, will also be exactly equal to $\Sigma x_1{}^2 + \Sigma x_2{}^2 = 100.4 + 67.6 = 168.00$. We shall have more to say about this in later discussions of the analysis of variance.

Substituting in formula (14.11), with the values calculated, we obtain

$$\Sigma y._x{}^2 = (127.33 + 68.90) - \frac{(160.80)^2}{168.00}$$

$$= 196.23 - 153.91$$

$$= 42.32$$

Then, by means of formula (14.14), we obtain for the standard error of the difference

$$s_{(\bar{y}_1 - \bar{y}_2)\cdot\bar{x}} = \sqrt{\left(\frac{42.32}{15 + 10 - 3}\right)\left(\frac{1}{15} + \frac{1}{10}\right)}$$

$$= .3206$$

$$= .57$$

We may now test for the significance of the difference between $\bar{Y}_1$

and $\bar{Y}_2$. We find that

$$t = \frac{7.33 - 5.10}{.57}$$

$$= 3.91$$

Entering the t table with $n_1 + n_2 - 3 = 22$ degrees of freedom, we find that a value of 2.069 will be significant at the 5 per cent level and a value of 1.714 at the 5 per cent point.[2] If we had tested the null hypotheses $m_1 \leqq m_2$ or $m_1 = m_2$, they would be rejected.

■ The Sign Test for Paired Observations

Consider the case where we have paired observations, as in Table 14.3, but, for one reason or another, we do not feel justified in assuming that the values of X are normally distributed. If one group represents a control group and the other an experimental group we may still wish to determine whether the two groups differ in their performance as measured by X. In this instance we may apply the "sign test" of Dixon and Mood (1946).

We observe the differences $X_1 - X_2$ of the pairs of observations. If the difference is positive, we give a plus sign to that pair of observations and if the difference is negative, we give a minus sign. If we have values of $X_1 - X_2$ that are equal to 0, we assign a plus to half of them and a minus to the other half. For example, in Table 14.3, we have two values, $8 - 8$ and $7 - 7$, that are equal to 0. We have given the first of these a plus sign and the other a minus sign.

If there is no difference in the performance of the two groups of subjects, then the probability that $X_1 > X_2$ will be equal to the probability that $X_2 > X_1$ or 1/2. Thus, if this null hypothesis is true, we should expect the number of plus signs to be approximately equal to the number of minus signs for our pairs of observations. If we have too many plus or too many minus signs, we shall reject the null hypothesis.

The null hypothesis may be evaluated in terms of the binomial distribution $(p + q)^n$, where p is equal to .5, q is equal to .5, and n is equal to the number of pairs of observations.[3] However, if we have at least 10 pairs of observations, we may make an approximate test by first finding the

---

[2] The development of the test of significance for the case described is based upon a technique known as the analysis of covariance. This technique is not discussed in its broader applications in this text, but the interested reader may consult Edwards (1950a), Lindquist (1940), Fisher (1942), Snedecor (1946), or McNemar (1949).

[3] See pp. 219–221.

Table 14.3—The Sign Test for Paired Observations

(1) X_1	(2) X_2	(3) $X_1 - X_2$	(4) *Signs*
4	6	−2	−
1	2	−1	−
4	9	−5	−
7	4	3	+
8	8	0	+
8	5	3	+
7	7	0	−
9	8	1	+
9	4	5	+
9	6	3	+
9	5	4	+
1	4	−3	−
7	3	4	+
1	9	−8	−
4	1	3	+

mean and standard deviation of the binomial distribution as given by formula (11.4) and formula (11.6), respectively.

For the data of Table 14.3, with n equal to 15 and taking p equal to .5, we have

$$m = (15)(.5) = 7.5$$

and

$$\sigma = \sqrt{(15)(.5)(.5)} = 1.94$$

Then we may use formula (11.9) to obtain

$$z = \frac{X - m}{\sigma}$$

where X is the observed frequency of plus or minus signs, whichever is the larger. The null hypothesis will be rejected at the 5 per cent *level* if the obtained value of z is equal to or greater than 1.96.

Substituting in formula (11.9) with the values of X, m, and σ, we obtain

$$z = \frac{9 - 7.5}{1.94} = .77$$

Since the obtained z of .77 is not significant, the null hypothesis will be regarded as tenable, and we conclude that our two groups do not differ in their performance as measured by X.

Correction for Continuity

Whereas the binomial distribution is discrete, the normal distribution is continuous. We may obtain a better approximation of the desired probability if we treat the discrete frequency X of formula (11.9) as occupying an interval ranging .5 of a unit below and .5 of a unit above the observed value.[4] We would then substitute the lower limit of the interval for the observed value of X in formula (11.9). For the data at hand, this would mean substituting 8.5 for 9 and then finding z. Thus

$$z = \frac{8.5 - 7.5}{1.94} = .52$$

One-Tailed Tests

A one-tailed test of the null hypothesis that $P(X_1 > X_2) \leqq \frac{1}{2}$ may also be made.[5] If this hypothesis is rejected, the alternative hypothesis that $P(X_1 > X_2) > \frac{1}{2}$ would be accepted. Evidence against this null hypothesis will be provided only if the number of plus signs for the differences $X_1 - X_2$ exceeds the number of minus signs. Therefore, in order to reject the null hypothesis at the 5 per cent *point*, the number of plus signs must exceed the number of minus signs and the z obtained from formula (11.9) must be at least equal to 1.645.

Similarly, a one-tailed test of the null hypothesis that the $P(X_1 > X_2) \geqq \frac{1}{2}$ may also be made. Rejecting this null hypothesis, the alternative hypothesis that $P(X_1 > X_2) < \frac{1}{2}$ would be accepted. Evidence against the null hypothesis, in this instance, will be provided only if the number of minus signs exceeds the number of plus signs for the differences $X_1 - X_2$. Thus, in order to reject the null hypothesis at the 5 per cent *point*, the number of minus signs must exceed the number of plus signs and the value of z obtained from formula (11.9) must be at least equal to 1.645.

We should perhaps caution again that one-tailed tests of significance are proper only if the experimenter has an a priori hypothesis concerning the outcome of the experiment. It would obviously not be legitimate to capitalize upon chance factors by first examining the data and then deciding that a one-tailed test was to be made.

---

[4] See page 224.

[5] Expressed in words, this null hypothesis states that the probability that X_1 exceeds X_2 is less than or equal to $\frac{1}{2}$.

We should also state that regardless of whether a one- or two-tailed test is to be made, the correction for continuity should be applied before calculating z. It may be noted, in terms of the above discussion, that the correction for continuity operates in such a way as to reduce the absolute value of the deviation $X - m$ by .5.

■ The Rank Test for Paired Observations

The data of Table 14.3 may be used to illustrate another distribution-free test that can be used with paired observations.[6] In columns (1) and (2) of Table 14.4 we repeat the X_1 and X_2 observations of Table 14.3. In column (3) of Table 14.4, we give the differences $X_1 - X_2$. We now rank these differences in terms of their absolute values, that is, without regard to their signs. These ranks are shown in column (4) of the table. In column (5) we have entered the ranks from column (4) corresponding to positive values of $X_1 - X_2$, and in column (6) we have entered the ranks corresponding to negative values of $X_1 - X_2$.

Table 14.4—The Rank Test for Paired Observations

(1) X_1	(2) X_2	(3) $X_1 - X_2$	(4) *Ranks*	(5) *Ranks* (+)	(6) *Ranks* (−)
4	6	−2	11		11
1	2	−1	12.5		12.5
4	9	−5	2.5		2.5
7	4	3	8	8	
8	8	0	14.5	14.5	
8	5	3	8	8	
7	7	0	14.5		14.5
9	8	1	12.5	12.5	
9	4	5	2.5	2.5	
9	6	3	8	8	
9	5	4	4.5	4.5	
1	4	−3	8		8
7	3	4	4.5	4.5	
1	9	−8	1		1
4	1	3	8	8	
Σ				70.5	49.5

[6] A distribution-free test is one that does not require any assumption concerning the form of the distribution of the measurements. In the t test, for example, we assume that the measures are from a normally distributed population. The sign test and the rank test, described in this section, do not involve this assumption.

It may be observed that we have two values of $X_1 - X_2$ equal to 0, and that in column (4) these two 0's have been given the rank 14.5 or the average of the ranks 14 and 15, for which they are tied. We have then assigned the rank for one of these 0's to the column of positive ranks and the other to the column of negative ranks. For any other *even* number of 0 differences, we would also give half of the corresponding ranks to the column of positive ranks and half to the column of negative ranks. If we had only one 0, then it would have the rank of 15 and, under this circumstance, we would have given half of this value to the positive ranks and half to the negative ranks. We would, in other words, have entered 7.5 in both column (5) and column (6). Similarly, if we had three or any other *odd* number of 0 differences, we would find the sum of the ranks for these 0 differences and give half of this sum to the column of positive ranks and half to the column of negative ranks.[7]

We may let the sum of ranks corresponding to positive values of $X_1 - X_2$ be T_1 and the sum of ranks corresponding to negative values of $X_1 - X_2$ be T_2. Then it should be clear that

$$T_1 + T_2 = \frac{n(n+1)}{2} \tag{14.15}$$

where n is the number of pairs of differences.[8]

Under the null hypothesis that the two groups of X_1 and X_2 observations are from a common population, the expectation is that T_1 will be equal to T_2 so that the average or expected total for either T_1 or T_2 will be

$$\bar{T} = \frac{n(n+1)}{4} \tag{14.16}$$

with standard deviation equal to[9]

$$\sigma = \sqrt{\frac{(2n+1)\bar{T}}{6}} \tag{14.17}$$

---

[7] For the data of Table 14.4, if we had three 0 differences, they would each be given 14 or the average of ranks 13, 14, and 15. Since the sum of ranks for these three 0 differences would be 42, we would enter 42/2 or 21 in both the column of positive ranks and the column of negative ranks.

[8] See p. 1 3.

[9] I am indebted to Lincoln Moses for calling my attention to an error in Wilcoxon's (1947) original formula for σ. This error was corrected in a later publication by Wilcoxon (1949).

Wilcoxon (1947) has pointed out that if the null hypothesis is true, and if n is at least 8, then the distribution of rank totals is sufficiently close to normal that we may make use of the table of the normal curve for our test of significance. Thus we may define

$$z = \frac{T_1 - \bar{T}}{\sigma} \tag{14.18}$$

where z = a normal deviate

T_1 = the sum of rank totals for the positive values of $X_1 - X_2$

$\bar{T}$ = the expected rank total as given by formula (14.16)

σ = the standard deviation of the rank total as given by formula (14.17)

For the data of Table 14.4, we have T_1 equal to 70.5 and T_2 equal to 49.5. Then, substituting in formula (14.16) and formula (14.17), we obtain

$$\bar{T} = \frac{(15)(16)}{4} = 60$$

and

$$\sigma = \sqrt{\frac{(30 + 1)(60)}{6}} = \sqrt{310} = 17.61$$

If we substitute in formula (14.18) with the values of T_1, $\bar{T}$, and σ, and make a two-tailed test of significance, we should be prepared to reject the null hypothesis at the 5 per cent level if we obtain an absolute value of z equal to or greater than 1.96. Substituting in formula (14.18), we obtain

$$z = \frac{70.5 - 60}{17.61} = .60$$

Since our observed value is not equal to or greater than 1.96, we may regard the null hypothesis as tenable for the data of Table 14.4.

It should be obvious that we could have made our test of significance using T_2 instead of T_1. In this instance we would have obtained

$$z = \frac{49.5 - 60}{17.61} = -.60$$

which is equal in absolute value to the z we obtained using T_1 in the test. Under the null hypothesis the distribution of the rank totals T_1 and T_2

will be symmetrical about the expected value $\bar{T}$, and the test of significance of formula (14.18) can be made using either T_1 or T_2.

Correction for Continuity

The distribution of rank totals is discrete, whereas the normal distribution is continuous. Therefore, we may obtain a better approximation of the desired probability if we first make a correction for continuity in the numerator of formula (14.18) before calculating z. This correction is made by reducing the *absolute value* of the deviation $T_1 - \bar{T}$ or $T_2 - \bar{T}$ by .5. Thus, making a continuity correction and using T_1 in the test of significance, we would have

$$z = \frac{|70.5 - 60| - .5}{17.61} = \frac{10}{17.61} = .57$$

and using T_2 and making a correction for continuity would give

$$z = \frac{|49.5 - 60| - .5}{17.61} = \frac{-10}{17.61} = -.57$$

Table of Significant Values of the Rank Totals

Wilcoxon (1945) has published a table for determining the significance of either T_1 or T_2, whichever is the smaller, for values of n from 7 to 16. The correspondence between his tabled values and those obtained from the normal-curve approximation are quite good, and there seems to be no practical reason for not using the normal-curve approximation. This is particularly true at the 5 per cent level of significance. For example, when n is equal to 8, Wilcoxon states that the probability of obtaining a value of T_1 or T_2, whichever is the smaller, equal to or less than 4 is .055. Let us see how well the normal curve will approximate this probability.

Substituting in formula (14.16) and formula (14.17) with n equal to 8, we obtain

$$\bar{T} = \frac{(8)(9)}{4} = 18$$

and

$$\sigma = \sqrt{\frac{(16 + 1)(18)}{6}} = \sqrt{51} = 7.14$$

Then, making a correction for continuity and solving formula (14.18) for

z, with $T_1 = 4$, $\bar{T} = 18$, and $\sigma = 7.14$, we get

$$z = \frac{|4 - 18| - .5}{7.14} = -1.89$$

From the table of the normal curve, we see that the area falling in the left tail beyond $z = -1.89$ is .0294. Since we want the probability corresponding to a two-tailed test of significance, we have $(2)(.0294) = .0588$. The corresponding probability tabled by Wilcoxon is .055. In general, it can be said that the agreement between the probabilities obtained by the normal-curve approximation and those tabled by Wilcoxon is quite good at the 5 per cent level for all values of n equal to or greater than 8.

One-Tailed Tests

For the two-tailed test of significance, the null hypothesis that we have tested is that $T_1 = T_2 = \bar{T}$, or that $T_1 = \bar{T}$. If this hypothesis is rejected, we shall accept the alternative hypothesis that $T_1 \neq \bar{T}$. The acceptance of this alternative implies that either $T_1 > T_2$ or that $T_1 < T_2$. Under some circumstances, we may wish to test the null hypothesis that $T_1 \leqq \bar{T}$. Evidence against this null hypothesis will be available only if $T_1 > \bar{T}$. If the probability of a Type I error is to be .05, this null hypothesis will be rejected only if $T_1 - \bar{T}$ results in a value of z equal to or greater than 1.645. If we reject this null hypothesis, then we shall accept the alternative hypothesis that $T_1 > \bar{T}$, and this, in turn, implies that $T_1 > T_2$.

Similarly, if we test the null hypothesis that $T_1 \geqq \bar{T}$, evidence against this hypothesis will be available only if $T_1 < \bar{T}$. If the probability of a Type I error is to be .05, this hypothesis will be rejected only if the obtained value of z is numerically equal to or greater than 1.645 and is also *negative* in sign. If we reject this null hypothesis we shall accept the alternative that $T_1 < \bar{T}$, and this, in turn, implies that $T_1 < T_2$.

■ The Rank Test and the Sign Test

It may sometimes be true that the null hypothesis tested by means of Wilcoxon's rank-order test will be rejected, whereas the null hypothesis tested in terms of the sign test, discussed earlier in this chapter, will not result in the rejection of the null hypothesis. If such discrepancies occur, they can be accounted for by the fact that the rank-order test is sensitive to the magnitude of the differences $X_1 - X_2$, whereas the sign test takes into account only the direction of the difference. For the sign test, all positive and all negative differences contribute equally, regardless of their magnitude.

■ EXAMPLES

14.1—One of the experiments in a series by Ansbacher (1944) was concerned with judgments of apparent movement. Subjects judged the apparent length of a 13-centimeter arc at various speeds of rotation. The data given below are for judgments of apparent length at zero speed and at 1 revolution per second. Test the hypothesis that $m_1 = m_2$.

Subject	*Rotation Speeds in Revolutions per Second*	
	0	1
1	10.0	9.3
2	12.3	9.1
3	11.3	8.7
4	10.3	8.1
5	8.9	6.7
6	10.0	7.7
7	9.9	8.4
8	10.5	8.4

14.2—Subjects were given an attitude test before and after viewing a motion picture designed to influence their attitudes favorably. A high score indicates a favorable attitude, and a low score an unfavorable attitude. Can we conclude that the motion picture resulted in a significant mean change in attitude?

Subject	*Pretest*	*Posttest*
1	2.6	2.5
2	4.6	5.7
3	8.9	9.3
4	5.5	6.7
5	1.9	1.5
6	6.2	7.8
7	4.6	4.7
8	5.6	5.9
9	6.9	7.3
10	6.6	7.0

14.3—A study by Bugelski (1942) was concerned with interference of recall of responses to stimuli after learning of new responses. The data given are for the per cent of original trials required for relearning where interference was expected to be present and where it was not. Can we conclude that the mean percentage of trials for relearning is greater for the interference condition than for the control condition?

Subject	*Control Condition*	*Interference Condition*
1	.706	.744
2	.862	.585
3	.711	.704
4	.554	.850
5	.556	.591
6	.553	.750
7	.700	1.000
8	1.323	1.345
9	.848	1.250
10	.967	1.000
11	.900	.711
12	.576	1.000
13	.750	1.154
14	.512	.778
15	.950	1.190
16	1.100	.689
17	.950	.895
18	.622	1.379
19	.679	.816
20	.759	.723

14.4—In a study by Thomas and Young (1942) subjects were required to reproduce a pattern of stimulation in successive practice periods. The data given below are for Trials I and II. Use the sign test to determine whether the number of correct reproductions differed significantly from Trial I to Trial II. Use the correction for continuity in making your test.

Subject	Trial I	Trial II
I	10	18
E	7	8
K	6	11
J	8	9
Q	7	7
S	6	9
R	10	12
B	5	8
U	5	6
D	3	6
P	2	8
O	7	10
H	4	7
N	3	6
V	4	4
M	2	5
A	4	3
G	4	6
F	5	8
L	3	2
T	4	2
C	0	2

14.5—The reaction time of mental patients to verbal questions was studied before and after the patients had received electroshock treatments. Can we conclude that the mean reaction time before electroshock does not differ significantly from the mean reaction time after shock? Data are from Janis and Astrachan (1951).

Patient	Before Electroshock	After Electroshock
1	12.75	23.71
2	8.24	7.50
3	3.26	12.95
4	9.07	12.56
5	6.22	14.14
6	8.20	9.90
7	7.11	8.95
8	4.52	6.32
9	6.12	5.42

14.6—A group of 15 and a group of 10 subjects were equated on an X variable. The two groups were then tested under different experimental conditions with Y measures as the dependent variable. Determine whether $\bar{Y}_1$ and $\bar{Y}_2$ differ significantly, using the standard error of the difference as given by formula (14.13).

Group 1		*Group 2*	
X	Y	X	Y
10	12	14	16
10	13	15	18
14	18	12	14
12	18	8	12
8	14	10	10
15	19	13	14
15	19	14	15
11	17	8	10
9	11	9	12
14	18	9	10
13	17		
8	12		
8	11		
10	14		
11	18		

14.7—An experiment involves 8 *pairs* of subjects. One group is tested under Experimental Condition A and the other under Experimental Condition B. The results are given below. Use the two-tailed rank test with correction for continuity to determine whether the two groups of observations differ.

A	*B*
20	15
12	8
25	32
18	15
19	8
23	7
16	10
10	9

CHAPTER FIFTEEN

The Significance of Correlation and Regression Coefficients

When n is large and the population value of the correlation coefficient is not excessively high, the sampling distribution of the correlation coefficient is approximately normal in form. When, however, n is small and the correlation in the population is high, say .80 or $-.80$, the sampling distribution of the correlation coefficient is markedly skew. One reason for this is that we have placed a limitation on one end of the sampling distribution. If the population value is .80, for example, then sample values could vary from -1.00 to 1.00, but they could exceed the population value by not more than .20 at one end of the distribution, whereas in the opposite direction they could deviate by as much as 1.80 from the population value.

If, however, n is as large as 300, then the restriction of unity at one end of the scale would no longer be an important determining factor in the sampling distribution. Sample values of the correlation coefficient based upon an n of 300 observations, even when drawn from a population in which the correlation is as high as .80, would not tend to range more than .05 on each side of the population value. But, if the population value was as high as .96, or higher, the restriction would again be a factor to consider.

Even when the population correlation is 0, the sampling distribution of the correlation coefficient for small samples departs slightly from normality. Figure 15.1 shows the distribution for samples of 8 pairs of observations that were drawn from a population where the correlation was 0 and from a population where the correlation was .80. The symbol that appears in the figure is *rho,* and we shall use this symbol to represent the population correlation.

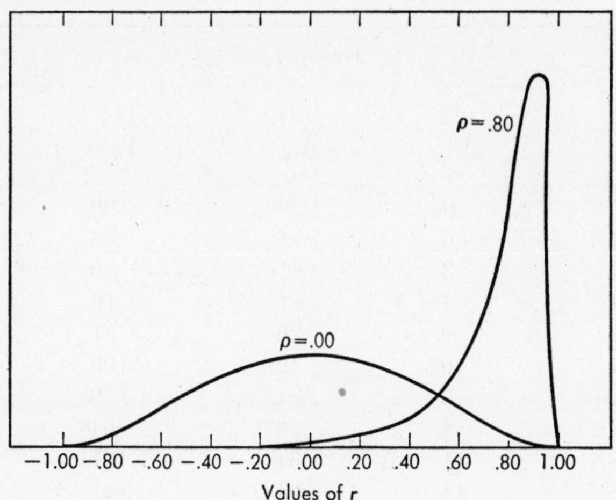

Fig. 15.1—Sampling distributions of the correlation coefficient for samples of eight pairs of observations drawn from two populations having the indicated values of ρ.

Testing the Hypothesis That the Population Correlation Is Zero

In Table 15.1 we repeat the data of Table 14.2. We shall use these data to illustrate some of the tests of significance that may be applied to correlation coefficients and regression coefficients.

Using formula (8.4), we find that the correlation coefficient for the combined group of $n_1 + n_2 = n$ subjects will be given by

$$r = \frac{837 - \dfrac{(105)(161)}{25}}{\sqrt{\left(609 - \dfrac{(105)^2}{25}\right)\left(1{,}263 - \dfrac{(161)^2}{25}\right)}}$$

$$= \frac{160.80}{\sqrt{(168.00)(226.16)}}$$

$$= .825$$

One hypothesis that we are often interested in testing, once we have

Table 15.1—Scores on an Independent Variable X and a Dependent Variable Y for a Group of 15 Subjects and a Group of 10 Subjects (Data Repeated from Table 14.2)

	Group 1				
	(1) X_1	(2) Y_1	(3) X_1^2	(4) Y_1^2	(5) X_1Y_1
	6	10	36	100	60
	1	6	1	36	6
	1	3	1	9	3
	1	4	1	16	4
	6	9	36	81	54
	7	10	49	100	70
	2	3	4	9	6
	4	8	16	64	32
	8	11	64	121	88
	8	11	64	121	88
	1	6	1	36	6
	5	10	25	100	50
	7	10	49	100	70
	3	5	9	25	15
	3	4	9	16	12
Σ	63	110	365	934	564
	Group 2				
	X_2	Y_2	X_2^2	Y_2^2	X_2Y_2
	3	2	9	4	6
	1	4	1	16	4
	1	2	1	4	2
	7	7	49	49	49
	6	6	36	36	36
	3	2	9	4	6
	1	4	1	16	4
	5	6	25	36	30
	8	10	64	100	80
	7	8	49	64	56
Σ	42	51	244	329	273
Σ	105	161	609	1,263	837

obtained a given value of r, is the hypothesis that the population correlation ρ is 0. If we test this null hypothesis, assuming that our sample value is the result of sampling variation or chance, then we may calculate

$$t = \frac{r}{\sqrt{1 - r^2}} \sqrt{n - 2} \tag{15.1}$$

where t = the t ratio with $n - 2$ degrees of freedom
r = the observed sample value of the correlation coefficient
n = the number of pairs of observations in the sample

The t obtained from formula (15.1) is distributed in accordance with the tabled values of t with degrees of freedom equal to $n - 2$, when the null hypothesis of zero correlation in the population is true. In other words, once we have obtained the value of t from the formula above, we may enter the t table to determine whether it is significant at the 5 or 1 per cent levels.[1]

For the data of Table 15.1 we have found that the sample value of r is .825. Substituting in formula (15.1), we obtain

$$t = \frac{.825}{\sqrt{1 - (.825)^2}} \sqrt{25 - 2}$$

$$= \left(\frac{.825}{.565}\right) 4.796$$

$$= 7.00$$

Entering the t table with 23 degrees of freedom, we find that a t of 2.807 will be significant at the 1 per cent level. Our obtained value of t is 7.00, and is, therefore, highly significant. We reject the hypothesis that $\rho = 0$ and accept the alternative hypothesis that $\rho \neq 0$. This hypothesis in turn implies that *either* $\rho > 0$ *or* that $\rho < 0$.

The Use of Table VI

There is a much simpler method for finding out whether an observed value of r is sufficiently large to cause us to reject the hypothesis that $\rho = 0$. Table VI, in the Appendix, gives the value of r that would be needed to meet the requirements of significance at the .10, .05, .02, and .01 *levels of significance*, that is, for a two-tailed test, for samples of various sizes.

---

[1] Table V, in the Appendix.

Table VI is entered with degrees of freedom equal to $n - 2$, where n is the number of pairs of observations. If we enter the table with the 23 degrees of freedom available for our sample value of r of .82, we find that r would need to be .505 to be significant at the 1 per cent level, that is, in order to reject the hypothesis that $\rho = 0$, with the probability of a Type I error of .01.

For the data of Table 15.1, we have reason to believe that the correlation should be positive, and we might wish to test the null hypothesis that $\rho \leqq 0$. If this hypothesis is tested and rejected, we shall accept the alternative hypothesis that $\rho > 0$. If the probability of a Type I error for the test of this null hypothesis is to be .05, then we will reject the hypothesis if the observed value of r equals or exceeds the value in Table VI under the column heading of .10, for the degrees of freedom available. For 23 degrees of freedom, for example, the hypothesis would be rejected if r equals or exceeds .337. Similarly, if we test the null hypothesis that $\rho \geqq 0$, then this hypothesis would be rejected if we obtained an r of $-.337$, if the probability of a Type I error is to be .05.

Table VI is similar to the t table in that it gives the *absolute* value of r that will be regarded as significant in terms of the probabilities given by the column headings. The tabled values are thus those corresponding to a two-tailed test of significance and represent levels of significance. If a one-tailed test of significance is to be made, the value of r significant at the 5 per cent *point* will be that given under the column heading .10, that is, at the 10 per cent *level.*

It should be evident from Table VI that small r's may be significant when they are based upon a large n, whereas large values of r may not be significant when based upon a small number of observations. An r of .55 based upon 10 pairs of observations, for example, may be expected to occur quite frequently as a result of sampling variation, even when there is no correlation in the population from which the sample was drawn. The larger the value of n, on the other hand, the smaller the value the observed correlation coefficient need be in order to consider the hypothesis of zero correlation untenable.

■ Significance of the Difference between Two Correlation Coefficients

If we compute the correlation coefficient separately for the two groups of observations in Table 15.1, we have for Group 1

$$r_1 = \frac{564 - \dfrac{(63)(110)}{15}}{\sqrt{\left(365 - \dfrac{(63)^2}{15}\right)\left(934 - \dfrac{(110)^2}{15}\right)}}$$

$$= \frac{102}{\sqrt{(100.40)(127.33)}}$$

$$= .90$$

and for Group 2 we have

$$r_2 = \frac{273 - \frac{(42)(51)}{10}}{\sqrt{\left(244 - \frac{(42)^2}{10}\right)\left(329 - \frac{(51)^2}{10}\right)}}$$

$$= \frac{58.80}{\sqrt{(67.60)(68.90)}}$$

$$= .86$$

The z' Transformation

We may now ask the question whether r_1 and r_2 differ significantly, that is, we may test the null hypothesis that $\rho_1 = \rho_2$. For reasons pointed out earlier, the sampling distribution of these correlation coefficients will not be normal; consequently, the sampling distribution of the differences will not be normal. Fisher (1921), however, has shown that if we make the transformation

$$z' = \tfrac{1}{2}[\log_e (1 + r) - \log_e (1 - r)] \tag{15.2}$$

then z' will be distributed in approximately normal form with standard error equal to

$$\sigma_{z}' = \frac{1}{\sqrt{n - 3}} \tag{15.3}$$

where n is the number of pairs of observations.

The standard error of the difference between two independent values of z' will then be given by

$$\sigma_{z_1' - z_2'} = \sqrt{\sigma_{z_1'}{}^2 + \sigma_{z_2'}{}^2}$$

$$= \sqrt{\frac{1}{n_1 - 3} + \frac{1}{n_2 - 3}} \tag{15.4}$$

Table VII, in the Appendix, shows the values of z' corresponding to given values of r. We enter the table with the observed value of r and obtain the value of z', as determined by formula (15.2), without the necessity of making the calculations. For $r_1 = .90$, for example, we find that $z_1' = 1.472$. And for $r_2 = .86$, we find that $z_2' = 1.293$.

Then the standard error of the difference between these two z' values, as determined by formula (15.4), will be

$$\sigma_{z_1'-z_2'} = \sqrt{\frac{1}{15-3} + \frac{1}{10-3}}$$

$$= \sqrt{.0833 + .1429}$$

$$= \sqrt{.2262}$$

$$= .48$$

If we divide the observed difference between the two z' values by the standard error of the difference, we will obtain a normal deviate, which may be evaluated by reference to the table of the normal curve. Thus

$$z = \frac{z_1' - z_2'}{\sigma_{z_1'-z_2'}} \tag{15.5}$$

For the present example, we obtain

$$z = \frac{1.472 - 1.293}{.48}$$

$$= .37$$

Entering the table of the normal curve with z equal to .37, we find that the probability of obtaining an absolute value of z equal to or greater than this is about .71, when the null hypothesis that $\rho_1 = \rho_2$ is true. We thus regard the null hypothesis as tenable and conclude that our two observed values of z' do not differ significantly and, therefore, that our two observed values of the correlation coefficient do not differ significantly.

You may have noticed that, since we made a two-tailed test of significance, appropriate to the null hypothesis $\rho_1 = \rho_2$, we took the area in *both* tails of the normal distribution, that is, beyond $z = \pm.37$, into account in arriving at our probability. One-tailed tests of significance appropriate to testing the null hypotheses that $\rho_1 \geqq \rho_2$ and that $\rho_1 \leqq \rho_2$ may also be made in terms of formula (15.5). Our procedure in this instance would be the same as that previously described in connection with one-tailed tests of significance of the difference between two means, and it will not be repeated here.[2]

Fiducial Limits for the Correlation Coefficients

If we have but a single value of the correlation coefficient, then we may use the z' transformation to establish the fiducial limits of the parameter, at some defined significance level, in the same manner in which we did this in the case of the mean. The lower fiducial limit $\bar{z}_1'$ and the upper fiducial limit $\bar{z}_2'$, at the 5 per cent level, for example, will be given by

$$\bar{z}_1' = z_r' - 1.96\sigma_{z_r'} \tag{15.6}$$

$$\bar{z}_2' = z_r' + 1.96\sigma_{z_r'} \tag{15.7}$$

where z_r' is the value of z' corresponding to the sample value of r, and $\sigma_{z_r'}$ is the standard error of z_r' as determined from formula (15.3). Having found the fiducial limits $\bar{z}_1'$ and $\bar{z}_2'$, we may express these limits in terms of the correlation coefficient by reference to Table VII. The interpretation to be placed upon these limits is similar to that previously described in connection with the fiducial limits for the mean.[3]

Testing Other Null Hypotheses

If we wish to make a one-tailed test of significance, appropriate to the null hypothesis that ρ is equal to or greater than some specified value or the null hypothesis that ρ is equal to or less than some specified value, we may do this also in terms of the z' transformation. For example, we might wish to test the null hypothesis that $\rho \leqq .85$. If this hypothesis is rejected, we shall accept the alternative that $\rho > .85$. Then

$$z = \frac{z_r' - z_\rho'}{\sigma_{z_r'}} \tag{15.8}$$

where z = a normal deviate
z_r' = the z' value for the observed correlation coefficient

---

[2] See page 258.
[3] See page 241.

$z_\rho{}' =$ the z' value for the hypothetical population value
$\sigma_{z_r}{}' =$ the standard error of $z_r{}'$ as given by formula (15.3)

The value of z obtained from formula (15.8) may be evaluated in terms of the table of the normal curve, with due consideration being given to the directional nature of the null hypothesis tested.

Significance of the Regression Coefficient

If we have found a regression coefficient b_{yx}, we may be interested in determining whether this value differs significantly from zero, that is, we may wish to test the hypothesis that population parameter is zero. We shall use the symbol β_{yx} to represent the population regression coefficient of Y on X. The standard error of the regression coefficient will be given by

$$s_{b_{yx}} = \frac{s_{y \cdot x}}{\sqrt{\sum x^2}} \tag{15.9}$$

where $s_{b_{yx}} =$ the standard error of the regression coefficient b_{yx}
$s_{y \cdot x} =$ the standard error of estimate as given by formula (7.20)
$\sum x^2 =$ the sum of squares for the X variable

For the data of Table 15.1, we find that for the combined group of $n_1 + n_2 = n$ subjects, $s_{y \cdot x}$ will be[4]

$$s_{y \cdot x} = \sqrt{\frac{226.16 - \dfrac{(160.80)^2}{168.00}}{25 - 2}}$$

$$= \sqrt{\frac{72.25}{23}}$$

$$= 1.772$$

and therefore $s_{b_{yx}}$ will be equal to

$$s_{b_{yx}} = \frac{1.772}{\sqrt{168.00}} = \frac{1.772}{12.961} = .137$$

[4] Using formulas (7.18) and (7.20) and the values found previously on page 301.

The regression coefficient b_{yx} for the combined group of n subjects may be obtained from formula (7.12). Thus, using the values previously calculated for $\sum xy$ and $\sum x^2$, we have

$$b_{yx} = \frac{\sum xy}{\sum x^2}$$

$$= \frac{160.80}{168.00}$$

$$= .957$$

If we test the null hypothesis that $\beta_{yx} = 0$, that is, that the population regression coefficient is zero, then we shall have

$$t = \frac{b_{yx} - \beta_{yx}}{s_{b_{yx}}} \tag{15.10}$$

$$= \frac{.957 - 0}{.137}$$

$$= 6.99$$

with $n - 2$ degrees of freedom.

Entering the t table with $n - 2 = 23$ degrees of freedom, we find that a value of 2.807 will be required for significance at the 1 per cent level. Since our obtained t is equal to 6.99, we reject the hypothesis of zero regression and accept the alternative hypothesis that $\beta_{yx} \neq 0$.

In the present example, since our expectation was a positive correlation coefficient, we should also expect a positive regression coefficient. Thus the null hypothesis that we would probably be interested in is that $\beta_{yx} \leqq 0$. If we reject this hypothesis, we shall accept the alternative hypothesis that $\beta_{yx} > 0$. This hypothesis would be rejected, with a probability of a Type I error of .05 or less, if we obtained a t equal to or greater than 1.714.

It may be observed that the t obtained from formula (15.10) is 6.99 and that this value is equal, within rounding errors, to the t of 7.00 that we obtained from formula (15.1) in testing the null hypothesis of zero correlation for the same data. The test of the null hypothesis that $\beta_{yx} = 0$, as given by formula (15.10), is equivalent to testing the null hypothesis that $\rho = 0$, as given by formula (15.1). Similarly, the t test of formula (15.1) for the null hypotheses $\rho \leqq 0$ and $\rho \geqq 0$ is equivalent to testing the corresponding null hypotheses $\beta_{yx} \leqq 0$ and $\beta_{yx} \geqq 0$, respectively. For all of these tests, formulas (15.10) and (15.1) will give identical values of t, within the limits of rounding errors which may be present.

Formula (15.10), however, can also be used to test additional null hypotheses about the population regression coefficient, whereas formula (15.1) is limited to the cases specified above. For example, we could substitute any hypothetical value for β_{yx} in formula (15.10) and determine whether the sample value b_{yx} deviates significantly from this hypothetical value. Thus we could test the null hypothesis that $\beta_{yx} \geqq 2.00$ in terms of formula (15.10). As we have seen, however, if we wish to test the hypothesis that the population correlation is equal to or greater than, say, .85, we must make use of the z' transformation. No such transformation is needed in testing hypotheses about the population regression coefficient.

Significance of the Difference between Two Regression Coefficients

In making a test of the significance of the difference between $\bar{Y}_1$ and $\bar{Y}_2$ for the data of Table 14.2, which we have reproduced in Table 15.1, we assumed that the regression of Y on X for the two groups was essentially the same. If we now test the hypothesis that $\beta_{y_1x} = \beta_{y_2x}$, we can determine whether or not b_{y_1x} and b_{y_2x} differ significantly.

We assume homogeneity of the residual variance for the two groups on the Y variable and obtain as an estimate of the common residual variance

$$s_{y.x}^2 = \frac{\left(\sum y_1^2 - \frac{(\sum x_1y_1)^2}{\sum x_1^2}\right) + \left(\sum y_2^2 - \frac{(\sum x_2y_2)^2}{\sum x_2^2}\right)}{n_1 + n_2 - 4} \tag{15.11}$$

$$= \frac{\left(127.33 - \frac{(102)^2}{100.4}\right) + \left(68.90 - \frac{(58.80)^2}{67.60}\right)}{15 + 10 - 4}$$

$$= \frac{23.70 + 17.75}{21}$$

$$= \frac{41.45}{21}$$

$$= 1.9738$$

and $$s_{y.x} = \sqrt{1.9738} = 1.40$$

The standard error of b_{y_1x} and b_{y_2x} will be given by formula (15.9). Using the value of $s_{y.x}$ obtained above in the numerator of formula (15.9), we get

$$s_{b_{y_1x}} = \frac{1.40}{\sqrt{100.40}} = \frac{1.40}{10.02} = .140$$

and $$s_{b_{y_2x}} = \frac{1.40}{\sqrt{67.60}} = \frac{1.40}{8.22} = .170$$

The standard error of the difference between b_{y_1x} and b_{y_2x} will be given by

$$s_{b_1-b_2} = \sqrt{s_{b_{y_1x}}{}^2 + s_{b_{y_2x}}{}^2} \tag{15.12}$$

$$= \sqrt{(.140)^2 + (.170)^2}$$

$$= \sqrt{.0196 + .0289}$$

$$= \sqrt{.0485}$$

$$= .22$$

Then we may test the significance of the difference between b_{y_1x} and b_{y_2x} by calculating

$$t = \frac{b_{y_1x} - b_{y_2x}}{s_{b_1-b}} \tag{15.13}$$

with $n_1 + n_2 - 4$ degrees of freedom.

For the data of Table 15.1, using formula (7.12), we have

$$b_{y_1x} = \frac{102.0}{100.4} = 1.02$$

and $$b_{y_2x} = \frac{58.8}{67.6} = .87$$

Then substituting in formula (15.13)

$$t = \frac{1.02 - .87}{.22}$$

$$= \frac{.15}{.22}$$

$$= .68$$

The t obtained from formula (15.13) may be evaluated by entering the t table with $n_1 + n_2 - 4 = 21$ degrees of freedom. For the two-tailed test of significance of the null hypothesis that $\beta_{y_1x} = \beta_{y_2x}$, a t of 2.080 would be required at the 5 per cent level of significance. Since our observed value of t is only .68, we regard the null hypothesis as tenable. We can say that the values of b_{y_1x} and b_{y_2x} do not differ sufficiently to result in our rejection of the null hypothesis.

As in the case of means and correlation coefficients, we may also, in particular cases, wish to test the null hypothesis that $\beta_{y_1x} \leqq \beta_{y_2x}$ or the null hypothesis that $\beta_{y_1x} \geqq \beta_{y_2x}$. If the test of these hypotheses is to be made in such a way that the probability of a Type I error is .05 or less, then we should make one-tailed tests of significance. The values of t significant at the 5 per cent *point*, as we have mentioned before, will be given in the column of the t table headed .10.

The t test of formula (15.13) may be useful in a variety of experiments. Let us suppose that we have done an experiment for which we have available two values of the regression coefficient b_{yx}. For example, we may have related some variable Y to X for two different groups of subjects. We assume that both relationships are linear, but the two regression coefficients are not necessarily the same. If X consisted of trials and Y consisted of some measure of performance, the regression coefficients would give the slopes of the lines relating performance to trials for each group and would indicate the change in performance with trials. We wish to determine whether the rate of change in the two groups is significantly different. We can make this test by determining whether the two regression coefficients differ significantly.

Homogeneity of Regression and the Test of Significance for the Difference between $\bar{Y}_1$ and $\bar{Y}_2$

In the previous chapter we tested the significance of the difference between $\bar{Y}_1 = 7.33$ and $\bar{Y}_2 = 5.10$ for the data of Table 15.1. In using formula (14.13) or formula (14.14) for the standard error of the difference between the means, we assumed that the regression of Y on X for the two groups was the same, within the limits of sampling error. We therefore used only the single regression coefficient, based upon the combined set of n_1 and n_2 observations, in calculating the residual sum of squares of formula (14.11). We thus had $(n_1 - 1) + (n_2 - 1) - 1 = n_1 + n_2 - 3$ degrees of freedom for our test of significance. The additional degree of freedom was lost because of our use of the regression coefficient $b_{yx} = \frac{160.80}{168.00} = .957$. The test of significance we have made in this chapter concerning the difference between b_{y_1x} and b_{y_2x} indicates that we were justified in using the single regression coefficient.

However, if we had found a significant difference between b_{y_1x} and b_{y_2x}, the test of significance for the difference between the means $\bar{Y}_1$ and $\bar{Y}_2$ would properly be made using formula (14.9) or formula (14.10) for the standard error of the difference. In this instance, we would make use of the two regression coefficients, $b_{y_1x} = 102.0/100.4 = 1.02$ and $b_{y_2x} = 58.8/67.6 = .87$, in calculating the residual sum of squares, and the degrees of freedom for t would be equal to $(n_1 - 2) + (n_2 - 2) = n_1 + n_2 - 4$.

EXAMPLES

15.1—We have values of X and Y available for a group of 15 subjects and another group of 10 subjects.

Group 1		*Group 2*	
X	Y	X	Y
10	12	14	16
10	13	15	18
14	18	12	14
12	18	8	12
8	14	10	10
15	19	13	14
15	19	13	14
11	17	8	10
9	11	9	12
14	18	9	10
13	17		
8	12		
8	11		
10	14		
11	18		

(a) Find the value of r for the combined group of $n_1 + n_2 = n$ subjects and the fiducial limits at the 5 per cent level.
(b) Find the values of r separately for the two groups and test the null hypothesis that $\rho_1 = \rho_2$.
(c) Find the value of b_{yx} for the combined group of $n_1 + n_2 = n$ subjects and test the null hypothesis that $\beta_{yx} = 0$.
(d) Find b_{y_1x} and b_{y_2x} for the two groups and test the null hypothesis that $\beta_{y_1x} = \beta_{y_2x}$.

15.2—An investigator reports an r of .88 for 10 pairs of observations. Is the hypothesis that the population correlation is 0 tenable?

15.3—Would a sample value of the correlation coefficient of .33 based upon 10 pairs of observations result in the rejection of the hypothesis that the population correlation is 0?

15.4—What value of the correlation coefficient would you need to obtain before rejecting the hypothesis that the population correlation is 0 for a sample of 50 pairs of observations?

15.5—An investigator reports a correlation coefficient of .25 for a sample of observations.

(a) How large would his sample have to be before you would reject the hypothesis of zero correlation?
(b) What if he had reported a correlation coefficient of .33?

15.6—Plot the values of (X_1,Y_1) and (X_2,Y_2) of Table 15.1 on the same sheet of coordinate paper. You can use x's to represent the points (X_1,Y_1) and small circles to represent the points (X_2,Y_2). Find the point corresponding to $(\bar{X}_1,\bar{Y}_1)$ and the point corresponding to $(\bar{X}_2,\bar{Y}_2)$ and plot them on the graph. Draw the regression line for Y_1 on X_1 and the regression line for Y_2 on X_2 on the graph. Using the results presented for the data of Table 15.1 in both this and the previous chapter, write as complete an interpretation as possible for the data presented in the graph.

CHAPTER SIXTEEN

The Analysis of Variance

The t test of significance is adequate for any experiment that involves only two groups and consequently a test of a single mean difference. But suppose we had an experimental design involving three groups, A, B, and C, with each group tested under a different set of experimental conditions. We could still use t to evaluate the differences between the means by comparing A and B, B and C, and A and C. This seems a relatively simple procedure and it is, as long as there are not too many groups in our experiment. But if we had five groups, the number of comparisons we would have to make would be 10. And if we had ten groups, then the number of comparisons would be 45. Obviously, some method of testing differences among all of the means at the same time would prove very valuable. The analysis of variance and the corresponding test of significance based upon the F distribution permits us to do this.

Nature of the Analysis of Variance

The analysis of variance, as the name indicates, deals with variances rather than with standard deviations and standard errors. The rationale of the analysis of variance is that the total sum of squares of a set of measurements composed of several groups can be analyzed or broken down into specific parts, each part identifiable with a given source of variation. In the simplest case, the total sum of squares is analyzed into two parts: a sum of squares based upon variation *within* the several groups, and a sum of squares based upon the variation *between* the group means.[1] Then, from

[1] See the earlier discussion in Chapter 10, p. 200.

these two sums of squares, *independent* estimates of the population variance are computed.

On the assumption that the groups or samples making up a total series of measurements are random samples from a common normal population, the two estimates of the population variance may be expected to differ only within the limits of random sampling. We may test this null hypothesis by dividing the larger variance by the smaller variance to get the variance ratio. The 5 and 1 per cent *points* of the variance ratio, which has been designated as F, have been tabled by Snedecor (1946) and are reproduced in Table VIII, in the Appendix. If the observed value of F equals or exceeds the tabled value, then the null hypothesis that the samples have been drawn from the same common normal population is considered untenable. If we reject the null hypothesis, the populations from which the samples have been drawn may differ in terms of either means or variances or both. If the variances are approximately the same, it is the means that differ.

This, basically, is the analysis of variance in its simplest form. Our first step will be to show that the total sum of squares for a series of measurements composed of several groups can be analyzed into the two parts mentioned above, one part associated with variation within groups and the other part associated with variation between group means.

■ Breakdown of the Sums of Squares

Let us take the data of Table 16.1. Assume that the values given are scores on an achievement test for a group taught by the lecture method, another

Table 16.1—Scores X and Squares of Scores X^2 on an Achievement Test for Subjects Taught by the Lecture, Discussion, and Project Methods

	Lecture Group		*Discussion Group*		*Project Group*	
	X	X^2	X	X^2	X	X^2
	7	49	4	16	2	4
	10	100	6	36	2	4
	10	100	7	49	3	9
	11	121	9	81	7	49
	12	144	9	81	6	36
Σ	50	514	35	263	20	102

group taught by the discussion method, and a third group taught by the project method.

The Total Sum of Squares

We first determine the total sum of squares by combining the scores of the three groups and treating them as one set of measurements. We could find the mean $\bar{X}$ of the combined distribution and subtract this value from each of the scores, square the deviations, and sum, to get the total sum of squares. We can also obtain this sum of squares by dealing with the measurements as they stand. Thus

$$\sum_{1}^{n}(X - \bar{X})^2 = \sum_{1}^{n} X^2 - \frac{\left(\sum_{1}^{n} X\right)^2}{n} \tag{16.1}$$

where $\sum_{1}^{n}(X - \bar{X})^2$ equals the total sum of squares. The n appearing over the summation sign in formula (16.1) indicates that the summation is over all $n = n_1 + n_2 + n_3$ observations. Then, for the data of Table 16.1, we have

$$\sum_{1}^{n}(X - \bar{X})^2 = 879 - \frac{(105)^2}{15}$$

$$= 879 - 735$$

$$= 144$$

The Sum of Squares within Groups

Now let us find the sum of squares *within* each group. That is, considering each group separately, we find the mean of each group and the sum of squared deviations within each group from its own mean. Again we shall use the formula for the scores as they stand. Then, letting the subscripts 1, 2, and 3 indicate the lecture, discussion, and project groups, respectively, and n_i the number of observations in each group, we have

$$\sum_{1}^{n_i}(X - \bar{X}_1)^2 = 514 - \frac{(50)^2}{5}$$

$$= 514 - 500$$

$$= 14$$

and $$\sum_{1}^{n_i}(X - \bar{X}_2)^2 = 263 - \frac{(35)^2}{5}$$

$$= 263 - 245$$

$$= 18$$

and $$\sum_{1}^{n_i}(X - \bar{X}_3)^2 = 102 - \frac{(20)^2}{5}$$

$$= 102 - 80$$

$$= 22$$

The sum of these three sums of squares, $14 + 18 + 22 = 54$, is called the sum of squares *within* groups. It is a measure of the variation of the individual observations about the means of the particular groups to which they belong. If we let n_i equal the number of observations in the ith group, $\bar{X}_i$, the mean of the ith group, and if we have k such groups, then, in general, the sum of squares within groups will be given by

$$\textit{Within groups} = \sum_{1}^{k}\sum_{1}^{n_i}(X - \bar{X}_i)^2 \qquad \textbf{(16.2)}$$

The Sum of Squares between Groups

The sum of squares within groups, 54, does not equal the total sum of squares, 144. The reason for this is that the total sum of squares is based upon the deviations of all n observations from the mean $\bar{X}$ of the combined groups, which is equal to 7. The sum of squares within groups, on the other hand, is based upon the deviations of each set of n_i observations about the particular means $\bar{X}_i$ of the groups to which they belong. For the lecture group, $\bar{X}_i = 10$; for the discussion group, $\bar{X}_i = 7$; and for the project group $\bar{X}_i = 4$. If these three means had been equal to the mean of the combined groups, the sum of squares within groups would have been exactly equal to the total sum of squares.[2] Because the means $\bar{X}_i$ do differ, the sum of squares within groups is not equal to the total sum of squares. We thus see that the remaining sum of squares, $144 - 54 = 90$, must be in some way associated with the variation of the group means.

---

[2] This point was mentioned earlier in the discussion of the correlation ratio. See page 202.

The mean of the combined groups is 7. We shall let the deviation of a group mean from the mean of the total be represented by d. Then

$$d_i^2 = (\bar{X}_i - \bar{X})^2 \tag{16.3}$$

where d_i is the deviation of the mean $\bar{X}_i$ of the ith group from the combined mean $\bar{X}$. Each of the squared deviations of formula (16.3), however, is based upon n_i observations. Consequently, these deviations must be weighted or multiplied by n_i, the number of observations in each group, to put them on a per individual basis. Then

$$n_i d_i^2 = n_i(\bar{X}_i - \bar{X})^2 \tag{16.4}$$

Letting the subscript i in formula (16.4) take the values 1, 2, and 3, corresponding to our lecture, discussion, and project groups, respectively, we have

$$n_1 d_1^2 = 5(10 - 7)^2$$

$$= 45$$

and

$$n_2 d_2^2 = 5(7 - 7)^2$$

$$= 0$$

and

$$n_3 d_3^2 = 5(4 - 7)^2$$

$$= 45$$

The sum of the three values found above is $45 + 0 + 45 = 90$, and it is called the sum of squares *between* groups. The sum of squares between groups is a measure of the variation of the group means about the combined mean. When the group means do not differ among themselves, the sum of squares between groups will be equal to zero. On the other hand, the greater the variation in the group means, the larger the sum of squares between groups. In general, if we have k groups, with n_i observations in each group, the sum of squares between groups will be given by

$$\textit{Between groups} = \sum_1^k n_i(\bar{X}_i - \bar{X})^2 \tag{16.5}$$

■ Degrees of Freedom and Mean Squares

It may now be noted that the sum of squares within groups plus the sum of squares between groups is equal to the total sum of squares. Then, in terms of formulas (16.1), (16.2), and (16.5), we may write for these sums of squares

$$\sum_{1}^{n}(X - \bar{X})^2 = \sum_{1}^{k}\sum_{1}^{n_i}(X - \bar{X}_i)^2 + \sum_{1}^{k}n_i(\bar{X}_i - \bar{X})^2 \qquad \textbf{(16.6)}$$

or, in terms of the names commonly assigned to the sums of squares,

$$\textit{Total} = \textit{Within} + \textit{Between} \qquad \textbf{(16.7)}$$

Each of these sums of squares has associated with it a specified number of degrees of freedom. For the total sum of squares, we already know that the degrees of freedom will be equal to $n - 1$. The number of degrees of freedom within each group is equal to $n_i - 1$, where n_i is the number of observations in each group. But, since we have more than one group, the number of degrees of freedom for the sum of squares within groups will be equal to $k(n_i - 1)$, where k is the number of groups. The number of degrees of freedom for the sum of squares between groups will be equal to $k - 1$, where k is the number of groups.

If we divide the sum of squares within groups by its degrees of freedom, we shall have an estimate of the common population variance that is independent of the variation in the group means. If we divide the sum of squares between groups by its degrees of freedom we shall have a second estimate of the population variance that is independent of the variation within groups. In the analysis of variance, these estimates of the population variance are called *mean squares*, and they are shown, for the present example, in Table 16.2, which summarizes the analysis.

Table 16.2—Analysis of Variance of Achievement Scores of Groups Taught by the Lecture, Discussion, and Project Methods

Source of Variation	*Sum of Squares*	*df*	*Mean Square*
Between groups	90.0	2	45.0
Within groups	54.0	12	4.5
Total	144.0	14	

■ The Test of Significance

We mentioned in an earlier discussion that if we have two estimates of the population variance, then F will be given by dividing the larger estimate by the smaller.[3] For the present analysis of variance problem, we may define

$$F = \frac{\textit{mean square between groups}}{\textit{mean square within groups}} \tag{16.8}$$

and, for the data of Table 16.2, we have

$$F = \frac{45.0}{4.5} = 10$$

To determine whether this value is significant at the 5 or 1 per cent *points*, we enter the column of Table VIII, in the Appendix, with the degrees of freedom of the numerator of the F ratio and run down this column until we find the row entry corresponding to the degrees of freedom of the denominator. The values of F significant at the 5 per cent point are given in lightface type, and those significant at the 1 per cent point are given in boldface type. For 2 and 12 degrees of freedom, we find, from the table of F, that a value of 6.93 will be significant at the 1 per cent point.

Since our observed value of 10 greatly exceeds the tabled value of 6.93 for 2 and 12 degrees of freedom, we may conclude that our observed value is significant. The null hypothesis that we have tested, namely, that our samples are random samples from a common normal population, will thus be rejected. We may conclude that the means of our groups differ significantly among themselves, that is, they show more variation than can be attributed to random sampling from populations with a common population mean. Consequently, we may infer that the differences in achievement between the three groups taught by different methods of instruction are indicative of real differences.

We have defined F as the mean square between groups divided by the mean square within groups. The null hypothesis that we are testing is that the samples are random samples from a common normally distributed population. If this hypothesis is true, then the mean square between groups estimates the common variance plus a component reflecting the variation in the population means.

We can draw some inference about the significance of the differences in the means of our samples only if the mean square between groups is

---

[3] See page 272.

larger than the mean square within groups. That is why the mean square based upon the variation of the means of the experimental groups is placed in the numerator of the F ratio and the mean square within groups in the denominator, and the test of significance is made on the right tail of the F distribution.

Only values of F, as defined by formula (16.8), greater than 1 will provide evidence against the null hypothesis in which we are interested. If the mean square between groups is smaller than the mean square within groups, then the value of F will be less than 1, and such values will not contradict the null hypothesis. In this case, there is no need to compute the F ratio, for it is obvious that the data offer no evidence against the null hypothesis.

■ The Case Where the Null Hypothesis Is True

In order to clarify further the notions we have presented in the previous sections concerning the analysis of variance in its simplest form, we show in Figure 16.1 three normal populations in which $m_1 = m_2 = m_3$ and $\sigma_1^2 = \sigma_2^2 = \sigma_3^2$. We may denote the common population mean by m and the common population variance by σ^2. Figure 16.1 describes the situation in which the null hypothesis, as tested by the F of formula (16.8), is *true.*

If we draw a random sample of n_i observations from each of the k populations, we can compute the sum of squares within groups as given by formula (16.2). Then, dividing this sum of squares by its degrees of freedom $k(n_i - 1)$, we obtain the mean square within groups. Thus

$$\textit{Mean square within groups} = \frac{\sum_1^k \sum_1^{n_i} (X - \bar{X}_i)^2}{k(n_i - 1)} \tag{16.9}$$

and this mean square will be an unbiased estimate of the common population variance σ^2.

We can also find the variation of each of the k sample means $\bar{X}_i$ about the mean $\bar{X}$ of the combined samples. Then, squaring these deviations, summing, and dividing the sum by $k - 1$, we obtain the variance of the means $s_{\bar{x}}^2$. Thus

$$s_{\bar{x}}^2 = \frac{\sum_1^k (\bar{X}_i - \bar{X})^2}{k - 1} \tag{16.10}$$

As long as we have the situation described in Figure 16.1, that is, as long as $m_1, m_2, \cdots, m_k$, are all equal to m, and $\sigma_1^2, \sigma_2^2, \cdots, \sigma_k^2$ are all equal to σ^2, the variance of the means of samples of n_i observations, each drawn from the *separate* populations, may be expected to be no greater than the

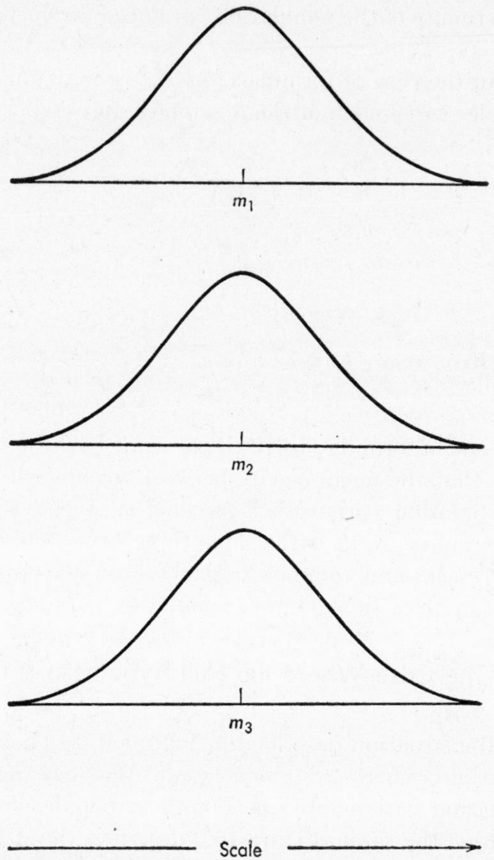

Fig. 16.1—Three normal populations with equal means and equal variances.

variance of means of samples of the same size drawn from any *one* of the populations.

When we have a sample of n observations drawn from a common normally distributed population, we have found that the variance of the means could be estimated by[4]

$$s_{\bar{x}}^2 = \frac{s^2}{n}$$

[4] See formula (13.1), page 246.

Multiplying both sides of this expression by n, we obtain

$$ns_{\bar{x}}^2 = s^2 \tag{16.11}$$

where s^2 is an estimate of the population variance σ^2 from which the sample was drawn.

Similarly, in the case of formula (16.10), we may multiply both sides by n_i, the sample size of each of the k samples, to obtain

$$n_i s_{\bar{x}}^2 = \frac{n_i \sum_1^k (\bar{X}_i - \bar{X})^2}{k - 1}$$

or

$$\textit{Mean square between groups} = \frac{n_i \sum_1^k (\bar{X}_i - \bar{X})^2}{k - 1} \tag{16.12}$$

Since the right side of formula (16.12) is the same as the left side of formula (16.11), we see that the mean square between groups will also be an estimate of the population variance σ^2. As long as we have samples from a common population or, what is the same thing, from separate populations with a common mean and common variance, formula (16.12) will give us an unbiased estimate of the common population variance.

■ The Case Where the Null Hypothesis Is False

Now consider the situation described in Figure 16.2. There we have three normal populations where $\sigma_1^2 = \sigma_2^2 = \sigma_3^2$. We may again denote the common population variance by σ^2. For these populations, however, m_1, m_2, and m_3 are *not* the same. Figure 16.2 describes the situation for which the null hypothesis in which we are interested is *false*.

If we have a random sample of n_i observations from each of the k populations of Figure 16.2, we can again compute the sum of squares within groups as given by formula (16.2). Dividing this sum of squares by $k(n_i - 1)$, we obtain the mean square within groups, as given by formula (16.9). Now, it should be clear that the mean square within groups will still be an unbiased estimate of the common population variance σ^2, despite the fact that the population means from which the samples were drawn differ. The reason for this is that the numerator of formula (16.9) is based upon the deviations of each set of n_i observations about the respective sample means $\bar{X}_i$. Consequently, any systematic differences in the sample means, resulting from differences in the population means, will not influence the sum of squares within groups.

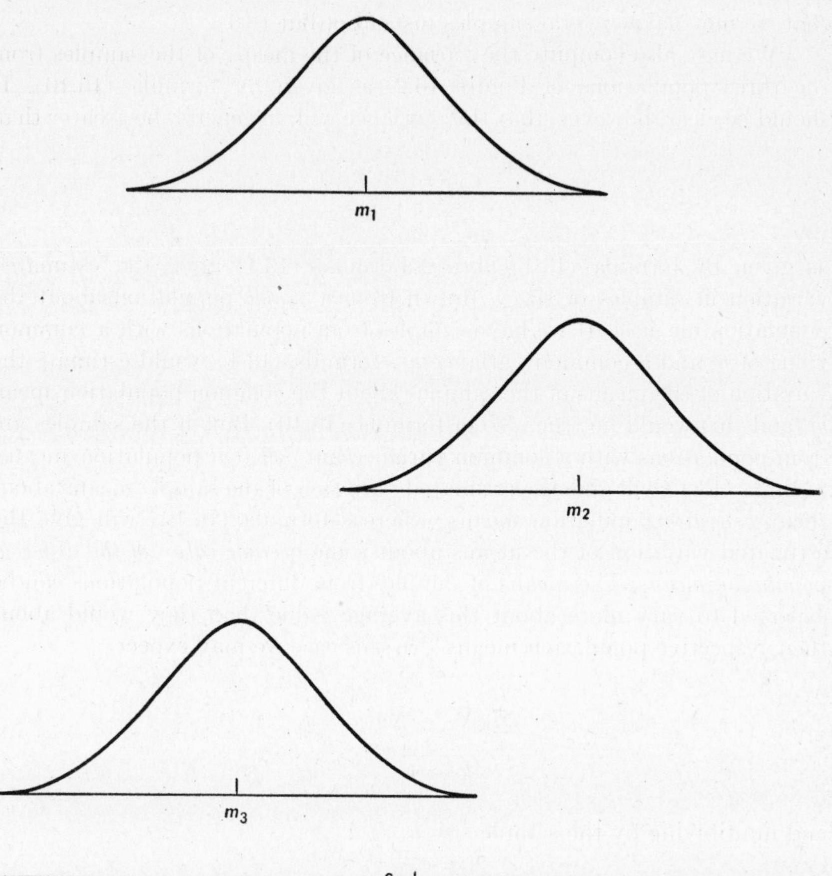

Fig. 16.2—Three normal populations with equal variances but different means.

Each of the variances obtainable from the separate samples, that is, the values of

$$s_i^2 = \frac{\sum_{1}^{n_i}(X - \bar{X}_i)^2}{n_i - 1} \qquad \textbf{(16.13)}$$

will be an estimate of the common population variance σ^2. In obtaining the mean square within groups of formula (16.9), we have merely pooled the sums of squares within each sample and their degrees of freedom to obtain an estimate of the common population variance. This is precisely the same procedure we followed in connection with the t test.[5] The only difference is that we now have several samples instead of but two.

We may also compute the variance of the means of the samples from the three populations of Figure 16.2, as given by formula (16.10). It should be clear, however, that this variance will, in general, be greater than

$$s_{\bar{x}}^2 = \frac{s^2}{n}$$

as given by formula (13.1) above. Formula (13.1) gives the estimated variation in samples of size n drawn from a *single* population about the population mean m. If we have samples from populations with a common value of m and a common variance σ^2, formula (13.1) would estimate the variation of the means of the samples about the common population mean m, and this would be true also of formula (16.10). But, if the samples are from populations with a common variance but *different* population means, formula (13.1) will give the estimated variation of the sample means about their *respective* population means, whereas formula (16.10) will give the estimated variation of the means about some *average value of the different population means.* The means of samples from different populations can be expected to vary more about this average value than they would about their respective population means.[6] In this case we may expect

$$\frac{\sum_{1}^{k}(\bar{X}_i - \bar{X})^2}{k - 1} > \frac{s^2}{n}$$

and multiplying by the sample size $n_i = n$

$$\frac{n_i\sum_{1}^{k}(\bar{X}_i - \bar{X})^2}{k - 1} > s^2$$

Substituting the unbiased estimate of s^2 from formula (16.9) in the above expression, we have

$$\frac{n_i\sum_{1}^{k}(\bar{X}_i - \bar{X})^2}{k - 1} > \frac{\sum_{1}^{k}\sum_{1}^{n_i}(X - \bar{X}_i)^2}{k(n_i - 1)}$$

---

[5] See page 253.

[6] We have already shown that the sum of squared deviations from a mean is at a minimum.

or *Mean square between groups* $>$ *Mean square within groups*

If our experimental conditions have any systematic influence upon the means of our experimental groups, we should expect the mean square between groups to be larger than the mean square within groups. We may test the null hypothesis that the mean square between groups is equal to or less than the mean square within groups in terms of F as defined by formula (16.8). If this hypothesis is rejected, we shall accept the alternative hypothesis that the mean square between groups is greater than the mean square within groups. If the mean square between groups is equal to or less than the mean square within groups, so that $F \leqq 1$, this outcome will not provide a basis for rejecting the null hypothesis. Only if the mean square between groups is greater than the mean square within groups, so that $F > 1$, will the data offer evidence against the null hypothesis. If the test of significance is to be made in such a way that the probability of a Type I error is to be .05, then the null hypothesis will be rejected only if the observed value of F is greater than 1 and falls within the class of those values of F greater than 1 that would occur 5 per cent of the time when the null hypothesis is true. Our test of significance is thus a one-tailed test, and we shall be concerned with a significance point rather than a level.

■ Estimates Based upon the Total Sum of Squares

For the situation described by Figure 16.1, where the null hypothesis is true, we could also obtain an unbiased estimate of the common population variance from the total sum of squares. This estimate would be given if we divided the total sum of squares of formula (16.1) by its degrees of freedom, $n - 1$.

If we have the situation described by Figure 16.2, however, where the null hypothesis is false, dividing the total sum of squares by its degrees of freedom will not result in an unbiased estimate of the common population variance. In this case the total sum of squares would measure the variation of the individual observations about some estimate of the average value of the different population means, and not about a common population mean. For the same reasons discussed in connection with the mean square between groups, for the case where the null hypothesis was false, we may expect the mean square based upon the total sum of squares to be larger than the unbiased estimate of the common population variance obtained from the sum of squares within groups.

■ Homogeneity of Variance

Our analysis and test of significance assume that the variation within groups is homogeneous, that is, that the variances within the several groups do not differ significantly among themselves. This is the usual case with experimental data and with random assignment of subjects to experimental groups. A separate test of the hypothesis of homogeneity of variance can be made if the variances within groups show marked discrepancies. This test is known as Bartlett's (1937) test and it is described in Edwards (1950*a*).

A simple approximate first test of homogeneity of variance may be made by dividing each of the separate sums of squares within the several groups by the corresponding degrees of freedom, or $n_i - 1$. For the present problem, these three estimates are: $s_1^2 = 14/4 = 3.5$; $s_2^2 = 18/4 = 4.5$; and $s_3^2 = 22/4 = 5.5$. It is these estimates that are assumed to be homogeneous.

If we now take the largest estimate and divide it by the smallest estimate, we have $F = 5.5/3.5 = 1.57$, with 4 and 4 degrees of freedom. From the table of F, we find that for 4 and 4 degrees of freedom a value of 15.98 will be required for significance at the 2 per cent level. Our observed value of 1.57 obviously is not significant.[7]

In general, if the two extreme estimates do not differ significantly, we may conclude that homogeneity of variance prevails. On the other hand, we may find that the two extreme estimates do differ significantly, but that the complete set of variances, as tested by Bartlett's test, are homogeneous.

■ Standard Errors

If we have an analysis of variance design involving several groups and we wish to find the standard error of one of the means, then we may use the mean square within groups as our estimate of the population variance. This assumes, of course, that homogeneity of variance prevails. Then

$$s_{\bar{x}} = \frac{s}{\sqrt{n}} \tag{16.14}$$

where $s_{\bar{x}}$ = the standard error of the mean
s = the square root of the mean square within groups
n = the number of subjects or observations in a given group

Then the standard error of the difference between two means will be given by

$$s_{\bar{x}_1 - \bar{x}_2} = \sqrt{s_{\bar{x}_1}{}^2 + s_{\bar{x}_2}{}^2}$$

[7] If we test the null hypothesis that $\sigma_3^2 = \sigma_1^2$ against the alternative that $\sigma_3^2 \neq \sigma_1^2$, this is a two-tailed test, and the 5 and 1 per cent points in the table of F correspond to the 10 and 2 per cent levels.

$$= \sqrt{\frac{s^2}{n_1} + \frac{s^2}{n_2}}$$

$$= s\sqrt{\frac{1}{n_1} + \frac{1}{n_2}} \qquad (16.15)$$

where $s_{\bar{x}_1-\bar{x}_2}$ = the standard error of the difference between the means
s = the square root of the mean square within groups
n_1 = the number of observations in Group 1
n_2 = the number of observations in Group 2

If the difference between the means $\bar{X}_1$ and $\bar{X}_2$ is now divided by the standard error of the difference as given by formula (16.15), the result will be the t ratio and may be evaluated in terms of the t table. The degrees of freedom available for entering the table of t will be those associated with s^2, the mean square within groups, as determined in the analysis of variance.

Comparison of Individual Means

The argument we made earlier, however, with respect to homogeneity of variance applies also to the case of means. Suppose, for example, that we have tested 10 groups of subjects under different experimental conditions. If we now take the two extreme means and test them for significance by means of the t test, we may find that they differ significantly. On the other hand, if we apply the analysis of variance to the data from the 10 groups, we may find that the mean square between groups is not significantly larger than the mean square within groups.

Both the t test and the F test involve the hypothesis that the samples have been drawn at random from a common population. In making the t test for the two extreme means, however, we have not selected two samples at random for comparison. A random selection of two means from the 10 available would result in our obtaining the two extremes but 1 time in 45, since there are 45 possible pairs of means. If we were to make all of the possible 45 t tests, we would expect, when the null hypothesis is true, to find 5 per cent of these t's, or approximately 2, to be significant at the 5 per cent level. It is obvious that we have biased the test of significance by selecting the two means to be compared in such a way that we obtain the largest possible t from the 45 values that could be computed.

Although Fisher (1942), warns that comparisons suggested *after* the data are in are open to suspicion, he recommends that, under these circumstances, the basis for rejecting the null hypothesis be, not the probability of 1 in 20 (5 per cent level), but a probability of 1 in $(n)(20)$, where n is the number of possible comparisons. For the case of 10 groups, for example, we should demand a probability of 1 in (45)(20) = 1 in 900, before rejecting the null hypothesis. In other words, t in this particular example would have to be equal to a value that could be expected to occur as a result of random sampling, when the null hypothesis is true, but 1 time in 900 rather than 1 time in 20. Fisher contends, nevertheless, that it would be better to regard such unforeseen comparisons "only as suggestions for future experimentation, in which they could be deliberately tested" (1942, p. 57).

Tukey's Procedure for Comparing Individual Means

Let us suppose, however, that in an analysis of variance problem the F test indicates that the means are not homogeneous. As Tukey (1949, p. 99) has pointed out, the experimenter wants to draw as many conclusions as are reasonable about the differences that are present among the means, and a statement, as a result of the F test, that "they are not all alike leaves him thoroughly unsatisfied." What we generally want to do is to classify the means into groups that are alike among themselves but differ from each other. Suppose, for example, that we arrange the means in order of magnitude, from lowest to highest. We would now like to section this ordering in such a way that we could say the means falling within a given section are alike in that they do not differ significantly among themselves, but that there are significant differences between sections.

Specifically, let us assume that we have 8 experimental conditions and that 10 subjects have been assigned to each condition. The resulting 8 means, arranged in order of magnitude and arbitrarily labeled A, B, C, D, E, F, G, and H, are as shown in Table 16.3. We have a total of 79 degrees of

Table 16.3—Means Obtained under Eight Experimental Conditions Arranged in Order of Magnitude and Assigned the Letters *A* to *H*

	Experimental Conditions							
	A	*B*	*C*	*D*	*E*	*F*	*G*	*H*
$\bar{X}$	19.70	36.70	50.60	51.40	55.10	61.30	65.30	72.00

freedom, with 72 degrees of freedom for the mean square within groups and 7 degrees of freedom for the mean square between groups. Let us also assume that the analysis of variance for the data is as shown in Table 16.4. The value of F equal to 31.54, with 7 and 72 degrees of freedom, indicates

Table 16.4—Analysis of Variance for Eight Groups of Ten Subjects Each Tested under Different Experimental Conditions

Source of Variation	*Sum of Squares*	*df*	*Mean Square*	*F*
Between groups	19,507.90	7	2,786.84	31.54
Within groups	6,361.92	72	88.36	
Total	25,869.82			

that there are significant differences among the 8 means shown in Table 16.3.

When real differences are present among a set of means, Tukey (1949, p. 101) has pointed out that one or all of the following conditions may be observed: (a) there is a wide gap between adjacent means when they are arranged in order of magnitude; (b) one of the means is a "straggler"; (c) the means taken as a group show excessive variability. Tukey proposes that we apply three tests in order to detect these conditions.

Test for a Significant Gap

The first test is applied by taking t at some defined level of significance, say at the 5 per cent level, for the degrees of freedom available and then solving for

$$\textit{Significant gap} = (t_{.05})(\sqrt{2})(s_{\bar{x}}) \tag{16.16}$$

where $s_{\bar{x}}$ is as defined by formula (16.14) and $t_{.05}$ is the tabled value of t at the 5 per cent level for the degrees of freedom associated with the mean square within groups.

For the data of Table 16.4, t at the 5 per cent level for 72 degrees of freedom is 1.99. Taking the square root of the mean square within groups we have $s = \sqrt{88.36} = 9.4$. Then $s_{\bar{x}}$ as given by formula (16.14) will be

$$s_{\bar{x}} = \frac{9.4}{\sqrt{10}} = 2.97$$

Substituting in formula (16.16) with these values, we have

$$\textit{Significant gap} = (1.99)(1.41)(2.97) = 8.33$$

If we now inspect the differences between adjacent pairs of means, when they are arranged in order of magnitude, any gap between adjacent pairs that is equal to or greater than the gap as obtained from formula

(16.16) is taken as a group boundary. For the means of Table 16.3 we have 36.70 − 19.70 = 15.00 and 50.60 − 36.70 = 13.90 as the only two differences that exceed 8.33. Thus the gap test has divided the 8 means into three groups: A by itself, B by itself, and C, D, E, F, G, and H as the third group.

Test for a "Straggler"

If the application of formula (16.16) separates the means into groups such that no group has more than two means, no further tests would be necessary. If, on the other hand, groups of three or more means exist after the application of formula (16.16), then, for each group of three or more means, we find the grand mean $\bar{X}$, the most straggling mean $\bar{X}_1$, and the difference between these two divided by $s_{\bar{x}}$ as given by formula (16.14). These ratios can be translated into approximate normal deviates or standard scores.

If there are only three means in a group, then we find

$$z = \frac{\left(\dfrac{\bar{X}_1 - \bar{X}}{s_{\bar{x}}}\right) - \dfrac{1}{2}}{3\left(\dfrac{1}{4} + \dfrac{1}{df}\right)} \tag{16.17}$$

where df is the number of degrees of freedom associated with the mean square within groups.

If there are more than three means in a group, then we find[8]

$$z = \frac{\left(\dfrac{\bar{X}_1 - \bar{X}}{s_{\bar{x}}}\right) - \dfrac{6}{5}\log k}{3\left(\dfrac{1}{4} + \dfrac{1}{df}\right)} \tag{16.18}$$

where k is the number of means in the group, and df is again the number of degrees of freedom associated with the mean square within groups.

Since the value of z significant at the 5 per cent level is 1.96, any straggling mean in a group that yields a z of 1.96 or greater would be separated from the group. If any means are separated from a group and the group still contains three or more means, the application of formula (16.17) or formula (16.18) would be repeated upon the remaining means in the group with the new values for $\bar{X}_1$, $\bar{X}$, and k. This process is continued until

[8] The logarithm of k is to base 10 as given in Table IX, in the Appendix.

no additional means are separated. All means separated on the same side are considered as belonging in a new subgroup. If any subgroup contains three or more means, we also apply formula (16.17) or formula (16.18) to the subgroup.

For the data under consideration, we have three groups of means: A by itself, B by itself, and the group C, D, E, F, G, and H. We shall test the set C, D, E, F, G, and H to determine whether we have any stragglers. The mean of these six means is

$$\bar{X} = \frac{50.60 + 51.40 + 55.10 + 61.30 + 65.30 + 72.00}{6} = 59.28$$

and the most straggling mean is H = 72.00. Then, since we have more than three means in the group, we apply formula (16.18). We have found $s_{\bar{x}}$ to be equal to 2.97, we have 72 degrees of freedom, and $\log k = \log 6 = .778$. Substituting in formula (16.18), we have

$$z = \frac{\left(\dfrac{72.00 - 59.28}{2.97}\right) - \dfrac{6}{5}.778}{3\left(\dfrac{1}{4} + \dfrac{1}{72}\right)}$$

$$= \frac{4.28 - .93}{.79}$$

$$= 4.24$$

Since 4.24 exceeds 1.96, we separate H from the group under consideration.

We now repeat the process for the set C, D, E, F, and G. The mean of these means is

$$\bar{X} = \frac{50.60 + 51.40 + 55.10 + 61.30 + 65.30}{5} = 56.74$$

and the most straggling mean is G = 65.30. We now have $k = 5$ and $\log k = .699$. The denominator of formula (16.18) will be the same as before, and we therefore have

$$z = \frac{\left(\dfrac{65.30 - 56.74}{2.97}\right) - \dfrac{6}{5}.699}{.79} = 2.58$$

Since 2.58 exceeds 1.96, we separate G from the group C, D, E, and F. Since G is separated on the same side as H, these two means form a new subgroup.

Repeating the same process with the remaining four means, we now have $\bar{X} = 54.60$ with the most straggling mean F = 61.30. With $k = 4$ and $\log k = .602$, formula (16.18) now results in a z of 1.95. This is of borderline significance and we shall assume that F = 61.30 is also separated from the group C, D, and E. Since F is separated on the same side as G and H, we have these three means in a subgroup apart from the group C, D, and E.

If we now consider the means C, D, and E, we have $\bar{X} = 52.37$ and E = 55.10 as the most straggling mean. Applying formula (16.17) we obtain $z = .92$, and this is not a significant value. No additional stragglers can be detected in the set C, D, and E. Similarly, taking the subgroup F, G, and H, we have $\bar{X} = 66.20$ and H = 72.00 as the most straggling mean. Applying formula (16.17), we obtain $z = 1.84$, and this is not a significant value. There are no excessive stragglers that can be detected in the subgroup F, G, and H.

Test for Excessive Variability

To apply Tukey's third criterion, that is, to determine whether there is excessive variability in any remaining group or subgroup with three or more means, the sum of squares of the deviations of the individual means $\bar{X}_i$ from the mean of the group $\bar{X}$ is found. Dividing this sum of squares by one less than the number of means involved will yield an estimate of the variance of the means in the group. Then we may calculate

$$F = \frac{\dfrac{\sum(\bar{X}_i - \bar{X})^2}{k - 1}}{s_{\bar{x}}^{\,2}} \tag{16.19}$$

where k is the number of means in the group and $s_{\bar{x}}^{\,2}$ is the square of the standard error of formula (16.14). The degrees of freedom for evaluating the F of formula (16.19) will be $k - 1$ for the numerator, and for the denominator the degrees of freedom will be those associated with the mean square within groups.

For the group C, D, and E, we have $\bar{X} = 52.37$ and $\sum(\bar{X}_i - \bar{X})^2 = 11.53$. Then, substituting in formula (16.19), we obtain

$$F = \frac{\dfrac{11.53}{3 - 1}}{(2.97)^2} = \frac{5.76}{8.82} < 1.00$$

Since the value of F is less than 1.00, we have no evidence of excessive variability in the set of means C, D, and E.

Making a similar test for the subgroup F, G, and H, we have $\bar{X} = 66.20$ and $\sum (\bar{X}_i - \bar{X})^2 = 58.46$. Then, substituting in formula (16.19), we get

$$F = \frac{\frac{58.46}{3 - 1}}{(2.97)^2} = \frac{29.23}{8.82} = 3.31$$

which for 2 and 72 degrees of freedom is significant at the 5 per cent point.

The three tests we have applied now enable us to draw the following conclusions about the 8 means. A = 19.7 is significantly smaller than B = 36.70, and B, in turn, is significantly smaller than C = 50.60, D = 51.40, and E = 55.10. C, D, and E, in turn, are significantly smaller than F = 61.30, G = 65.30, and H = 72.00. There is no evidence of significant variability within the set C, D, and E, but the members of group F, G, and H do show variability that is significant at the 5 per cent point. It seems fairly evident that F and H differ, but we cannot determine whether F and G perhaps belong together in a subgroup or whether G and H form a subgroup.

A Simple Method of Calculating the Sum of Squares between Groups

We shall now show another method for computing the sum of squares between groups. This method does not involve finding the means of the various groups and then expressing these as deviations from the combined mean, as was necessary with formula (16.5). If we have k groups with n_i observations in each group and with $n = \sum n_i$, then the sum of squares between groups will be given by

$$\textit{Between groups} = \sum_{1}^{k} \frac{\left(\sum_{1}^{n_i} X\right)^2}{n_i} - \frac{\left(\sum_{1}^{n} X\right)^2}{n} \tag{16.20}$$

For the data of Table 16.1, we may obtain the sum of squares between groups by means of formula (16.20). Then

$$\begin{aligned}\textit{Between groups} &= \frac{50^2}{5} + \frac{(35)^2}{5} + \frac{(20)^2}{5} - \frac{(105)^2}{15} \\ &= 825 - 735 \\ &= 90\end{aligned}$$

which is the same value we obtained by working with the deviations of the group means from the combined mean.

It should be apparent also that if our calculations are correct, and if we have available the total sum of squares, the sum of squares within groups may be obtained by subtraction. Thus

$$\textit{Within groups} = \textit{Total} - \textit{Between groups} \qquad \textbf{(16.21)}$$

Summary of Calculations

We may summarize the computations needed for a simple case of analysis of variance in Table 16.5. The necessary formulas and methods of determining the appropriate degrees of freedom are included also for convenient reference.

In Table 16.5, we assume that we have the same number of observations in each group. This is not necessary in the experimental design, and it may so happen that we have groups with a varying number of subjects in each. When this is the case, we find the total sum of squares, between-groups sum of squares, and within-groups sum of squares, in the usual way. The degrees of freedom for the total sum of squares will still be equal to $n - 1$, where n is equal to $\sum n_i$. The degrees of freedom for the between groups sum of squares will be equal to $k - 1$, where k is the number of groups. The degrees of freedom for the sum of squares within groups will then be equal to the sum of the degrees of freedom within each of the several groups, or $\sum_1^k (n_i - 1) = \sum_1^k n_i - k$, where the k over the summation sign indicates that our summation extends over the k groups.

The Case of Two Groups

Perhaps you are wondering whether the analysis of variance could be applied in testing the significance of the difference between the means when we have but two experimental groups. It can, indeed, and if we were to apply the analysis of variance to the data of Table 13.1, we would note a very interesting thing. The value of F that we would obtain would be equal to the value of t^2. In the case of but two means, the degrees of freedom for the numerator of the F ratio of formula (16.8) will be equal to 1, and when this is true the tabled values of F are those for the corresponding values of t^2. For example, you will note that when we have 1 and 30 degrees of freedom, F at the 5 per cent *point* is 4.17. From the table of t we find that for 30 degrees of freedom, t at the 5 per cent *level* is 2.042 and that $(2.042)^2 = 4.17$.

Table 16.5—Summary of Computations in Analysis of Variance for k Groups with n_i Independent Observations in Each Group—Total Sum of Squares Analyzed into Two Parts

Measurements			
Group 1	*Group 2*	*Group 3*	*Group k*
X_{11}	X_{12}	X_{13}	X_{1k}
X_{21}	X_{22}	X_{23}	X_{2k}
X_{31}	X_{32}	X_{33}	X_{3k}
X_{41}	X_{42}	X_{43}	X_{4k}
.	.	.	.
.	.	.	.
.	.	.	.
X_{n_i1}	X_{n_i2}	X_{n_i3}	X_{n_ik}
$\sum X_1$	$\sum X_2$	$\sum X_3$	$\sum X_k$

Computations:

1. Total sum of scores $= \sum_1^{n_i} X_1 + \sum_1^{n_i} X_2 + \sum_1^{n_i} X_3 + \cdots + \sum_1^{n_i} X_k = \sum_1^{n} X$

2. Correction for origin $= \dfrac{\left(\sum_1^n X\right)^2}{n}$

3. Total sum of squares $= \sum_1^n X^2 - \dfrac{\left(\sum_1^n X\right)^2}{n}$

4. Sum of squares between groups =

$$\frac{\left(\sum_1^{n_i} X_1\right)^2}{n_i} + \frac{\left(\sum_1^{n_i} X_2\right)^2}{n_i} + \frac{\left(\sum_1^{n_i} X_3\right)^2}{n_i} + \cdots + \frac{\left(\sum_1^{n_i} X_k\right)^2}{n_i} - \frac{\left(\sum_1^{n} X\right)^2}{n}$$

Degrees of freedom:

1. Between groups $= k - 1$
2. Within groups $= \sum(n_i - 1) = \sum n_i - k = n - k$
3. Total $= \sum n_i - 1 = n - 1$

For the case of but two groups, the probability associated with F in the table of F is the corresponding probability associated with t^2. Since either $t = 2.042$ or $t = -2.042$ will result in a t^2 of 4.17, we need the probability as given by the area in the *two* tails of the t distribution. Thus, for 1 and 30 degrees of freedom, the probability of obtaining an F of 4.17 is .05 and the probability of obtaining a t^2 of 4.17 is also .05.

■ EXAMPLES

16.1—The following data consist of samples selected from the population we used earlier to study the sampling distribution of means. Assume that each value represents a score made by an individual assigned at random to one of five different experimental groups.

(*a*) Find the total sum of squares, the sum of squares between groups, and the sum of squares within groups.

(*b*) Code the scores by subtracting 60 from each one. Does this influence the values obtained for the various sums of squares? Is the value of F changed?

A	*B*	*C*	*D*	*E*
68	49	64	67	61
55	59	63	55	59
60	61	54	65	70
67	60	52	64	69
60	61	62	59	61

16.2—Apply the analysis of variance to the measurements obtained from the subjects in each of the experimental groups.

A	*B*	*C*	*D*	*E*
18	18	4	7	9
13	9	13	3	16
21	15	11	11	26
14	25	11	11	21
25	14	15	7	18
14	6	15	13	11
7	12	11	10	14
20	9	12	10	13

16.3—The following data consist of measurements of an experimental and a control group.

(*a*) Apply the t test and find the value of t^2.
(*b*) Apply the analysis of variance and compare the value of F with t^2.

Experimental	*Control*
21	9
19	10
18	20
13	14
15	18
20	5
22	8
25	11
17	12
10	13

16.4—Forty subjects were divided at random into 4 groups of 10 subjects each. The groups were then assigned at random to experimental conditions A, B, C, and D. Find the mean square between groups, the mean square within groups, and the value of F.

A	*B*	*C*	*D*
8	9	5	6
5	4	3	1
6	8	7	1
8	4	5	6
9	3	3	5
10	6	1	4
9	7	5	3
7	6	4	6
8	7	3	4
10	6	4	4

CHAPTER SEVENTEEN

Further Applications of the Analysis of Variance

Let us now consider a somewhat more complicated application of the analysis of variance. Suppose that we wished to study simultaneously the interaction of two or more variables, each varying in several ways. Specifically, we might be interested in the differential effects of three methods of instruction (the lecture method, the discussion method, and the project method) upon three different types of achievement as measured by three different but comparable tests (a test of factual information, a test of understanding of general principles, and a test of ability to make applications). The questions that we might be interested in answering by the experiment might be these: which of the three methods of instruction will result in the greatest over-all achievement, that is to say, on the combined tests? Will achievement be greatest in the area of facts, applications, or principles? Is achievement in each area independent of method of instruction or will achievement in the various areas be dependent upon the type of instruction?

A Two-Part Analysis

For purposes of illustration, let us assume that we have 45 subjects and that they are assigned at random to one of the 9 experimental conditions of Table 17.1, so that we have 5 subjects in each group. In the table, we have designated type of achievement as the A variable which is varied in three ways, A_1, A_2, and A_3. Method of instruction we have designated as the B variable which is also varied in three ways, B_1, B_2, and B_3. Thus the cell entry A_1B_1 represents factual achievement under the lecture method, and a similar interpretation can be made for each of the other cell entries. The row total A_1 represents factual achievement over all methods of instruction, and similar interpretations may be given each of the other row and column totals.

Table 17.1—Experimental Design for Studying the Influence of Three Different Methods of Instruction upon Three Different Kinds of Achievement

A: Type of Achievement	*B: Method of Instruction*			
	1. Lecture	*2. Discussion*	*3. Project*	Σ
1. Facts	A_1B_1	A_1B_2	A_1B_3	A_1
2. Principles	A_2B_1	A_2B_2	A_2B_3	A_2
3. Applications	A_3B_1	A_3B_2	A_3B_3	A_3
Σ	B_1	B_2	B_3	

With the border totals alone, in Table 17.1, we would have 3 comparisons to make for achievement and 3 comparisons to make for methods of instruction. If we compared every cell in the table, that is, every experimental condition with every other experimental condition, we would have 36 additional comparisons to make. Since we do not know whether any of these differences are significant or not, we shall make over-all comparisons first by means of the F test. We may then use the t test for the specific comparisons we are interested in, if F is significant. The results of the outcomes on the various achievement tests for each subject are given in Table 17.2. We proceed with the calculation of the sums of squares in the manner already familiar.

$$\begin{aligned} \textit{Total} &= (7)^2 + (10)^2 + (10)^2 + \cdots + (10)^2 - \frac{(340)^2}{45} \\ &= 2{,}938.00 - 2{,}568.89 \\ &= 369.11 \end{aligned}$$

$$\begin{aligned} \textit{Between} &= \frac{(50)^2}{5} + \frac{(40)^2}{5} + \frac{(25)^2}{5} + \cdots + \frac{(45)^2}{5} - \frac{(340)^2}{45} \\ &= 2{,}770.00 - 2{,}568.89 \\ &= 201.11 \end{aligned}$$

Table 17.2—Scores on Three Different Measures of Achievement for Groups Taught by Three Different Methods of Instruction

Type of Achievement	*Ind.*	*Method*			*Sum and Mean for Achievement*
		Lecture	*Discussion*	*Project*	
Facts	1	7	4	2	
	2	10	6	2	
	3	10	7	3	
	4	11	9	7	
	5	12	9	6	
	Σ	50	35	20	105
	Mean	10	7	4	7
Principles	1	6	10	5	
	2	5	10	4	
	3	8	11	7	
	4	9	11	8	
	5	12	13	11	
	Σ	40	55	35	130
	Mean	8	11	7	8.67
Applications	1	3	4	7	
	2	3	6	9	
	3	4	7	9	
	4	8	8	10	
	5	7	10	10	
	Σ	25	35	45	105
	Mean	5	7	9	7
Sum for Method		115	125	100	340
Mean for Method		7.67	8.33	6.67	7.56

$$\textit{Within groups} = 369.11 - 201.11$$

$$= 168.00$$

Before analyzing further the sum of squares between groups, let us test the significance of the mean square between groups (cells). Table 17.3 summarizes the analysis of variance. Then

$$F = \frac{25.14}{4.67} = 5.38$$

We enter the column of the table of F with the 8 degrees of freedom for the numerator and find the row entry corresponding to the 36 degrees of freedom of the denominator and find that an F of 3.04 will be significant

Table 17.3—Analysis of Variance of Scores on Three Different Measures of Achievement for Groups Taught by Three Different Methods of Instruction

Source of Variation	*Sum of Squares*	*df*	*Mean Square*	*F*
Between groups	201.11	8	25.14	5.38
Within groups	168.00	36	4.67	
Total	369.11	44		

Degrees of freedom:

1. Between groups $= k - 1$
2. Within groups $= k(n_i - 1) = kn_i - k = n - k$
3. Total $= kn_i - 1 = n - 1$

where k = the number of experimental groups
n_i = the number in each experimental group
n = the total number of subjects

at the 1 per cent point. According to the standards agreed upon, our obtained F of 5.38 is highly significant. We find the null hypothesis untenable, since if there were no differences in the populations the divergence between our estimates of the variance would occur as a result of sampling variation less than 1 per cent of the time. Hence we infer that the observed differences between our groups are not the result of chance.

Analysis of the Sum of Squares between Groups

But the information we have at the present time is not entirely satisfactory. We are pretty confident that there are differences between the 9 experimental groups, but what about differences in type of achievement? And are the methods of instruction equally effective as far as total achievement is concerned? Or is one method more effective with one type of achievement;

another method of instruction more effective with another kind of achievement? Let us analyze the sum of squares between groups to see if we can get any additional information that would assist us in answering these questions.

We may compute a sum of squares for achievement, by squaring the sum of scores for each type of achievement, that is, A_1, A_2, and A_3, dividing each of these squares by the number of observations on which it is based, summing, and then subtracting the correction term for origin. Thus the sum of squares for achievement will be

$$\textit{Achievement} = \frac{(105)^2}{15} + \frac{(130)^2}{15} + \frac{(105)^2}{15} - \frac{(340)^2}{45}$$

$$= 2{,}596.67 - 2{,}568.89$$

$$= 27.78$$

and the sum of squares for methods will be

$$\textit{Methods} = \frac{(115)^2}{15} + \frac{(125)^2}{15} + \frac{(100)^2}{15} - \frac{(340)^2}{45}$$

$$= 2{,}590.00 - 2{,}568.89$$

$$= 21.11$$

The sum of the sums of squares for achievement and methods is equal to $27.78 + 21.11 = 48.89$, and this is not equal to the sum of squares between groups, which we have found to be equal to 201.11. We have a remainder or residual which is called the sum of squares for *interaction*. The interaction sum of squares may be found by subtraction. Thus

$$\textit{Interaction} = \textit{Between groups} - (\textit{Methods} + \textit{Achievement}) \qquad \textbf{(17.1)}$$

$$= 201.11 - (21.11 + 27.78)$$

$$= 152.22$$

Let us see what we have accomplished. First we analyzed the total sum of squares into two parts, one part associated with variation between each of the cells or groups of Table 17.1, the second part associated with variation within each of the groups. We then proceeded to analyze further the sum of squares between groups. One part can be traced to variation between methods of instruction, another to variation between types of achievement. The third, or remainder, is called interaction, since it is the result of the joint effect of a particular method of instruction and a particular kind of achievement.

We summarize the results of our analysis in Table 17.4, showing what has happened to the total sum of squares and how the total number of degrees of freedom has been partitioned. Note that we have 9 experimental groups with 5 subjects in each group. Consequently, we have 4 degrees of freedom within each of these groups or $(9)(4) = 36$ degrees of freedom within groups. In the previous analysis we had 8 degrees of freedom available for the sum of squares based upon differences between the 9 experimental groups. The degrees of freedom between groups and within groups made up our total of $n - 1$ or 44 degrees of freedom. But we have further analyzed the sum of squares between groups into an achievement sum of squares, a methods sum of squares, and a residual or interaction sum of squares. And the 8 degrees of freedom must also be divided among these sums of squares. The methods sum of squares and the achievement sum of squares are each based upon 3 groups each and consequently each of these sums of squares will have 2 degrees of freedom. Thus, if 2 of the 8 degrees of freedom are allotted to methods and 2 to achievement, we have a remainder of 4 degrees of freedom for the residual or interaction sum of squares. The degrees of freedom for interaction may also be obtained by multiplying the number of degrees of freedom allotted to methods by the number of degrees of freedom allotted to achievement, as shown in Table 17.4.

The Tests of Significance

In Table 17.4 we have divided each of the sums of squares by the corresponding degrees of freedom to obtain the mean squares shown. In the column headed F the methods, achievement, and interaction mean squares have been divided by the mean square within groups. Each of the values of F must be evaluated according to the number of degrees of freedom involved in computing it. For achievement and method of instruction, the degrees of freedom are the same, 2 and 36, and from the table of F we find that a value of 3.26 will be required for significance at the 5 per cent point. Since our observed values of F for achievement and methods are 2.97 and 2.26, respectively, neither is significant at the 5 per cent point. The failure of the F for methods to be significant indicates that the differences in total achievement of groups taught by the different methods are not significant. Likewise, since the F for achievement is not significant, we cannot conclude that our subjects tend to learn facts better than principles or applications.

Table 17.4—Further Analysis of Variance of Scores on Three Different Measures of Achievement for Groups Taught by Three Different Methods of Instruction

Source of Variation	*Sum of Squares*	*df*	*Mean Square*	*F*
Type of achievement	27.78	2	13.89	2.97
Method of instruction	21.11	2	10.56	2.26
Interaction	152.22	4	38.06	8.15
Between groups	201.11	8	25.14	5.38
Within groups	168.00	36	4.67	
Total	369.11	44		

Degrees of freedom:

1. Type of achievement $= A - 1$
2. Method of instruction $= B - 1$
3. Interaction $= (A - 1)(B - 1)$
4. Between groups $= k - 1$
5. Within groups $= k(n_i - 1) = n - k$
6. Total $= kn_i - 1 = n - 1$

where A = the number of achievement groups or means
B = the number of methods groups or means
k = the total number of experimental groups or means
n_i = the number of subjects in each experimental group
n = the total number of subjects

The interaction F is based upon 4 and 36 degrees of freedom and from the table of F we find that a value of 3.89 will be significant at the 1 per cent point. Our observed value is 8.15 and is therefore highly significant. How may we interpret this? The interaction mean square, as we have said before, is a product of the joint effect of method of instruction and type of achievement. The fact that it is significant indicates that the effectiveness of a particular method of instruction depends upon the kind of achievement we are interested in measuring. One method of instruction is, in other words, more effective with one kind of achievement than another. Note again that the F test does not tell us specifically which method is most effective with which kind of achievement. But we may gain some insight into this matter by examining the means of the various groups as shown in Table 17.2. There we see that the lecture method seems to be most effective in factual achievement, the discussion method in the learning of principles, and the project method in the learning of applications.

We should complete our analysis of the data of Table 17.2 by using the t test for various comparisons of the means in which we are interested. The standard error of the mean of a single group will be given by formula (16.14) and the standard error of the difference between two means will be given by formula (16.15). Tukey's procedure for comparing individual means, described in the previous chapter, could also be applied to the group of 9 means.

A Further Discussion of Interaction

We may see more clearly the nature of an interaction between two variables if we consider a simplified experimental design in which each variable is varied in two ways. We shall let the A variable be method of instruction, with A_1 corresponding to the discussion method and A_2 to the lecture method. We shall let the B variable be type of achievement, with B_1 corresponding to factual information and B_2 to the learning of principles. We shall assume that n subjects have been divided at random into four groups of n_i subjects each. The groups are then assigned at random to one of the four possible combinations of experimental conditions. The mean scores of the four experimental groups are as shown below:

Group:	A_1B_1	A_1B_2	A_2B_1	A_2B_2
Mean:	84.0	76.0	60.0	46.0

These means may be arranged as shown in Table 17.5.

To determine whether the A variable, method of instruction, is a significant variable, we would test the difference between the means 80.0 and 53.0. To determine if the B variable, type of achievement, is a significant variable, we would test the difference between the means 72.0 and 61.0.

If there is *no interaction* between the two variables, method of instruction and type of achievement, then we would expect the difference in the fact and principle means to be the same, within random errors, regardless of the method of instruction. We see, however, that the difference between the fact and principle means is 8.0 for the discussion method, whereas the

Table 17.5—Mean Scores for Four Groups of Subjects Tested under Different Experimental Conditions

Method of Instruction		*Type of Achievement*			
		Facts B_1	*Principles* B_2	$\bar{X}_A$	$B_1 - B_2$
Discussion	A_1	84.0	76.0	80.0	8.0
Lecture	A_2	60.0	46.0	53.0	14.0
$\bar{X}_B$		72.0	61.0		
$A_1 - A_2$		24.0	30.0		

difference is 14.0 for the lecture method. Both of these differences should, in the absence of interaction, estimate the same quantity, the difference in type of achievement. The average of the two differences would be

$$\frac{8.0 + 14.0}{2} = 11.0$$

and this value represents the *main effect* of the B variable, type of achievement. It can be seen that this value is the same as the difference between the factual mean and the principle mean, referred to earlier, that is, $72.0 - 61.0 = 11.0$.

Again, assuming no interaction, the difference between the fact means for the discussion and lecture methods, $84.0 - 60.0 = 24.0$, and the difference between the principle means for the discussion and lecture methods, $76.0 - 46.0 = 30.0$, should be the same. Both differences, in the absence of interaction, should estimate the same quantity, the difference between the two methods of instruction. The average of these two differences is

$$\frac{24.0 + 30.0}{2} = 27.0$$

and this value represents the *main effect* of the A variable, method of instruction. It can be seen that the value 27.0, just obtained, is the same as the difference between the discussion and lecture means, that is, $80.0 - 53.0 = 27.0$.

In the present example, an interaction effect seems to be present. The discrepancy between the values 8.0 and 14.0, which supposedly estimate the same quantity, the difference attributable to type of achievement, is fairly large. It would seem that the superiority of factual achievement over the learning of principles is less in the case of the discussion method than it is in the case of the lecture method. The degree of superiority of factual achievement over the learning of principles, in other words, is influenced by the second variable, method of instruction, and we call this an *interaction effect.*

We may also approach the interaction effect from the point of view of the A variable instead of the B variable. For example, consider the two values 24.0 and 30.0 which we assumed to be estimates of the influence of the A variable, method of instruction. From the discrepancy between these two values, it is apparent that the superiority of the discussion method over the lecture method is greater in the case of the learning of general principles than it is in the case of factual learning. In other words, the degree of superiority of the discussion method over the lecture method is dependent upon the kind of achievement we measure. Again, we call this an interaction effect between the two variables, and it is the same interaction that we discussed before. We have simply approached it from the A variable instead of from the B variable.[1]

A Three-Part Analysis

You may recall that when we discussed the t test applied to two groups in which the observations were paired, we were forced to modify the formula for the standard error of the difference between the means to take into account the possible correlation involved. If we have several such groups, in which observations are paired, and we wish to apply the analysis of variance, we must also make certain modifications of the procedures described in the last chapter.

We shall assume, for example, that we have 5 subjects and that each subject is tested under 5 different experimental conditions. The observations on the dependent variable may be arranged as shown in Table 17.6. Each row of this table corresponds to the performance of a single subject, and each column corresponds to a different experimental condition. If we had but two experimental conditions so that we had but two columns, our design would be exactly comparable to the case described earlier for the t test applied to paired observations. All that we have done is to extend the case of two groups of paired observations to several groups.

---

[1] The interaction effect, in the present example, is measured by the absolute difference between 8.0 and 14.0, or between 24.0 and 30.0, which is 6. It can be shown that the interaction sum of squares is based upon the value of this absolute difference. See, for example, Edwards (1950*a*, pp. 217–218).

Table 17.6—Outcomes of an Experiment with Five Subjects Tested under Five Different Experimental Conditions

Subjects	*Experimental Conditions* 1	2	3	4	5	Σ	$\bar{X}$
1	8	10	10	11	11	50	10.0
2	7	9	9	10	10	45	9.0
3	6	7	8	9	10	40	8.0
4	6	6	7	8	8	35	7.0
5	6	6	5	7	6	30	6.0
Σ	33	38	39	45	45	200	
$\bar{X}$	6.6	7.6	7.8	9.0	9.0		8.0

The total sum of squares for the data of Table 17.6 may now be analyzed into three component parts. One sum of squares will be based upon the variation of the column means, a second upon the variation of the row means, and the third will be a residual which remains after we have removed the row and column variation from the total. We shall go through the calculations involved and the test of significance and then come back and examine the nature of the residual sum of squares more closely.

Sums of Squares

We may obtain the total sum of squares, the sum of squares between columns, and the sum of squares between rows, in the manner already familiar. Then

$$\textit{Total} = (8)^2 + (7)^2 + (6)^2 + \cdots + (8)^2 + (6)^2 - \frac{(200)^2}{25}$$

$$= 1{,}678.00 - 1{,}600.00$$

$$= 78.00$$

$$\textit{Between columns} = \frac{(33)^2}{5} + \frac{(38)^2}{5} + \cdots + \frac{(45)^2}{5} - \frac{(200)^2}{25}$$

$$= 1{,}620.80 - 1{,}600.00$$

$$= 20.80$$

$$\textit{Between rows} = \frac{(50)^2}{5} + \frac{(45)^2}{5} + \cdots + \frac{(30)^2}{5} - \frac{(200)^2}{25}$$

$$= 1{,}650.00 - 1{,}600.00$$

$$= 50.00$$

The residual sum of squares may then be obtained by subtracting the sum of squares for columns and the sum of squares for rows from the total sum of squares. Thus

$$\textit{Residual} = \textit{Total} - (\textit{Between columns} + \textit{Between rows}) \qquad \textbf{(17.2)}$$

$$= 78.00 - (20.80 + 50.00)$$

$$= 7.20$$

Degrees of Freedom and Mean Squares

The results of our analysis are summarized in Table 17.7. For the row sum of squares we have $n - 1$ degrees of freedom, where n is equal to the number of rows, and for the column sum of squares we have $k - 1$ degrees of freedom, where k is equal to the number of columns. The degrees of freedom for the total sum of squares will be equal to the total number of

Table 17.7—Analysis of Variance of the Data of Table 17.6

Source of Variation	*Sum of Squares*	*df*	*Mean Square*	*F*
Between columns	20.8	4	5.20	11.56
Between rows	50.0	4	12.50	27.78
Residual	7.2	16	.45	
Total	78.0	24		

Degrees of freedom:

1. Between columns = $k - 1$
2. Between rows = $n - 1$
3. Residual = $(n - 1)(k - 1)$
4. Total = $nk - 1$

where k = the number of columns or experimental conditions
n = the number of rows or subjects

observations minus 1, or $nk - 1$. The degrees of freedom for the residual sum of squares may be obtained by subtraction of the degrees of freedom for rows and columns from the total. The degrees of freedom for the residual sum of squares will also be given by the product of the degrees of freedom for the row and column sums of squares, or $(n - 1)(k - 1)$. Dividing the row, column, and residual sums of squares by their respective degrees of freedom, we obtain the mean squares shown in the table.

Tests of Significance

If we test the column mean square for significance, using the residual mean square as the denominator of the F ratio, we have F equal to 11.56 with 4 and 16 degrees of freedom. From the table of F we find that a value of 4.77 will be significant at the 1 per cent point for 4 and 16 degrees of freedom, and we may infer that the differences in the column means are indicative of real differences in the experimental conditions. Although we are not primarily interested in the significance of the row means, we find that F is 27.78, and this is highly significant for 4 and 16 degrees of freedom also. This simply tells us what we might have already guessed: that our subjects show significant differences in their mean performance.

The Residual Sum of Squares

Now let us examine the nature of the residual sum of squares in greater detail. In Table 17.8, we give a schematic representation of the experimental design, with n subjects tested under k conditions, so that our total

Table 17.8—Schematic Representation of Observations Obtained from n Subjects with Each Subject Tested under k Conditions

	Experimental Conditions							
Subjects	*1*	*2*	*3*	·	*j*	·	*k*	*Means*
1	X_{11}	X_{12}	X_{13}	·	X_{1j}	·	X_{1k}	$\bar{X}_{1.}$
2	X_{21}	X_{22}	X_{23}	·	X_{2j}	·	X_{2k}	$\bar{X}_{2.}$
3	X_{31}	X_{32}	X_{33}	·	X_{3j}	·	X_{3k}	$\bar{X}_{3.}$
·	·	·	·	·	·	·	·	·
i	X_{i1}	X_{i2}	X_{i3}	·	X_{ij}	·	X_{ik}	$\bar{X}_{i.}$
·	·	·	·	·	·	·	·	·
n	X_{n1}	X_{n2}	X_{n3}	·	X_{nj}	·	X_{nk}	$\bar{X}_{n.}$
Means	$\bar{X}_{.1}$	$\bar{X}_{.2}$	$\bar{X}_{.3}$	·	$\bar{X}_{.j}$	·	$\bar{X}_{.k}$	$\bar{X}_{..}$

number of observations is nk. The score for the ith subject under the jth condition is X_{ij}. The mean score for the ith subject is represented by $\bar{X}_{i\cdot}$, and the mean score for the jth experimental condition is represented by $\bar{X}_{\cdot j}$. The mean of all nk observations is represented by $\bar{X}_{\cdot\cdot}$. Using this notation, let us express the scores of Table 17.6 in terms of their deviations from the mean $\bar{X}_{\cdot\cdot}$ of all nk observations, as shown in Sub-Table A of Table 17.9.

You will note that the sum of the deviations in Sub-Table A is equal to zero and that the sum of squares of the values is equal to the total sum of squares. That is, squaring and summing over all nk observations, we have

$$\begin{aligned} Total &= \sum_{j=1}^{k} \sum_{i=1}^{n} (X_{ij} - \bar{X}_{\cdot\cdot})^2 \qquad \textbf{(17.3)} \\ &= 78.00 \end{aligned}$$

It is this total sum of squares that is to be further analyzed into the sum of squares between columns, between rows, and the residual sum of squares.

You may observe, in Sub-Table A, that the row and column means are now expressed in terms of their deviations from the combined mean, that is, in terms of $\bar{X}_{i\cdot} - \bar{X}_{\cdot\cdot}$ and $\bar{X}_{\cdot j} - \bar{X}_{\cdot\cdot}$, respectively. For example, in Table 17.6 we see that the mean for Experimental Condition 1 is 6.6. The combined mean is equal to 8.0. If we subtract the combined mean from 6.6 we have $6.6 - 8.0 = -1.4$, and this is the mean of the values for Experimental Condition 1 in Sub-Table A. Similarly, the mean for Subject 1 in Table 17.6 is 10.0. Subtracting the combined mean from this row mean, we have $10.0 - 8.0 = 2.0$, and this is the mean for Subject 1 in Sub-Table A.

Let us now remove from the individual observations of Sub-Table A the variation attributable to the column means. In other words, we shall set the column means all equal to zero by subtracting the mean of each column of the sub-table from the corresponding entries in the column. We have just seen that the column means of Sub-Table A are equal to $\bar{X}_{\cdot j} - \bar{X}_{\cdot\cdot}$, so that the resulting deviations will be given by

$$(X_{ij} - \bar{X}_{\cdot\cdot}) - (\bar{X}_{\cdot j} - \bar{X}_{\cdot\cdot}) = X_{ij} - \bar{X}_{\cdot j} \qquad \textbf{(17.4)}$$

These deviations are shown in Sub-Table B. Squaring formula (17.4) and summing over all nk observations, we then have[2]

$$\sum_{j=1}^{k} \sum_{i=1}^{n} (X_{ij} - \bar{X}_{\cdot\cdot})^2 - n \sum_{j=1}^{k} (\bar{X}_{\cdot j} - \bar{X}_{\cdot\cdot})^2 = \sum_{j=1}^{k} \sum_{i=1}^{n} (X_{ij} - \bar{X}_{\cdot j})^2 \qquad \textbf{(17.5)}$$

[2] All cross-product terms disappear upon summation.

or

$$78.0 - 20.8 = 57.2$$

The sum of squares 57.2 is the sum of squares within columns or the total sum of squares minus the sum of squares between columns. It is apparent

Table 17.9—Deviation Values of the Scores in Table 17.6

Sub-Table A: $X_{ij} - \bar{X}_{..}$

	1	*2*	*3*	*4*	*5*	Σ	*Means*
1	0	2	2	3	3	10.0	2.0
2	−1	1	1	2	2	5.0	1.0
3	−2	−1	0	1	2	0.0	.0
4	−2	−2	−1	0	0	−5.0	−1.0
5	−2	−2	−3	−1	−2	−10.0	−2.0
Σ	−7.0	−2.0	−1.0	5.0	5.0		
Means	−1.4	−.4	−.2	1.0	1.0		.0

Sub-Table B: $X_{ij} - \bar{X}_{.j}$

	1	*2*	*3*	*4*	*5*	Σ	*Means*
1	1.4	2.4	2.2	2.0	2.0	10.0	2.0
2	.4	1.4	1.2	1.0	1.0	5.0	1.0
3	−.6	−.6	.2	.0	1.0	.0	.0
4	−.6	−1.6	−.8	−1.0	−1.0	−5.0	−1.0
5	−.6	−1.6	−2.8	−2.0	−3.0	−10.0	−2.0
Σ	.0	.0	.0	.0	.0		.0

Sub-Table C: $X_{ij} - \bar{X}_{.j} - \bar{X}_{i.} + \bar{X}_{..}$

	1	*2*	*3*	*4*	*5*	Σ
1	−.6	.4	.2	.0	.0	.0
2	−.6	.4	.2	.0	.0	.0
3	−.6	−.6	.2	.0	1.0	.0
4	.4	−.6	.2	.0	.0	.0
5	1.4	.4	−.8	.0	−1.0	.0
Σ	.0	.0	.0	.0	.0	.0

then, in Sub-Table B, that in setting the column means equal to zero, we have removed from the total sum of squares the sum of squares based upon variation in the column means.

You will note, however, that the row means of Sub-Table B are exactly the same as those of Sub-Table A. We have not as yet removed from the observations the variation attributable to the row means. We can do so, however, by setting the row means equal to zero. Each of the row means of Sub-Table B is equal to $\bar{X}_{i\cdot} - \bar{X}_{\cdot\cdot}$, and if we subtract these values from both sides of formula (17.4), we obtain

$$(X_{ij} - \bar{X}_{\cdot\cdot}) - (\bar{X}_{\cdot j} - \bar{X}_{\cdot\cdot}) - (\bar{X}_{i\cdot} - \bar{X}_{\cdot\cdot}) = X_{ij} - \bar{X}_{\cdot j} - \bar{X}_{i\cdot} + \bar{X}_{\cdot\cdot} \quad \textbf{(17.6)}$$

These deviations are shown in Sub-Table C. Squaring formula (17.6) and summing over all nk observations, we would then have[3]

$$\sum_{j=1}^{k} \sum_{i=1}^{n} (X_{ij} - \bar{X}_{\cdot\cdot})^2 - n \sum_{j=1}^{k} (\bar{X}_{\cdot j} - \bar{X}_{\cdot\cdot})^2 - k \sum_{i=1}^{n} (\bar{X}_{i\cdot} - \bar{X}_{\cdot\cdot})^2$$
$$= \sum_{j=1}^{k} \sum_{i=1}^{n} (X_{ij} - \bar{X}_{\cdot j} - \bar{X}_{i\cdot} + \bar{X}_{\cdot\cdot})^2 \quad \textbf{(17.7)}$$

or

$$78.0 - 20.8 - 50.0 = 7.2$$

which is the total sum of squares minus the sum of squares between columns and the sum of squares between rows.

The sum of squares of the deviations in Sub-Table C, or the right-hand side of formula (17.7), thus gives the residual sum of squares of the analysis of variance. The residual sum of squares represents the remaining variation in our original data after we have removed the variation attributable to the row and column means.

The residual sum of squares corresponds to an interaction sum of squares between rows and columns of our original data. It is thus a measure of the tendency of the subjects to respond differentially to the experimental conditions. Our interest is in being able to generalize about the average performance of the subjects under the different experimental conditions. The fact that the mean square between columns (experimental conditions) was significantly larger than the residual or interaction mean square means that, although there may be some tendency for the different subjects to respond differentially to the various experimental conditions, on the average the subjects do better under certain conditions than under others.[4]

---

[3] All cross-product terms again disappear upon summation.

[4] We cannot test the significance of the residual or interaction mean square in this example because we have no mean square within groups with which to compare it.

Examination of the means for the experimental conditions, shown in Table 17.6, indicates that Experimental Conditions 4 and 5 produce the higher means.

Standard Errors

We could now complete our analysis of the experimental design in which n subjects are tested under k conditions, by making t tests for the comparisons of interest. The standard error of a single mean will be given by

$$s_{\bar{x}} = \frac{s}{\sqrt{n}} \tag{17.8}$$

where $s_{\bar{x}}$ = the standard error of the mean
s = the square root of the residual mean square with $(n-1)(k-1)$ degrees of freedom
n = the number of observations on which the mean is based

The standard error of the difference between two means will then be given by

$$s_{\bar{x}_1-\bar{x}_2} = \sqrt{s_{\bar{x}_1}{}^2 + s_{\bar{x}_2}{}^2}$$

$$= \sqrt{\frac{s^2}{n_1} + \frac{s^2}{n_2}}$$

$$= s\sqrt{\frac{1}{n_1} + \frac{1}{n_2}} \tag{17.9}$$

where s is again the square root of the residual mean square. If we take the difference between two means and divide the difference by the standard error of the difference, as given by formula (17.9), we shall have a value of t. This t may be evaluated in the table of t with degrees of freedom equal to those associated with the residual mean square of the analysis of variance. Tukey's procedure for comparing individual means, described in the previous chapter, could also be applied to the 5 experimental means. In this instance we would take $s_{\bar{x}}$ as given by formula (17.8) and s as the square root of the residual mean square with df equal to $(n - 1)(k - 1)$.

Equating Groups

The three-part analysis of variance just described would also be applicable to any case where we have observations paired or equated across the rows of the table of experimental data. For example, we might have given subjects an initial test and arranged them in rank order in terms of their performance on this test. If we had 5 experimental conditions, we might then take the 5 subjects with the highest scores and assign at random one subject to each of the experimental conditions. Thus the first row of the table would consist of subjects of comparable levels on the initial test. Similarly, we could take the next 5 subjects and assign one at random to each of the experimental conditions. The second row of our table would also consist of subjects of comparable levels on the initial test. This process could be repeated until all of the subjects had been assigned, the only requirement being that the total number of subjects is some multiple of the number of experimental conditions. The analysis of variance for the experimental observations would be a three-part analysis of the kind described.

Test for Linearity of Regression

In Table 17.10 we have values of a dependent variable Y obtained under different experimental conditions, that is, for an independent variable X. Let us assume that a total of 80 subjects were assigned at random to the 8 experimental conditions so that we have 10 subjects for each condition. The subjects practiced with experimental materials until they reached a certain criterion of learning. Then we shall assume that the subjects in each group were given a retention test upon the material learned, with the Y variable representing a measure of *loss* in retention, that is, the greater the value of Y the greater the loss in retention. The X variable corresponds to the time elapsed between the learning period and the test of retention. For simplicity, we shall let the elapsed times represent 1-day intervals, so that Group 1 was tested 1 day after learning, Group 2 was tested 2 days after learning, and so on.

We find the total sum of squares for the Y variable in the usual way. Thus

$$\begin{aligned} \textit{Total} &= (37)^2 + (22)^2 + (22)^2 + \cdots + (63)^2 + (58)^2 - \frac{(4{,}521)^2}{80} \\ &= 25{,}886.0 \end{aligned}$$

The sum of squares between groups or columns will be given by

$$\begin{aligned} \textit{Between} &= \frac{(247)^2}{10} + \frac{(417)^2}{10} + \cdots + \frac{(770)^2}{10} - \frac{(4{,}521)^2}{80} \\ &= 19{,}507.9 \end{aligned}$$

Table 17.10—Observations on a Dependent Variable Y for Eight Groups of Ten Subjects Each, Tested under Different Experimental Conditions X

	Experimental Conditions								
	1	*2*	*3*	*4*	*5*	*6*	*7*	*8*	
	37	36	67	43	76	67	74	94	
	22	45	60	75	66	64	74	85	
	22	47	54	66	43	70	64	80	
	25	23	51	46	62	65	86	81	
	11	43	49	56	65	60	68	80	
	27	43	38	62	43	55	72	80	
	23	54	55	51	42	57	62	69	
	24	45	56	63	60	66	64	80	
	25	41	68	52	78	79	78	63	
	31	40	58	50	66	80	61	58	
$\sum Y_i$	247	417	556	564	601	663	703	770	$4{,}521 = \sum Y$
Means	24.7	41.7	55.6	56.4	60.1	66.3	70.3	77.0	
X	1	2	3	4	5	6	7	8	
nX	10	20	30	40	50	60	70	80	$360 = \sum X$
nX^2	10	40	90	160	250	360	490	640	$2{,}040 = \sum X^2$
$X \sum Y_i$	247	834	1,668	2,256	3,005	3,978	4,921	6,160	$23{,}069 = \sum XY$

The sum of squares within groups or columns may then be found by subtracting the sum of squares between columns from the total sum of squares. Then

$$\textit{Within columns} = 25{,}886.0 - 19{,}507.9$$

$$= 6{,}378.1$$

The results of our analysis are summarized in Table 17.11. We see that the mean square between columns divided by the mean square within columns gives us an F equal to 31.46. From the table of F we find that for 7 and 72 degrees of freedom the value of 31.46 is highly significant with a probability of much less than .01. We conclude that the means do differ significantly.

Table 17.11—Analysis of Variance of the Scores of Table 17.10

Source of Variation	*Sum of Squares*	*df*	*Mean Square*	*F*
Between columns	19,507.9	7	2,786.843	31.46
Within columns	6,378.1	72	88.585	
Total	25,886.0	79		

In Figure 17.1 we have plotted the Y means against the corresponding time intervals. The question we now raise is whether the trend of the means can be represented adequately by a straight line. This question is a general

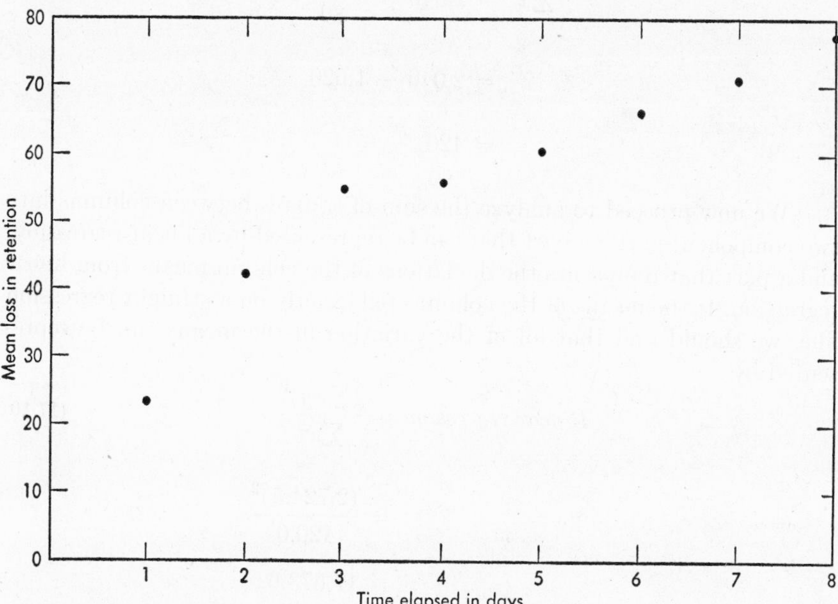

Fig. 17.1—Mean loss in retention plotted against elapsed time. Data are from Table 17.10.

one and applies to any correlation table where we compute a product-moment correlation coefficient to represent degree of linear relationship between a Y variable and an X variable. What we now propose is a test of the hypothesis of linear regression.

At the bottom of Table 17.10, we show the calculations necessary for obtaining the product sum in terms of formula (7.11). Substituting in this formula, we obtain

$$\Sigma xy = 23{,}069 - \frac{(360)(4{,}521)}{80}$$

$$= 23{,}069 - 20{,}344.5$$

$$= 2{,}724.5$$

We may also obtain the total sum of squared deviations for X from the row sums at the bottom of Table 17.10. Then

$$\Sigma x^2 = 2{,}040 - \frac{(360)^2}{80}$$

$$= 2{,}040 - 1{,}620$$

$$= 420$$

We now proceed to analyze the sum of squares between columns into two component parts: a part that can be represented by a linear regression, and a part that represents the deviations of the column means from linear regression. If the means of the columns fell exactly on a straight regression line, we should find that all of the variation in the means can be represented by

$$\textit{Linear regression} = \frac{(\Sigma xy)^2}{\Sigma x^2} \qquad \textbf{(17.10)}$$

$$= \frac{(2{,}724.5)^2}{420.0}$$

$$= 17{,}673.6$$

Then, if we subtract the above quantity from the sum of squares between columns, we shall be left with a residual which represents the deviations of the means of the columns from the linear regression line. Thus

$$\textit{Deviations from regression} = \textit{Between columns} - \textit{Linear regression} \qquad \textbf{(17.11)}$$

$$= 19{,}507.9 - 17{,}673.6$$

$$= 1{,}834.3$$

We know, from the previous discussions of regression, that the sum of squares obtained from formula (17.11) will have degrees of freedom equal to 1 less than the number of degrees of freedom associated with the first term on the right.[5] In the present example, this is the sum of squares between columns, and it has 7 degrees of freedom. Then the sum of squares representing deviations from regression, as given by formula (17.11), will have degrees of freedom equal to 1 less than the degrees of freedom between groups or columns. In the present example, this will be 6 degrees of freedom. The 1 degree of freedom that we lose in formula (17.11) is associated with the sum of squares for linear regression of formula (17.10).

Table 17.12 summarizes our analysis. We find that the mean square for deviations from linear regression is equal to 305.717. The mean square within columns or groups is equal to 88.585. We obtain a value of F by

Table 17.12—Test for Linearity of Regression of the Means of Table 17.10

Source of Variation	*Sum of Squares*	*df*	*Mean Square*	*F*
Linear regression	17,673.6	1	17,673.600	
Deviations from regression	1,834.3	6	305.717	3.45
Between columns	19,507.9	7	2,786.843	31.46
Within columns	6,378.1	72	88.585	
Total	25,886.0	79		

dividing the mean square for deviations from linear regression by the mean square within groups. The value of F obtained is equal to 3.45 with 6 and 72 degrees of freedom. From the table of F, we observe that our obtained value is significant beyond the 1 per cent point. We conclude, therefore, that the column means deviate significantly from the linear regression line.

The Case of Unequal n's in the Columns

It should be emphasized that although for the data of Table 17.10 we have equal n's in the columns, this is not a necessary condition for testing for linearity of regression. The test described can be applied to any correlation table. All that is necessary is that we find the sum of squares between columns for Y and the sum of squares within columns. Then, if we find the product sum for X and Y, and the sum of squares for X, we can solve for the sum of squares for linear regression of formula (17.10) and the sum of squares for deviations from linear regression of formula (17.11).

[5] See the discussion on page 313.

Then the sum of squares between columns will be analyzed into the two parts mentioned previously: a sum of squares corresponding to linear regression with 1 degree of freedom, and a sum of squares representing deviations from linear regression with $k - 2$ degrees of freedom, where k is the number of columns in the correlation table. The test of significance is made by finding the mean square for deviations from linear regression and dividing this mean square by the mean square within columns to obtain F. The obtained value of F can then be evaluated with reference to the table of F with the degrees of freedom involved.

■ Test of Significance of the Correlation Ratio

If you will go back to Chapter 10 and examine the various formulas for the correlation ratio squared, you will find that, in the analysis of variance terms, the correlation ratio squared, for Y on X, is merely

$$\eta_{yx}^2 = \frac{\textit{Sum of squares between groups or columns}}{\textit{Total sum of squares}} \tag{17.12}$$

To determine whether the correlation ratio is significantly greater than zero is to determine whether the variation between the means of the columns of the correlation table is significantly greater than the variation within columns. This can easily be tested by finding

$$F = \frac{\textit{Sum of squares between columns}/(k - 1)}{\textit{Sum of squares within columns}/(n - k)} \tag{17.13}$$

where k is the number of columns in the correlation table, and n is the total number of observations. It should be clear that the F obtained above is merely the ratio of the mean square between columns to the mean square within columns in the analysis of variance. Then the table of F will be entered with $k - 1$ degrees of freedom for the numerator and $n - k$ degrees of freedom for the denominator. If the value of F obtained from formula (17.13) is significant, we may conclude that the correlation ratio is significantly greater than zero.

In calculating the correlation ratio squared η_{yx}^2, we ordinarily compute the total sum of squares and the sum of squares between columns. It may be emphasized again that the sum of squares within columns may be obtained by subtracting the sum of squares between columns from the total sum of squares.

■ EXAMPLES

17.1—Assume that we are interested in studying differences in retention between groups that have been presented with material by different methods. We are also interested in studying the relative effectiveness of the methods of presentation, as far as retention is concerned, at three different age levels. We have 30 subjects at each age level. Within each age level subjects have been assigned at random to one of the three methods groups. The hypothetical outcomes of our experiment are listed below.

	Methods		
Age Groups	*A*	*B*	*C*
	8	9	5
	5	4	3
	6	8	7
	8	4	5
I	9	3	3
	10	6	1
	9	7	5
	7	6	4
	8	7	3
	10	6	4
	6	6	9
	1	5	8
	1	9	9
	6	7	11
II	5	5	8
	4	6	11
	3	6	10
	6	5	7
	4	4	8
	4	7	9
	7	7	5
	3	5	9
	6	8	8
	2	5	7
III	3	5	7
	5	8	8
	3	6	6
	3	6	8
	4	6	5
	4	4	7

(*a*) Find the total sum of squares, the sum of squares within groups, and the sum of squares between the 9 groups.
(*b*) Analyze the sum of squares between groups into a sum of squares for methods, age levels, and interaction.
(*c*) Make the various tests of significance and interpret your results.

17.2—Here is a set of scores for practice.

	Experimental Conditions		
Subjects	*A*	*B*	*C*
1	11	10	12
2	10	9	11
3	10	9	12
4	8	9	10
5	8	7	8
6	8	8	9
7	8	6	9
8	6	5	8
9	6	3	5
10	5	4	6

(*a*) Find the total sum of squares, the sum of squares within columns, and the sum of squares between columns. Find the value of F, using the mean square within columns as the error term.
(*b*) Find the sum of squares between rows and subtract it from the sum of squares within columns. The remainder will be the row $\times$ column interaction sum of squares. Test the mean square for columns for significance, using the interaction mean square as your error term. Compare the results of this analysis, assuming subjects have been matched across rows, with the results obtained in the first analysis.

17.3—The statement was made in the text that if the means of the columns in a correlation table fell exactly on a linear regression line, then all of the variation in the means could be accounted for by formula (17.10). The data given below illustrate this.

Trials		
1	2	3
3	4	6
1	0	11
2	8	1

Find the total sum of squares, the sum of squares within columns, and the between columns sum of squares. Let the observations in the table be the values of the dependent Y variable, and let the independent variable X be the trials, with values of 1, 2, and 3, as shown. Find the product sum for all 9 observations and the sum of squares for the X values. Then find the sum of squares for linear regression of formula (17.10). Is this equal to the sum of squares between columns?

17.4—Given the following correlation table, test for linearity of regression.

	35–39	1				
	30–34	1	2		2	
	25–29		1	2		
Y Variable	20–24	1	1	2	1	
	15–19		1	1		
	10–14				1	2
	5– 9					1
		1	2	3	4	5

X Variable

17.5—The following table will illustrate another point made in the text.

Experimental Conditions

A	*B*	*C*	*D*
5	2	7	4
4	3	6	3
3	4	5	2
2	5	4	1
1	6	3	0

(*a*) Find the total sum of squares, the sum of squares within columns, and the sum of squares between columns. Find the value of F.

(*b*) Now find the sum of squares between rows, assuming each row corresponds to a single subject tested under all 4 conditions. Subtract the row sum of squares from the sum of squares within columns to obtain the residual or interaction sum of squares. Test the between-columns mean square for significance, using the interaction mean square as an error term. How would you explain the results of these two analyses?

The χ^2 Test of Significance

In research we often encounter problems in which our interest is in the number of subjects, objects, or measurements falling in each of various categories. For example, the items in a test might be classified in terms of whether they were primarily concerned with facts, principles, vocabulary, and so forth. We would then have a certain observed number of items in each of the various classes or categories. Or we might have a group of subjects who could be classified in terms of whether they passed or failed an item on a test. We would then have a certain observed number of subjects in each of the two categories, pass and fail. When we make a frequency distribution, we may regard the class intervals as categories, with the frequencies representing the observed number of measurements falling within each category or class interval.

When we wanted to make an inference concerning the population mean, on the basis of a sample mean, we found that we could approach the problem by setting up some null hypothesis about the population mean. Then, by finding the deviation of our observed sample mean from the hypothetical value and dividing this deviation by the standard error of the mean, we arrived at a statistic called t. And, since the sampling distribution of t under the null hypothesis was known, we were able to make a probability statement concerning the frequency with which values of t as large as, or larger than, the one we obtained would occur by chance, assuming the hypothesis to be true.

Similarly, in problems dealing with the *observed number* of observations falling in each of various categories, we may test any null hypothesis that will yield an *expected number* for each of the various categories. By "expected number" or "expected frequency" we shall mean a number obtained from the testing of the null hypothesis. These numbers are sometimes called "theoretical numbers" or "theoretical frequencies" and also "hypothetical numbers" or "hypothetical frequencies." In general, if we have k categories, with $n_1, n_2, n_i, \cdots, n_k$ observations in the respective categories, we shall also have $n_1', n_2', n_i', \cdots, n_k'$ expected observations in the respective categories, with $\sum_1^k n_i = \sum_1^k n_i'$.

The expected numbers are obtained from the null hypothesis that specifies the proportion of the observations in the population falling in each of the categories. If we let p_i represent the proportion in the ith category in terms of the null hypothesis, with $\sum_1^k p_i = 1.00$, then

$$np_i = n_i' \tag{18.1}$$

where n = the sample size or $\sum_1^k n_i$

p_i = the theoretical proportion in the ith category

n_i' = the expected number in the ith category

The null hypothesis may be tested in terms of the χ^2 distribution. The calculations are simple. We merely take the difference between each observed and expected number, square these discrepancies, divide each squared discrepancy by the corresponding expected number, and sum. The result is a value of χ^2. Thus

$$\chi^2 = \sum_1^k \frac{(n_i - n_i')^2}{n_i'} \tag{18.2}$$

where χ^2 = chi square

n_i = the observed number of observations in the ith category

n_i' = the expected number of observations in the ith category and the k over the summation sign indicates that we sum over all k categories.

■ A Simple Example

Suppose that we have interviewed a random sample of 50 students at a given college. We have presented each student with two proposed titles for a new college magazine and have asked each student to choose one of the two. We find that 30 of the students say they prefer Title 1 and that 20 say they prefer Title 2. In this problem, the hypothesis we are probably most interested in testing is that we have a random sample from a population in which the proportion favoring Title 1 is .5 and the proportion favoring Title 2 is .5. If this hypothesis is true, then, with a sample of 50 observations, we should expect 25 observations in Category 1, that is, favoring Title 1, and 25 in Category 2, that is, favoring Title 2. Our sample data will offer evidence against this hypothesis either if the observed number in Category 1 is greater than 25 or if the number in Category 1 is less than 25. Substituting in formula (18.2) with the observed and expected numbers, we obtain

$$\chi^2 = \frac{(30 - 25)^2}{25} + \frac{(20 - 25)^2}{25}$$

$$= \frac{(5)^2}{25} + \frac{(-5)^2}{25}$$

$$= 1.0 + 1.0$$

$$= 2.0$$

We have presented the calculation of χ^2 in some detail because we wish to make it perfectly clear that the same deviations or discrepancies would arise if the observed numbers in our sample were such that 20 preferred Title 1 and 30 preferred Title 2. The deviations of 5 and -5 that we have above would merely shift positions, and we would, in this case also, obtain a value of χ^2 equal to 2.0. The value of χ^2 as calculated, therefore, takes into account possible deviations from the null hypothesis in either direction.

To evaluate the χ^2 of 2.0, we must enter the table of χ^2—Table IV, in the Appendix—with the number of degrees of freedom involved. We stated earlier that the concept of degrees of freedom may be regarded as having to do with the number of observations that are free to vary once certain restrictions are placed upon the data. In the present problem the single restriction that we place upon the data in using formula (18.2) is that $\sum_1^k (n_i - n_i') = \sum_1^k n_i - \sum_1^k n_i' = 0$. This restriction is apparent from formula (18.1), where we may observe that if we sum both sides of the formula we obtain $n\sum_1^k p_i = \sum_1^k n_i'$ and, since $\sum_1^k p_i = 1.00$, we have $n = \sum n_i'$. In the present problem we have $k = 2$ categories, and, because of the restriction placed upon the data, only one of the two deviations is free to vary. We thus have $k - 1 = 1$ degree of freedom to evaluate the χ^2 of 2.0.

The column headings of the table of χ^2—Table IV, in the Appendix—show the proportion of the total area in the χ^2 distribution falling to the right of ordinates erected at the tabled entries of χ^2. If we enter the table of χ^2 with 1 degree of freedom, we find that our observed value of χ^2 would have to be equal to or greater than 3.841, if it is to be one of those values that would occur by chance 5 per cent of the time or less when the null hypothesis is true. Values of 2.0 or greater would occur somewhere between 10 and 20 per cent of the time when the null hypothesis is true. If we have decided to reject the null hypothesis only if the probability of a Type I error does not exceed .05, we shall have to regard the null hypothesis as tenable in the present example.

Relationship between the Sample Size, the Deviations, and χ^2

The example we have just discussed may be used to illustrate several things about the relationship between the sample size n, the deviations $n_i - n_i'$, and χ^2. If the deviation $n_i - n_i'$ is constant and the sample size is increased, the value of χ^2 will decrease. For the title data, for example, we had a deviation of 5, with n equal to 50 and χ^2 equal to 2.0. If the sample size is increased to 100, with the deviation remaining 5, then χ^2 will be equal to 1.0. Doubling the sample size and holding the deviation constant has, in other words, reduced χ^2 by one half. If the sample size is increased to 200, with the deviation remaining 5, then χ^2 will be .5. Quadrupling the sample size and holding the deviation constant has reduced χ^2 by one fourth. Since it is true that the smaller the value of χ^2 the greater the probability of its being equaled or exceeded, we can interpret this to mean that, while a deviation of 5 may be expected to occur relatively infrequently in a sample of 50, it can be expected to occur much more frequently as the sample size is increased.

If we increase the sample size from 50 to 100 and also increase the deviation from 5 to 10, then the value of χ^2 will also be doubled, that is, we shall now have a χ^2 of 4.0 instead of 2.0. If we increase the sample size from 50 to 200, that is, multiply it by 4, and also multiply the deviation by 4 so that we now have a deviation of 20 instead of 5, then the obtained value of χ^2 will also be 4 times larger than our original value. χ^2 will now be 8.0 instead of 2.0. Since the larger the value of χ^2, the smaller the probability of its being equaled or exceeded, we can interpret this to mean that a deviation that is 10 per cent of the sample size will occur relatively infrequently when the sample is 50 and even less frequently in larger samples.

The deviation that has an equal likelihood of occurrence with an increase in the sample size is the one that will result in the same value of χ^2 as obtained with the smaller sample. If we multiply the sample size by some value k, then the deviation that has an equal likelihood of occurrence will be one that is $\sqrt{k}$ times the original deviation. For the title data, for example, if the sample size is multipled by 4, that is, increased from 50 to 200, the deviation that has an equal likelihood of occurrence will be $\sqrt{4}\,(5) = 10$. A deviation of 10 for the increased sample size will give us exactly the same value of 2.0 for χ^2 that we obtained from our original sample.

■ χ^2 and the Normal Deviate z

If we have but two categories in which our observations will fall, and if the theoretical proportion for one of these categories is p, then the theoretical proportion for the second category will be $1 - p = q$. If the total number of observations in the sample is n, then the binomial expansion

$$(p + q)^n$$

will enable us to determine the probability of obtaining any given number of observations in the two categories.

We have previously pointed out that if np (or nq, if q is smaller than p) is equal to or greater than 5, then the binomial probabilities can be approximated by means of the normal deviate z, as given by formula (11.9). It is also true that when we have a χ^2 with 1 degree of freedom, the probability associated with this value of χ^2 is equal to the probability associated with the corresponding value of z^2.

In the case of the title data, we have $p = .5$ and $n = 50$. From formula (11.4) we obtain the mean of the binomial

$$m = np = (50)(.5) = 25$$

and from formula (11.6) we obtain the standard deviation

$$\sigma = \sqrt{npq} = \sqrt{(50)(.5)(.5)} = 3.536$$

Then, substituting in formula (11.9), with X equal to the number of observations in Category 1, that is, the number preferring Title 1, we have

$$z = \frac{30 - 25}{3.536} = 1.414$$

and $z^2 = (1.414)^2 = 2.0$.

But it is also true that

$$z = \frac{20 - 25}{3.536} = -1.414$$

and $(-1.414)^2 = 2.0$. Thus, since $z^2 = 2.0$ can arise from either a positive or a negative value of z, the probability associated with z^2 will be given by the area in the *two* tails of the normal distribution falling beyond $z = 1.414$ and $z = -1.414$. From the table of the normal curve we find that the sum of the two areas will be approximately $(2)(.08) = .16$, and this is the probability of obtaining $z^2 = 2.0$. It is also the probability associated with $\chi^2 = 2.0$, for 1 degree of freedom.

In general, for any χ^2 test involving 1 degree of freedom there is a corresponding test in terms of the normal distribution involving z^2. The probabilities obtained from the two tests will be the same, and both are approximations of the probabilities that would be given in terms of the binomial distribution. Applications of the χ^2 test, however, are not limited to the binomial distribution, as we shall see later, but can be extended to multinomial distributions, that is, where we have more than two categories in which the observations may fall.

Testing Hypotheses about Population Ratios

The null hypothesis we have tested for the title data is sometimes put in a slightly different form. It might be said, for example, that we are testing the null hypothesis that we have a random sample from a population in which the population ratio is 1 : 1. This means that for every observation in the first category, we expect an observation in the second category, or that the probability of an observation falling in the first category is $1/(1 + 1) = 1/2$, and that the probability of an observation falling in the second category is $1/(1 + 1) = 1/2$. This is but another way of stating the null hypothesis that the theoretical proportions for the two categories are .5 and .5.

In the same manner in which we tested the hypothesis that the population ratio was 1 : 1, in the case of the title data, we might test any other hypothesis concerning a population ratio. Suppose, for example, that on the basis of past experience we know that 75 per cent of the members of a general-psychology class passed an item on a test. We now have a new class consisting of 200 students. On the basis of past experience, we could test the hypothesis that our sample of 200 students is a random sample from a population in which the theoretical proportion passing the item is .75 and the theoretical proportion failing is .25. This would be the same as testing the hypothesis that the population ratio is 3 : 1, that is, for every 3 observations in the passing category, we would expect 1 in the failing category.[1]

Suppose that we give the test and find that 137 students pass the item and that 63 fail it. Then our expected numbers, as given by formula (18.1) will be (200)(.75) = 150 and (200)(.25) = 50, respectively. Substituting in formula (18.2) we have

$$\chi^2 = \frac{(137 - 150)^2}{150} + \frac{(63 - 50)^2}{50}$$

$$= 3.38 + 1.13$$

$$= 4.51$$

We again have 1 degree of freedom, and from the table of χ^2 we find that values of 3.84 or greater will occur 5 per cent of the time or less when the null hypothesis is true. Thus, if the null hypothesis is true, we have a value, 4.51, which would occur as a result of random-sampling variation less than 5 per cent of the time. According to the standards we have used before, we would reject the null hypothesis and conclude that our sample was not drawn from a population in which the proportion passing the item is .75 and the proportion failing is .25.

χ^2 Applied to More Than Two Categories

As we pointed out before, the χ^2 test is not limited to the case where we have but 2 categories or a binomial distribution. It can be used when we have a sample in which the observations are distributed over 3 or more categories. Suppose, for example, we polled 60 students and asked their opinions concerning a contemplated change in the hours during which the library is open. We allow for 3 categories of response: favorable, indifferent, and unfavorable. In the absence of any information about how the responses would be distributed in the population, we may test the null hypothesis that the probability of occurrence of the responses in the 3 categories is the same. If this hypothesis is true, then the population ratio is 1 : 1 : 1, and we should expect an equal number of observations in each

---

[1] If the hypothesis is put in this form, the probability of an observation falling in the passing category would be $3/(3 + 1) = 3/4$, and the probability of an observation falling in the failing category would be $1/(3 + 1) = 1/4$. These probabilities give the theoretical proportions .75 and .25.

category. With a total of 60 students polled, this means that our expected number will be 20 in each of the 3 categories. The observed number in each category in our sample is shown in Table 18.1, along with the expected numbers. Then, from formula (18.2), we obtain

$$\chi^2 = \frac{(15 - 20)^2}{20} + \frac{(10 - 20)^2}{20} + \frac{(35 - 20)^2}{20}$$

$$= 1.25 + 5.00 + 11.25$$

$$= 17.50$$

Table 18.1—Observed Numbers and Expected Numbers in Three Categories Assuming a Uniform Distribution in the Population

	Response to Item			
	Favorable	*Indifferent*	*Unfavorable*	Σ
Observed numbers	15	10	35	60
Expected numbers	20	20	20	60

How many degrees of freedom will we now have to evaluate the χ^2 of 17.50? The restriction that we have placed upon the data is that $\sum(n_i - n_i') = 0$, and therefore only two of the three deviations are free to vary. In general, in problems of this nature, the number of degrees of freedom will be equal to $k - 1$, where k equals the number of categories. Thus, if we have 2 categories, we have 1 degree of freedom, if we have 3 categories, we have 2 degrees of freedom, and so on.

According to the table of χ^2, a value of 17.5, with 2 degrees of freedom, would occur less than 1 per cent of the time when the null hypothesis is true. We reject the hypothesis that our sample was drawn from a population in which the theoretical proportion in each of the 3 categories is the same. We conclude that the population ratio must be other than 1 : 1 : 1.

■ Two Criteria of Classification

In the problems considered so far, we have had but a single basis for classifying our observations. We now consider the case of a sample of observations in which we have two criteria of classification. In general, if we have two criteria of classification, A and B, with r categories or classes for A, and k classes or categories for B, we can set up a two-way table as shown in

Table 18.2. In terms of the notation of this table, the number of subjects in the ith category of A and the jth category of B is n_{ij}. The sum or total

Table 18.2—Schematic Representation of a Two-Way Contingency Table with r Categories for A and k Categories for B

A Criterion	*B* Criterion B_1	B_2	B_3	·	B_j	·	B_k	Σ
A_1	n_{11}	n_{12}	n_{13}	·	n_{1j}	·	n_{1k}	$n_{1\cdot}$
A_2	n_{21}	n_{22}	n_{23}	·	n_{2j}	·	n_{2k}	$n_{2\cdot}$
A_3	n_{31}	n_{32}	n_{33}	·	n_{3j}	·	n_{3k}	$n_{3\cdot}$
·	·	·	·	·	·	·	·	·
A_i	n_{i1}	n_{i2}	n_{i3}	·	n_{ij}	·	n_{ik}	$n_{i\cdot}$
·	·	·	·	·	·	·	·	·
A_r	n_{r1}	n_{r2}	n_{r3}	·	n_{rj}	·	n_{rk}	$n_{r\cdot}$
Σ	$n_{\cdot 1}$	$n_{\cdot 2}$	$n_{\cdot 3}$	·	$n_{\cdot j}$	·	$n_{\cdot k}$	n

number of observations in the ith category of A is obtained by summing the ith row over the k columns, so that

$$n_{i\cdot} = \sum_{j=1}^{k} n_{ij} \tag{18.3}$$

The sum or total number of observations in the jth category of B is obtained by summing the jth column of the table over the r rows, so that

$$n_{\cdot j} = \sum_{i=1}^{r} n_{ij} \tag{18.4}$$

If we sum all of the cell entries we obtain the total number of observations, and we represent this total by n. Then

$$n = \sum_{i=1}^{r} \sum_{j=1}^{k} n_{ij} \tag{18.5}$$

The total number of observations can also be obtained by summing the row totals or the column totals, so that we also have

$$n = \sum_{i=1}^{r} n_{i\cdot} = \sum_{j=1}^{k} n_{\cdot j} \tag{18.6}$$

Tables such as Table 18.1 are often called *contingency tables.*

When we have observations arranged in the form of a contingency table, we can determine whether there is any relationship between the two criteria of classification, that is, whether or not they are independent. For example, we might believe that there should be some tendency for subjects with different amounts of education to respond differentially to an item in an opinion poll. If we obtained a sample of subjects and classified them according to their level of education and also in terms of their response to the item, we could then test the null hypothesis that the first classification, level of education, is independent of the second classification, response to the item.

Suppose, for example, that we have a sample of 250 subjects and that for each subject we have available a response to an opinion item. We have 3 categories of response—agree, undecided, and disagree—with 65, 115, and 70 subjects, respectively, in the 3 categories. If this were our only basis of classification, the problem would correspond to those we have previously considered. But let us suppose that we also have available a second criterion of classification, the level of education of the subjects. We shall assume that we have 3 categories here also: college graduates, high-school graduates, and elementary-school graduates, with 95, 70, and 85 subjects, respectively, in the 3 categories. These marginal totals are shown in Table 18.3. The cells of the table give the number of subjects falling in a

Table 18.3—Two-Way Contingency Table for Level of Education and Response to an Item in an Opinion Poll with Observed Numbers n_{ij} in Each Cell

Level of Education		*Response to Item*				
		Agree B_1	*Undecided* B_2	*Disagree* B_3	Σ	Σ/n
College graduate	A_1	10	35	50	95	.38
High-school graduate	A_2	20	40	10	70	.28
Elementary-school graduate	A_3	35	40	10	85	.34
Σ		65	115	70	250	
Σ/n		.26	.46	.28		1.00

given category of the row criterion (level of education) and a given category of the column criterion (response to the item).

An examination of the cells of Table 18.3 would seem to indicate that there is some tendency for the college graduates to give more disagree responses than high-school and elementary-school graduates. In accordance with the notation of Table 18.2, we may designate the row classification, level of education, as A, and the column classification, response to the item, as B. We wish to test the null hypothesis that the two criteria of classification are independent. If this hypothesis is true, the probability of an individual falling in the jth category of B will be independent of the particular A category in which the individual falls.

Obtaining the Expected Numbers

Let us indicate the probability of an observation falling in the ith category of A as $p_{i\cdot}$. Using the notation of Table 18.2, we may take as our estimate of this probability

$$p_{i\cdot} = \frac{n_{i\cdot}}{n} \tag{18.7}$$

Then for the data of Table 18.3, we have as the probability of an observation falling in the first row

$$p_{1\cdot} = \frac{95}{250} = .38$$

In the same way we obtain, from formula (18.7), the probability of an observation falling in the second row and the probability of an observation falling in the third row for the data of Table 18.3. These three probabilities are shown in Table 18.3. If we sum these probabilities over the r rows of the table, we would have

$$\sum_{i=1}^{r} p_{i\cdot} = \frac{\sum_{i=1}^{r} n_{i\cdot}}{n} = 1.00 \tag{18.8}$$

since formula (18.6) tells us that $\sum_{i=1}^{r} n_{i\cdot} = n$, or the total number of observations.

Similarly, we may indicate the probability of an observation falling in the jth category of B as $p_{\cdot j}$. We may take as our estimate of this probability

$$p_{\cdot j} = \frac{n_{\cdot j}}{n} \tag{18.9}$$

Then, for the data of Table 18.3, we have as the probability of an observation falling in the first column

$$p_{\cdot 1} = \frac{65}{250} = .26$$

In the same way we obtain, from formula (18.9), the probability of an observation falling in the second column and the probability of an observation falling in the third column. These probabilities are shown in Table 18.3. If we sum these probabilities over all k columns of the table, we would have

$$\sum_{j=1}^{k} p_{\cdot j} = \frac{\sum_{j=1}^{k} n_{\cdot j}}{n} = 1.00 \tag{18.10}$$

since formula (18.6) tells us that $\sum_{j=1}^{k} n_{\cdot j} = n$, or the total number of observations.

Assuming independence of the two criteria of classification, the probability p_{ij} of an observation falling in the ijth cell of the contingency table will be

$$p_{ij} = p_{i\cdot}p_{\cdot j}$$

$$= \frac{n_{i\cdot}n_{\cdot j}}{n^2} \tag{18.11}$$

For the data of Table 18.3, we would then have as the probability of an observation falling in the cell where the first row and first column of the table intersect

$$p_{11} = \frac{(95)(65)}{(250)^2} = .0988$$

The p_{ij}'s obtained from formula (18.11) will give the probabilities or theoretical proportions for each of the cells of the contingency table. If we multiply the p_{ij}'s by n, the total number of observations, we shall obtain the expected numbers n_{ij}' for the cells of the table. Thus

$$n_{ij}' = np_{i\cdot}p_{\cdot j} \tag{18.12}$$

or, substituting from formula (18.11), we have

$$n_{ij}' = n\frac{n_{i\cdot}n_{\cdot j}}{n^2}$$

$$= \frac{n_{i\cdot}n_{\cdot j}}{n} \tag{18.13}$$

The expected number for the cell in the first row and first column of Table 18.3, as given by formula (18.13), will be

$$n_{11}' = \frac{(95)(65)}{250} = 24.7$$

The expected numbers for the other cells may be obtained by substituting the appropriate marginal totals in formula (18.13). We show these expected numbers in Table 18.4 for purposes of illustration. However, as we shall show later in connection with formula (18.23), it is not necessary to calculate these expected numbers in order to calculate χ^2.

Table 18.4—Expected Numbers n_{ij}' for the Data of Table 18.3

Level of Education		*Response to Item*			
		Agree B_1	*Undecided* B_2	*Disagree* B_3	Σ
College graduate	A_1	24.7	43.7	26.6	95.0
High-school graduate	A_2	18.2	32.2	19.6	70.0
Elementary-school graduate	A_3	22.1	39.1	23.8	85.0
Σ		65.0	115.0	70.0	250.0

Restrictions on the Data

For any given row, say the ith of the contingency table, n and $p_{i\cdot}$ will be constants, while $p_{\cdot j}$ will vary. Then, summing the expected numbers of formula (18.12) across the k columns for a single row, say the ith, we have

$$\sum_{j=1}^{k} n_{ij}' = np_{i\cdot} \sum_{j=1}^{k} p_{\cdot j} \tag{18.14}$$

If we multiply both sides of formula (18.7) by n, we see that $np_{i\cdot} = n_{i\cdot}$, and formula (18.10) tells us that $\sum_{j=1}^{k} p_{\cdot j} = 1.00$. Therefore, we may write formula (18.14) as

$$\sum_{j=1}^{k} n_{ij}' = n_{i\cdot} \tag{18.15}$$

and this restriction will be true for every row of the contingency table. In the same way we could show that

$$\sum_{i=1}^{r} n_{ij}' = n_{\cdot j} \tag{18.16}$$

and this restriction will be true for every column of the contingency table.

If we now sum formula (18.15) over all r rows of the contingency table, we have

$$\sum_{i=1}^{r} \sum_{j=1}^{k} n_{ij}' = \sum_{i=1}^{r} n_{i\cdot} \tag{18.17}$$

and we have shown in formula (18.6) that $\sum_{i=1}^{r} n_{i\cdot} = n$, or the total number of observations. Thus we see that

$$\sum_{i=1}^{r} \sum_{j=1}^{k} n_{ij}' = n \tag{18.18}$$

Since it is also true that $n_{ij}' = np_{i\cdot}p_{\cdot j}$, it follows that

$$\sum_{i=1}^{r} \sum_{j=1}^{k} n_{ij}' = n \sum_{i=1}^{r} \sum_{j=1}^{k} p_{i\cdot}p_{\cdot j} \tag{18.19}$$

But $\sum_{i=1}^{r} \sum_{j=1}^{k} n_{ij}' = n$, and therefore

$$n = n \sum_{i=1}^{r} \sum_{j=1}^{k} p_{i\cdot}p_{\cdot j} \tag{18.20}$$

Dividing both sides of this expression by n, we see that

$$\sum_{i=1}^{r} \sum_{j=1}^{k} p_{i\cdot}p_{\cdot j} = 1.00 \tag{18.21}$$

Calculation of χ^2

We have an observed number in each of the cells of Table 18.3, and in Table 18.4 we have corresponding expected numbers as obtained from formula (18.13). If we take the difference between each observed and expected number, square these discrepancies, divide each squared discrepancy by the corresponding expected number, and sum, we shall have a value of χ^2. Thus

$$\chi^2 = \sum_{i=1}^{r} \sum_{j=1}^{k} \frac{(n_{ij} - n_{ij}')^2}{n_{ij}'} \tag{18.22}$$

Substituting for n_{ij}' from formula (18.13) we also have

$$\chi^2 = \sum_{i=1}^{r} \sum_{j=1}^{k} \frac{\left(n_{ij} - \dfrac{n_{i}.n._{j}}{n}\right)^2}{\dfrac{n_{i}.n._{j}}{n}}$$

or

$$\chi^2 = \frac{1}{n} \sum_{i=1}^{r} \sum_{j=1}^{k} \frac{(nn_{ij} - n_{i}.n._{j})^2}{n_{i}.n._{j}} \tag{18.23}$$

Formula (18.23) is convenient for calculating χ^2, but since we have already obtained the expected numbers, n_{ij}', we have used formula (18.22) in the calculation of χ^2 in Table 18.5. The value we obtain is 53.38.

Table 18.5—Calculation of χ^2 Using Observed Numbers n_{ij} of Table 18.3 and Expected Numbers n_{ij}' of Table 18.4

(1) n_{ij}	(2) n_{ij}'	(3) $n_{ij} - n_{ij}'$	(4) $(n_{ij} - n_{ij}')^2$	(5) $(n_{ij} - n_{ij}')^2/n_{ij}'$
10	24.7	−14.7	216.09	8.75
35	43.7	− 8.7	75.69	1.73
50	26.6	23.4	547.56	20.58
20	18.2	1.8	3.24	.18
40	32.2	7.8	60.84	1.89
10	19.6	− 9.6	92.16	4.70
35	22.1	12.9	166.41	7.53
40	39.1	.9	.81	.02
10	23.8	−13.8	190.44	8.00
				$\chi^2 = 53.38$

Degrees of Freedom

In order to evaluate the χ^2 of 53.38, we must enter the table of χ^2 with the number of degrees of freedom available. Since it is true that the sum of the expected numbers in any row of the table will be equal to the sum of the observed numbers,[2] that is, since $\sum_{j=1}^{k} n_{ij}' = n_{i}.$, it is also true that

$$\sum_{j=1}^{k} (n_{ij} - n_{ij}') = 0 \tag{18.24}$$

[2] See formula (18.15).

Consequently, for any given row only $k - 1$ of the discrepancies will be free to vary. Similarly, it is true that the sum of the expected numbers for any given column will be equal to the sum of the observed numbers, that is, $\sum_{i=1}^{r} n_{ij}' = n_{.j}$, and it is also true that

$$\sum_{i=1}^{r} (n_{ij} - n_{ij}') = 0 \tag{18.25}$$

Consequently, for any given column, only $r - 1$ of the discrepancies will be free to vary. Thus, for any $r \times k$ contingency table, the number of degrees of freedom will be given by

$$df = (r - 1)(k - 1) \tag{18.26}$$

For our problem we have $r = 3$ and $k = 3$, so that we have 4 degrees of freedom available. From the table of χ^2 we find that, for 4 degrees of freedom, values of χ^2 equal to or greater than 13.277 will occur less than 1 per cent of the time when the null hypothesis is true. Since our obtained value of 53.38 exceeds 13.277, we shall reject the null hypothesis that the two criteria of classification are independent. In other words, we reject the hypothesis that $p_{ij} = p_{i\cdot}p_{\cdot j}$ and conclude that the probability of a given individual falling in the ith category of A *is* influenced by the particular category of B in which the individual falls.

■ The Contingency Coefficient and χ^2

The *contingency coefficient* C is a measure of association which is sometimes used when data have been arranged in an $r \times k$ contingency table.[3] The contingency coefficient can vary between 0 and 1, but it can reach its maximum value only when the number of categories for both criteria of classification is large.[4] For a 3×3 table, such as Table 18.3, for example, C cannot exceed .816, and for a 10×10 table, the maximum value of C is .949.

The contingency coefficient can be obtained directly from χ^2. Thus

$$C = \sqrt{\frac{\chi^2}{n + \chi^2}} \tag{18.27}$$

[3] If the categories of both criteria can be ordered, we could, of course, code the ordered categories 0, 1, 2, 3, and so forth, and calculate a product-moment coefficient of correlation for the contingency table. If the categories of only one of the criteria can be ordered, they could be coded, and we could compute the correlation ratio as a measure of association for the contingency table.

[4] For a further discussion of this coefficient and its limitations, see Kelley (1923), and Yule and Kendall (1947).

where n is the total number of observations in the contingency table. For the data of Table 18.3, we found χ^2 was equal to 53.38 and n was equal to 250. Substituting in formula (18.27) with these values, we get[5]

$$C = \sqrt{\frac{53.38}{250 + 53.38}}$$

$$= .42$$

As we pointed out in the previous section, χ^2 provides a test of the null hypothesis that the two criteria of classification are independent. χ^2 can also be said to test the null hypothesis that $C = 0$. Therefore, if χ^2 is significant, we would reject this null hypothesis and conclude that $C > 0$.

■ The Phi Coefficient and χ^2

We discussed earlier the use of the phi coefficient to measure the degree of association or relationship between two variables when each variable is a dichotomy, that is, when we have a 2×2 contingency table. We have just seen in this chapter that it would also be possible to compute χ^2 for data arranged in a 2×2 table. Thus χ^2 can be used to provide us with a test of the significance of r_ϕ. If χ^2 is significant, then we may conclude that r_ϕ differs significantly from zero.

The phi coefficient and χ^2 are related in the following way

$$r_\phi = \sqrt{\frac{\chi^2}{n}} \qquad \textbf{(18.28)}$$

and

$$\chi^2 = nr_\phi{}^2 \qquad \textbf{(18.29)}$$

where n is the total number of observations in the 2×2 table.

If we have computed r_ϕ as a measure of association and wish to test the

---

[5] Coding the categories of the A criterion of classification 0, 1, and 2, and making a similar coding for the B categories, we obtain a product-moment coefficient of correlation equal to .42 also. However, this agreement between the product-moment correlation coefficient and the contingency coefficient is not always to be expected. As we pointed out in the above discussion, as the relationship between the two criteria of classification increases in the 3×3 table, the contingency coefficient will approach its maximum value of .816, whereas the correlation coefficient will approach its maximum value of 1.00. Because the maximum value of the contingency coefficient is dependent upon the number of categories for the two criteria of classification, contingency coefficients obtained from tables with varying numbers of categories are not comparable.

null hypothesis that the population correlation is zero, we need merely square the obtained value and multiply by n to obtain χ^2. If χ^2, with 1 degree of freedom, is significant, then we reject the null hypothesis. For the data of Table 10.2 we found r_ϕ was equal to .23, with n equal to 200. Then, substituting in formula (18.29), we get

$$\chi^2 = (200)(.23)^2$$
$$= 10.58$$

By reference to the table of χ^2 we find that for 1 degree of freedom a value of χ^2 equal to 10.58 would occur less than 1 per cent of the time when the null hypothesis is true. Therefore, we reject the null hypothesis.

We could, of course, reverse the procedure and compute χ^2 first. This would tell us whether or not there was any association present and whether we could reject the null hypothesis at some defined probability value. If we were then interested in getting some indication of the strength of the relationship we could substitute in formula (18.28) and solve for r_ϕ.

If we substitute from formula (10.6) for $r_\phi{}^2$ in formula (18.29) we obtain a convenient method for calculating χ^2 for a 2×2 contingency table. Thus

$$\chi^2 = \frac{n(bc - ad)^2}{(a + c)(b + d)(a + b)(c + d)} \tag{18.30}$$

Correction for Continuity

When we have but a single degree of freedom and we apply the χ^2 test, we should also apply a correction for continuity, suggested by Yates (1934). With a single criterion of classification, the correction consists of reducing the absolute value of the deviations $(n_i - n_i')$ of formula (18.2) by .5 before calculating χ^2. Thus

$$\chi_c{}^2 = \sum_1^k \frac{(|n_i - n_i'| - .5)^2}{n_i'} \tag{18.31}$$

where $\chi_c{}^2$ is chi square corrected for continuity.

Assume, for example, that we have frequencies of 18 and 12 for two categories and we wish to test a 1 : 1 hypothesis. The values of $(n_i - n_i')$ would be equal to 3 and -3. Then χ^2, calculated in the usual way from formula (18.2), would give us a value of 1.2. Making the correction for continuity, in terms of formula (18.31), would give us deviations of 2.5 and -2.5, and χ^2 would now be equal to .83.

In the case of a 2×2 contingency table, the correction for continuity can be made very readily in terms of formula (18.30). Applying the correction, we would have

$$\chi_c^2 = \frac{n\left(|bc - ad| - \frac{n}{2}\right)^2}{(a + c)(b + d)(a + b)(c + d)} \tag{18.32}$$

where χ_c^2 is chi square corrected for continuity for the 2×2 table.

The basis of the correction for continuity is that, whereas our frequencies are discrete, χ^2 is a continuous distribution or curve. The correction made for χ^2 is comparable to the one we made in using the normal curve to evaluate binomial probabilities.[6] This point is discussed in greater detail in Edwards (1950*a*).

Small Expected Frequencies

It seems to be generally agreed that χ^2 should not ordinarily be applied when any one of the expected frequencies is less than 5.[7] If we have but a single criterion of classification with only 2 categories and if we have an expected frequency of less than 5, we can use the binomial expansion $(p + q)^n$ to determine the probability of obtaining the observed frequencies upon the basis of the null hypothesis tested. If we have a 2×2 table and if an expected cell entry is less than 5, an exact test may be applied. This test is described by Fisher (1936). The tables published by Finney (1948) make the exact test for the 2×2 table relatively easy to perform.

If we have more than 1 degree of freedom, for either a single criterion of classification or for two criteria of classification, it may be possible to combine categories in order to increase the expected cell frequencies. For example, if we have 5 categories—strongly agree, agree, undecided, disagree, and strongly disagree—in response to an opinion item, it might be possible to combine the strongly agree and agree categories, if either has a relatively small expected frequency. Similarly, the strongly disagree and disagree categories might be combined, if necessary.

Testing Goodness of Fit

In Table 18.6 we have a frequency distribution of scores obtained on a psychological test. We have let n_i represent the number of scores falling in

---

[6] See the discussion on page 224.

[7] See the discussion by Yates (1934), Lewis and Burke (1949), and Edwards (1950*b*).

Table 18.6—Fitting a Normal Distribution to an Observed Distribution with Mean Equal to 60.1 and Standard Deviation Equal to 10.2

(1) *Intervals*	(2) n_i	(3) *Upper Limit*	(4) x	(5) z	(6) *Proportion Below*	(7) *Proportion Within*	(8) n_i'	
85–89	2	89.5	29.4	—	—	.0084	.8	
80–84	1	84.5	24.4	2.39	.9916	.0203	2.0	7.9
75–79	4	79.5	19.4	1.90	.9713	.0506	5.1	
70–74	9	74.5	14.4	1.41	.9207	.0995	10.0	
65–69	13	69.5	9.4	.92	.8212	.1548	15.5	
60–64	26	64.5	4.4	.43	.6664	.1903	19.0	
55–59	19	59.5	−.6	−.06	.4761	.1849	18.5	
50–54	12	54.5	−5.6	−.55	.2912	.1420	14.2	
45–49	8	49.5	−10.6	−1.04	.1492	.0862	8.6	
40–44	3	44.5	−15.6	−1.53	.0630	.0413	4.1	
35–39	2	39.5	−20.6	−2.02	.0217	.0157	1.6	6.3
30–34	1	34.5	−25.6	−2.51	.0060	.0060	.6	

the various intervals, and these frequencies are shown in column (2) of the table. The distribution appears, upon inspection, to be somewhat normal in form. We could get a better indication of the extent to which the distribution is normal by plotting the cumulative-proportion distribution on normal-probability paper, in the manner described earlier.[8] In terms of the discussion of this chapter, however, it should also be apparent that χ^2 can be used to provide a test of the hypothesis that the distribution is normal in form. We have an observed frequency n_i for each of the class intervals. If we can obtain an expected frequency n_i' for each of the intervals, in terms of a normal distribution, we could apply formula (18.2) and calculate χ^2.

We obtain our expected frequencies in the manner shown in Table 18.6. In column (3) of the table we give the upper limits of the class intervals. Calculation would show that the mean of the observed distribution is 60.1 and the standard deviation is 10.2. In column (4) we have subtracted the mean from each of the upper limits of the class intervals, to put them in deviation form. In column (5) we have divided the deviations by the standard deviation of the distribution to obtain the z values or normal deviates corresponding to the upper limits of the intervals. In column (6) we have the proportion of the total area in a normal distribution falling below each of the z values shown in column (5). We obtained these proportions from the table

[8] See Chapter 5.

of the normal curve—Table III, in the Appendix. For example, from the table of the normal curve we find that .0060 of the total area will fall below z equal to -2.51, and .0217 of the total area will fall below z equal to -2.02.

In column (7) we show the proportion of the area falling within each of the intervals. The first value, .0060, is recorded directly from column (6). The other proportions are obtained by subtraction of the successive entries in column (6). For example, the second entry is given by $.0217 - .0060 = .0157$. The third entry is given by $.0630 - .0217 = .0413$. We continue in this way until we come to the last entry .0084. This is obtained by subtracting .9916 from 1.000, which gives .0084. We have included all of the area falling beyond the limit 84.5 in the interval 85.5 to 89.5. Similarly, we have included all of the area falling below the limit 34.5 in the interval 29.5 to 34.5.

In column (8) we have multiplied the proportions in column (7) by n, the total number of observations, and have rounded the products to one decimal place. The entries in column (8) are our *theoretical or expected frequencies for a normal distribution with the same n, mean, and standard deviation as our observed frequency distribution.*

Since the bottom two intervals and the top two intervals in column (8) contain expected numbers that are less than 5, we have combined the first three classes and the last three classes. This gives us $.6 + 1.6 + 4.1 = 6.3$ for the expected number for the combined bottom three categories, and $5.1 + 2.0 + .8 = 7.9$ for the expected number for the combined top three intervals. We must also combine the observed frequencies in the bottom three intervals and those in the top three intervals. This gives us $1 + 2 + 3 = 6$ for the observed frequency for the bottom three intervals. Combining the top three intervals for the observed distribution gives us $4 + 1 + 2 = 7$ for our observed number for these combined categories. These distributions of observed and expected numbers are shown in column (2) and column (3), respectively, of Table 18.7.

In column (4) of Table 18.7, we have subtracted the expected numbers from the observed numbers to obtain the deviations $n_i - n_i'$. The squares of these discrepancies are given in column (5), and in column (6) we give the squares divided by the corresponding expected numbers. The sum of column (6) gives us χ^2, which is equal to 3.595.

To evaluate our χ^2 of 3.595 we must enter the table of χ^2 with the number of degrees of freedom available. Ordinarily, in problems of this kind we have had $k - 1$ degrees of freedom, where k is equal to the number of categories or classes. In the present problem, however, we have placed additional restrictions upon the data. Not only have we placed the restriction that $\sum n_i = \sum n_i'$ upon the data, but we have placed the further restrictions that the mean and standard deviation must remain the same

Table 18.7—χ^2 Test of Goodness of Fit for the Observed and Theoretical Distributions of Table 18.6

(1) *Intervals*	(2) n_i	(3) n_i'	(4) $n_i - n_i'$	(5) $(n_i - n_i')^2$	(6) $(n_i - n_i')^2/n_i'$
Above 74	7	7.9	−.9	.81	.102
70–74	9	10.0	−1.0	1.00	.100
65–69	13	15.5	−2.5	6.25	.403
60–64	26	19.0	7.0	49.00	2.579
55–59	19	18.5	.5	.25	.014
50–54	12	14.2	−2.2	4.84	.341
45–49	8	8.6	−.6	.36	.042
Below 45	6	6.3	−.3	.09	.014
Σ	100	100.0	.0		$\chi^2 = 3.595$

for the expected distribution as for the observed distribution.[9] Consequently, we have three restrictions upon the data, and our degrees of freedom will be $k - 3$. Since we have used $k = 8$ classes in computing χ^2, we shall have $8 - 3 = 5$ degrees of freedom available.

From the table of χ^2 we find that for 5 degrees of freedom a value of 3.595 will occur more than 50 per cent of the time when the null hypothesis is true. We consider the null hypothesis, in this instance, to be tenable. Our observed distribution, we conclude, does not differ significantly from a normal distribution with the same n, mean, and standard deviation.

■ The Median Test

Suppose that we have measures X_1 for n_1 subjects in an experimental group and measures X_2 for n_2 subjects in a control group. We are interested in comparing the difference in average performance for the two groups, but, for one reason or another, we may not be able to assume normality of distribution. Then, instead of testing some null hypothesis about the means in terms of the t test, which would involve the assumption of normality, we shall use a somewhat different approach. We can test the null hypothesis that the two groups are random samples from a population with a common

[9] And they do, within errors involved in reading the theoretical proportions from the table of the normal curve and in rounding in the calculations. The mean of the theoretical distribution of column (8) in Table 18.6 is 60.1, and the standard deviation is 10.3, as compared with the mean of 60.1 and standard deviation of 10.2 for the observed distribution of column (2) in the same table.

median. The test of this null hypothesis will not involve any assumption concerning the nature of the distribution of the X measures, that is, we shall not have to make any assumption about normality.[10]

In table 18.8 we show the X_1 values for 15 subjects in a control group and the X_2 values for 19 subjects in an experimental group. The frequency

Table 18.8—Scores for a Control and Experimental Group. Plus Signs Have Been Given to Scores above the Common Median of 6.17 and Minus Signs to Those below the Median

Control Group		*Experimental Group*	
X_1	*Sign*	X_2	*Sign*
4	−	2	−
7	+	6	−
6	−	11	+
3	−	3	−
8	+	1	−
10	+	6	−
9	+	7	+
5	−	10	+
1	−	8	+
5	−	4	−
1	−	5	−
7	+	9	+
2	−	3	−
3	−	3	−
7	+	8	+
		10	+
		11	+
		9	+
		8	+

distribution of the combined $n_1 + n_2 = 34$ observations is shown in Table 18.9. Using formula (3.11), we find that the median of this distribution is

$$Mdn = 5.5 + \left(\frac{17 - 15}{3}\right)$$

$$= 6.17$$

[10] This test is described by Mood (1950, pp. 394–395). Mood points out that the test is primarily sensitive to differences in location and is relatively uninfluenced by differences in the shapes of the distributions.

Table 18.9—Frequency Distribution for the Combined n_1 and n_2 Scores of Table 18.8

X	f
11	2
10	3
9	3
8	4
7	4
6	3
5	3
4	2
3	5
2	2
1	3

Now, if the samples come from a population with a common median, we would expect approximately half of the X_1 values to be above the median of 6.17 and approximately half below. Similarly, we would expect about half of the X_2 values to be above the median of 6.17 and about half below.

In Table 18.8 we have assigned a plus to every observation that is above the median and a minus to every observation that is below. For the control group we have 6 plus values and 9 minus values. For the experimental group we have 10 plus values and 9 minus values. These frequencies have been entered in Table 18.10.

We may now apply the χ^2 test to the data of Table 18.10. Using formula (18.32), with the correction for continuity, we obtain

$$\chi_c^2 = \frac{34\left(|(10)(9) - (9)(6)| - \frac{34}{2}\right)^2}{(18)(16)(19)(15)}$$

$$= .15$$

Our obtained value of χ_c^2 is .15 with 1 degree of freedom. It is obvious that this is not a significant value and we conclude that the null hypothesis is tenable. The two groups of observations may very well be samples from a population with a common median. For the data of Table 18.8, this conclusion was to be expected. The values entered in the table for the two groups were obtained at random from the table of random numbers—Table I, in the Appendix.

The median test can be generalized for more than two groups. For example, if we have k groups of observations, we would combine the data

Table 18.10—The 2 × 2 Table for the Observations of Table 18.8

Groups	*Signs* −	+	*Total*
Experimental group	9	10	19
Control group	9	6	15
Total	18	16	34

for all groups into a single distribution and find the median of this combined distribution. Then we would count the number of observations in each group falling above and below the common median and calculate χ^2 for the resulting $2 \times k$ table.

In Table 18.11, we show the counts above and below a common median for each of 4 groups of 25 observations. The obtained value of χ^2 for this table is 13.28 with 3 degrees of freedom, and the probability of obtaining a

Table 18.11—Number of Observations Falling Above and Below a Common Median for Each of Four Groups of 25 Observations

	Groups *A*	*B*	*C*	*D*	*Total*
Above median	8	12	20	10	50
Below median	17	13	5	15	50
Total	25	25	25	25	100

value of χ^2 as large as this, when the null hypothesis is true, is less than .01. We would therefore conclude that these samples are not from a population with a common median.

Tests of significance, such as the one described above, which do not depend upon an assumption concerning the nature of the population distribution of the observations are called *distribution-free* or *nonparametric* tests. The χ^2 test for independence of the observations, in the 2 × 2 table, or for the general case of the $r \times k$ table, is one such test. The "sign test" discussed in Chapter 14 is another distribution-free or nonparametric test. In the next chapter we shall discuss some additional nonparametric tests.[11]

[11] Mood (1950) and Dixon and Massey (1951) describe a number of additional nonparametric tests. Moses (1952) gives an excellent nontechnical review of nonparametric tests that may be useful in psychological research.

■ The Significance of a Set of Results

In some stages of research, the experimenter may find it desirable to evaluate the results of a set of tests of significance. Let us suppose that the tests have been made in such a way that the null hypothesis will be rejected if the probability of the outcome is .05 or less when the null hypothesis is true. If n *independent* tests of significance are made, the probability of obtaining any given number of significant outcomes will be given by the binomial[12]

$$(p + q)^n$$

which, for the present example, will be

$$(.05 + .95)^n$$

If two tests of significance are made, for example, then

$$(.05 + .95)^2 = (.05)^2 + (2)(.05)(.95) + (.95)^2$$

$$= .0025 + .0950 + .9025$$

and the probability of obtaining two significant outcomes will be .0025, and the probability of obtaining one *or more* will be $.0025 + .0950 = .0975$.

Wilkinson (1951) has prepared tables based upon the expansion $(p + q)^n$ to give the probability of obtaining a given number of significant statistics by chance, when from 1 to 25 tests of significance are made. These tables were constructed by setting p equal to .05 and .01 and then expanding the binomial. It may be noted now, and we shall return to this point later, that the binomial, or Wilkinson's tables based upon the binomial, should be used only when the several tests of significance are *independent*. If the tests are independent, the binomial can be used to determine the probability of obtaining one or more significant outcomes at some defined level, when n tests are made.

Another approach to the problem of determining the significance of a set of independent outcomes involves the χ^2 distribution. The χ^2 test takes into account the obtained probabilities for each of the several tests and not merely whether or not these probabilities meet some specified criterion of significance. For example, an experimenter may have available the outcomes of several independent experiments bearing upon some hypothesis of interest. None of the several tests of significance yields a probability of .05

[12] See the discussion of the binomial on page 219.

or less, but the general impression gained from the group of experiments is that the outcomes are consistent in an expected direction. The experimenter wishes to know whether or not the composite probability for the several experiments may be regarded as significant.

The χ^2 test is based upon the fact that the natural logarithm (base e) of a probability p is equal to $-\frac{1}{2}\chi^2$ with 2 degrees of freedom, and that the sum of a number of independent values of χ^2 is also distributed as χ^2 with degrees of freedom equal to the sum of the degrees of freedom for the individual χ^2 values. Thus

$$-\tfrac{1}{2}\chi^2 = \log_e p \tag{18.33}$$

Multiplying both sides of formula (18.33) by -2 and changing from natural logarithms (base e) to common logarithms with base 10, we have

$$\chi^2 = (-2)(2.3026)\log_{10} p \tag{18.34}$$

The product of $(-2)(2.3026)$ will be a constant for each of the probabilities p, and we have as χ^2 for the sum of k such values

$$\chi^2 = (-2)(2.3026)\sum_1^k \log_{10} p \tag{18.35}$$

with $2k$ degrees of freedom, where k is the number of independent probabilities to be combined.

To illustrate the χ^2 test, let us assume that three independent tests of significance have yielded probabilities of .09, .20, and .12. From the table of logarithms in the Appendix, we find the $\log_{10} p$ values and $\sum_1^k \log_{10} p$ as given below:

p	$\log_{10} p$		
.09	8.9542 − 10.0000		
.20	9.3010 − 10.0000		
.12	9.0792 − 10.0000		
$\sum_1^k \log_{10} p$ =	27.3344 − 30.0000	=	−2.6656

Then applying formula (18.35) we have

$$\chi^2 = (-2)(2.3026)(-2.6656) = 12.2756$$

with $(2)(3) = 6$ degrees of freedom. The tabled value of χ^2 with a probability of .05 for 6 degrees of freedom is 12.592, and the probability of obtaining the three experimental outcomes with probabilities of .09, .20, and .12, by chance is, therefore, just slightly greater than .05.

In both the binomial and the χ^2 test of the significance of a set of results, the fundamental assumption involved is that of the *independence* of the several outcomes. This assumption is likely to be justified only when *different* samples of subjects are used in each experiment. It is not likely to be justified when a number of tests of significance have been made with the *same* sample.

Suppose, for example, that the responses of the same two groups of subjects are compared on each of a number of items in a test. It is found that a given number of the items differentiate significantly between the two groups, and the investigator would like to know whether the number of significant outcomes exceeds the number expected to be significant by chance. In general, the binomial cannot be used to answer this question nor can the χ^2 test be used to evaluate the combined probabilities. The reason for this is that it is unlikely that the assumption of independence of the several outcomes will be justified. In the case described, the assumption of independence specifies that the items must be uncorrelated or that the inter-item correlations are randomly distributed about zero. If a test of significance is applied to one item, for example, and a significant result is obtained, the test of significance applied to any other item that is correlated with the first item will not be independent of the results obtained in the first test, and the assumption of independence involved in the binomial or χ^2 tests will not be met.[13]

EXAMPLES

Make continuity corrections for all problems involving 1 degree of freedom

18.1—Previous experience with a particular achievement test indicated that for seventh-grade children the ratio of those receiving a passing mark to those failing was 3 to 1. We wish to test whether this hypothesis (3 : 1) holds also for sixth-grade children. In a sample of 100 students drawn from the sixth grade, we find that 60 pass the test and 40 fail. Is the hypothesis tenable?

[13] This point is discussed in an article by Jones and Fiske (1953) which reviews in detail the problem of testing the significance of the combined results of several experiments.

18.2—A poll of fraternity men on a university campus showed that the ratio of those on the honor list to those not on the list was 1 : 4. To find out whether this ratio would hold for sorority members, a sample of 150 sorority members was drawn. Forty of the sorority members were on the honor list and 110 were not. Should we abandon the 1 : 4 hypothesis?

18.3—A chairman of a committee confronted with a choice between the use of two slogans decided to sample a number of individuals to determine which they preferred. In a sample of 80 he found that 50 approved Slogan 1 and 30 approved Slogan 2. Test the hypothesis that the population ratio is 1 : 1.

18.4—Sixty cases in a mental hospital responded to an item in a personality inventory. For each patient we also have available the psychiatric diagnosis. Test for independence of the two criteria of classification for the data given below.

	Response to Item		
Psychiatric Diagnosis	*Yes*	*?*	*No*
Schizoid	18	9	3
Manic	6	9	15

18.5—A group of 200 subjects responded to an item in an attitude test. Five categories of response were permitted. We also have available the sex classification of the subjects. Test for the independence of the two criteria of classification for the data given below.

	Response to Item				
Sex	*Strongly Disagree*	*Disagree*	*Undecided*	*Agree*	*Strongly Agree*
Men	5	5	12	18	60
Women	25	25	20	20	10

18.6—Kuo (1930) reared kittens under three different conditions: (1) one group of kittens was isolated from all contact with rats except on the experimental test; (2) the kittens in another group were reared with their mothers whom they saw kill a rat or mouse every four days outside the cage; (3) one group lived with a single rodent from age 6–8 days onward. The test situation consisted of putting a kitten together with a rat to determine whether or not the kitten would kill. The data are given below. Test for the independence of the two criteria of classification.

Experimental Condition	*Response to Rodent*	
	Kills	*Does Not Kill*
Reared in isolation	9	11
Reared with mother	18	3
Reared with rodent	3	15

18.7—One hundred and seventy patients in a mental hospital were rated in terms of whether they showed improvement or no improvement after therapy. We also have available information concerning which of two therapeutic procedures was used for each patient. Test for the independence of the two criteria of classification for the data given below.

Method Used	*Rating after Therapy*	
	No Improvement	*Improvement*
Procedure 1	10	42
Procedure 2	58	60

18.8—Rosenzweig (1943) has studied the recall of subjects for finished and unfinished tasks when they worked on the tasks under differing sets of instructions. The "informal" group was told that the experimenter was interested in knowing something about the task, that the ability of the subjects was not under investigation. The "formal" group, on the other hand, was under the impression that the tasks were an intelligence test. Test the independence of the two criteria of classification for the data given below.

Test Situation	*Kind of Recall*		
	Recalls More Finished Tasks	*Recalls More Unfinished Tasks*	*No Difference*
Informal	7	19	4
Formal	17	8	5

18.9—Sixty subjects were observed leaving a classroom. They could leave through either one of two doors. Thirty-six of the subjects went out through one of the doors and twenty-four went out through the other. Test a 1 : 1 hypothesis.

18.10—An item on an examination was based upon a discussion of a topic that was treated in each of two textbooks. One hundred subjects had read the discussion in one of the books, and 100 subjects had read the discussion in the other textbook. We have available information concerning whether the subjects passed or failed the item on the examination. Test for the independence of the two criteria of classification for the data given below.

	Response to Item	
Textbook Read	*Failed*	*Passed*
Text No. 1	10	90
Text No. 2	30	70

18.11—A group of 100 subjects was asked to choose between the aromas of two pipe tobaccos. We have available information concerning which tobacco was chosen and also the sex classification of the subjects. Test for the independence of the two criteria of classification for the data given below.

	Tobacco Chosen	
Sex	*Brand 1*	*Brand 2*
Men	10	40
Women	20	30

18.12—A total of 572 members of the Kansas State Alumni Association were sent cards concerning their membership in the association. The subjects were divided in such a way that approximately 1/4 received a white card, 1/4 a yellow card, 1/4 a blue card, and 1/4 a cherry-colored card. We have available information concerning whether the members responded to the card and also concerning the color of the card received. Test for the independence of the two criteria of classification for the data given below. Data are from Dunlap (1950).

Color of Card Received	Response to Card	
	Returned	*Not Returned*
White	60	87
Yellow	73	71
Blue	65	76
Cherry	54	86

18.13—Eight bottles of each of 6 brands of beer were given to each of 20 families for 5 days, and then 12 bottles of each brand were given on the sixth day for use over the week end. No charge was made for the beer. All brands carried the same plain label. We have available the number of bottles consumed for each brand and the number not consumed. Test for the independence of the two criteria of classification for the data given below. Data are from Fleishman (1951).

Brand	*Reaction to Brand*	
	Consumed	*Not Consumed*
A	625	415
B	613	427
C	591	449
D	566	474
E	514	526
F	497	543

18.14—Test the significance of the phi coefficient for the data of Example 10.5.

18.15—Use the median test to compare the two sets of observations given below.

Group 1		*Group 2*	
14	8	6	3
8	18	14	10
9	15	11	12
14	12	11	10
12	9	16	8
18	12	11	10
15	14	13	11
16	13	2	11
11	11	11	12
16	15	13	5

18.16—Three independent tests of significance yield probabilities of .04, .20, and .05, respectively. Using the χ^2 test, can we assume that these results, taken as a group, would occur by chance?

■ CHAPTER NINETEEN

Significance Tests for Ranked Data[1]

We have previously shown that the rank correlation coefficient r' is the product-moment correlation coefficient between two sets of ranks.[2] It is a measure of the degree of relationship between two sets of ranks. The rank correlation coefficient may range in value from -1.0 to 1.0, the former indicating a perfect negative relationship, the latter a perfect positive relationship. In the absence of any relationship between the two sets of ranks, the value of r' is zero.

Two problems to which the rank correlation coefficient is applicable may be distinguished. In the first, the objects to be ranked have no known intrinsic order established by any criterion. Two judges rank the objects with respect to some attribute, and the rank correlation coefficient between the two sets of ranks is computed. In this case, the value of r' is a measure of the degree of agreement between the two judges.

In the second problem, an order for the objects has already been established by the experimenter in terms of some criterion. It is the task of the judge to duplicate this order to the best of his ability. The rank correlation coefficient is based upon the ranks previously established by the experimenter and those assigned by the judge. In this instance, the value of r' is a

[1] Some of the material of this chapter is based upon a report (Edwards, 1951) prepared for the Instructional Film Research Program. I am indebted to Dr. C. R. Carpenter, Director of the Instructional Film Research Program, for permission to quote freely from this report.

[2] The τ coefficient can also be used, with certain advantages, in place of the rank correlation coefficient. In general, however, it is easier to calculate r' than τ. The relative merits of r' and τ are discussed by Kendall (1948).

measure of the ability of the rater to judge in accordance with a standard set by the experimenter. Application of the rank correlation coefficient to problems of this sort could be used in the selection of judges or in the segregation of judges into groups with varying degrees of ability to make the required judgments in accordance with the standard set by the experimenter.

Although the statistical analysis is the same for the two problems described above, the interpretation to be placed upon the value of r' is essentially different. In the first problem, we are merely testing the agreement between the ranks assigned by the two judges and without any knowledge about the order of the objects in terms of some criterion. It is possible, for example, for two judges to show a high degree of agreement about an order that is not necessarily "correct"—assuming that the correct order is known in terms of a defined criterion. In the second problem, we are testing the ability of the judges to agree with a known order. We are testing, in other words, the ability of a judge to rank the objects in accordance with an imposed standard. The value of r' is a measure of this ability.

Significance of the Rank Correlation Coefficient

In Table 19.1 we show the ranks assigned to 10 stimuli in terms of an external criterion, A. The ranks assigned to these same objects by two judges, B and C, are also shown. The rows labeled D^2 represent the squared

Table 19.1—Rank Order of Ten Stimuli in Terms of a Criterion A and Ranks Assigned by Each of Two Judges B and C

	Objects										
Orders	*a*	*b*	*c*	*d*	*e*	*f*	*g*	*h*	*i*	*j*	
Criterion A	1	2	3	4	5	6	7	8	9	10	
Judge B	1	2	5	6	4	3	9	10	7	8	
Judge C	6	4	5	1	8	10	2	3	9	7	
Values of D^2											$\sum D^2$
$(A - B)^2$	0	0	4	4	1	9	4	4	4	4	34
$(A - C)^2$	25	4	4	9	9	16	25	25	0	9	126
$(B - C)^2$	25	4	0	25	16	49	49	49	4	1	222

differences between the indicated sets of ranks. The data will thus illustrate both the problems described above to which the rank correlation coefficient is applicable. Let us first determine the agreement between

Judges B and C. The value of r' will be given by formula (10.19). Thus

$$r_{bc}' = 1 - \frac{(6)(222)}{990} = -.345$$

The negative value of r' indicates that there is some tendency for the second judge to assign high ranks to the stimuli to which low ranks are assigned by the first judge. We inquire now whether the value of r' is significant or whether it is sufficiently small to indicate that the relationship could very well be the result of chance or sampling variation.

We may test the null hypothesis that the population correlation is zero. Since either negative or positive values of r' will provide evidence against this hypothesis, we shall make a two-tailed test of significance. Table XIII, in the Appendix, shows the values of r' at selected significance points for values of n from 4 to 10.[3] From Table XIII, we find that for $n = 10$, positive or negative values of r' equal to or greater than .345 will occur more than 20 per cent of the time when the null hypothesis is true.[4] We conclude that the observed value of r' is not significantly greater than zero. We do not have sufficient evidence, in other words, to indicate that the two judges show anything more than chance agreement or, more accurately, disagreement in their rankings.

How well do the two judges agree with the set of ranks established by the experimenter? The rank correlation coefficients for Judge B and Judge C with the experimenter's order A are

$$r_{ab}' = 1 - \frac{(6)(34)}{990} = .794$$

and

$$r_{ac}' = 1 - \frac{(6)(126)}{990} = .236$$

By reference to Table XIII, we find that r_{ab}' is significant ($p < .02$), whereas r_{ac}' may be regarded as a chance value ($p > .20$). Consequently, we may conclude that Judge B is able to rank the 10 stimuli in an order that is significantly related to that established by the experimenter, whereas Judge C is not. If we tested a series of judges, we could, in this way, select

[3] Olds (1938) tabled the values of $\sum D^2$ for n from 2 through 7 in terms of the exact frequencies, and for n equal to 8, 9, and 10 by means of an approximation function. We have used his table to compute the corresponding values of r'. These are given in Table XIII, in the Appendix.

[4] As indicated in Table XIII, the probabilities given are for a one-tailed test of significance. If we make a two-tailed test, we must double the tabled probabilities.

those who showed a relatively high degree of the ability required and eliminate those who did not.

When n is greater than 10, the sampling distribution of r', under the null hypothesis of zero correlation, may be approximated by the t distribution. If we write

$$t = \frac{r'}{\sqrt{1 - r'^2}} \sqrt{n - 2} \tag{19.1}$$

then we may enter the table of t with the value obtained from formula (19.1) to determine whether the null hypothesis is tenable. The degrees of freedom available will be equal to $n - 2$, where n is the number of pairs of observations.

It may be observed that formula (19.1) corresponds to formula (15.1) which we used in testing the null hypothesis of zero correlation in connection with the Pearson product-moment correlation coefficient. As we pointed out earlier, Table VI, in the Appendix, is based upon formula (15.1) and enables us to evaluate the correlation coefficient directly, without the necessity of computing t. Table VI, therefore, may also be used to test the null hypothesis of zero correlation for the rank correlation coefficient when n is greater than 10. The table is entered with degrees of freedom equal to $n - 2$.

■ The Coefficient of Concordance

Just as the rank correlation coefficient is a measure of the degree of agreement between two sets of ranks, so is Kendall's (1948) *coefficient of concordance W* a measure of the degree of agreement among m sets of n ranks. If we have a group of n objects ranked by each of m judges, the coefficient of concordance tells us the degree of agreement among the m sets of ranks. The coefficient of concordance, unlike the rank correlation coefficient, however, can only be positive in sign and ranges from 0 to 1. It will be 1 when the ranks assigned by each judge are exactly the same as those assigned by the other judges, and it will be 0 when there is maximum disagreement among the judges.

It is important to note that it is the agreement among the judges that is measured by the coefficient of concordance. The fact that W may be high does not necessarily mean that the order established by the rankings is correct. As we have pointed out before, judges may agree with respect to an order that is incorrect in terms of some external standard. A high value of W may indicate, however, that the judges are applying essentially the same standard to the objects being ranked, regardless of other considerations. Such a finding may be of considerable importance when no external criterion of the order of the objects is available. For example, in investigating the relative merits of a set of objects in terms of some attribute for which we have no direct measure, we are dealing essentially with opinions and value judgments. If an objective order of merit were possible for the objects, we could test the judgments of each rater against this objective order by means of the rank correlation coefficient. We would, in essence, be testing the ability of the rater to judge in accordance with an imposed, objective standard. But in the absence of an objective order, we can rely only upon the community of agreement among judges as a means of establishing an order.[5]

This problem may be regarded from a slightly different point of view. Suppose, for example, that the judges have been asked to rank a set of objects in terms of several criteria. On some of the criteria we find a high degree of agreement, as measured by W, and on others very little. This might be taken as indicating that a common standard or frame of reference is possible for some of the attributes ranked, but not for others. Obviously, great disagreement among judges will be present if they are applying different standards or different interpretations of the same standard. In either case, the variable being judged is scientifically meaningless, for the judges at hand, for the essence of science is agreement among competent observers. The coefficient of concordance may thus be used to detect and eliminate variables that are ambiguous or are of such a nature that they cannot be reliably judged.

Analysis of Variance and *m* Sets of *n* Ranks

Consider the general case in which we have n objects that have been ranked by each of m judges. These rankings can be arranged in an $m \times n$ table such as Table 19.2. In terms of the notation of this table, the cell entry X_{ij} is the rank assigned by the ith judge to the jth object. We let $\bar{X}_{.j}$ represent a column mean and $\bar{X}_{i.}$ a row mean, with $\bar{X}_{..}$ representing the mean of all of the mn observations.

Table 19.2 is set up in the same way that Table 17.8 was arranged when we made a three-part analysis of variance. Without concerning ourselves for the moment with the fact that we now have ranks in the various cells, we could, for data so arranged, find the total sum of squares, the sum of squares between columns, and the sum of squares between rows. We could then obtain the residual or interaction sum of squares by subtracting the sum of squares between rows and the sum of squares between columns

[5] This is the basis of psychological scaling methods such as the method of paired comparisons, the method of equal-appearing intervals, and the method of successive intervals.

Table 19.2—Schematic Representation for Ranks Assigned to n Objects by m Judges

	Objects								
Judges	1	2	3	·	j	·	n		*Means*
1	X_{11}	X_{12}	X_{13}	·	X_{1j}	·	X_{1n}		$\bar{X}_{1.}$
2	X_{21}	X_{22}	X_{23}	·	X_{2j}	·	X_{2n}		$\bar{X}_{2.}$
3	X_{31}	X_{32}	X_{33}	·	X_{3j}	·	X_{3n}		$\bar{X}_{3.}$
·							·		·
i	X_{i1}	X_{i2}	X_{i3}	·	X_{ij}	·	X_{in}		$\bar{X}_{i.}$
·							·		·
m	X_{m1}	X_{m2}	X_{m3}	·	X_{mj}	·	X_{mn}		$\bar{X}_{m.}$
Means	$\bar{X}_{.1}$	$\bar{X}_{.2}$	$\bar{X}_{.3}$	·	$\bar{X}_{.j}$	·	$\bar{X}_{.n}$		$\bar{X}_{..}$

from the total sum of squares.[6] Thus, in terms of formula (17.2), we would have

$$\textit{Interaction} = \textit{Total} - (\textit{Between columns} + \textit{Between rows})$$

However, if ranks from 1 to n are present in each row of Table 19.2, then it is obvious that the row sums would all be the same and consequently the row means would all be the same. Since the row sum of squares is based upon the variation of the row means, the absence of any variation tells us that the row sum of squares will have to be zero. Then we may note that

$$\textit{Interaction} = \textit{Total} - \textit{Between columns} \tag{19.2}$$

and, since the right-hand side of formula (19.2) is the sum of squares within columns, we have the identity

$$\textit{Interaction} = \textit{Within columns} \tag{19.3}$$

Formula (19.3) gives us an important identity, which we shall find useful in later discussions.

The Case of Perfect Agreement

Now, let us assume that $m = 10$ and that $n = 5$. Let us assume also that there is perfect agreement among the m judges. If this is true, then we

[6] It would be worth while, at this point, if the section dealing with a three-part analysis of variance in Chapter 17 were reviewed.

would find that each judge had assigned the same rank to a given object that every other judge had assigned. One of the columns of Table 19.2 would have to be filled with nothing but 1's, another with nothing but 2's, another with 3's, another with 4's, and another with nothing but 5's. The column sums would, therefore, have to be 10, 20, 30, 40, and 50, and the column means would have to be 1, 2, 3, 4, and 5—but not necessarily in this order.

Now suppose, in analysis of variance terms, that we found the total sum of squares for these entries. We could then analyze this sum of squares into the sum of squares between columns and the sum of squares within columns. We would find, however, that the sum of squares within columns is zero. The reason for this is that the mean of a given column will be exactly equal to the individual entries in the column; consequently, the sum of squares within the column has to be zero. Since this will be true for every column in the table, the sum of squares within columns must be equal to zero. All of the variation in the entries in the table can be accounted for by the variation in the column means.

Let us now define W, the coefficient of concordance, as

$$W = \frac{\textit{Sum of squares between columns}}{\textit{Total sum of squares}} \tag{19.4}$$

Then, as we have just seen, if there is perfect agreement among the judges, the sum of squares between columns will be equal to the total sum of squares, and the coefficient of concordance will be equal to 1.0.

You may observe also that the formula for W as given above is the same as formula (10.24) for the correlation ratio squared. W is, in other words, the correlation ratio squared for ranked data.[7]

The Case of Maximum Disagreement

Now consider the case where there is no agreement among the judges. Again we shall let $m = 10$ and $n = 5$. We shall assume, in this instance, that the ranks are much the same as they would be if each judge had assigned them at random to the objects. We should, therefore, expect approximately the same number of 1's, 2's, 3's, and 4's, and 5's, to be present in each of the columns, within the limits of random or chance differences. If this is true, then the column sums would, in general, be equal to one another, as would the column means. The total sum of squares we would obtain from a random arrangement of the ranks in a 10×5 table will obviously be the same as that we would obtain from any other arrange-

[7] See Wallis (1939).

ment for a 10×5 table, since in any case exactly the same numbers will be used. But if the ranks are assigned at random, the sum of squares between columns will be zero, within the limits of random error, and the sum of squares within columns will be equal to the total sum of squares. Thus, the coefficient of concordance, as given by formula (19.4), will be zero when the null hypothesis of random assignment is true, that is, when there is no agreement at all among the judges.

Calculation of the Sums of Squares

We have previously shown[8] that the sum of ranks for any one judge or row of Table 19.2 will be given by formula (10.12) or

$$\sum_1^n X = \frac{n(n+1)}{2}$$

and that the sum of squared ranks for any one row of Table 19.2 will be given by formula (10.13) or

$$\sum_1^n X^2 = \frac{n(n+1)(2n+1)}{6}$$

and that the sum of squared deviations for the ranks from 1 to n for any one row of Table 19.2 will be given by formula (10.14) or

$$\sum_1^n x^2 = \frac{n^3 - n}{12}$$

where the n over the summation sign now indicates that we are concerned only with the ranks obtained from one of the judges.

If we now have m judges who have ranked the same n objects, it should be clear that the sum of ranks for any one judge will be equal to the sum of ranks for any other judge and consequently, using the notation of Table 19.2,

$$\bar{X}_{1\cdot} = \bar{X}_{2\cdot} = \bar{X}_{3\cdot} = \bar{X}_{i\cdot} = \bar{X}_{m\cdot} \tag{19.5}$$

Since the row sums will all be equal, the sum of all m sets of n ranks will be given by multiplying formula (10.12) by m. Then

$$\sum_{i=1}^{m} \sum_{j=1}^{n} X_{ij} = \frac{mn(n+1)}{2} \tag{19.6}$$

---

[8] See page 193.

It is also true that since the row means of Table 19.2 are all equal to the mean $\bar{X}_{..}$ of all m sets of n ranks, the total sum of squares for all mn observations will be given by multiplying formula (10.14) by m. Thus

$$Total = \frac{m(n^3 - n)}{12} \tag{19.7}$$

Then, using a variation of formula (16.20) for the sum of squares between groups, we have

$$Between = \frac{\sum_{j=1}^{n} (\sum_{i=1}^{m} X_{ij})^2}{m} - \frac{mn(n+1)^2}{4} \tag{19.8}$$

The sum of squares within columns can then be obtained by subtracting the sum of squares between columns from the total sum of squares, as shown by formula (16.21). Thus

$$Within\ columns = Total - Between\ columns$$

A Numerical Example

To illustrate one application of the coefficient of concordance, we have some data obtained by the Instructional Film Research Program at Pennsylvania State College. Five films were shown to a group of 10 film specialists and to a group of 9 subjects with no more than ordinary experience in viewing films. The members of each group were asked to rank the five films from best to worst. The rankings were done on the basis of an over-all evaluation of content, production, casting, and so forth. The ranks thus probably represent judgments of a rather complex standard.

The obtained ranks for the two groups of subjects are shown in Table 19.3 along with the sum of ranks and the mean rank for each film. Let us calculate the value of W for the film specialists. The sum of squares between columns as given by formula (19.8) will be

$$Between = \frac{(23)^2 + (26)^2 + \cdots + (48)^2}{10} - \frac{(10)(5)(6)^2}{4}$$

$$= 47.4$$

and the total sum of squares, as given by formula (19.7), will be

$$Total = \frac{10(5^3 - 5)}{12}$$

$$= 100.0$$

Table 19.3—Ranks Assigned to Five Films by Ten Film Specialists and Nine Naïve Judges

	Films				
Film Specialists	*A*	*B*	*C*	*D*	*E*
1	5	2	1	4	3
2	1	2	3	4	5
3	1	2	4	3	5
4	1	3	2	4	5
5	1	3	2	4	5
6	4	3	1	2	5
7	3	2	1	4	5
8	1	3	4	2	5
9	3	4	2	1	5
10	3	2	1	4	5
$\sum$	23	26	21	32	48
Mean	2.30	2.60	2.10	3.20	4.80

	Films				
Naïve Judges	*A*	*B*	*C*	*D*	*E*
1	3	4	1	5	2
2	4	1	2	5	3
3	4	2	3	5	1
4	2	4	3	1	5
5	4	3	1	2	5
6	4	2	1	3	5
7	1	2	4	3	5
8	2	5	3	1	4
9	4	1	3	2	5
$\sum$	28	24	21	27	35
Mean	3.11	2.67	2.33	3.00	3.89

and we obtain the sum of squares within columns by subtraction. Thus

$$Within = 100.0 - 47.4$$

$$= 52.6$$

Then, from formula (19.4), we obtain as the value of the coefficient of concordance,

$$W = \frac{47.4}{100.0} = .474$$

Significance of the Coefficient of Concordance

In research work, of course, we are usually not only interested in determining the degree of agreement among several or more sets of ranks, but also in testing some null hypothesis about the agreement. The null hypothesis of interest here is that the observed agreement among the rankings is a matter of chance. If this null hypothesis is true, then, as we have shown, the expected value of W will be zero. We need to determine how frequently values of W equal to or greater than .474 will arise by chance when the null hypothesis is true. If we set the probability of a Type I error as .05, we shall reject the null hypothesis if our observed value is such that it would occur 5 per cent of the time or less when the null hypothesis is true.

Continuity Corrections

The sampling distribution of W under the null hypothesis has been investigated by Kendall (1948), who reports that W may be tested for significance in terms of the F distribution. For small values of m, however, Kendall and Smith (1939) have shown that the probabilities given by the F distribution show greatest agreement with those of the exact distribution, if we first make continuity corrections in W before testing it for significance. W with continuity corrections is given by

$$W_c = \frac{\textit{Sum of squares between columns} - \dfrac{1}{m}}{\textit{Total sum of squares} + \dfrac{2}{m}} \tag{19.9}$$

where m is again the number of judges or sets of ranks available.[9]

For the film specialists of Table 19.3, we would then have

$$W_c = \frac{47.4 - \frac{1}{10}}{100.0 + \frac{2}{10}} = .472$$

instead of the value of .474 we obtained without the continuity correction.

[9] It should be apparent from formula (19.9) that, as m becomes large, the continuity correction becomes relatively unimportant.

The *F* Test

The value of W_c can be tested for significance by finding

$$F = \frac{(m - 1)W_c}{1 - W_c} \tag{19.10}$$

If we let df_1 be the degrees of freedom for the numerator of the F ratio of formula (19.10) and df_2 be the degrees of freedom for the denominator, then we have

$$df_1 = (n - 1) - \frac{2}{m} \tag{19.11}$$

degrees of freedom for the numerator and

$$df_2 = (m - 1)\left[(n - 1) - \frac{2}{m}\right] \tag{19.12}$$

degrees of freedom for the denominator.[10]

Table of Significant Values of W_c

In order to simplify the test of significance, values of W_c significant at the 5 and 1 per cent points for the values of n from 3 to 7 and for selected

---

[10] Since W is the correlation ratio squared for a set of ranks, and since we have previously shown that the significance of the correlation ratio is a matter of determining whether the mean square between columns is significantly greater than the mean square within columns, we might expect the F of formula (19.10) to be closely related to that obtained in testing the significance of the correlation ratio. Neglecting the correction for continuity, we show in answer to one of the examples at the end of the chapter that formula (19.10) may also be written

$$F = \frac{\textit{Sum of squares between columns}/n - 1}{\textit{Sum of squares within columns}/(n - 1)(m - 1)}$$

As formula (19.3) shows, the sum of squares within columns for ranked data is equal to the interaction sum of squares, and for the interaction sum of squares we have $(m - 1)(n - 1)$ degrees of freedom. Thus, the test of significance of formula (19.10), neglecting the continuity correction, is

$$F = \frac{\textit{Mean square between columns}}{\textit{Interaction mean square}}$$

with $n - 1$ degrees of freedom for the numerator and $(n - 1)(m - 1)$ degrees of freedom for the denominator. In essence, then, we are making the same test as in the case of the correlation ratio.

values of m from 3 to 20 have been calculated and are given in Table XIV, in the Appendix.[11] By reference to Table XIV we find that values of W_c equal to or greater than .307 would occur 1 per cent of the time or less when the null hypothesis is true and when $m = 10$ and $n = 5$. Since our observed value of .472 exceeds .307, we reject the null hypothesis and conclude that the agreement among the film specialists is sufficiently good that it cannot be accounted for by chance.

The χ_r^2 Test for W

For values of n and m not included in Table XIV, W_c can be tested for significance by means of formula (19.10). It is also true that a χ^2 test of the significance of W, as given by formula (19.4), may be made. This test is due to Friedman (1937, 1940) who showed that the distribution of χ^2 for ranks arranged in an $m \times n$ table tends to that of χ^2 with $n - 1$ degrees of freedom as m becomes indefinitely large. We may define χ^2 computed from the $m \times n$ table of ranks as

$$\chi_r^2 = \frac{(n - 1)(\textit{Sum of squares between columns})}{(n^3 - n)/12} \qquad \textbf{(19.13)}$$

Substituting in formula (19.13) with the data for the 10 film specialists, we get

$$\chi_r^2 = \frac{(5 - 1)(47.4)}{(5^3 - 5)/12}$$

$$= \frac{189.6}{10}$$

$$= 18.96$$

Then entering the table of χ^2 with $n - 1 = 4$ degrees of freedom, we see that our obtained value of χ_r^2 of 18.96 would also occur less than 1 per cent of the time when the null hypothesis is true.

Relation between χ_r^2 and W

χ_r^2 and W, as may be evident from the above discussion, are closely related. Thus

$$W = \frac{\chi_r^2}{m(n - 1)} \qquad \textbf{(19.14)}$$

[11] The values of W_c in Table XIV are based upon Friedman's (1940) Table II.

and $$\chi_r^2 = (W)(m)(n - 1) \tag{19.15}$$

Having calculated W, we may test its significance by means of χ_r^2, with the restrictions mentioned above, or, having found a significant value of χ_r^2, we may then express the degree of agreement in terms of W.

For the data presented in Table 19.3, we found that W_c was equal to .472 for the 10 film specialists. The corresponding value for the 9 naïve subjects is .134 and, as Table XIV shows, for $m = 9$ and $n = 5$, this is not sufficiently large for us to reject the null hypothesis. We may thus conclude that whereas the film specialists show substantial agreement among themselves in evaluating the films, the naïve subjects do not.

■ Mean Value of the Possible Rank Correlation Coefficients

In some problems it may be desirable to know the average value of all of the $m(m - 1)/2$ possible rank correlation coefficients in the $m \times n$ table. It is not necessary to compute the separate rank correlation coefficients, for this average value can be readily obtained from the coefficient of concordance. Thus

$$\bar{r}' = \frac{mW - 1}{m - 1} \tag{19.16}$$

where $\bar{r}'$ = the average value of the $m(m - 1)/2$ rank correlation coefficients
m = the number of judges or sets of ranks
W = the coefficient of concordance

Substituting in formula (19.16) with the data for the 10 film specialists we obtain

$$\bar{r}' = \frac{(10)(.474) - 1}{10 - 1} = .416$$

whereas for the 9 naïve subjects the corresponding value is .027.

■ Reliability of Average Ranks

For the ranks given to the five films by the 10 film specialists, shown in Table 19.3, we found that the value of W_c was significant and indicated substantial agreement among the judges in terms of the ranks assigned to the films. It is not expected in experimental work that m sets of ranks will show perfect agreement, but only that the agreement is sufficiently good among the judges to rule out the possibility that it is merely the result of chance. Obviously, any one of the m sets of ranks throws some light upon the ordering of the objects. Since each of the sets of ranks is an estimate of their order, we may inquire whether the various estimates may be combined to yield a single best estimate.

It is a commonplace of measurement that the average of two or more estimates of an unknown parameter is more likely to be closer to the true value than a single estimate. Similarly, with respect to ranks, we expect the average values of the m sets of ranks to provide a better estimate of the order of the n objects than a single set of ranks.

Having obtained the average values of the m ranks for each of the n objects, we raise a further question. How reliable are the averages thus obtained? Suppose, for example, the same objects were ranked by another set of m comparable judges. If we also find the average ranks assigned by the second set of judges, to what extent may we expect these averages to agree with those obtained from our first set of judges?

A reliability coefficient applicable to this case has been developed by Horst (1949) and may be symbolized by $r_{\bar{x}\bar{x}}$. This reliability coefficient may be obtained from the ranks assigned by one group of m judges. It is a measure of the degree to which we may expect the average ranks obtained from two groups of m comparable judges to agree.

Horst's formula for the general case of the reliability of the mean *ratings* assigned to n objects by m judges, where X_{ij} is the rating given by the ith judge to the jth object is, in terms of the notation of Table 19.2,

$$r_{\bar{x}\bar{x}} = 1 - \frac{\sum_{j=1}^{n} \left[\frac{\frac{\sum_{i=1}^{m} X_{ij}^2}{m} - \left(\frac{\sum_{i=1}^{m} X_{ij}}{m} \right)^2}{m-1} \right]}{\sum_{j=1}^{n} \left(\frac{\sum_{i=1}^{m} X_{ij}}{m} \right)^2 - \frac{\left[\sum_{j=1}^{n} \left(\frac{\sum_{i=1}^{m} X_{ij}}{m} \right) \right]^2}{n}} \tag{19.17}$$

In the special case where the ratings consist of rankings, so that we have the ranks assigned to n objects by each of m judges arranged in an $m \times n$ table, then formula (19.17) reduces to[12]

[12] In analysis of variance terms, formula (19.18) is

$$r_{\bar{x}\bar{x}} = 1 - \frac{s_1^2}{s_2^2}$$

$$r_{\bar{x}\bar{x}} = 1 - \frac{\textit{Sum of squares within columns}/(m-1)(n-1)}{\textit{Sum of squares between columns}/(n-1)} \tag{19.18}$$

$$r_{\bar{x}\bar{x}} = 1 - \frac{\textit{Sum of squares within columns}}{(m-1)(\textit{Sum of squares between columns})} \tag{19.19}$$

We have already found, for the film specialists of Table 19.3, that the total sum of squares is equal to 100.0 and the sum of squares between columns is equal to 47.4. Then, for the sum of squares within columns, we have

$$\textit{Within} = 100.0 - 47.4$$

$$= 52.6$$

Substituting in formula (19.19) for the reliability of the mean ranks, we get

$$r_{\bar{x}\bar{x}} = 1 - \frac{52.6}{(10-1)(47.4)}$$

$$= .877$$

as a measure of the reliability of the mean ranks obtained from the 10 film specialists. The corresponding value for the 9 naïve subjects is .205, and this value is, as we might expect, much lower than that obtained for the film specialists.

Relation between $r_{\bar{x}\bar{x}}$ and $\bar{r}'$

It can also be shown that the value of $r_{\bar{x}\bar{x}}$, as given by formula (19.18), is related to $\bar{r}'$ of formula (19.16) in terms of the Spearman-Brown

---

where s_1^2 is the residual or interaction mean square and s_2^2 is the mean square between groups. As we have pointed out earlier, when we have a table of $m \times n$ ranks the row sum of squares will be zero and the within-columns sum of squares is equal to the interaction sum of squares. We may compare this formula with formula (9.13) which we previously developed for the reliability coefficient. Thus

$$r_{x_1x_2} = 1 - \frac{s_e^2}{s_x^2}$$

where s_e^2 was an error variance. In the analysis of variance, the mean square for interaction s_1^2 is regarded as an error variance.

prophecy formula.[13] Thus

$$r_{\bar{x}\bar{x}} = \frac{m\bar{r}'}{1 + (m - 1)\bar{r}'} \tag{19.20}$$

where m is the number of judges or sets of ranks.

For the 10 film specialists of Table 19.3, we found $\bar{r}'$ was equal to .416. Then, substituting in formula (19.20), we obtain

$$r_{\bar{x}\bar{x}} = \frac{(10)(.416)}{1 + (10 - 1)(.416)}$$

$$= .877$$

which is the same value we obtained before.

Analysis of Variance of Ranks for a Two-Way Classification

Suppose that a film has been shown to a large group of college students. Each subject has been asked to express his like or dislike of the film. In addition to the response of like or dislike, we have available for each subject two criteria of classification: a score on an aptitude test and the college status of the subject. We now set up an $m \times n$ contingency table in which the m rows correspond to aptitude levels and the n columns to educational status, that is, college freshmen, sophomores, juniors, and seniors. For each cell in this table we have a certain number of subjects. This is the kind of contingency table to which, in the previous chapter, we applied the χ^2 test for the independence of the two criteria of classification.

Suppose, however, that our interest is not in testing the independence of the row and column criteria, that is, aptitude level and college status, but rather in the liking or disliking of the film. Let us keep the same $m \times n$ table, but let us now record in each cell the per cent of the subjects in the cell who say they like the film. We now inquire whether liking the film is in any way related to college status.[14] It is not necessary to assume that the relationship, if it exists, is linear, although we may detect the presence of a linear relationship as well as one that departs from linearity.

If our cell entries consisted of measures that we could assume to be

[13] The Spearman-Brown formula is discussed on page 176.

[14] We may, of course, also inquire whether liking the film is in any way related to aptitude level, and we shall discuss procedures for answering this question later.

normally distributed, we could obtain an answer to our question by a three-part analysis of variance, in which the significance of the column mean square would be tested in terms of the interaction or residual mean square. But the per cents we have recorded in the table may not reasonably be assumed to be normally distributed.

Let us rank the per cents in each row of the table. It may be noted that in ranking the per cents in the rows, we have in effect controlled the row criterion of classification, aptitude level, for the same set of ranks will appear in each row, and consequently the row means will now all be equal.[15] It should also be emphasized that in assigning ranks within rows, no assumption need be made concerning the form of the distribution of the entries that are ranked, that is, we do not need to assume that the entries are normally distributed.

We have already shown that if the row entries in the $m \times n$ table represent ranks from 1 to n, then the correlation ratio squared for this table will be equal to the coefficient of concordance W.[16] Then if the value of W is calculated and tested for significance, we are in effect testing whether there is any relationship between liking of the film and college status—with aptitude level controlled. The test involved is thus essentially one of determining whether there is any tendency for the column means to vary with the column classification.

If we desire to test for the relationship between the row criterion of classification (aptitude level) and liking of the film, we would assign the ranks within columns instead of within rows. In this way the influence of college status would be controlled, for the column means would now all be equal. We would then find the total sum of squares, the sum of squares within rows, and the sum of squares between rows, and use these sums of squares in the calculation of W and the test of significance. In testing the significance of W, in this instance, we would be testing the relationship between aptitude level and liking the film, with college status controlled. In essence, we would be testing for the tendency of the row means to vary with the row classification.

The use of W and its test of significance for problems in which the observed variable is subject to a two-way classification is not used extensively in research at the present time. It would seem, however, that this technique may prove extremely valuable in psychological, educational, and sociological research. For in this way we may study the relationship between the cell entries and the row or column classification, regardless of the

---

[15] See the discussion on page 404.

[16] In fact, Wallis (1939), working independently, developed the same statistic as W which he called the correlation ratio for ranks.

nature of the original cell entries, if only they can be ranked. We are thus not limited by any assumption concerning the population distribution of the cell entries.

It may also be emphasized that there is no necessity for the column or row classification to be quantitative variables. The row criterion might be different schools, or different test groups, and the column classification might be different films. The only requirement is that the observations or cell entries of the $m \times n$ table be capable of being ranked.

■ A Rank Test for the Significance of the Difference between Two Groups[17]

Let us suppose that we have two sets of observations and we wish to determine whether the means of the two sets differ significantly. If we can assume that the measurements are normally distributed, we should use the t test with our data. But suppose that the measurements, for one reason or another, cannot be assumed to be normally distributed. We may again make use of ranking methods without the necessity of making any assumption about the form of distribution of the observations.

Ranking methods for determining the significance of the difference between two sets of observations have been investigated by Wilcoxon (1945, 1947, 1949), Festinger (1946), Mann and Whitney (1947), and by White (1952). In the discussion that follows, we make use of the procedures developed by White.

Let us assume that we have two groups of $n_1 + n_2 = n$ observations where it is not necessary that n_1 and n_2 be equal. A single distribution of the n observations is made and ranks from 1 to n are assigned to the observations in such a way that rank 1 is given to the largest numerical observation. In case our data do not consist of numerical observations, we assume that rank 1 is assigned to the subject or object that has most of the attribute in which we are interested and that the subject or object with the least amount of the attribute is assigned the rank of n.

We shall let n_1 correspond to the group with the smaller number of observations and let T be equal to the sum of ranks for this group. We may also let T' be the conjugate total or the sum of ranks for the group with the smaller number of observations when the smallest numerical observation, or the subject with the least amount of the attribute, has been given the rank of 1 and the largest value the rank of n. The conjugate

[17] Kruskal and Wallis (1952) have developed a generalized test for comparing several sets of ranks. In the case of two groups the Kruskal-Wallis test and White's test yield the same results. The Kruskal-Wallis test is discussed later in this chapter.

total will be given by

$$T' = n_1(n_1 + n_2 + 1) - T$$

$$= n_1(n + 1) - T \tag{19.21}$$

so that there is no necessity for reranking the observations. The test of significance will be made by using either T or T', whichever is the smaller.

Table XV, in the Appendix, gives the values of T or T', whichever is the smaller, at the 5 and 1 per cent levels of significance, that is, for a two-tailed test. We may illustrate the use of Table XV with the data of Wright (1946), cited by White (1952). These data are given in Table 19.4.

Table 19.4—Survival Time in Minutes of the Peroneal Nerve under Anoxic Conditions for 4 Cats and 14 Rabbits*

Animal	*Survival Time*		*Cat Ranks*	*Rabbit Ranks*
	Minutes	*Ranks*	$n_1 = 4$	$n_2 = 14$
Cat	45	1	1	
Cat	43	2	2	
Rabbit	35	3.5		3.5
Rabbit	35	3.5		3.5
Cat	33	5	5	
Rabbit	30	6.5		6.5
Rabbit	30	6.5		6.5
Rabbit	28	8.5		8.5
Rabbit	28	8.5		8.5
Cat	25	10	10	
Rabbit	23	11		11
Rabbit	22	12.5		12.5
Rabbit	22	12.5		12.5
Rabbit	20	14		14
Rabbit	17	15		15
Rabbit	16	16.5		16.5
Rabbit	16	16.5		16.5
Rabbit	15	18		18
Σ			18.0	153.0

* Data from Wright (1946).

The values recorded in Table 19.4 are the survival times in minutes of the peroneal nerve of rabbits and cats under anoxic conditions. We have arranged the observations in order of magnitude. We wish to determine whether the survival times tend to be longer in one of the species than in the other. We might say that the null hypothesis we wish to test is that the two sets of observations are from a common population, without making any assumption concerning the distribution of the measures in this population.

We have assigned ranks to the observations in Table 19.4 based upon the combined distributions. You will note that, in assigning the ranks, we have given tied values the average of the ranks they would ordinarily occupy. For example, when we come to rank 3, we have two values of 35 minutes. We give these two values the average of ranks 3 and 4, or 3.5.

For the data of Table 19.4, we see that T for the smaller group of n_1 observations is 18. From formula (19.21) we find that

$$T' = 4(18 + 1) - 18$$

$$= 58$$

In this instance, T is smaller than T'. Consequently, we evaluate the rank total $T = 18$ in terms of the value in Table XV for $n_1 = 4$ and $n_2 = 14$. From Table XV we find that a value equal to or less than 19 will occur 5 per cent of the time or less when the null hypothesis is true. Since our observed value is less than 19, we reject the null hypothesis and conclude that the survival times in the two groups do differ.

Summary of the Rank-Order Test

We may summarize the procedure of applying the rank test in the following steps.

1. Let the group with the smaller number of observations be n_1 and the other group n_2. If the same number of observations is present in each group, one of the groups may be arbitrarily designated n_1 and the other n_2.
2. Combine the $n_1 + n_2 = n$ observations and rank them, with rank 1 being assigned to the largest numerical observation and rank n to the smallest.
3. If ties are present, give the tied observations the average of the ranks they would otherwise occupy.
4. Find the sum of ranks T for the group with the smaller number of observations.
5. Calculate T' in terms of formula (19.21)
6. Find the tabled value in Table XV for n_1 and n_2 observations. If either T or T' is equal to or less than the tabled value, reject the null hypothesis.

One-Tailed Tests for T and T'

The test summarized above is a two-tailed test, and the probabilities of .05 and .01 for the entries of Table XV refer to the probability of obtaining either a value of T or T' as small as the tabled entry. Now, if the n_1 observations are, in general, numerically larger than the n_2 observations, the n_1 observations will tend to have the smaller ranks, and the rank sum T will tend to be small and less than T'. On the other hand, if the n_1 observations are, in general, numerically smaller than the n_2 observations, the n_1 observations will tend to have the larger ranks, and the rank total T will tend to be large and greater than T'.

We might argue, therefore, that if $T < T'$, then, in general $m_1 > m_2$, whereas if $T > T'$, then, in general, $m_1 < m_2$. If we wish to test the null hypothesis that $m_1 \leqq m_2$, evidence against this hypothesis will be provided only if $\bar{X}_1 > \bar{X}_2$ so that $T < T'$. Therefore, if we reject the null hypothesis only if T is equal to or less than the tabled value in Table XV, we are making a one-tailed test and the probabilities of .05 and .01 will now correspond to .025 and .005, respectively. If this null hypothesis is rejected, we shall accept the alternative that $m_1 > m_2$. We shall conclude, in other words, that the mean for the n_1 observations is significantly greater than the mean for the n_2 observations.

Similarly, we might make a test of the null hypothesis that $m_1 \geqq m_2$. Evidence against this null hypothesis will be provided only if $\bar{X}_1 < \bar{X}_2$ so that $T > T'$. We would, therefore, reject this null hypothesis only if T' is equal to or less than the value in Table XV. This is also a one-tailed test, and the probabilities of .05 and .01 will correspond to .025 and .005, respectively. If this null hypothesis is rejected, we shall accept the alternative that $m_1 < m_2$.

Normal-Curve Approximations

White (1952) has pointed out that the distribution of T approaches normality as n_1 and n_2 become large. The expected or mean value of T for the n_1 observations is

$$\bar{T} = \frac{n_1(n_1 + n_2 + 1)}{2}$$

$$= \frac{n_1(n + 1)}{2} \tag{19.22}$$

and its standard deviation is

$$\sigma = \sqrt{\frac{n_1 n_2(n_1 + n_2 + 1)}{12}}$$

$$= \sqrt{\frac{n_1 n_2 (n + 1)}{12}} \tag{19.23}$$

where $n = n_1 + n_2$.

Then, if we have values of n_1 and n_2 that exceed those given in Table XV, we may express the observed value of T as a normal deviate. Thus

$$z = \frac{T - \bar{T}}{\sigma} \tag{19.24}$$

where z = a normal deviate
T = the sum of ranks for the n_1 observations
$\bar{T}$ = the expected or mean value of T as given by formula (19.22)
σ = the standard deviation obtained from formula (19.23)

If we apply formula (19.22) to the data of Table 19.4, we get

$$\bar{T} = \frac{4(18 + 1)}{2} = 38$$

and formula (19.23) gives us

$$\sigma = \sqrt{\frac{(4)(14)(18 + 1)}{12}} = 9.416$$

We have already found that the rank total T for the n_1 observations is 18 and that T' is equal to 58. It is also true that if T had been equal to 58, then T' would have been equal to 18. As we have emphasized, Table XV is so arranged as to make use of either T or T', whichever is the smaller, with the probabilities of .05 and .01 corresponding to a two-tailed test. As a matter of convenience, we have expressed formula (19.24) in terms of T only and not T'. If T is smaller than T', then the value of z that we obtain from formula (19.24) will be negative in sign, whereas if T is larger than T', then the value of z that we obtain will be positive in sign. Consequently, if we wish to make a two-tailed test corresponding to that of Table XV, at say the 5 per cent level, we should be prepared to reject the null hypothesis if the z we obtain from formula (19.24) is either plus 1.96 or minus 1.96.

Substituting in formula (19.24), we obtain

$$z = \frac{18 - 38}{9.416} = -2.124$$

and the null hypothesis would be rejected. We may observe that if the value of T' had been equal to 18, so that T would be equal to 58, then we would have

$$z = \frac{58 - 38}{9.416} = 2.124$$

Thus by considering both positive and negative values of z in the test of significance, we are making a test that corresponds to the one made in using Table XV, that is, a two-tailed test.

Correction for Continuity

As we have pointed out before, the rank total will, in general, be integral, whereas the normal distribution is continuous.[18] Therefore, we may make a continuity correction which consists of reducing the absolute value of the deviation $T - \bar{T}$ or $T' - \bar{T}$ by .5 before calculating z.

Making the continuity correction, we obtain, for the data of Table 19.4,

$$z = \frac{|18 - 38| - .5}{9.416} = -2.07$$

and

$$z = \frac{|58 - 38| - .5}{9.416} = 2.07$$

It may be noted that the continuity correction will always serve to reduce the value of the normal deviate.

From Table XV we see that the tabled value of T for $n_1 = 4$ and $n_2 = 14$ is 19 at the 5 per cent level. Then, as we have just seen, $\bar{T}$ will be equal to 38 and σ will be equal to 9.416. If we substitute these values in formula (19.24) and solve for z corrected for continuity, we should expect to obtain a value that is close to -1.96, that is, the normal deviate that would be significant at the 5 per cent level.

Making these substitutions, we obtain

$$z = \frac{|19 - 38| - .5}{9.416} = -1.965$$

which differs by only .005 from the expected value of -1.96. We see, therefore, that, with $n_1 = 4$ and $n_2 = 14$, the normal-curve approximation is quite satisfactory at the 5 per cent level of significance.

---

[18] See page 224.

The *H* Test for More Than Two Groups

Suppose that we have more than two groups of observations and that the observations in each group consist of ranks based upon the total number of observations. For example, in Table 19.5 we have three groups with 5 observations in each group. If we now arrange these 15 observations in order of magnitude and then rank them, we obtain the ranks shown in the table alongside of the original observations. We have given observations that are tied the average of the ranks they would ordinarily occupy.

Table 19.5—Scores and Ranks for Three Groups of Five Subjects Each

	Group 1		*Group 2*		*Group 3*	
	Score	*Rank*	*Score*	*Rank*	*Score*	*Rank*
	7	8	4	12	2	14.5
	10	3.5	6	10.5	2	14.5
	10	3.5	7	8	3	13
	11	2	9	5.5	7	8
	12	1	9	5.5	6	10.5
T		18.0		41.5		60.5
$T^2/5$		64.80		344.45		732.05

We now wish to test the null hypothesis that these samples have been drawn at random from identical populations. This null hypothesis may be tested in terms of a statistic developed by Kruskal and Wallis (1952) which they call H. This statistic is given by

$$H = \left[\frac{12}{n(n+1)}\right]\left[\sum_{1}^{k} \frac{T_i^2}{n_i}\right] - 3(n+1) \tag{19.25}$$

where k = the number of groups

n_i = the number of observations in the ith group

n = $\sum n_i$, the total number of observations

T_i = the sum of ranks for the ith group

It should be obvious from formula (19.25) that there is no necessity for the number of observations in each group to be equal, as happens to be the case for the data of Table 19.5.

In Table 19.5 we show the sum of ranks for each group and the squares of these sums divided by the corresponding values of n_i. We see that $\sum_{1}^{k} \frac{T_i^2}{n_i} = 1{,}141.30$. Then, substituting in formula (19.25), we obtain

$$H = \frac{12(1{,}141.30)}{15(15+1)} - 3(15+1)$$

$$= \frac{13{,}695.60}{240} - 48$$

$$= 57.065 - 48$$

$$= 9.065$$

Kruskal and Wallis (1952) show that if the null hypothesis is true, and if the number of observations in each group is not too small, then H is distributed as χ^2 with $k - 1$ degrees of freedom.[19] Consequently, we may determine whether or not the null hypothesis is tenable by entering the table of χ^2 with the value of H obtained from formula (19.25) and with degrees of freedom equal to 1 less than the number of groups. For the data of Table 19.5, k is equal to 3, and we therefore have 2 degrees of freedom. From the table of χ^2—Table IV, in the Appendix—we find that for 2 degrees of freedom the probability of obtaining a value of H equal to or greater than 9.065 is somewhere between .02 and .01.[20] Consequently, we shall reject the null hypothesis for the data of Table 19.5.

The null hypothesis tested by H is that the samples come from identical populations. If this hypothesis is rejected, we shall accept the alternative hypothesis that the populations are not identical. As in the case of F, however, our experimental interest is usually in means and not in variances or other characteristics of the populations. Kruskal and Wallis (1952, p. 599) offer reasons to believe that the H test may be relatively insensitive to differences in variances. In general, therefore, the test may be useful in testing differences among means, without the necessity of assuming homogeneity of variance. That is, if the null hypothesis is rejected, we shall, in general, be able to conclude that the population means are not equal.

---

[19] The χ^2 table may be used, in general, if we have three or more samples and the n_i are all greater than 5. Kruskal and Wallis (1952) give tables for the exact distribution of H for three samples with all $n_i \leqq 5$. They also suggest approximations which may be used when more than three samples are to be evaluated and some of the n_i are less than 5.

[20] The Kruskal and Wallis (1952) tables show that the probability is less than .01.

Relationship between the Kruskal-Wallis Test and White's Test for the Case of Two Groups

Let us apply the Kruskal-Wallis test to the data of Table 19.4, where we have but two groups of observations. The sum of ranks for the group with 4 observations is 18, and the sum of ranks for the group with 14 observations is 153. Then

$$\sum_{1}^{k} \frac{T_i^2}{n_i} = \frac{(18)^2}{4} + \frac{(153)^2}{14}$$

$$= 81.000 + 1{,}672.071$$

$$= 1{,}753.071$$

If we now substitute in formula (19.25) we obtain

$$H = \frac{(12)(1{,}753.071)}{(18)(19)} - (3)(18+1)$$

$$= 61.511 - 57$$

$$= 4.511$$

Since we have but two groups, we have but 1 degree of freedom, and from the table of χ^2 we find that the probability of obtaining H equal to or greater than 4.511 is somewhere between .05 and .02.

In the discussion of White's rank-order test for the data of Table 19.4, we found that the normal-curve approximation gave us z equal to 2.124. We have already shown[21] that for 1 degree of freedom, the probability of a given value of χ^2 can be obtained by finding the probability for the corresponding value of z^2. In the present example, we see that either z equal to plus 2.124 or minus 2.124 will give z^2 equal to 4.511. The probability of obtaining $z^2 = 4.511$ will therefore be given by the area in the two tails of the normal curve falling beyond -2.124 and 2.124 or, approximately, $(2)(.0169) = .0338$. This is also the probability of obtaining $\chi^2 = 4.511$, with 1 degree of freedom.

Thus the Kruskal-Wallis test, in the case of but two groups, is the same

[21] See page 170.

as White's test, which uses the normal-curve approximation and makes a two-tailed test of significance.[22]

The Case of Tied Ranks

We have suggested earlier, in connection with the rank correlation coefficient, that if observations are tied for a given rank, then they should be assigned the average value of the ranks they would otherwise occupy. We also followed this procedure in applying White's rank-order test for the difference between two groups and the H test of Kruskal and Wallis. Although tied observations did not enter into the discussion of the coefficient of concordance, we may at this time point out that if tied observations are present in problems dealing with this coefficient, we may also give the tied observations the average value of the ranks they would otherwise occupy. As long as the number of ties is not too large, corrections that could be introduced for taking the ties into account will have relatively little influence.[23] However, if the number of tied ranks is large, a correction for this condition should be made.

The effect of tied ranks is to reduce the sum of squares $\sum(X - \bar{X})^2$, as given by formula (10.14), below the value of $(n^3 - n)/12$. We shall, therefore, need to introduce a correction factor into formula (10.14) which will take the presence of ties into account. We may define this correction factor for each group of ties as

$$C = \frac{k^3 - k}{12} \tag{19.26}$$

where k represents the number of observations in a group tied for a given rank. Thus, if we have 2 observations tied for a given rank, $C = (2^3 - 2)/12 = .5$. If we have 3 observations tied for a given rank, $C = (3^3 - 3)/12 = 2.0$. Values of C for k up to 15 are given in Table 19.6. It may be noted that Table 19.6 can be used to obtain the values of $(n^3 - n)/12$ for n up to 15 also.

---

[22] We have shown the relationship between z^2 and H. A similar relationship exists between z^2, corrected for continuity, and H with a continuity correction. The continuity adjustment for H in the case of 1 degree of freedom is described by Kruskal and Wallis (1952).

[23] This is true, as Kendall (1948) shows, for both the rank correlation coefficient and the coefficient of concordance. It is also true for H, and consequently for White's rank-difference test for two groups, as Kruskal and Wallis (1952) point out.

Table 19.6—Values of the Correction Factor $C = (k^3 - k)/12$ for Tied Ranks

Number of Ties k	*Correction* $(k^3 - k)/12$ C
2	.5
3	2.0
4	5.0
5	10.0
6	17.5
7	28.0
8	42.0
9	60.0
10	82.5
11	110.0
12	143.0
13	182.0
14	227.5
15	280.0

We may now define the sum of squares for a set of n ranks as

$$\sum(X - \bar{X})^2 = \frac{n^3 - n}{12} - \sum C \tag{19.27}$$

where $\sum C$ indicates that we must sum the correction factor for each group of tied ranks. If there are no tied ranks, then $\sum C$ will equal zero and the sum of squares will be equal to $(n^3 - n)/12$.

The Rank Correlation Coefficient and Tied Ranks

In Table 19.7 we have a set of X and Y scores. We have assigned ranks to the X and Y scores, giving the tied observations the average of the ranks they would ordinarily occupy. Squaring the differences between the pairs of ranks and summing, we find $\sum D^2 = 13$. Then, substituting in formula (10.19) for the rank correlation coefficient, we obtain

$$r' = 1 - \frac{(6)(13)}{990} = .921$$

If we now make corrections for the presence of ties in the X ranks and

Table 19.7—Scores and Ranks for Ten Pairs of Observations

Scores		*Ranks*		*Rank Difference*
X	*Y*	*X*	*Y*	*D*
32	18	1.0	1.0	.0
20	16	2.5	2.0	.5
20	11	2.5	4.5	−2.0
18	11	4.5	4.5	.0
18	11	4.5	4.5	.0
10	11	6.5	4.5	2.0
10	5	6.5	8.0	−1.5
5	5	8.0	8.0	.0
4	5	9.5	8.0	1.5
2	2	9.5	10.0	− .5

the Y ranks, we may designate these two correction factors as $\sum C_x$ and $\sum C_y$, respectively. For the X ranks we have 4 groups of $k = 2$ tied observations. For each of these groups $C_x = (2^3 - 2)/12 = .5$, and $\sum C_x = 2.0$. For the Y ranks we have one group of $k = 3$ tied observations and another group of $k = 4$ tied observations. Table 19.6 shows that the two corresponding values of C_y will be 2.0 and 5.0, respectively, and we have $\sum C_y = 7.0$.

The sum of squares for the X ranks, as given by formula (19.27), which takes the ties into account, will be

$$\sum x^2 = \frac{10^3 - 10}{12} - 2.0 = 80.5$$

and for the Y ranks the sum of squares will be

$$\sum y^2 = \frac{10^3 - 10}{12} - 7.0 = 75.5$$

Then, by substitution in formula (10.16), we obtain as the value of the rank correlation coefficient, taking the tied ranks into account,

$$r' = \frac{80.5 + 75.5 - 13.0}{2\sqrt{(80.5)(75.5)}} = .917$$

In the present example, the correction factors are relatively small compared with $(n^3 - n)/12$, and the value of the rank correlation coefficient obtained with the correction factor for ties differs but little from that obtained without taking the tied ranks into account.

White's Rank Test and Tied Ranks

In our discussion of White's rank test for the significance of the difference between two groups, we gave as the denominator of the z ratio

$$\sigma = \sqrt{\frac{n_1 n_2 (n + 1)}{12}}$$

where $n_1 + n_2 = n$.

If there are ties present in the set of n ranks, then we may apply a correction factor to the above formula, so that we have

$$\sigma = \sqrt{\left(\frac{n_1 n_2}{n(n - 1)}\right)\left(\frac{n^3 - n}{12} - \Sigma C\right)} \quad \textbf{(19.28)}$$

where C is defined as in formula (19.26). If there are no ties in the set of n ranks, then ΣC will be equal to zero, and formula (19.28) reduces to formula (19.23).

In Table 19.8 we give values of a dependent variable X obtained by Group 1 and Group 2. We have assigned ranks to the X values, giving the

Table 19.8—Scores and Ranks for Two Groups of Subjects

	Group 1		*Group 2*	
	X	*Rank*	X	*Rank*
	60	4.5	50	10.0
	55	7.0	49	11.0
	75	2.0	52	8.5
	58	6.0	48	12.0
	72	3.0	60	4.5
	80	1.0	45	13.0
			52	8.5
Σ *Ranks*		23.5		67.5

tied observations the average of the ranks they would ordinarily occupy. If we apply formula (19.23), which does not take the presence of ties into account, we have as the denominator of the z ratio

$$\sigma = \sqrt{\frac{(6)(7)(13 - 1)}{12}} = 7.0$$

Then $\bar{T}$ as obtained from formula (19.22) will be equal to

$$\bar{T} = \frac{n_1(n + 1)}{2} = \frac{(6)(14)}{2} = 42.0$$

and, without making continuity corrections, we have

$$z = \frac{23.5 - 42.0}{7.0} = -2.643$$

If we now apply formula (19.28), which takes the presence of ties into account, we have two groups of $k = 2$ tied observations, with $C = .5$ for each group, and $\sum C = 1.00$. Then, for formula (19.28), we have

$$\sigma = \sqrt{\left(\frac{(6)(7)}{(13)(13 + 1)}\right)\left(\frac{13^3 - 13}{12} - 1.00\right)} = 6.981$$

and, without making continuity corrections, we have

$$z = \frac{23.5 - 42.0}{6.981} = -2.650$$

Again, in the present example, the correction factor is relatively small compared with $(n^3 - n)/12$, and the value of z obtained with the correction factor for tied ranks differs but little from that obtained by taking the tied ranks into account.

The Coefficient of Concordance and Tied Ranks

We defined the coefficient of concordance in terms of formula (19.4) as

$$W = \frac{\textit{Sum of squares between columns}}{\textit{Total sum of squares}}$$

where the total sum of squares was defined by formula (19.7) as

$$\textit{Total} = \frac{m(n^3 - n)}{12}$$

If there are tied ranks present within any one of the set of m ranks, then we may apply a correction to the total sum of squares, as defined by formula (19.7), to obtain

$$Total = \frac{m(n^3 - n)}{12} - \sum C \tag{19.29}$$

where C is defined as in formula (19.26). If there are no ties present in any of the m sets of ranks, then $\sum C$ will be equal to zero, and the total sum of squares will be equal to $m(n^3 - n)/12$.

The coefficient of concordance, taking tied ranks into account, will then be given by the sum of squares between columns divided by the total sum of squares, as given by formula (19.29), or

$$W = \frac{\textit{Sum of squares between columns}}{\dfrac{m(n^3 - n)}{12} - \sum C} \tag{19.30}$$

We illustrate the correction factor for tied ranks in terms of data supplied by Kogan and Pumroy (1952). Eleven patients were rated by 4 psychiatrists on a diagnostic rating scale. These ratings were transformed to ranks, and the tied ratings for each psychiatrist were given the average of the ranks they would ordinarily occupy. These rankings are shown in Table 19.9.

Table 19.9—Ranks Assigned to Ratings Given by 4 Psychiatrists to Each of 11 Patients with Tied Ratings Assigned Average Ranks*

Psychiatrists	*Patients*											Σ
	A	*B*	*C*	*D*	*E*	*F*	*G*	*H*	*I*	*J*	*K*	
1	7.0	1.5	7.0	7.0	7.0	7.0	7.0	1.5	7.0	7.0	7.0	66.0
2	7.5	2.5	7.5	7.5	1.0	2.5	7.5	7.5	7.5	7.5	7.5	66.0
3	6.5	6.5	6.5	6.5	6.5	6.5	6.5	6.5	6.5	1.0	6.6	66.0
4	6.5	6.5	1.0	6.5	6.5	6.5	6.5	6.5	6.5	6.5	6.5	66.0
Σ	27.5	17.0	22.0	27.5	21.0	22.5	27.5	22.0	27.5	22.0	27.5	264.0

* Data from Kogan and Pumroy (1952).

The sum of squares between columns will be given by formula (19.8) and is equal to

$$Between = \frac{(27.5)^2 + (17.0)^2 + \cdots + (27.5)^2}{4} - \frac{(4)(11)(12)^2}{4}$$

$$= 33.375$$

If we fail to take the presence of ties into account, then the total sum of squares, as given by formula (19.7), will be equal to

$$Total = \frac{4(11^3 - 11)}{12} = 440$$

and the coefficient of concordance, as given by formula (19.4), will equal

$$W = \frac{Sum\ of\ squares\ between\ columns}{Total\ sum\ of\ squares} = \frac{33.375}{440} = .076$$

We now correct the total sum of squares, taking the presence of tied ranks into account. For the first psychiatrist we have two groups of ties with $k = 2$ and $k = 9$. The corresponding values of C are .5 and 60.0. For the second psychiatrist we have two groups of ties with $k = 2$ and $k = 8$. The corresponding values of C are .5 and 42.0. For the third psychiatrist we have one group of ties with $k = 10$. The corresponding value of C is 82.5. The fourth psychiatrist also has one group of ties with $k = 10$ and $C = 82.5$. For $\sum C$ we have 268. Subtracting this correction in formula (19.29), we obtain

$$Total = 440 - 268 = 172$$

Dividing the sum of squares between columns by the total sum of squares, corrected for the presence of ties, we have for the coefficient of concordance

$$W = \frac{33.375}{172} = .194$$

which differs considerably from the value of W obtained without taking the presence of tied ranks into account.

If we wish to test W, adjusted for tied ranks, for significance in terms of formula (19.13), then χ_r^2 becomes

$$\chi_r^2 = \frac{m(n-1)\ (Sum\ of\ squares\ between\ columns)}{\dfrac{m(n^3 - n)}{12} - \sum C} \qquad \textbf{(19.31)}$$

which for the data of Table 19.8 gives

$$\chi_r^2 = \frac{4(10)(33.375)}{440 - 268} = 7.76$$

Since we have already made the adjustment for tied ranks in W, as given by formula (19.30), if we use formula (19.15) to test this W for significance, no further correction is necessary. Thus

$$\chi_r^2 = (W)(m)(n-1)$$

$$= (.194)(4)(10)$$

$$= 7.76$$

The Kruskal-Wallis Test and Tied Ranks

If we have three or more groups and the Kruskal-Wallis test is used to evaluate the differences between the groups, there may be tied ranks present. If the tied ranks are given the average of the ranks they would ordinarily occupy, then H as given by formula (19.25) may be divided by

$$1 - \frac{\sum C}{(n^3 - n)/12}$$

where C is defined as in formula (19.26). If there are no ties present, then $\sum C$ will be zero, and H will be unchanged.

■ EXAMPLES

19.1—At a neuropsychiatric hospital, three psychiatrists were asked to rank 7 patients according to the judged severity of the patients' psychological problems. Each psychiatrist made his rankings independently, that is, without knowledge of the ranks assigned to the patients by the other psychiatrists.

(*a*) Find the value of W and of W_c.
(*b*) Is W_c significant?
(*c*) What is the reliability of the average ranks?

Psychiatrists	Patients						
	A	B	C	D	E	F	G
1	5	2	1	6	3	4	7
2	2	1	3	7	5	4	6
3	5	2	1	4	6	3	7

19.2—Uhrbrock (1948) had 7 interviewers rank 11 applicants for a position. The applicants had been preselected from various colleges on the basis of psychological tests and preliminary interviews.

(*a*) Find the value of W.
(*b*) Test W for significance, using χ_r^2.
(*c*) What is the reliability of the average ranks as given by formula (19.21)?
(*d*) Using the formula for W, find the average intercorrelation of the ranks.
(*e*) Check the value obtained for $r_{\bar{x}\bar{x}}$ in terms of formula (19.22).

Inter-viewers	Applicants										
	Jn	Wy	De	Sn	Pt	Mc	Le	Bw	Bn	Dy	Ls
1	3	10	9	8	1	6	4	7	11	2	5
2	8	9	7	10	2	1	5	3	11	4	6
3	4	9	5	10	1	2	3	8	11	6	7
4	3	7	4	9	1	2	6	8	11	5	10
5	1	6	8	7	5	4	10	3	9	11	2
6	5	11	8	7	1	10	2	4	9	3	6
7	5	9	4	8	2	1	6	10	11	3	7

19.3—Anderson (1934) had 25 occupations ranked by 673 North Carolina State College students. The occupations were ranked in terms of (A) social contribution, (B) social prestige, and (C) economic return. The ranks based upon the combined judgments of the 673 students are given below.

(*a*) Find the three possible rank correlation coefficients.
(*b*) Use W to determine how much agreement there is among the three sets of ranks.
(*c*) Use χ_r^2 to test the significance of W.
(*d*) Average the three coefficients obtained in (*a*) and see that this average checks with that given by formula (19.16).

Occupation	*A* *Social Contribution*	*B* *Social Prestige*	*C* *Economic Return*	Σ
Clergyman	1	3	16	20
Physician	2	2	3	7
Professor	3	5	10	18
Banker	4	1	1	6
Schoolteacher	5	11	19	35
Manufacturer	6	6	2	14
Lawyer	7	4	4	15
Farmer	8	14	12	34
Engineer	9	9	5	23
Artist	10	7	8	25
Merchant	11	12	9	32
Factory manager	12	10	6	28
Machinist	13	18	11	42
Carpenter	14	19	17	50
Bookkeeper	15	17	18	50
Insurance agent	16	15	13	44
Salesman	17	16	14	47
Factory operative	18	21	20	59
Barber	19	20	21	60
Blacksmith	20	22	22	64
Baseball player	21	13	7	41
Soldier	22	23	24	69
Chauffeur	23	24	23	70
Man of leisure	24	8	15	47
Ditch digger	25	25	25	75

19.4—Dulsky and Krout (1950) had fourteen factory supervisors ranked on promotion potential by three executives who had observed the supervisors at work. Two psychologists also ranked the supervisors on the basis of an information blank and various psychological tests. The ranks are given below.

(*a*) Compute the three rank correlation coefficients for the executive rankings and also the rank correlation coefficient for the ranks assigned by the two psychologists.

(*b*) Find the coefficient of concordance using the ranks obtained from all five judges.

(*c*) Test W for significance using χ_r^2.

(*d*) Find the reliability of the average ranks.

Supervisor	Rankings by Three Executives 1	2	3	Rankings by Two Psychologists 4	5	Σ
A	7	4	8	9	8	36
B	2	1	2	3	3	11
C	1	2	1	10	7	21
D	5	3	6	5	5	24
E	4	8	7	4	2	25
F	3	5	5	8	13	34
G	6	6	4	1	1	18
H	9	11	9	6	4	39
I	11	7	10	7	10	45
J	14	10	12	12	14	62
K	10	9	11	14	9	53
L	12	14	13	11	11	61
M	8	12	3	2	6	31
N	13	13	14	13	12	65

19.5—Sixteen graduate students in psychology took the Ph.D. qualifying examination in statistics. Their papers were read and graded by two examiners. The grades given the papers by each examiner have been translated into ranks and the ranks are given below.

(*a*) Find the value of r'.
(*b*) Can we conclude that the agreement between the two examiners is significantly greater than chance?

Students	Examiner A	Examiner B	Students	Examiner A	Examiner B
1	1	1	9	3	3
2	2	2	10	10	5.5
3	7	10	11	8.5	11
4	4	5.5	12	12	13.5
5	11	9	13	14.5	15.5
6	5	5.5	14	13	12
7	8.5	5.5	15	16	15.5
8	6	8	16	14.5	13.5

19.6—Schultz (1945) collected data on the socio-economic level, aptitude level, and college attendance of male high school graduates. Ranks within rows were assigned on the basis of the per cent of college attendance for the number of subjects falling in each cell of the row.

(*a*) Compute the coefficient of concordance.
(*b*) Test *W* for significance using χ_r^2.
(*c*) Interpret your results.

Aptitude Intervals	*Socio-Economic Status* 0–14	15–18	19–22	23–26	27–30	31 plus
100 plus	6	2	4.5	4.5	3	1
90–99	5	4	2	3	6	1
80–89	6	4	2	3	5	1
70–79	6	4	1	5	3	2
60–69	6	4	5	2	3	1
50–59	5.5	5.5	3	6	4	1
40–49	2	5	3	6	4	1
15–39	4	6	2	5	3	1
Sum	40.5	34.5	21.5	32.5	30.0	9.0

19.7—Weise and Bitterman (1951) tested two groups of 10 rats each under different conditions. Two lamps were located at each choice point. For one group, both lamps were on. For the other group, one lamp at each choice point was on and the other was off. The scores given below are error scores based on 24 days of training.

One Lamp	*Both Lamps*
164	69
157	117
123	102
196	39
209	62
188	101
174	54
136	65
117	92
109	86

(*a*) Arrange the combined observations in order of magnitude and assign ranks from 1 to 20.

(*b*) Use White's test and Table XV to determine whether the two groups differ.
(*c*) Without making a correction for continuity, find the value of z.
(*d*) Show that the value of z^2 is equal to H.

19.8—Twenty-two subjects were divided at random into two groups of 11 subjects each. One group was then tested under Experimental Condition A and the other under Experimental Condition B. The measures obtained on the dependent variable are given below.

(*a*) Arrange the combined observations in order of magnitude and assign ranks from 1 to 22.
(*b*) Use White's test and Table XV to determine whether the two groups differ.

Experimental Condition A	*Experimental Condition B*
36	33
50	29
100	80
90	62
38	45
95	34
70	43
76	98
79	60
75	40
44	30

19.9—Make a correction for continuity and find the value of z for the data of Example 19.8.

19.10—Use the H test to determine whether the hypothesis that the following four sets of observations are from identical populations is tenable.

Group 1	*Group 2*	*Group 3*	*Group 4*
30	19	22	38
28	17	24	45
36	20	32	42
29	20	29	39
36	15	24	36
34	16		32
36	29		
	13		
	27		
	18		
	17		

19.11—Use the H test to determine whether the hypothesis that the following three sets of observations are from identical populations is tenable.

Group A	*Group B*	*Group C*
38	22	32
55	24	33
54	42	30
44	41	35
48	31	30
22	32	28

19.12—Show that formula (19.10), without continuity corrections, can also be written

$$F = \frac{\textit{Sum of squares between columns}/n - 1}{\textit{Sum of squares within columns})/(n - 1)(m - 1}$$

Bibliography

Adkins, Dorothy C. and Others. 1947. *Construction and analysis of achievement tests*. Washington: Government Printing Office.

Anastasi, Anne. 1937. *Differential psychology*. New York: Macmillan.

Anderson, W. W. 1934. The occupational attitudes of college men. *J. soc. Psychol.*, **5**, 435–466.

Ansbacher, H. L. 1944. Distortion in the perception of real movement. *J. exp. Psychol.*, **34**, 1–23.

Baker, K. H. 1937. Pre-experimental set in distraction experiments. *J. gen. Psychol.*, **16**, 471–488.

Bartlett, M. S. 1937. Some examples of statistical methods of research in agriculture and applied biology. *J. R. statist. Soc. Suppl.*, **4**, 137–170.

Berkshire, J. R. (Ed.) 1951. *Improvement of grading practices for Air Training Command schools*. Air Training Command, Scott Air Force Base, Illinois, ATRC Manual 50–900–9.

Bugelski, B. R. 1942. Interference with recall of original responses after learning new responses to old stimuli. *J. exp. Psychol.*, **30**, 368–379.

Burke, C. J. 1953. A brief note on one-tailed tests. *Psychol. Bull.*, **50**, 384–386.

Cheshire, L., Saffir, M., & Thurstone, L. L. 1933. *Computing diagrams for the tetrachoric correlation coefficient*. Chicago: University of Chicago Bookstore.

Cochran, W. G. 1947. Some consequences when the assumptions for the analysis of variance are not satisfied. *Biometrics*, **3**, 22–38.

Cochran, W. G., & Cox, Gertrude M. 1950. *Experimental designs*. New York: Wiley.

Conrad, H. S. 1948. Characteristics and uses of item-analysis data. *Psychol. Monogr.*, **62**, 295.

Crespi, L. P. 1942. Quantitative variation of incentive and performance in the white rat. *Amer. J. Psychol.*, **55**, 467–517.

Cronbach, L. J. 1949. *Essentials of psychological testing.* New York: Harper.

Curtis, J. W. 1943. A study of the relationship between hypnotic susceptibility and intelligence. *J. exp. Psychol.*, **33**, 337–339.

Davidoff, M. D., & Goheen, H. W. 1953. A table for the rapid determination of the tetrachoric correlation coefficient. *Psychometrika*, **18**, 115–121.

Dixon, W. J., & Massey, F. J., Jr. 1951. *Introduction to statistical analysis.* New York: McGraw-Hill.

Dixon, W. J., & Mood, A. M. 1946. The statistical sign test. *J. Amer. statist. Ass.*, **41**, 557–566.

Dorcus, R. M. 1944. A brief study of the Humm-Wadsworth Temperament Scale and the Guilford-Martin Personnel Inventory in an industrial situation. *J. appl. Psychol.*, **28**, 302–307.

Dulsky, S. G., & Krout, M. H. 1950. Predicting promotion potential on the basis of psychological tests. *Personnel Psychol.* **3**, 345–351.

Dunlap, J. W. 1950. The effect of color in direct mail advertising. *J. appl. Psychol.*, **34**, 280–281.

Edwards, A. L. 1950*a*. *Experimental design in psychological research.* New York: Rinehart.

Edwards, A. L. 1950*b*. On "the use and misuse of the chi-square test"—the case of the 2 × 2 contingency table. *Psychol. Bull.*, **47**, 341–346.

Edwards, A. L. 1951. *Applications of ranking in film research and the statistical analysis of ranks.* Instructional Film Research Program: Pennsylvania State College.

Edwards, A. L., & Thurstone, L. L. 1952. An internal consistency check for scale values determined by the method of successive intervals. *Psychometrika*, **17**, 169–180.

Festinger, L. 1946. The significance of the difference between means without reference to the frequency distribution function. *Psychometrika*, **11**, 97–105.

Finney, D. J. 1948. The Fisher-Yates test of significance in 2 by 2 contingency tables. *Biometrika*, **35**, 145–156.

Fisher, R. A. 1921. On the "probable error" of a coefficient of correlation. *Metron*, **1**, Part 4, 1–32.

Fisher, R. A. 1936. *Statistical methods for research workers.* (6th ed.) Edinburgh: Oliver & Boyd.

Fisher, R. A. 1942. *The design of experiments.* (3d ed.) Edinburgh: Oliver & Boyd.

Fisher, R. A., & Yates, F. 1949. *Statistical tables for biological, agricultural and medical research.* (3d ed.) New York: Hafner.

Fleishman, E. A. 1951. An experimental consumer panel technique. *J. appl. Psychol.*, **35**, 133–135.

Fosdick, S. J. 1939. Report to the National Retail Dry Goods Association. Quoted in Hartmann, G. W., and Newcomb, T. M. (Eds.) *Industrial conflict.* New York: Cordon, p. 119.

Friedman, M. 1937. The use of ranks to avoid the assumption of normality implicit in the analysis of variance. *J. Amer. statist. Ass.*, **32**, 675–701.

Friedman, M. 1940. A comparison of alternative tests of significance for the problem of *m* rankings. *Ann. math. Statist.*, **11**, 86–92.

Garrett, H. E. 1937. *Statistics in psychology and education.* (2d ed.) New York: Longmans, Green.

Gilliland, A. R., & Clark, E. L. 1939. *Psychology of individual differences.* New York: Prentice-Hall.

Goodenough, Florence L. 1949. *Mental testing.* New York: Rinehart.

Guilford, J. P. 1936. *Psychometric methods.* New York: McGraw-Hill.

Gulliksen, H. 1950. *Theory of mental tests.* New York: Wiley.

Hick, W. E. 1952. A note on one-tailed and two-tailed tests. *Psychol. Rev.*, **59**, 316–317.

Hoel, P. G. 1947. *Introduction to mathematical statistics.* New York: Wiley.

Horst, P. 1949. A generalized expression for the reliability of measures. *Psychometrika*, **14**, 21–31.

Janis, I. L., & Astrachan, Myrtle A. 1951. The effects of electroconvulsive treatment on memory efficiency. *J. abnorm. soc. Psychol.*, **46**, 501–511.

Jenkins, J. G., & Dallenbach, K. M. 1924. Obliviscence during sleep and waking. *Amer. J. Psychol.*, **35**, 605–612.

Johnson, P. O. 1949. *Statistical methods in research.* New York: Prentice-Hall.

Jones, L. V. 1952. Tests of hypotheses: one-sided vs. two-sided alternatives. *Psychol. Bull.*, **49**, 43–46.

Jones, L. V., & Fiske, D. W. 1953. Models for testing the significance of combined results. *Psychol. Bull.*, **50**, 375–382.

Keating, Elizabeth, Paterson, D. G., & Stone, C. H. 1950. Validity of work histories obtained by interview. *J. appl. Psychol.*, **34**, 6–11.

Kellar, B. 1934. The construction and validation of a scale for measuring attitude toward any home-making activity. In Remmers, H. H. (Ed.) *Studies in attitudes: Bull. Purdue Univ.*, **35**, 47–63.

Kelley, T. L. 1923. *Statistical method.* New York: Macmillan.

Kelly, E. L., and Fiske, D. W. 1950. The prediction of success in the VA training program in clinical psychology. *Amer. Psychologist*, **5**, 395–406.

Kempthorne, O. 1952. *The design and analysis of experiments.* New York: Wiley.

Kendall, M. G. 1948. *Rank correlation methods.* London: Griffin.

Kendall, M. G., and Smith, B. B. 1939. The problem of *m* rankings. *Ann. math. Statist.*, **10**, 275–287.

Kogan, W. S., & Pumroy, Shirley. 1952. Unpublished data from a paper presented before the Western Psychological Association.

Kruskal, W. H., & Wallis, W. A. 1952. Use of ranks in one-criterion variance analysis. *J. Amer. statist. Ass.*, **47**, 583–621.

Kuo, Z. Y. 1930. The genesis of the cat's response to the rat. *J. comp. Psychol.*, **11**, 1–30.

Levine, A. S. 1950. Minnesota Psycho-Analogies Test. *J. appl. Psychol.*, **34**, 300–305.

Lewis, D., & Burke, C. J. 1949. The use and misuse of the chi-square test. *Psychol. Bull.*, **46**, 433–489.

Lindquist, E. F. 1940. *Statistical analysis in educational research.* Boston: Houghton Mifflin.

Locke, B., & Grimm, C. H. 1949. Odor selection preferences and identification. *J. appl. Psychol.*, **33**, 167–174.

Mangus, A. R. 1936. Relationships between the young woman's conception of her intimate male associates and of her ideal husband. *J. soc. Psychol.*, **7**, 403–420.

Mann, H. B., & Whitney, D. R. 1947. On a test of whether one of two random variables is stochastically larger than the other. *Ann. math. Statist.*, **18**, 50–60.

Marks, E. S. 1943. Standardization of a race attitude test for Negro youth. *J. soc. Psychol.*, **18**, 245–278.

Marks, M. R. 1951. Two kinds of experiment distinguished in terms of statistical operations. *Psychol. Rev.*, **58**, 179–184.

Mather, K. 1947. *Statistical analysis in biology.* (2d ed.) New York: Interscience.

McNemar, Q. 1949. *Psychological statistics.* New York: Wiley.

Mood, A. M. 1950. *Introduction to the theory of statistics.* New York: McGraw-Hill.

Moses, L. E. 1952. Non-parametric statistics for psychological research. *Psychol. Bull.*, **49**, 122–143.

Olds, E. G. 1938. Distributions of sums of squares of rank differences for small numbers of individuals. *Ann. math. Statist.*, **9**, 133–148.

Olds, E. G. 1949. The 5% significance levels for sums of squares of rank differences and a correction. *Ann. math. Statist.*, **20**, 117–118.

Pearson, K. 1901. On the correlation of characters not quantitatively measureable. *Philosophical Transactions*, Series A, **195**, 1–47.

Perry, N. C., Kettner, N. W., Hertzka, A. F., & Bouvier, E. A. 1953. Estimating the tetrachoric correlation coefficient via I. A cosine-pi table and II. Correction graphs for nonmedian dichotomization. *Studies of aptitudes of high-level personnel.* Technical Memorandum No. 2. Los Angeles: University of Southern California.

Peters, C. C., & Van Voorhis, W. R. 1940. *Statistical procedures and their mathematical bases.* New York: McGraw-Hill.

Pronko, N. H., & Herman, D. T. 1950. Identification of cola beverages. IV. Postscript. *J. appl. Psychol.*, **34**, 68–69.

Reagan, L. M., Ott, E. R., & Sigley, D. T. 1948. *College algebra.* (Rev. ed.) New York: Rinehart.

Rosenzweig, S. 1943. An experimental study of "repression" with special reference to need-persistive and ego-defensive reactions to frustration. *J. exp. Psychol.*, **32**, 64–74.

Schultz, F. G. 1945. Recent developments in the statistical analysis of rank data adapted to educational research. *J. exp. Educ.*, **13**, 149–152.

Selover, R. B., & Vogel, J. 1948. The value of a testing program in a tight labor market. *Personnel Psychol.*, **1**, 447–456.

Shaffer, L. F. 1936. *The psychology of adjustment.* Boston: Houghton Mifflin.

Shipley, W. C., Coffin, Judith E., & Hadsell, Kathryn C. 1945. Affective distance and other factors determining reaction time in judgments of color preferences. *J. exp. Psychol.*, **34**, 206–215.

Smith, D. E., Reeve, W. D., & Morss, E. L. 1928. *Elementary mathematical tables.* Boston: Ginn.

Snedecor, G. W. 1946. *Statistical methods.* (4th ed.) Ames, Iowa: State College Press.

Thomas, W. F., & Young, P. T. 1942. A study of organic set: immediate reproduction, by different muscle groups, of patterns presented by successive visual flashes. *J. exp. Psychol.*, **30**, 347–367.

Thurstone, L. L. 1935. *The reliability and validity of tests.* Ann Arbor, Michigan: Edwards.

Tippett, L. H. C. 1925. On the extreme individuals and the range of a sample from a normal population. *Biometrika*, **17**, 364–387.

Tippett, L. H. C. 1941. *The methods of statistics.* (3d ed.) London: Williams & Norgate.

Tukey, J. W. 1949. Comparing individual means in the analysis of variance. *Biometrics*, **5**, 99–114.

Tyler, Leona E. 1947. *The psychology of human differences.* New York: Appleton-Century-Crofts.

Uhrbrock, R. S. 1948. The personnel interview. *Personnel Psychol.*, **1**, 273–302.

Walker, Helen M. 1943. *Elementary statistical methods.* New York: Holt.

Walker, Helen M. 1951. *Mathematics essential for elementary statistics.* (Rev. ed.) New York: Holt.

Wallis, W. A. 1939. The correlation ratio for ranked data. *J. Amer. statist. Ass.*, **34**, 533–538.

Watson, K. B. 1942. The nature and measurement of musical meanings. *Psychol. Monogr.*, **54**, No. 224.

Weise, P., & Bitterman, M. E. 1951. Response-selection in discriminative learning. *Psychol. Rev.*, **58**, 185–194.

White, C. 1952. The use of ranks in a test of significance for comparing two treatments. *Biometrics*, **8**, 33–41.

Wilcoxon, F. 1945. Individual comparisons by ranking methods. *Biometrics*, **1**, 80–82.

Wilcoxon, F. 1947. Probability tables for individual comparisons by ranking methods. *Biometrics*, **3**, 119–122.

Wilcoxon, F. 1949. *Some rapid approximate statistical procedures.* American Cyanamid Co.

Wilkinson, B. 1951. A statistical consideration in psychological research. *Psychol. Bull.*, **48**, 156–158.

Wright, E. B. 1946. A comparative study of the effects of oxygen lack on peripheral nerve. *Amer. J. Physiol.*, **147**, 78–89.

Yates, F. 1934. Contingency tables involving small numbers and the χ^2 test. *J. R. statist. Soc. Suppl.*, **1**, 217–235.

Yule, G. U., & Kendall, M. G. 1947. *An introduction to the theory of statistics.* (13th ed.) London: Griffin.

List of Formulas

The numbers given in the parentheses are used throughout the text to refer to the formula. The page on which the formula appears in the text is given at the left.

Page	*Number*	*Formula*
36	**(3.1)**	$R = X_h - X_l$
37	**(3.2)**	$\bar{X} = \dfrac{X_1 + X_2 + X_3 + X_4 + X_5 + \cdots + X_n}{n}$
37	**(3.3)**	$\bar{X} = \dfrac{\sum X}{n}$
38	**(3.4)**	$n\bar{X} = \sum X$
38	**(3.5)**	$x = X - \bar{X}$
38	**(3.6)**	$\sum x = 0$
39	**(3.7)**	$AD = \dfrac{\sum \lvert x \rvert}{n}$
40	**(3.8)**	$s^2 = \dfrac{\sum (X - \bar{X})^2}{n - 1} = \dfrac{\sum x^2}{n - 1}$

Page	*Number*	*Formula*
40	**(3.9)**	$s = \sqrt{\frac{\sum(X - \bar{X})^2}{n - 1}} = \sqrt{\frac{\sum x^2}{n - 1}}$
41	**(3.10)**	$(n - 1)(s^2) = \sum x^2$
46	**(3.11)**	$Mdn = l + \left(\frac{\frac{n}{2} - \sum f_b}{f_w}\right) i$
46	**(3.12)**	$Mdn = u - \left(\frac{\frac{n}{2} - \sum f_a}{f_w}\right) i$
47	**(3.13)**	$Q = \frac{Q_3 - Q_1}{2}$
59	**(4.1)**	$\sum x^2 = \sum X^2 - \frac{(\sum X)^2}{n}$
61	**(4.2)**	$X' = X - M'$
61	**(4.3)**	$\bar{X} = M' + \frac{\sum X'}{n}$
62	**(4.4)**	$\sum x^2 = \sum X'^2 - \frac{(\sum X')^2}{n}$
64	**(4.5)**	$x' = \frac{X}{i}$
64	**(4.6)**	$\bar{X} = \left(\frac{\sum x'}{n}\right) i$
65	**(4.7)**	$\sum x^2 = \left[\sum x'^2 - \frac{(\sum x')^2}{n}\right] i^2$
66	**(4.8)**	$\bar{X} = M' + \left(\frac{\sum x'}{n}\right) i$

Page	*Number*	*Formula*
72	(**4.9**)	$\bar{X} = M' + \left(\frac{\sum fx'}{n}\right) i$
73	(**4.10**)	$\sum x^2 = \left[\sum fx'^2 - \frac{(\sum fx')^2}{n}\right] i^2$
74	(**4.11**)	$\sum fx'' = \sum fx' + n$
74	(**4.12**)	$\sum fx''^2 = \sum fx'^2 + (2)(\sum fx') + n$
101	(**6.1**)	$z = \frac{X - \bar{X}}{s} = \frac{x}{s}$
103	(**6.2**)	$\bar{z} = 0$
103	(**6.3**)	$s_z{}^2 = 1.00$
106	(**6.4**)	$Z = a + b\left(\frac{X - \bar{X}}{s}\right)$
117	(**7.1**)	$Y = bX$
117	(**7.2**)	$Y = a + bX$
119	(**7.3**)	$b = \frac{Y_2 - Y_1}{X_2 - X_1}$
121	(**7.4**)	$\tilde{Y} = a + bX$
122	(**7.5**)	$Y - \tilde{Y} = Y - (a + bX)$
122	(**7.6**)	$\sum(Y - \tilde{Y})^2 = \sum[Y - (a + bX)]^2$
122	(**7.7**)	$\sum Y = na + b\sum X$
123	(**7.8**)	$\sum XY = a\sum X + b\sum X^2$
123	(**7.9**)	$a = \bar{Y} - b\bar{X}$

Page	*Number*	*Formula*
123	**(7.10)**	$b = \dfrac{\sum XY - \dfrac{(\sum X)(\sum Y)}{n}}{\sum X^2 - \dfrac{(\sum X)^2}{n}}$
124	**(7.11)**	$\sum xy = \sum (X - \bar{X})(Y - \bar{Y}) = \sum XY - \dfrac{(\sum X)(\sum Y)}{n}$
124	**(7.12)**	$b = \dfrac{\sum xy}{\sum x^2}$
125	**(7.13)**	$\sum xy = \left[\sum x'y' - \dfrac{(\sum x')(\sum y')}{n}\right] i_x i_y$
125	**(7.14)**	$\sum xy = \left[\sum Xy' - \dfrac{(\sum X)(\sum y')}{n}\right] i_y$
125	**(7.15)**	$\sum \tilde{Y} = \sum Y$
126	**(7.16)**	$\sum (Y - \tilde{Y}) = \sum Y - \sum \tilde{Y} = 0$
126	**(7.17)**	$\tilde{y} = bx$
127	**(7.18)**	$\sum (y - \tilde{y})^2 = \sum y^2 - \dfrac{(\sum xy)^2}{\sum x^2}$
128	**(7.19)**	$s_{y \cdot x}{}^2 = \dfrac{\sum (y - \tilde{y})^2}{n - 2}$
128	**(7.20)**	$s_{y \cdot x} = \sqrt{\dfrac{\sum (y - \tilde{y})^2}{n - 2}}$
129	**(7.21)**	$Y = aX^b$
129	**(7.22)**	$\log Y = \log a + b \log X$
132	**(7.23)**	$Y = a10^{bX}$
133	**(7.24)**	$\log Y = \log a + bX$

Page	*Number*	*Formula*
135	**(7.25)**	$Y = a + b \log X$
146	**(8.1)**	$r = \dfrac{\dfrac{\sum xy}{n-1}}{\sqrt{\left(\dfrac{\sum x^2}{n-1}\right)\left(\dfrac{\sum y^2}{n-1}\right)}}$
146	**(8.2)**	$r = \dfrac{\sum xy}{\sqrt{\sum x^2 \sum y^2}}$
146	**(8.3)**	$r\sqrt{\sum x^2 \sum y^2} = \sum xy$
147	**(8.4)**	$r = \dfrac{\sum XY - \dfrac{(\sum X)(\sum Y)}{n}}{\sqrt{\left(\sum X^2 - \dfrac{(\sum X)^2}{n}\right)\left(\sum Y^2 - \dfrac{(\sum Y)^2}{n}\right)}}$
148	**(8.5)**	$r = \dfrac{\sum X'Y' - \dfrac{(\sum X')(\sum Y')}{n}}{\sqrt{\left(\sum X'^2 - \dfrac{(\sum X')^2}{n}\right)\left(\sum Y'^2 - \dfrac{(\sum Y')^2}{n}\right)}}$
148	**(8.6)**	$r = \dfrac{\sum x'y' - \dfrac{(\sum x')(\sum y')}{n}}{\sqrt{\left(\sum x'^2 - \dfrac{(\sum x')^2}{n}\right)\left(\sum y'^2 - \dfrac{(\sum y')^2}{n}\right)}}$
153	**(8.7)**	$d = x - y$
154	**(8.8)**	$s_d^2 = s_x^2 + s_y^2 - 2rs_xs_y$
154	**(8.9)**	$r = \dfrac{s_x^2 + s_y^2 - s_d^2}{2s_xs_y}$

Page	*Number*	*Formula*
159	(8.10)	$b_{xy} = \dfrac{\dfrac{\sum xy}{n-1}}{\dfrac{\sum y^2}{n-1}} = \dfrac{\sum xy}{\sum y^2}$
159	(8.11)	$\tilde{X} = a + b_{xy}Y$
159	(8.12)	$a = \bar{X} - b_{xy}\bar{Y}$
159	(8.13)	$\sum(x - \tilde{x})^2 = \sum x^2 - \dfrac{(\sum xy)^2}{\sum y^2}$
159	(8.14)	$s_{x \cdot y}{}^2 = \dfrac{\sum(x - \tilde{x})^2}{n-2}$
159	(8.15)	$s_{x \cdot y} = \sqrt{\dfrac{\sum(x-\tilde{x})^2}{n-2}}$
160	(8.16)	$b_{yx} = r\dfrac{s_y}{s_x}$
160	(8.17)	$b_{xy} = r\dfrac{s_x}{s_y}$
161	(8.18)	$\pm\sqrt{r^2} = \pm\sqrt{(b_{yx})(b_{xy})}$
162	(8.19)	$\sum(y - \tilde{y})^2 = \sum y^2 - r^2\sum y^2$
162	(8.20)	$r^2 = \dfrac{\sum y^2 - \sum(y - \tilde{y})^2}{\sum y^2}$
162	(8.21)	$r^2 = 1 - \dfrac{\sum(y - \tilde{y})^2}{\sum y^2}$
162	(8.22)	$\sum(y - \tilde{y})^2 = \sum y^2(1 - r^2)$
162	(8.23)	$s_{y \cdot x}{}^2 = \dfrac{\sum y^2(1 - r^2)}{n-2}$

Page	*Number*	*Formula*
162	(**8.24**)	$\sum(x - \bar{x})^2 = \sum x^2(1 - r^2)$
162	(**8.25**)	$s_{x \cdot y}{}^2 = \dfrac{\sum x^2(1 - r^2)}{n - 2}$
163	(**8.26**)	$\sum y^2 = \sum y^2(1 - r^2) + r^2 \sum y^2$
163	(**8.27**)	$1.00 = (1 - r^2) + r^2$
163	(**8.28**)	$s_y{}^2 = (1 - r^2)s_y{}^2 + r^2 s_y{}^2$
171	(**9.1**)	$e = X - X_t$
171	(**9.2**)	$X = X_t + e$
172	(**9.3**)	$x = x_t + e$
172	(**9.4**)	$\sum x^2 = \sum x_t{}^2 + \sum e^2 + 2\sum x_t e$
172	(**9.5**)	$\sum x^2 = \sum x_t{}^2 + \sum e^2$
172	(**9.6**)	$\sum x_t{}^2 = \sum x^2 - \sum e^2$
173	(**9.7**)	$\sum xy = \sum (x_t + e_1)(y_t + e_2)$
173	(**9.8**)	$\sum xy = \sum x_t y_t + \sum x_t e_2 + \sum y_t e_1 + \sum e_1 e_2$
173	(**9.9**)	$\sum xy = \sum x_t y_t$
174	(**9.10**)	$r = \dfrac{\sum xy}{\sqrt{(\sum x_t{}^2 + \sum e_1{}^2)(\sum y_t{}^2 + \sum e_2{}^2)}}$
175	(**9.11**)	$r_{x_1 x_2} = \dfrac{\sum x_t{}^2}{\sum x^2}$
175	(**9.12**)	$r_{x_1 x_2} = 1 - \dfrac{\sum e^2}{\sum x^2}$

Page	*Number*	*Formula*
175	**(9.13)**	$r_{x_1x_2} = 1 - \frac{{s_e}^2}{{s_x}^2}$
176	**(9.14)**	$r_{kk} = \frac{mr_{nn}}{1 + (m - 1)r_{nn}}$
177	**(9.15)**	$r_{kk} = \frac{2r_{nn}}{1 + r_{nn}}$
177	**(9.16)**	$r_{x_ty_t} = \frac{\sum x_ty_t}{\sqrt{\sum {x_t}^2 \sum {y_t}^2}}$
177	**(9.17)**	$r_{x_1x_2} \sum x^2 = \sum {x_t}^2$
178	**(9.18)**	$r_{x_ty_t} = \frac{r_{xy}}{\sqrt{r_{x_1x_2}\, r_{y_1y_2}}}$
178	**(9.19)**	$r_{xy} = r_{x_ty_t} \sqrt{r_{x_1x_2}\, r_{y_1y_2}}$
184	**(10.1)**	$r_{pb} = \frac{\sum {y_1}' - \frac{n_1 \sum y'}{n}}{\sqrt{\left(n_1 - \frac{(n_1)^2}{n}\right)\left(\sum y'^2 - \frac{(\sum y')^2}{n}\right)}}$
184	**(10.2)**	$r_{pb} = \frac{\sum {y_1}' - \frac{n_1 \sum y'}{n}}{\sqrt{\left(\frac{n_0 n_1}{n}\right)\left(\sum y'^2 - \frac{(\sum y')^2}{n}\right)}}$
184	**(10.3)**	$r_{pb} = \frac{n \sum {y_1}' - n_1 \sum y'}{\sqrt{(n_0 n_1)[n \sum y'^2 - (\sum y')^2]}}$
185	**(10.4)**	$r_{pb} = \frac{n \sum Y_1 - n_1 \sum Y}{\sqrt{(n_0 n_1)[n \sum Y^2 - (\sum Y)^2]}}$

Page	*Number*	*Formula*
187	**(10.5)**	$r_\phi = \dfrac{b - \dfrac{(b+d)(a+b)}{n}}{\sqrt{\left[(b+d) - \dfrac{(b+d)^2}{n}\right]\left[(a+b) - \dfrac{(a+b)^2}{n}\right]}}$
187	**(10.6)**	$r_\phi = \dfrac{bc - ad}{\sqrt{(a+c)(b+d)(a+b)(c+d)}}$
188	**(10.7)**	$r_b = \dfrac{n\sum y_1{}' - n_1\sum y'}{\sqrt{(n_0 n_1)[n\sum y'^2 - (\sum y')^2]}}\left(\dfrac{\sqrt{p_1 q}}{y_p}\right)$
189	**(10.8)**	$r_b = \dfrac{\sum y_1{}' - p_1\sum y'}{y_p\sqrt{n\sum y'^2 - (\sum y')^2}}$
189	**(10.9)**	$r_b = \dfrac{\sum Y_1 - p_1\sum Y}{y_p\sqrt{n\sum Y^2 - (\sum Y)^2}}$
192	**(10.10)**	$k = \dfrac{bc}{ad}$
192	**(10.11)**	$\dfrac{1}{k} = \dfrac{1}{\dfrac{bc}{ad}} = \dfrac{ad}{bc}$
193	**(10.12)**	$\sum X = \dfrac{n(n+1)}{2}$
193	**(10.13)**	$\sum X^2 = \dfrac{n(n+1)(2n+1)}{6}$
194	**(10.14)**	$\sum x^2 = \dfrac{n^3 - n}{12}$
194	**(10.15)**	$\bar{X} = \dfrac{n+1}{2}$

Page	*Number*	*Formula*
194	(**10.16**)	$r = \dfrac{\sum x^2 + \sum y^2 - \sum d^2}{2\sqrt{\sum x^2 \sum y^2}}$
195	(**10.17**)	$r' = 1 - \dfrac{6\sum d^2}{n^3 - n}$
195	(**10.18**)	$d = X - Y = D$
195	(**10.19**)	$r' = 1 - \dfrac{6\sum D^2}{n(n^2 - 1)}$
200	(**10.20**)	$\sum_1^n (Y - \bar{Y})^2 = \sum_1^k n_i(\bar{Y}_i - \bar{Y})^2 + \sum_1^k \sum_1^{n_i} (Y - \bar{Y}_i)^2$
200	(**10.21**)	$Total = \sum_1^n (Y - \bar{Y})^2 = \sum {y_t}^2$
200	(**10.22**)	$Between = \sum_1^k n_i(\bar{Y}_i - \bar{Y})^2 = \sum {y_b}^2$
200	(**10.23**)	$Within = \sum_1^k \sum_1^{n_i} (Y - \bar{Y}_i)^2 = \sum {y_w}^2$
201	(**10.24**)	${\eta_{yx}}^2 = \dfrac{\sum {y_b}^2}{\sum {y_t}^2}$
201	(**10.25**)	$\eta_{yx} = \sqrt{\dfrac{\sum {y_b}^2}{\sum {y_t}^2}}$
201	(**10.26**)	${\eta_{yx}}^2 = \dfrac{\sum {y_b}'^2}{\sum {y_t}'^2}$
201	(**10.27**)	$\sum {y_b}'^2 = \sum_1^k \dfrac{\left(\sum_1^{n_i} {y_i}'\right)^2}{n_i} - \dfrac{\left(\sum_1^n y'\right)^2}{n}$
201	(**10.28**)	$\sum {y_t}'^2 = \sum y'^2 - \dfrac{(\sum y')^2}{n}$

Page	*Number*	*Formula*
202	(10.29)	$\sum y_b^2 = \sum y_t^2 - \sum y_w^2$
202	(10.30)	$\eta_{yx}^2 = 1 - \dfrac{\sum y_w^2}{\sum y_t^2}$
203	(10.31)	$s_w^2 = \dfrac{\sum y_w^2}{n - k}$
203	(10.32)	$s_w = \sqrt{\dfrac{\sum y_w^2}{n - k}}$
205	(10.33)	$\eta_{xy}^2 = \dfrac{\sum x_b^2}{\sum x_t^2}$
205	(10.34)	$\eta_{xy} = \sqrt{\dfrac{\sum x_b^2}{\sum x_t^2}}$
205	(10.35)	$\eta_{xy}^2 = \dfrac{\sum x_b'^2}{\sum x_t'^2}$
205	(10.36)	$\sum x_b'^2 = \sum_1^k \dfrac{\left(\sum_1^{ni} x_i'\right)^2}{n_i} - \dfrac{\left(\sum_1^n x'\right)^2}{n}$
205	(10.37)	$\sum x_t'^2 = \sum x'^2 - \dfrac{(\sum x')^2}{n}$
205	(10.38)	$\sum x_b^2 = \sum x_t^2 - \sum x_w^2$
206	(10.39)	$\eta_{xy}^2 = 1 - \dfrac{\sum x_w^2}{\sum x_t^2}$
206	(10.40)	$s_w^2 = \dfrac{\sum x_w^2}{n - k}$
206	(10.41)	$s_w = \sqrt{\dfrac{\sum x_w^2}{n - k}}$

Page	*Number*	*Formula*
216	(**11.1**)	${}_nC_r = \dfrac{n!}{(n-r)!(r)!}$
217	(**11.2**)	${}_nC_rp^rq^{n-r} = \dfrac{n!}{(n-r)!(r)!}\,p^rq^{n-r}$
220	(**11.3**)	$N(p+q)^n = Np^n + N(np^{n-1}q) + N\left(\dfrac{n(n-1)}{(1)(2)}\,p^{n-2}q^2\right) + N\left(\dfrac{n(n-1)(n-2)}{(1)(2)(3)}\,p^{n-3}q^3\right) + \cdots + Nq^n$
222	(**11.4**)	$m = np$
222	(**11.5**)	$\sigma^2 = npq$
222	(**11.6**)	$\sigma = \sqrt{npq}$
223	(**11.7**)	$m = p$
223	(**11.8**)	$\sigma = \sqrt{\dfrac{pq}{n}}$
223	(**11.9**)	$z = \dfrac{X-m}{\sigma}$
225	(**11.10**)	$\sigma^2 = pq = \dfrac{n_1 - \dfrac{(n_1)^2}{n}}{n}$
232	(**12.1**)	$y = \dfrac{1}{\sqrt{2\pi}}\,e^{-(1/2)z^2}$
234	(**12.2**)	$X_1 = m - (1.96)(\sigma)$
234	(**12.3**)	$X_2 = m + (1.96)(\sigma)$

Page	*Number*	*Formula*
236	**(12.4)**	$\sigma_{\bar{x}}^2 = \frac{\sigma^2}{n}$
237	**(12.5)**	$\sigma_{\bar{x}} = \frac{\sigma}{\sqrt{n}}$
240	**(12.6)**	$z = \frac{\bar{X} - m}{\sigma_{\bar{x}}}$
242	**(12.7)**	$m_1 = \bar{X} - (1.96)(\sigma_{\bar{x}})$
243	**(12.8)**	$m_2 = \bar{X} + (1.96)(\sigma_{\bar{x}})$
246	**(13.1)**	$s_{\bar{x}}^2 = \frac{s^2}{n}$
246	**(13.2)**	$s_{\bar{x}} = \frac{s}{\sqrt{n}}$
247	**(13.3)**	$t = \frac{\bar{X} - m}{s_{\bar{x}}}$
249	**(13.4)**	$m_1 = \bar{X} - (t)(s_{\bar{x}})$
249	**(13.5)**	$m_2 = \bar{X} + (t)(s_{\bar{x}})$
253	**(13.6)**	$s_{\bar{x}_1 - \bar{x}_2} = \sqrt{s_{\bar{x}_1}^2 + s_{\bar{x}_2}^2}$
253	**(13.7)**	$s_{\bar{x}_1 - \bar{x}_2} = \sqrt{\frac{s_1^2}{n_1} + \frac{s_2^2}{n_2}}$
253	**(13.8)**	$s^2 = \frac{\sum x_1^2 + \sum x_2^2}{n_1 + n_2 - 2}$
253	**(13.9)**	$s_{\bar{x}_1 - \bar{x}_2} = \sqrt{\left(\frac{\sum x_1^2 + \sum x_2^2}{n_1 + n_2 - 2}\right)\left(\frac{1}{n_1} + \frac{1}{n_2}\right)}$
254	**(13.10)**	$t = \frac{\bar{X}_1 - \bar{X}_2}{s_{\bar{x}_1 - \bar{x}_2}}$

Page	*Number*	*Formula*
272	**(13.11)**	$F = \frac{s_1^2}{s_2^2} \quad \text{or} \quad F = \frac{s_2^2}{s_1^2}$
274	**(13.12)**	$t_{.05} = \frac{(s_{\bar{x}_1}^2)(t_1) + (s_{\bar{x}_2}^2)(t_2)}{s_{\bar{x}_1}^2 + s_{\bar{x}_2}^2}$
278	**(14.1)**	$s_{\bar{x}_1-\bar{x}_2} = \sqrt{s_{\bar{x}_1}^2 + s_{\bar{x}_2}^2 - 2rs_{\bar{x}_1}s_{\bar{x}_2}}$
279	**(14.2)**	$s_{\bar{x}_1-\bar{x}_2} = \frac{s_d}{\sqrt{n}}$
279	**(14.3)**	$\sum d^2 = \sum D^2 - \frac{(\sum D)^2}{n}$
279	**(14.4)**	$s_d^2 = \frac{\sum d^2}{n-1}$
280	**(14.5)**	$s_d = \sqrt{\frac{\sum d^2}{n-1}}$
283	**(14.6)**	$s_{y \cdot x}^2 = \frac{\sum y^2 - \frac{(\sum xy)^2}{\sum x^2}}{n-2}$
283	**(14.7)**	$s_{\bar{y} \cdot \bar{x}}^2 = \frac{s_{y \cdot x}^2}{n}$
284	**(14.8)**	$s_{\bar{y} \cdot \bar{x}} = \frac{s_{y \cdot x}}{\sqrt{n}}$
284	**(14.9)**	$s_{(\bar{y}_1-\bar{y}_2) \cdot \bar{x}} = \sqrt{s_{\bar{y}_1 \cdot \bar{x}}^2 + s_{\bar{y}_2 \cdot \bar{x}}^2}$
284	**(14.10)**	$s_{(\bar{y}_1-\bar{y}_2) \cdot \bar{x}} = \sqrt{\frac{s_{y_1 \cdot x}^2}{n_1} + \frac{s_{y_2 \cdot x}^2}{n_2}}$
284	**(14.11)**	$\sum y_{\cdot x}^2 = (\sum y_1^2 + \sum y_2^2) - \frac{(\sum xy)^2}{\sum x^2}$

Page	*Number*	*Formula*
285	**(14.12)**	$s_{y\cdot x}{}^2 = \dfrac{\sum y_{\cdot x}{}^2}{n_1 + n_2 - 3}$
285	**(14.13)**	$s_{(\bar{y}_1 - \bar{y}_2)\cdot \bar{x}} = \sqrt{\dfrac{s_{y\cdot x}{}^2}{n_1} + \dfrac{s_{y\cdot x}{}^2}{n_2}}$
285	**(14.14)**	$s_{(\bar{y}_1 - \bar{y}_2)\cdot \bar{x}} = \sqrt{\left(\dfrac{\sum y_{\cdot x}{}^2}{n_1 + n_2 - 3}\right)\left(\dfrac{1}{n_1} + \dfrac{1}{n_2}\right)}$
292	**(14.15)**	$T_1 + T_2 = \dfrac{n(n+1)}{2}$
292	**(14.16)**	$\bar{T} = \dfrac{n(n+1)}{4}$
292	**(14.17)**	$\sigma = \sqrt{\dfrac{(2n+1)\bar{T}}{6}}$
293	**(14.18)**	$z = \dfrac{T_1 - \bar{T}}{\sigma}$
303	**(15.1)**	$t = \dfrac{r}{\sqrt{1 - r^2}}\sqrt{n - 2}$
305	**(15.2)**	$z' = \frac{1}{2}[\log_e(1 + r) - \log_e(1 - r)]$
305	**(15.3)**	$\sigma_{z'} = \dfrac{1}{\sqrt{n - 3}}$
305	**(15.4)**	$\sigma_{z_1' - z_2'} = \sqrt{\dfrac{1}{n_1 - 3} + \dfrac{1}{n_2 - 3}}$
306	**(15.5)**	$z = \dfrac{z_1' - z_2'}{\sigma_{z_1' - z_2'}}$
307	**(15.6)**	$\bar{z}_1' = z_r' - 1.96\sigma_{z_r'}$
307	**(15.7)**	$\bar{z}_2' = z_r' + 1.96\sigma_{z_r'}$

Page	*Number*	*Formula*
307	**(15.8)**	$z = \dfrac{z_r' - z_\rho'}{\sigma_{z_r'}}$
308	**(15.9)**	$s_{b_{yx}} = \dfrac{s_{y \cdot x}}{\sqrt{\sum x^2}}$
309	**(15.10)**	$t = \dfrac{b_{yx} - \beta_{yx}}{s_{b_{yx}}}$
310	**(15.11)**	$s_{y \cdot x}{}^2 = \dfrac{\left(\sum y_1{}^2 - \dfrac{(\sum x_1 y_1)^2}{\sum x_1{}^2}\right) + \left(\sum y_2{}^2 - \dfrac{(\sum x_2 y_2)^2}{\sum x_2{}^2}\right)}{n_1 + n_2 - 4}$
311	**(15.12)**	$s_{b_1 - b_2} = \sqrt{s_{b_{y_1 x}}{}^2 + s_{b_{y_2 x}}{}^2}$
311	**(15.13)**	$t = \dfrac{b_{y_1 x} - b_{y_2 x}}{s_{b_1 - b_2}}$
317	**(16.1)**	$\sum_1^n (X - \bar{X})^2 = \sum_1^n X^2 - \dfrac{\left(\sum_1^n X\right)^2}{n}$
318	**(16.2)**	$Within\ groups = \sum_1^k \sum_1^{ni} (X - \bar{X}_i)^2$
319	**(16.3)**	$d_i^2 = (\bar{X}_i - \bar{X})^2$
319	**(16.4)**	$n_i d_i^2 = n_i(\bar{X}_i - \bar{X})^2$
319	**(16.5)**	$Between\ groups = \sum_1^k n_i(\bar{X}_i - \bar{X})^2$
320	**(16.6)**	$\sum_1^n (X - \bar{X})^2 = \sum_1^k \sum_1^{ni} (X - \bar{X}_i)^2 + \sum_1^k n_i(\bar{X}_i - \bar{X})^2$
320	**(16.7)**	$Total = Within + Between$
321	**(16.8)**	$F = \dfrac{mean\ square\ between\ groups}{mean\ square\ within\ groups}$

Page	*Number*	*Formula*
322	(**16.9**)	*Mean square within groups* $= \dfrac{\sum_1^k \sum_1^{n_i} (X - \bar{X}_i)^2}{k(n_i - 1)}$
322	(**16.10**)	$s_{\bar{x}}^2 = \dfrac{\sum_1^k (\bar{X}_i - \bar{X})^2}{k - 1}$
324	(**16.11**)	$ns_{\bar{x}}^2 = s^2$
324	(**16.12**)	*Mean square between groups* $= \dfrac{n_i \sum_1^k (\bar{X}_i - \bar{X})^2}{k - 1}$
325	(**16.13**)	$s_i^2 = \dfrac{\sum_1^{n_i} (X - \bar{X}_i)^2}{n_i - 1}$
328	(**16.14**)	$s_{\bar{x}} = \dfrac{s}{\sqrt{n}}$
329	(**16.15**)	$s_{\bar{x}_1 - \bar{x}_2} = s \sqrt{\dfrac{1}{n_1} + \dfrac{1}{n_2}}$
331	(**16.16**)	*Significant gap* $= (t_{.05})(\sqrt{2})(s_{\bar{x}})$
332	(**16.17**)	$z = \dfrac{\left(\dfrac{\bar{X}_1 - \bar{X}_2}{s_{\bar{x}}}\right) - \dfrac{1}{2}}{3\left(\dfrac{1}{4} + \dfrac{1}{df}\right)}$
332	(**16.18**)	$z = \dfrac{\left(\dfrac{\bar{X}_1 - \bar{X}_2}{s_{\bar{x}}}\right) - \dfrac{6}{5}\log k}{3\left(\dfrac{1}{4} + \dfrac{1}{df}\right)}$
334	(**16.19**)	$F = \dfrac{\dfrac{\sum (\bar{X}_i - \bar{X})^2}{k - 1}}{s_{\bar{x}}^2}$

Page	*Number*	*Formula*
335	**(16.20)**	$\text{Between groups} = \sum_{1}^{k} \frac{\left(\sum_{1}^{n_i} X\right)^2}{n_i} - \frac{\left(\sum_{1}^{n} X\right)^2}{n}$
336	**(16.21)**	$\text{Within groups} = \text{Total} - \text{Between groups}$
344	**(17.1)**	$\text{Interaction} = \text{Between groups} - (\text{Methods} + \text{Achievement})$
351	**(17.2)**	$\text{Residual} = \text{Total} - (\text{Between columns} + \text{Between rows})$
353	**(17.3)**	$\text{Total} = \sum_{j=1}^{k} \sum_{i=1}^{n} (X_{ij} - \bar{X}_{..})^2$
353	**(17.4)**	$(X_{ij} - \bar{X}_{..}) - (\bar{X}_{.j} - \bar{X}_{..}) = X_{ij} - \bar{X}_{.j}$
353	**(17.5)**	$\sum_{j=1}^{k} \sum_{i=1}^{n} (X_{ij} - \bar{X}_{..})^2 - n \sum_{j=1}^{k} (\bar{X}_{.j} - \bar{X}_{..})^2 = \sum_{j=1}^{k} \sum_{i=1}^{n} (X_{ij} - \bar{X}_{.j})^2$
355	**(17.6)**	$(X_{ij} - \bar{X}_{..}) - (\bar{X}_{.j} - \bar{X}_{..}) - (\bar{X}_{i.} - \bar{X}_{..}) = X_{ij} - \bar{X}_{.j} - \bar{X}_{i.} + \bar{X}_{..}$
355	**(17.7)**	$\sum_{j=1}^{k} \sum_{i=1}^{n} (X_{ij} - \bar{X}_{..})^2 - n \sum_{j=1}^{k} (\bar{X}_{.j} - \bar{X}_{..})^2 - k \sum_{i=1}^{n} (\bar{X}_{i.} - \bar{X}_{..})^2 = \sum_{j=1}^{k} \sum_{i=1}^{n} (X_{ij} - \bar{X}_{.j} - \bar{X}_{i.} + \bar{X}_{..})^2$
356	**(17.8)**	$s_{\bar{x}} = \frac{s}{\sqrt{n}}$
356	**(17.9)**	$s_{\bar{x}_1 - \bar{x}_2} = s\sqrt{\frac{1}{n_1} + \frac{1}{n_2}}$

Page	*Number*	*Formula*
360	(17.10)	$\text{Linear regression} = \dfrac{(\sum xy)^2}{\sum x^2}$
360	(17.11)	*Deviations from regression = Between columns − Linear regression*
362	(17.12)	$\eta_{yx}{}^2 = \dfrac{\text{Sum of squares between groups or columns}}{\text{Total sum of squares}}$
362	(17.13)	$F = \dfrac{\text{Sum of squares between columns}/(k-1)}{\text{Sum of squares within columns}/(n-k)}$
367	(18.1)	$np_i = n_i{}'$
367	(18.2)	$\chi^2 = \sum_1^k \dfrac{(n_i - n_i{}')^2}{n_i{}'}$
374	(18.3)	$n_{i\cdot} = \sum_{j=1}^{k} n_{ij}$
374	(18.4)	$n_{\cdot j} = \sum_{i=1}^{r} n_{ij}$
374	(18.5)	$n = \sum_{i=1}^{r} \sum_{j=1}^{k} n_{ij}$
374	(18.6)	$n = \sum_{i=1}^{r} n_{i\cdot} = \sum_{j=1}^{k} n_{\cdot j}$
376	(18.7)	$p_{i\cdot} = \dfrac{n_{i\cdot}}{n}$
376	(18.8)	$\sum_{i=1}^{r} p_{i\cdot} = \dfrac{\sum_{i=1}^{r} n_{i\cdot}}{n} = 1.00$
376	(18.9)	$p_{\cdot j} = \dfrac{n_{\cdot j}}{n}$

Page	*Number*	*Formula*
377	**(18.10)**	$\sum_{j=1}^{k} p_{\cdot j} = \frac{\sum_{j=1}^{k} n_{\cdot j}}{n} = 1.00$
377	**(18.11)**	$p_{ij} = \frac{n_{i\cdot} n_{\cdot j}}{n^2}$
377	**(18.12)**	$n_{ij}' = np_{i\cdot} p_{\cdot j}$
377	**(18.13)**	$n_{ij}' = \frac{n_{i\cdot} n_{\cdot j}}{n}$
378	**(18.14)**	$\sum_{j=1}^{k} n_{ij}' = np_{i\cdot} \sum_{j=1}^{k} p_{\cdot j}$
378	**(18.15)**	$\sum_{j=1}^{k} n_{ij}' = n_{i\cdot}$
379	**(18.16)**	$\sum_{i=1}^{r} n_{ij}' = n_{\cdot j}$
379	**(18.17)**	$\sum_{i=1}^{r} \sum_{j=1}^{k} n_{ij}' = \sum_{i=1}^{r} n_{i\cdot}$
379	**(18.18)**	$\sum_{i=1}^{r} \sum_{j=1}^{k} n_{ij}' = n$
379	**(18.19)**	$\sum_{i=1}^{r} \sum_{j=1}^{k} n_{ij}' = n \sum_{i=1}^{r} \sum_{j=1}^{k} p_{i\cdot} p_{\cdot j}$
379	**(18.20)**	$n = n \sum_{i=1}^{r} \sum_{j=1}^{k} p_{i\cdot} p_{\cdot j}$
379	**(18.21)**	$\sum_{i=1}^{r} \sum_{j=1}^{k} p_{i\cdot} p_{\cdot j} = 1.00$
379	**(18.22)**	$\chi^2 = \sum_{i=1}^{r} \sum_{j=1}^{k} \frac{(n_{ij} - n_{ij}')^2}{n_{ij}'}$

Page	*Number*	*Formula*
380	**(18.23)**	$\chi^2 = \frac{1}{n}\sum_{i=1}^{r}\sum_{j=1}^{k}\frac{(nn_{ij} - n_i.n._j)^2}{n_i.n._j}$
380	**(18.24)**	$\sum_{j=1}^{k}(n_{ij} - n_{ij}') = 0$
381	**(18.25)**	$\sum_{i=1}^{r}(n_{ij} - n_{ij}') = 0$
381	**(18.26)**	$df = (r - 1)(k - 1)$
381	**(18.27)**	$C = \sqrt{\frac{\chi^2}{n + \chi^2}}$
382	**(18.28)**	$r_\phi = \sqrt{\frac{\chi^2}{n}}$
382	**(18.29)**	$\chi^2 = nr_\phi{}^2$
383	**(18.30)**	$\chi^2 = \frac{n(bc - ad)^2}{(a + c)(b + d)(a + b)(c + d)}$
383	**(18.31)**	$\chi_c{}^2 = \sum_{1}^{k}\frac{(\lvert n_i - n_i'\rvert - .5)^2}{n_i'}$
384	**(18.32)**	$\chi_c{}^2 = \frac{n\left(\lvert bc - ad\rvert - \frac{n}{2}\right)^2}{(a + c)(b + d)(a + b)(c + d)}$
392	**(18.33)**	$-\frac{1}{2}\chi^2 = \log_e p$
392	**(18.34)**	$\chi^2 = (-2)(2.3026)\log_{10}p$
392	**(18.35)**	$\chi^2 = (-2)(2.3026)\sum_{1}^{k}\log_{10}p$
402	**(19.1)**	$t = \frac{r'}{\sqrt{1 - r'^2}}\sqrt{n - 2}$

Page	*Number*	*Formula*
404	(**19.2**)	$\text{Interaction} = \text{Total} - \text{Between columns}$
404	(**19.3**)	$\text{Interaction} = \text{Within columns}$
405	(**19.4**)	$W = \dfrac{\text{Sum of squares between columns}}{\text{Total sum of squares}}$
406	(**19.5**)	$\bar{X}_{1\cdot} = \bar{X}_{2\cdot} = \bar{X}_{3\cdot} = \bar{X}_{i\cdot} = \bar{X}_{m\cdot}$
406	(**19.6**)	$\sum_{i=1}^{m}\sum_{j=1}^{n} X_{ij} = \dfrac{mn(n+1)}{2}$
407	(**19.7**)	$\text{Total} = \dfrac{m(n^3 - n)}{12}$
407	(**19.8**)	$\text{Between} = \dfrac{\sum_{j=1}^{n}(\sum_{i=1}^{m} X_{ij})^2}{m} - \dfrac{mn(n+1)^2}{4}$
409	(**19.9**)	$W_c = \dfrac{\text{Sum of squares between columns} - \dfrac{1}{m}}{\text{Total sum of squares} + \dfrac{2}{m}}$
410	(**19.10**)	$F = \dfrac{(m-1)W_c}{1 - W_c}$
410	(**19.11**)	$df_1 = (n-1) - \dfrac{2}{m}$
410	(**19.12**)	$df_2 = (m-1)\left[(n-1) - \dfrac{2}{m}\right]$
411	(**19.13**)	$\chi_r^2 = \dfrac{(n-1)(\text{Sum of squares between columns})}{(n^3 - n)/12}$
411	(**19.14**)	$W = \dfrac{\chi_r^2}{m(n-1)}$

Page	*Number*	*Formula*
412	**(19.15)**	$\chi_r^2 = (W)(m)(n-1)$
412	**(19.16)**	$\bar{r}' = \dfrac{mW-1}{m-1}$
413	**(19.17)**	$r_{\bar{x}\bar{x}} = 1 - \dfrac{\displaystyle\sum_{j=1}^{n}\left[\dfrac{\dfrac{\sum_{i=1}^{m} X_{ij}^2}{m} - \dfrac{\left(\sum_{i=1}^{m} X_{ij}\right)^2}{m}}{m-1}\right]}{\displaystyle\sum_{j=1}^{n}\left(\dfrac{\sum_{i=1}^{m} X_{ij}}{m}\right)^2 - \dfrac{\left[\displaystyle\sum_{j=1}^{n}\left(\dfrac{\sum_{i=1}^{m} X_{ij}}{m}\right)\right]^2}{n}}$
414	**(19.18)**	$r_{\bar{x}\bar{x}} = 1 - \dfrac{\textit{Sum of squares within columns}/(m-1)(n-1)}{\textit{Sum of squares between columns}/(n-1)}$
414	**(19.19)**	$r_{\bar{x}\bar{x}} = 1 - \dfrac{\textit{Sum of squares within columns}}{(m-1)(\textit{Sum of squares between columns})}$
415	**(19.20)**	$r_{\bar{x}\bar{x}} = \dfrac{m\bar{r}'}{1+(m-1)\bar{r}'}$
418	**(19.21)**	$T' = n_1(n+1) - T$
420	**(19.22)**	$\bar{T} = \dfrac{n_1(n+1)}{2}$
421	**(19.23)**	$\sigma = \sqrt{\dfrac{n_1 n_2 (n+1)}{12}}$
421	**(19.24)**	$z = \dfrac{T - \bar{T}}{\sigma}$
423	**(19.25)**	$H = \left[\dfrac{12}{n(n+1)}\right]\left[\sum_{1}^{k}\dfrac{T_i^2}{n_i}\right] - 3(n+1)$
426	**(19.26)**	$C = \dfrac{k^3 - k}{12}$

Page	*Number*	*Formula*
427	**(19.27)**	$\sum(X - \bar{X})^2 = \frac{n^3 - n}{12} - \sum C$
429	**(19.28)**	$\sigma = \sqrt{\left(\frac{n_1 n_2}{n(n-1)}\right)\left(\frac{n^3 - n}{12} - \sum C\right)}$
431	**(19.29)**	$Total = \frac{m(n^3 - n)}{12} - \sum C$
431	**(19.30)**	$W = \frac{Sum\ of\ squares\ between\ columns}{\frac{m(n^3 - n)}{12} - \sum C}$
432	**(19.31)**	$\chi_r{}^2 = \frac{m(n-1)(Sum\ of\ squares\ between\ columns)}{\frac{m(n^3 - n)}{12} - \sum C}$

Appendix

TABLE I. *Table of Random Numbers**

Row	Column Number							
	00000 01234	00000 56789	11111 01234	11111 56789	22222 01234	22222 56789	33333 01234	33333 56789
	1st Thousand							
00	23157	54859	01837	25993	76249	70886	95230	36744
01	05545	55043	10537	43508	90611	83744	10962	21343
02	14871	60350	32404	36223	50051	00322	11543	80834
03	38976	74951	94051	75853	78805	90194	32428	71695
04	97312	61718	99755	30870	94251	25841	54882	10513
05	11742	69381	44339	30872	32797	33118	22647	06850
06	43361	28859	11016	45623	93009	00499	43640	74036
07	93806	20478	38268	04491	55751	18932	58475	52571
08	49540	13181	08429	84187	69538	29661	77738	09527
09	36768	72633	37948	21569	41959	68670	45274	83880
10	07092	52392	24627	12067	06558	45344	67338	45320
11	43310	01081	44863	80307	52555	16148	89742	94647
12	61570	06360	06173	63775	63148	95123	35017	46993
13	31352	83799	10779	18941	31579	76448	62584	86919
14	57048	86526	27795	93692	90529	56546	35065	32254
15	09243	44200	68721	07137	30729	75756	09298	27650
16	97957	35018	40894	88329	52230	82521	22532	61587
17	93732	59570	43781	98885	56671	66826	95996	44569
18	72621	11225	00922	68264	35666	59434	71687	58167
19	61020	74418	45371	20794	95917	37866	99536	19378
20	97839	85474	33055	91718	45473	54144	22034	23000
21	89160	97192	22232	90637	35055	45489	88438	16361
22	25966	88220	62871	79265	02823	52862	84919	54883
23	81443	31719	05049	54806	74690	07567	65017	16543
24	11322	54931	42362	34386	08624	97687	46245	23245

* Table I is reproduced from M. G. Kendall and B. B. Smith. Randomness and random sampling numbers. *J. R. statist. Soc.*, **101** (1938), 147–166, by permission of the Royal Statistical Society.

TABLE I. *Table of Random Numbers*—Continued*

Row	Column Number							
	00000 01234	00000 56789	11111 01234	11111 56789	22222 01234	22222 56789	33333 01234	33333 56789
				2nd Thousand				
00	64755	83885	84122	25920	17696	15655	95045	95947
01	10302	52289	77436	34430	38112	49067	07348	23328
02	71017	98495	51308	50374	66591	02887	53765	69149
03	60012	55605	88410	34879	79655	90169	78800	03666
04	37330	94656	49161	42802	48274	54755	44553	65090
05	47869	87001	31591	12273	60626	12822	34691	61212
06	38040	42737	64167	89578	39323	49324	88434	38706
07	73508	30908	83054	80078	86669	30295	56460	45336
08	32623	46474	84061	04324	20628	37319	32356	43969
09	97591	99549	36630	35106	62069	92975	95320	57734
10	74012	31955	59790	96982	66224	24015	96749	07589
11	56754	26457	13351	05014	90966	33674	69096	33488
12	49800	49908	54831	21998	08528	26372	92923	65026
13	43584	89647	24878	56670	00221	50193	99591	62377
14	16653	79664	60325	71301	35742	83636	73058	87229
15	48502	69055	65322	58748	31446	80237	31252	96367
16	96765	54692	36316	86230	48296	38352	23816	64094
17	38923	61550	80357	81784	23444	12463	33992	28128
18	77958	81694	25225	05587	51073	01070	60218	61961
19	17928	28065	25586	08771	02641	85064	65796	48170
20	94036	85978	02318	04499	41054	10531	87431	21596
21	47460	60479	56230	48417	14372	85167	27558	00368
22	47856	56088	51992	82439	40644	17170	13463	18288
23	57616	34653	92298	62018	10375	76515	62986	90756
24	08300	92704	66752	66610	57188	79107	54222	22013

* Table I is reproduced from M. G. Kendall and B. B. Smith. Randomness and random sampling numbers. *J. R. statist. Soc.*, **101** (1938), **147–166**, by permission of the Royal Statistical Society.

TABLE I. *Table of Random Numbers*—Continued*

Row	00000 01234	00000 56789	11111 01234	11111 56789	22222 01234	22222 56789	33333 01234	33333 56789
				3rd Thousand				
00	89221	02362	65787	74733	51272	30213	92441	39651
01	04005	99818	63918	29032	94012	42363	01261	10650
02	98546	38066	50856	75045	40645	22841	53254	44125
03	41719	84401	59226	01314	54581	40398	49988	65579
04	28733	72489	00785	25843	24613	49797	85567	84471
05	65213	83927	77762	03086	80742	24395	68476	83792
06	65553	12678	90906	90466	43670	26217	69900	31205
07	05668	69080	73029	85746	58332	78231	45986	92998
08	39302	99718	49757	79519	27387	76373	47262	91612
09	64592	32254	45879	29431	38320	05981	18067	87137
10	07513	48792	47314	83660	68907	05336	82579	91582
11	86593	68501	56638	99800	82839	35148	56541	07232
12	83735	22599	97977	81248	36838	99560	32410	67614
13	08595	21826	54655	08204	87990	17033	56258	05384
14	41273	27149	44293	69458	16828	63962	15864	35431
15	00473	75908	56238	12242	72631	76314	47252	06347
16	86131	53789	81383	07868	89132	96182	07009	86432
17	33849	78359	08402	03586	03176	88663	08018	22546
18	61870	41657	07468	08612	98083	97349	20775	45091
19	43898	65923	25078	86129	78491	97653	91500	80786
20	29939	39123	04548	45985	60952	06641	28726	46473
21	38505	85555	14388	55077	18657	94887	67831	70819
22	31824	38431	67125	25511	72044	11562	53279	82268
23	91430	03767	13561	15597	06750	92552	02391	38753
24	38635	68976	25498	97526	96458	03805	04116	63514

* Table I is reproduced from M. G. Kendall and B. B. Smith. Randomness and random sampling numbers. *J. R. statist. Soc.*, **101** (1938), 147–166, by permission of the Royal Statistical Society.

TABLE I. *Table of Random Numbers*—Continued*

Row	Column Number							
	00000 01234	00000 56789	11111 01234	11111 56789	22222 01234	22222 56789	33333 01234	33333 56789
				4th Thousand				
00	02490	54122	27944	39364	94239	72074	11679	54082
01	11967	36469	60627	83701	09253	30208	01385	37482
02	48256	83465	49699	24079	05403	35154	39613	03136
03	27246	73080	21481	23536	04881	89977	49484	93071
04	32532	77265	72430	70722	86529	18457	92657	10011
05	66757	98955	92375	93431	43204	55825	45443	69265
06	11266	34545	76505	97746	34668	26999	26742	97516
07	17872	39142	45561	80146	93137	48924	64257	59284
08	62561	30365	03408	14754	51798	08133	61010	97730
09	62796	30779	35497	70501	30105	08133	00997	91970
10	75510	21771	04339	33660	42757	62223	87565	48468
11	87439	01691	63517	26590	44437	07217	98706	39032
12	97742	02621	10748	78803	38337	65226	92149	59051
13	98811	06001	21571	02875	21828	83912	85188	61624
14	51264	01852	64607	92553	29004	26695	78583	62998
15	40239	93376	10419	68610	49120	02941	80035	99317
16	26936	59186	51667	27645	46329	44681	94190	66647
17	88502	11716	98299	40974	42394	62200	69094	81646
18	63499	38093	25593	61995	79867	80569	01023	38374
19	36379	81206	03317	78710	73828	31083	60509	44091
20	93801	22322	47479	57017	59334	30647	43061	26660
21	29856	87120	56311	50053	25365	81265	22414	02431
22	97720	87931	88265	13050	71017	15177	06957	92919
23	85237	09105	74601	46377	59938	15647	34177	92753
24	75746	75268	31727	95773	72364	87324	36879	06802

* Table I is reproduced from M. G. Kendall and B. B. Smith. Randomness and random sampling numbers. *J. R. statist. Soc.*, **101** (1938), **147–166**, by permission of the Royal Statistical Society.

TABLE I. *Table of Random Numbers*—Concluded*

Row	Column Number							
	00000 01234	00000 56789	11111 01234	11111 56789	22222 01234	22222 56789	33333 01234	33333 56789
				5th Thousand				
00	29935	06971	63175	52579	10478	89379	61428	21363
01	15114	07126	51890	77787	75510	13103	42942	48111
02	03870	43225	10589	87629	22039	94124	38127	65022
03	79390	39188	40756	45269	65959	20640	14284	22960
04	30035	06915	79196	54428	64819	52314	48721	81594
05	29039	99861	28759	79802	68531	39198	38137	24373
06	78196	08108	24107	49777	09599	43569	84820	94956
07	15847	85493	91442	91351	80130	73752	21539	10986
08	36614	62248	49194	97209	92587	92053	41021	80064
09	40549	54884	91465	43862	35541	44466	88894	74180
10	40878	08997	14286	09982	90308	78007	51587	16658
11	10229	49282	41173	31468	59455	18756	08908	06660
12	15918	76787	30624	25928	44124	25088	31137	71614
13	13403	18796	49909	94404	64979	41462	18155	98335
14	66523	94596	74908	90271	10009	98648	17640	68909
15	91665	36469	68343	17870	25975	04662	21272	50620
16	67415	87515	08207	73729	73201	57593	96917	69699
17	76527	96996	23724	33448	63392	32394	60887	90617
18	19815	47789	74348	17147	10954	34355	81194	54407
19	25592	53587	76384	72575	84347	68918	05739	57222
20	55902	45539	63646	31609	95999	82887	40666	66692
21	02470	58376	79794	22482	42423	96162	47491	17264
22	18630	53263	13319	97619	35859	12350	14632	87659
23	89673	38230	16063	92007	59503	38402	76450	33333
24	62986	67364	06595	17427	84623	14565	82860	57300

* Table I is reproduced from M. G. Kendall and B. B. Smith. Randomness and random sampling numbers. *J. R. statist. Soc.*, **101** (1938), **147–166**, by permission of the Royal Statistical Society.

TABLE II. *Table of Squares, Square Roots, and Reciprocals of Numbers from 1 to 1,000**

N	N^2	$\sqrt{N}$	$1/N$	N	N^2	$\sqrt{N}$	$1/N$
1	1	1.0000	1.000000	41	1681	6.4031	.024390
2	4	1.4142	.500000	42	1764	6.4807	.023810
3	9	1.7321	.333333	43	1849	6.5574	.023256
4	16	2.0000	.250000	44	1936	6.6332	.022727
5	25	2.2361	.200000	45	2025	6.7082	.022222
6	36	2.4495	.166667	46	2116	6.7823	.021739
7	49	2.6458	.142857	47	2209	6.8557	.021277
8	64	2.8284	.125000	48	2304	6.9282	.020833
9	81	3.0000	.111111	49	2401	7.0000	.020408
10	100	3.1623	.100000	50	2500	7.0711	.020000
11	121	3.3166	.090909	51	2601	7.1414	.019608
12	144	3.4641	.083333	52	2704	7.2111	.019231
13	169	3.6056	.076923	53	2809	7.2801	.018868
14	196	3.7417	.071429	54	2916	7.3485	.018519
15	225	3.8730	.066667	55	3025	7.4162	.018182
16	256	4.0000	.062500	56	3136	7.4833	.017857
17	289	4.1231	.058824	57	3249	7.5498	.017544
18	324	4.2426	.055556	58	3364	7.6158	.017241
19	361	4.3589	.052632	59	3481	7.6811	.016949
20	400	4.4721	.050000	60	3600	7.7460	.016667
21	441	4.5826	.047619	61	3721	7.8102	.016393
22	484	4.6904	.045455	62	3844	7.8740	.016129
23	529	4.7958	.043478	63	3969	7.9373	.015873
24	576	4.8990	.041667	64	4096	8.0000	.015625
25	625	5.0000	.040000	65	4225	8.0623	.015385
26	676	5.0990	.038462	66	4356	8.1240	.015152
27	729	5.1962	.037037	67	4489	8.1854	.014925
28	784	5.2915	.035714	68	4624	8.2462	.014706
29	841	5.3852	.034483	69	4761	8.3066	.014493
30	900	5.4772	.033333	70	4900	8.3666	.014286
31	961	5.5678	.032258	71	5041	8.4261	.014085
32	1024	5.6569	.031250	72	5184	8.4853	.013889
33	1089	5.7446	.030303	73	5329	8.5440	.013699
34	1156	5.8310	.029412	74	5476	8.6023	.013514
35	1225	5.9161	.028571	75	5625	8.6603	.013333
36	1296	6.0000	.027778	76	5776	8.7178	.013158
37	1369	6.0828	.027027	77	5929	8.7750	.012987
38	1444	6.1644	.026316	78	6084	8.8318	.012821
39	1521	6.2450	.025641	79	6241	8.8882	.012658
40	1600	6.3246	.025000	80	6400	8.9443	.012500

* Portions of Table II have been reproduced from J. W. Dunlap and A. K. Kurtz. *Handbook of Statistical Nomographs, Tables, and Formulas,* World Book Company, New York (1932), by permission of the authors and publishers.

TABLE II. *Table of Squares, Square Roots, and Reciprocals of Numbers from 1 to 1,000*—Continued*

N	N^2	$\sqrt{N}$	$1/N$	N	N^2	$\sqrt{N}$	$1/N$
81	6561	9.0000	.012346	121	14641	11.0000	.00826446
82	6724	9.0554	.012195	122	14884	11.0454	.00819672
83	6889	9.1104	.012048	123	15129	11.0905	.00813008
84	7056	9.1652	.011905	124	15376	11.1355	.00806452
85	7225	9.2195	.011765	125	15625	11.1803	.00800000
86	7396	9.2736	.011628	126	15876	11.2250	.00793651
87	7569	9.3274	.011494	127	16129	11.2694	.00787402
88	7744	9.3808	.011364	128	16384	11.3137	.00781250
89	7921	9.4340	.011236	129	16641	11.3578	.00775194
90	8100	9.4868	.011111	130	16900	11.4018	.00769231
91	8281	9.5394	.010989	131	17161	11.4455	.00763359
92	8464	9.5917	.010870	132	17424	11.4891	.00757576
93	8649	9.6437	.010753	133	17689	11.5326	.00751880
94	8836	9.6954	.010638	134	17956	11.5758	.00746269
95	9025	9.7468	.010526	135	18225	11.6190	.00740741
96	9216	9.7980	.010417	136	18496	11.6619	.00735294
97	9409	9.8489	.010309	137	18769	11.7047	.00729927
98	9604	9.8995	.010204	138	19044	11.7473	.00724638
99	9801	9.9499	.010101	139	19321	11.7898	.00719424
100	10000	10.0000	.010000	140	19600	11.8322	.00714286
101	10201	10.0499	.00990099	141	19881	11.8743	.00709220
102	10404	10.0995	.00980392	142	20164	11.9164	.00704225
103	10609	10.1489	.00970874	143	20449	11.9583	.00699301
104	10816	10.1980	.00961538	144	20736	12.0000	.00694444
105	11025	10.2470	.00952381	145	21025	12.0416	.00689655
106	11236	10.2956	.00943396	146	21316	12.0830	.00684932
107	11449	10.3441	.00934579	147	21609	12.1244	.00680272
108	11664	10.3923	.00925926	148	21904	12.1655	.00675676
109	11881	10.4403	.00917431	149	22201	12.2066	.00671141
110	12100	10.4881	.00909091	150	22500	12.2474	.00666667
111	12321	10.5357	.00900901	151	22801	12.2882	.00662252
112	12544	10.5830	.00892857	152	23104	12.3288	.00657895
113	12769	10.6301	.00884956	153	23409	12.3693	.00653595
114	12996	10.6771	.00877193	154	23716	12.4097	.00649351
115	13225	10.7238	.00869565	155	24025	12.4499	.00645161
116	13456	10.7703	.00862069	156	24336	12.4900	.00641026
117	13689	10.8167	.00854701	157	24649	12.5300	.00636943
118	13924	10.8628	.00847458	158	24964	12.5698	.00632911
119	14161	10.9087	.00840336	159	25281	12.6095	.00628931
120	14400	10.9545	.00833333	160	25600	12.6491	.00625000

* Portions of Table II have been reproduced from J. W. Dunlap and A. K. Kurtz. *Handbook of Statistical Nomographs, Tables, and Formulas*, World Book Company, New York (1932), by permission of the authors and publishers.

TABLE II. *Table of Squares, Square Roots, and Reciprocals of Numbers from 1 to 1,000*—Continued*

N	N^2	$\sqrt{N}$	$1/N$	N	N^2	$\sqrt{N}$	$1/N$
161	25921	12.6886	.00621118	201	40401	14.1774	.00497512
162	26244	12.7279	.00617284	202	40804	14.2127	.00495050
163	26569	12.7671	.00613497	203	41209	14.2478	.00492611
164	26896	12.8062	.00609756	204	41616	14.2829	.00490196
165	27225	12.8452	.00606061	205	42025	14.3178	.00487805
166	27556	12.8841	.00602410	206	42436	14.3527	.00485437
167	27889	12.9228	.00598802	207	42849	14.3875	.00483092
168	28224	12.9615	.00595238	208	43264	14.4222	.00480769
169	28561	13.0000	.00591716	209	43681	14.4568	.00478469
170	28900	13.0384	.00588235	210	44100	14.4914	.00476190
171	29241	13.0767	.00584795	211	44521	14.5258	.00473934
172	29584	13.1149	.00581395	212	44944	14.5602	.00471698
173	29929	13.1529	.00578035	213	45369	14.5945	.00469484
174	30276	13.1909	.00574713	214	45796	14.6287	.00467290
175	30625	13.2288	.00571429	215	46225	14.6629	.00465116
176	30976	13.2665	.00568182	216	46656	14.6969	.00462963
177	31329	13.3041	.00564972	217	47089	14.7309	.00460829
178	31684	13.3417	.00561798	218	47524	14.7648	.00458716
179	32041	13.3791	.00558659	219	47961	14.7986	.00456621
180	32400	13.4164	.00555556	220	48400	14.8324	.00454545
181	32761	13.4536	.00552486	221	48841	14.8661	.00452489
182	33124	13.4907	.00549451	222	49284	14.8997	.00450450
183	33489	13.5277	.00546448	223	49729	14.9332	.00448430
184	33856	13.5647	.00543478	224	50176	14.9666	.00446429
185	34225	13.6015	.00540541	225	50625	15.0000	.00444444
186	34596	13.6382	.00537634	226	51076	15.0333	.00442478
187	34969	13.6748	.00534759	227	51529	15.0665	.00440529
188	35344	13.7113	.00531915	228	51984	15.0997	.00438596
189	35721	13.7477	.00529101	229	52441	15.1327	.00436681
190	36100	13.7840	.00526316	230	52900	15.1658	.00434783
191	36481	13.8203	.00523560	231	53361	15.1987	.00432900
192	36864	13.8564	.00520833	232	53824	15.2315	.00431034
193	37249	13.8924	.00518135	233	54289	15.2643	.00429185
194	37636	13.9284	.00515464	234	54756	15.2971	.00427350
195	38025	13.9642	.00512821	235	55225	15.3297	.00425532
196	38416	14.0000	.00510204	236	55696	15.3623	.00423729
197	38809	14.0357	.00507614	237	56169	15.3948	.00421941
198	39204	14.0712	.00505051	238	56644	15.4272	.00420168
199	39601	14.1067	.00502513	239	57121	15.4596	.00418410
200	40000	14.1421	.00500000	240	57600	15.4919	.00416667

* Portions of Table II have been reproduced from J. W. Dunlap and A. K. Kurtz. *Handbook of Statistical Nomographs, Tables, and Formulas*, World Book Company, New York (1932), by permission of the authors and publishers.

TABLE II. *Table of Squares, Square Roots, and Reciprocals of Numbers from 1 to 1,000*—Continued*

N	N^2	$\sqrt{N}$	$1/N$	N	N^2	$\sqrt{N}$	$1/N$
241	58081	15.5242	.00414938	281	78961	16.7631	.00355872
242	58564	15.5563	.00413223	282	79524	16.7929	.00354610
243	59049	15.5885	.00411523	283	80089	16.8226	.00353357
244	59536	15.6205	.00409836	284	80656	16.8523	.00352113
245	60025	15.6525	.00408163	285	81225	16.8819	.00350877
246	60516	15.6844	.00406504	286	81796	16.9115	.00349650
247	61009	15.7162	.00404858	287	82369	16.9411	.00348432
248	61504	15.7480	.00403226	288	82944	16.9706	.00347222
249	62001	15.7797	.00401606	289	83521	17.0000	.00346021
250	62500	15.8114	.00400000	290	84100	17 0294	.00344828
251	63001	15.8430	.00398406	291	84681	17.0587	.00343643
252	63504	15.8745	.00396825	292	85264	17.0880	.00342466
253	64009	15.9060	.00395257	293	85849	17.1172	.00341297
254	64516	15.9374	.00393701	294	86436	17.1464	.00340136
255	65025	15.9687	.00392157	295	87025	17.1756	.00338983
256	65536	16.0000	.00390625	296	87616	17.2047	.00337838
257	66049	16.0312	.00389105	297	88209	17.2337	.00336700
258	66564	16.0624	.00387597	298	88804	17.2627	.00335570
259	67081	16.0935	.00386100	299	89401	17.2916	.00334448
260	67600	16.1245	.00384615	300	90000	17.3205	.00333333
261	68121	16.1555	.00383142	301	90601	17.3494	.00332226
262	68644	16.1864	.00381679	302	91204	17.3781	.00331126
263	69169	16.2173	.00380228	303	91809	17.4069	.00330033
264	69696	16.2481	.00378788	304	92416	17.4356	.00328947
265	70225	16.2788	.00377358	305	93025	17.4642	.00327869
266	70756	16.3095	.00375940	306	93636	17.4929	.00326797
267	71289	16.3401	.00374532	307	94249	17.5214	.00325733
268	71824	16.3707	.00373134	308	94864	17.5499	.00324675
269	72361	16.4012	.00371747	309	95481	17.5784	.00323625
270	72900	16.4317	.00370370	310	96100	17.6068	.00322581
271	73441	16.4621	.00369004	311	96721	17.6352	.00321543
272	73984	16.4924	.00367647	312	97344	17.6635	.00320513
273	74529	16.5227	.00366300	313	97969	17.6918	.00319489
274	75076	16.5529	.00364964	314	98596	17.7200	.00318471
275	75625	16.5831	.00363636	315	99225	17.7482	.00317460
276	76176	16.6132	.00362319	316	99856	17.7764	.00316456
277	76729	16.6433	.00361011	317	100489	17.8045	.00315457
278	77284	16.6733	.00359712	318	101124	17.8326	.00314465
279	77841	16.7033	.00358423	319	101761	17.8606	.00313480
280	78400	16.7332	.00357143	320	102400	17.8885	.00312500

* Portions of Table II have been reproduced from J. W. Dunlap and A. K. Kurtz. *Handbook of Statistical Nomographs, Tables, and Formulas,* World Book Company, New York (1932), by permission of the authors and publishers.

TABLE II. *Table of Squares, Square Roots, and Reciprocals of Numbers from 1 to 1,000*—Continued*

N	N^2	$\sqrt{N}$	$1/N$	N	N^2	$\sqrt{N}$	$1/N$
321	103041	17.9165	.00311526	361	130321	19.0000	.00277008
322	103684	17.9444	.00310559	362	131044	19.0263	.00276243
323	104329	17.9722	.00309598	363	131769	19.0526	.00275482
324	104976	18.0000	.00308642	364	132496	19.0788	.00274725
325	105625	18.0278	.00307692	365	133225	19.1050	.00273973
326	106276	18.0555	.00306748	366	133956	19.1311	.00273224
327	106929	18.0831	.00305810	367	134689	19.1572	.00272480
328	107584	18.1108	.00304878	368	135424	19.1833	.00271739
329	108241	18.1384	.00303951	369	136161	19.2094	.00271003
330	108900	18.1659	.00303030	370	136900	19.2354	.00270270
331	109561	18.1934	.00302115	371	137641	19.2614	.00269542
332	110224	18.2209	.00301205	372	138384	19.2873	.00268817
333	110889	18.2483	.00300300	373	139129	19.3132	.00268097
334	111556	18.2757	.00299401	374	139876	19.3391	.00267380
335	112225	18.3030	.00298507	375	140625	19.3649	.00266667
336	112896	18.3303	.00297619	376	141376	19.3907	.00265957
337	113569	18.3576	.00296736	377	142129	19.4165	.00265252
338	114244	18.3848	.00295858	378	142884	19.4422	.00264550
339	114921	18.4120	.00294985	379	143641	19.4679	.00263852
340	115600	18.4391	.00294118	380	144400	19.4936	.00263158
341	116281	18.4662	.00293255	381	145161	19.5192	.00262467
342	116964	18.4932	.00292398	382	145924	19.5448	.00261780
343	117649	18.5203	.00291545	383	146689	19.5704	.00261097
344	118336	18.5472	.00290698	384	147456	19.5959	.00260417
345	119025	18.5742	.00289855	385	148225	19.6214	.00259740
346	119716	18.6011	.00289017	386	148996	19.6469	.00259067
347	120409	18.6279	.00288184	387	149769	19.6723	.00258398
348	121104	18.6548	.00287356	388	150544	19.6977	.00257732
349	121801	18.6815	.00286533	389	151321	19.7231	.00257069
350	122500	18.7083	.00285714	390	152100	19.7484	.00256410
351	123201	18.7350	.00284900	391	152881	19.7737	.00255754
352	123904	18.7617	.00284091	392	153664	19.7990	.00255102
353	124609	18.7883	.00283286	393	154449	19.8242	.00254453
354	125316	18.8149	.00282486	394	155236	19.8494	.00253807
355	126025	18.8414	.00281690	395	156025	19.8746	.00253165
356	126736	18.8680	.00280899	396	156816	19.8997	.00252525
357	127449	18.8944	.00280112	397	157609	19.9249	.00251889
358	128164	18.9209	.00279330	398	158404	19.9499	.00251256
359	128881	18.9473	.00278552	399	159201	19.9750	.00250627
360	129600	18.9737	.00277778	400	160000	20.0000	.00250000

* Portions of Table II have been reproduced from J. W. Dunlap and A. K. Kurtz. *Handbook of Statistical Nomographs, Tables, and Formulas*, World Book Company, New York (1932), by permission of the authors and publishers.

TABLE II. *Table of Squares, Square Roots, and Reciprocals of Numbers from 1 to 1,000*—Continued*

N	N^2	$\sqrt{N}$	$1/N$	N	N^2	$\sqrt{N}$	$1/N$
401	160801	20.0250	.00249377	441	194481	21.0000	.00226757
402	161604	20.0499	.00248756	442	195364	21.0238	.00226244
403	162409	20.0749	.00248139	443	196249	21.0476	.00225734
404	163216	20.0998	.00247525	444	197136	21.0713	.00225225
405	164025	20.1246	.00246914	445	198025	21.0950	.00224719
406	164836	20.1494	.00246305	446	198916	21.1187	.00224215
407	165649	20.1742	.00245700	447	199809	21.1424	.00223714
408	166464	20.1990	.00245098	448	200704	21.1660	.00223214
409	167281	20.2237	.00244499	449	201601	21.1896	.00222717
410	168100	20.2485	.00243902	450	202500	21.2132	.00222222
411	168921	20.2731	.00243309	451	203401	21.2368	.00221729
412	169744	20.2978	.00242718	452	204304	21.2603	.00221239
413	170569	20.3224	.00242131	453	205209	21.2838	.00220751
414	171396	20.3470	.00241546	454	206116	21.3073	.00220264
415	172225	20.3715	.00240964	455	207025	21.3307	.00219780
416	173056	20.3961	.00240385	456	207936	21.3542	.00219298
417	173889	20.4206	.00239808	457	208849	21.3776	.00218818
418	174724	20.4450	.00239234	458	209764	21.4009	.00218341
419	175561	20.4695	.00238663	459	210681	21.4243	.00217865
420	176400	20.4939	.00238095	460	211600	21.4476	.00217391
421	177241	20.5183	.00237530	461	212521	21.4709	.00216920
422	178084	20.5426	.00236967	462	213444	21.4942	.00216450
423	178929	20.5670	.00236407	463	214369	21.5174	.00215983
424	179776	20.5913	.00235849	464	215296	21.5407	.00215517
425	180625	20.6155	.00235294	465	216225	21.5639	.00215054
426	181476	20.6398	.00234742	466	217156	21.5870	.00214592
427	182329	20.6640	.00234192	467	218089	21.6102	.00214133
428	183184	20.6882	.00233645	468	219024	21.6333	.00213675
429	184041	20.7123	.00233100	469	219961	21.6564	.00213220
430	184900	20.7364	.00232558	470	220900	21.6795	.00212766
431	185761	20.7605	.00232019	471	221841	21.7025	.00212314
432	186624	20.7846	.00231481	472	222784	21.7256	.00211864
433	187489	20.8087	.00230947	473	223729	21.7486	.00211416
434	188356	20.8327	.00230415	474	224676	21.7715	.00210970
435	189225	20.8567	.00229885	475	225625	21.7945	.00210526
436	190096	20.8806	.00229358	476	226576	21.8174	.00210084
437	190969	20.9045	.00228833	477	227529	21.8403	.00209644
438	191844	20.9284	.00228311	478	228484	21.8632	.00209205
439	192721	20.9523	.00227790	479	229441	21.8861	.00208768
440	193600	20.9762	.00227273	480	230400	21.9089	.00208333

* Portions of Table II have been reproduced from J. W. Dunlap and A. K. Kurtz: *Handbook of Statistical Nomographs, Tables, and Formulas*, World Book Company, New York (1932), by permission of the authors and publishers.

TABLE II. *Table of Squares, Square Roots, and Reciprocals of Numbers from 1 to 1,000*—Continued*

N	N^2	$\sqrt{N}$	$1/N$	N	N^2	$\sqrt{N}$	$1/N$
481	231361	21.9317	.00207900	521	271441	22.8254	.00191939
482	232324	21.9545	.00207469	522	272484	22.8473	.00191571
483	233289	21.9773	.00207039	523	273529	22.8692	.00191205
484	234256	22.0000	.00206612	524	274576	22.8910	.00190840
485	235225	22.0227	.00206186	525	275625	22.9129	.00190476
486	236196	22.0454	.00205761	526	276676	22.9347	.00190114
487	237169	22.0681	.00205339	527	277729	22.9565	.00189753
488	238144	22.0907	.00204918	528	278784	22.9783	.00189394
489	239121	22.1133	.00204499	529	279841	23.0000	.00189036
490	240100	22.1359	.00204082	530	280900	23.0217	.00188679
491	241081	22.1585	.00203666	531	281961	23.0434	.00188324
492	242064	22.1811	.00203252	532	283024	23.0651	.00187970
493	243049	22.2036	.00202840	533	284089	23.0868	.00187617
494	244036	22.2261	.00202429	534	285156	23.1084	.00187266
495	245025	22.2486	.00202020	535	286225	23.1301	.00186916
496	246016	22.2711	.00201613	536	287296	23.1517	.00186567
497	247009	22.2935	.00201207	537	288369	23.1733	.00186220
498	248004	22.3159	.00200803	538	289444	23.1948	.00185874
499	249001	22.3383	.00200401	539	290521	23.2164	.00185529
500	250000	22.3607	.00200000	540	291600	23.2379	.00185185
501	251001	22.3830	.00199601	541	292681	23.2594	.00184843
502	252004	22.4054	.00199203	542	293764	23.2809	.00184502
503	253009	22.4277	.00198807	543	294849	23.3024	.00184162
504	254016	22.4499	.00198413	544	295936	23.3238	.00183824
505	255025	22.4722	.00198020	545	297025	23.3452	.00183486
506	256036	22.4944	.00197628	546	298116	23.3666	.00183150
507	257049	22.5167	.00197239	547	299209	23.3880	.00182815
508	258064	22.5389	.00196850	548	300304	23.4094	.00182482
509	259081	22.5610	.00196464	549	301401	23.4307	.00182149
510	260100	22.5832	.00196078	550	302500	23.4521	.00181818
511	261121	22.6053	.00195695	551	303601	23.4734	.00181488
512	262144	22.6274	.00195312	552	304704	23.4947	.00181159
513	263169	22.6495	.00194932	553	305809	23.5160	.00180832
514	264196	22.6716	.00194553	554	306916	23.5372	.00180505
515	265225	22.6936	.00194175	555	308025	23.5584	.00180180
516	266256	22.7156	.00193798	556	309136	23.5797	.00179856
517	267289	22.7376	.00193424	557	310249	23.6008	.00179533
518	268324	22.7596	.00193050	558	311364	23.6220	.00179211
519	269361	22.7816	.00192678	559	312481	23.6432	.00178891
520	270400	22.8035	.00192308	560	313600	23.6643	.00178571

* Portions of Table II have been reproduced from J. W. Dunlap and A. K. Kurtz. *Handbook of Statistical Nomographs, Tables, and Formulas*, World Book Company, New York (1932), by permission of the authors and publishers.

TABLE II. *Table of Squares, Square Roots, and Reciprocals of Numbers from 1 to 1,000**—Continued*

N	N^2	$\sqrt{N}$	$1/N$	N	N^2	$\sqrt{N}$	$1/N$
561	314721	23.6854	.00178253	601	361201	24.5153	.00166389
562	315844	23.7065	.00177936	602	362404	24.5357	.00166113
563	316969	23.7276	.00177620	603	363609	24.5561	.00165837
564	318096	23.7487	.00177305	604	364816	24.5764	.00165563
565	319225	23.7697	.00176991	605	366025	24.5967	.00165289
566	320356	23.7908	.00176678	606	367236	24.6171	.00165017
567	321489	23.8118	.00176367	607	368449	24.6374	.00164745
568	322624	23.8328	.00176056	608	369664	24.6577	.00164474
569	323761	23.8537	.00175747	609	370881	24.6779	.00164204
570	324900	23.8747	.00175439	610	372100	24.6982	.00163934
571	326041	23.8956	.00175131	611	373321	24.7184	.00163666
572	327184	23.9165	.00174825	612	374544	24.7386	.00163399
573	328329	23.9374	.00174520	613	375769	24.7588	.00163132
574	329476	23.9583	.00174216	614	376996	24.7790	.00162866
575	330625	23.9792	.00173913	615	378225	24.7992	.00162602
576	331776	24.0000	.00173611	616	379456	24.8193	.00162338
577	332929	24.0208	.00173310	617	380689	24.8395	.00162075
578	334084	24.0416	.00173010	618	381924	24.8596	.00161812
579	335241	24.0624	.00172712	619	383161	24.8797	.00161551
580	336400	24.0832	.00172414	620	384400	24.8998	.00161290
581	337561	24.1039	.00172117	621	385641	24.9199	.00161031
582	338724	24.1247	.00171821	622	386884	24.9399	.00160772
583	339889	24.1454	.00171527	623	388129	24.9600	.00160514
584	341056	24.1661	.00171233	624	389376	24.9800	.00160256
585	342225	24.1868	.00170940	625	390625	25.0000	.00160000
586	343396	24.2074	.00170648	626	391876	25.0200	.00159744
587	344569	24.2281	.00170358	627	393129	25.0400	.00159490
588	345744	24.2487	.00170068	628	394384	25.0599	.00159236
589	346921	24.2693	.00169779	629	395641	25.0799	.00158983
590	348100	24.2899	.00169492	630	396900	25.0998	.00158730
591	349281	24.3105	.00169205	631	398161	25.1197	.00158479
592	350464	24.3311	.00168919	632	399424	25.1396	.00158228
593	351649	24.3516	.00168634	633	400689	25.1595	.00157978
594	352836	24.3721	.00168350	634	401956	25.1794	.00157729
595	354025	24.3926	.00168067	635	403225	25.1992	.00157480
596	355216	24.4131	.00167785	636	404496	25.2190	.00157233
597	356409	24.4336	.00167504	637	405769	25.2389	.00156986
598	357604	24.4540	.00167224	638	407044	25.2587	.00156740
599	358801	24.4745	.00166945	639	408321	25.2784	.00156495
600	360000	24.4949	.00166667	640	409600	25.2982	.00156250

* Portions of Table II have been reproduced from J. W. Dunlap and A. K. Kurtz. *Handbook of Statistical Nomographs, Tables, and Formulas*, World Book Company, New York (1932), by permission of the authors and publishers.

TABLE II. *Table of Squares, Square Roots, and Reciprocals of Numbers from 1 to 1,000*—Continued*

N	N^2	$\sqrt{N}$	$1/N$	N	N^2	$\sqrt{N}$	$1/N$
641	410881	25.3180	.00156006	681	463761	26.0960	.00146843
642	412164	25.3377	.00155763	682	465124	26.1151	.00146628
643	413449	25.3574	.00155521	683	466489	26.1343	.00146413
644	414736	25.3772	.00155280	684	467856	26.1534	.00146199
645	416025	25.3969	.00155039	685	469225	26.1725	.00145985
646	417316	25.4165	.00154799	686	470596	26.1916	.00145773
647	418609	25.4362	.00154560	687	471969	26.2107	.00145560
648	419904	25.4558	.00154321	688	473344	26.2298	.00145349
649	421201	25.4755	.00154083	689	474721	26.2488	.00145138
650	422500	25.4951	.00153846	690	476100	26.2679	.00144928
651	423801	25.5147	.00153610	691	477481	26.2869	.00144718
652	425104	25.5343	.00153374	692	478864	26.3059	.00144509
653	426409	25.5539	.00153139	693	480249	26.3249	.00144300
654	427716	25.5734	.00152905	694	481636	26.3439	.00144092
655	429025	25.5930	.00152672	695	483025	26.3629	.00143885
656	430336	25.6125	.00152439	696	484416	26.3818	.00143678
657	431649	25.6320	.00152207	697	485809	26.4008	.00143472
658	432964	25.6515	.00151976	698	487204	26.4197	.00143266
659	434281	25.6710	.00151745	699	488601	26.4386	.00143062
660	435600	25.6905	.00151515	700	490000	26.4575	.00142857
661	436921	25.7099	.00151286	701	491401	26.4764	.00142653
662	438244	25.7294	.00151057	702	492804	26.4953	.00142450
663	439569	25.7488	.00150830	703	494209	26.5141	.00142248
664	440896	25.7682	.00150602	704	495616	26.5330	.00142045
665	442225	25.7876	.00150376	705	497025	26.5518	.00141844
666	443556	25.8070	.00150150	706	498436	26.5707	.00141643
667	444889	25.8263	.00149925	707	499849	26.5895	.00141443
668	446224	25.8457	.00149701	708	501264	26.6083	.00141243
669	447561	25.8650	.00149477	709	502681	26.6271	.00141044
670	448900	25.8844	.00149254	710	504100	26.6458	.00140845
671	450241	25.9037	.00149031	711	505521	26.6646	.00140647
672	451584	25.9230	.00148810	712	506944	26.6833	.00140449
673	452929	25.9422	.00148588	713	508369	26.7021	.00140252
674	454276	25.9615	.00148368	714	509796	26.7208	.00140056
675	455625	25.9808	.00148148	715	511225	26.7395	.00139860
676	456976	26.0000	.00147929	716	512656	26.7582	.00139665
677	458329	26.0192	.00147710	717	514089	26.7769	.00139470
678	459684	26.0384	.00147493	718	515524	26.7955	.00139276
679	461041	26.0576	.00147275	719	516961	26.8142	.00139082
680	462400	26.0768	.00147059	720	518400	26.8328	.00138889

* Portions of Table II have been reproduced from J. W. Dunlap and A. K. Kurtz. *Handbook of Statistical Nomographs, Tables, and Formulas,* World Book Company, New York (1932), by permission of the authors and publishers.

TABLE II. *Table of Squares, Square Roots, and Reciprocals of Numbers from 1 to 1,000*—Continued*

N	N^2	$\sqrt{N}$	$1/N$	N	N^2	$\sqrt{N}$	$1/N$
721	519841	26.8514	.00138696	761	579121	27.5862	.00131406
722	521284	26.8701	.00138504	762	580644	27.6043	.00131234
723	522729	26.8887	.00138313	763	582169	27.6225	.00131062
724	524176	26.9072	.00138122	764	583696	27.6405	.00130890
725	525625	26.9258	.00137931	765	585225	27.6586	.00130719
726	527076	26.9444	.00137741	766	586756	27.6767	.00130548
727	528529	26.9629	.00137552	767	588289	27.6948	.00130378
728	529984	26.9815	.00137363	768	589824	27.7128	.00130208
729	531441	27.0000	.00137174	769	591361	27.7308	.00130039
730	532900	27.0185	.00136986	770	592900	27.7489	.00129870
731	534361	27.0370	.00136799	771	594441	27.7669	.00129702
732	535824	27.0555	.00136612	772	595984	27.7849	.00129534
733	537289	27.0740	.00136426	773	597529	27.8029	.00129366
734	538756	27.0924	.00136240	774	599076	27.8209	.00129199
735	540225	27.1109	.00136054	775	600625	27.8388	.00129032
736	541696	27.1293	.00135870	776	602176	27.8568	.00128866
737	543169	27.1477	.00135685	777	603729	27.8747	.00128700
738	544644	27.1662	.00135501	778	605284	27.8927	.00128535
739	546121	27.1846	.00135318	779	606841	27.9106	.00128370
740	547600	27.2029	.00135135	780	608400	27.9285	.00128205
741	549081	27.2213	.00134953	781	609961	27.9464	.00128041
742	550564	27.2397	.00134771	782	611524	27.9643	.00127877
743	552049	27.2580	.00134590	783	613089	27.9821	.00127714
744	553536	27.2764	.00134409	784	614656	28.0000	.00127551
745	555025	27.2947	.00134228	785	616225	28.0179	.00127389
746	556516	27.3130	.00134048	786	617796	28.0357	.00127226
747	558009	27.3313	.00133869	787	619369	28.0535	.00127065
748	559504	27.3496	.00133690	788	620944	28.0713	.00126904
749	561001	27.3679	.00133511	789	622521	28.0891	.00126743
750	562500	27.3861	.00133333	790	624100	28.1069	.00126582
751	564001	27.4044	.00133156	791	625681	28.1247	.00126422
752	565504	27.4226	.00132979	792	627264	28.1425	.00126263
753	567009	27.4408	.00132802	793	628849	28.1603	.00126103
754	568516	27.4591	.00132626	794	630436	28.1780	.00125945
755	570025	27.4773	.00132450	795	632025	28.1957	.00125786
756	571536	27.4955	.00132275	796	633616	28.2135	.00125628
757	573049	27.5136	.00132100	797	635209	28.2312	.00125471
758	574564	27.5318	.00131926	798	636804	28.2489	.00125313
759	576081	27.5500	.00131752	799	638401	28.2666	.00125156
760	577600	27.5681	.00131579	800	640000	28.2843	.00125000

* Portions of Table II have been reproduced from J. W. Dunlap and A. K. Kurtz. *Handbook of Statistical Nomographs, Tables, and Formulas,* World Book Company, New York (1932), by permission of the authors and publishers.

TABLE II. *Table of Squares, Square Roots, and Reciprocals of Numbers from 1 to 1,000*—Continued*

N	N^2	$\sqrt{N}$	$1/N$	N	N^2	$\sqrt{N}$	$1/N$
801	641601	28.3019	.00124844	841	707281	29.0000	.00118906
802	643204	28.3196	.00124688	842	708964	29.0172	.00118765
803	644809	28.3373	.00124533	843	710649	29.0345	.00118624
804	646416	28.3549	.00124378	844	712336	29.0517	.00118483
805	648025	28.3725	.00124224	845	714025	29.0689	.00118343
806	649636	28.3901	.00124069	846	715716	29.0861	.00118203
807	651249	28.4077	.00123916	847	717409	29.1033	.00118064
808	652864	28.4253	.00123762	848	719104	29.1204	.00117925
809	654481	28.4429	.00123609	849	720801	29.1376	.00117786
810	656100	28.4605	.00123457	850	722500	29.1548	.00117647
811	657721	28.4781	.00123305	851	724201	29.1719	.00117509
812	659344	28.4956	.00123153	852	725904	29.1890	.00117371
813	660969	28.5132	.00123001	853	727609	29.2062	.00117233
814	662596	28.5307	.00122850	854	729316	29.2233	.00117096
815	664225	28.5482	.00122699	855	731025	29.2404	.00116959
816	665856	28.5657	.00122549	856	732736	29.2575	.00116822
817	667489	28.5832	.00122399	857	734449	29.2746	.00116686
818	669124	28.6007	.00122249	858	736164	29.2916	.00116550
819	670761	28.6182	.00122100	859	737881	29.3087	.00116414
820	672400	28.6356	.00121951	860	739600	29.3258	.00116279
821	674041	28.6531	.00121803	861	741321	29.3428	.00116144
822	675684	28.6705	.00121655	862	743044	29.3598	.00116009
823	677329	28.6880	.00121507	863	744769	29.3769	.00115875
824	678976	28.7054	.00121359	864	746496	29.3939	.00115741
825	680625	28.7228	.00121212	865	748225	29.4109	.00115607
826	682276	28.7402	.00121065	866	749956	29.4279	.00115473
827	683929	28.7576	.00120919	867	751689	29.4449	.00115340
828	685584	28.7750	.00120773	868	753424	29.4618	.00115207
829	687241	28.7924	.00120627	869	755161	29.4788	.00115075
830	688900	28.8097	.00120482	870	756900	29.4958	.00114943
831	690561	28.8271	.00120337	871	758641	29.5127	.00114811
832	692224	28.8444	.00120192	872	760384	29.5296	.00114679
833	693889	28.8617	.00120048	873	762129	29.5466	.00114548
834	695556	28.8791	.00119904	874	763876	29.5635	.00114416
835	697225	28.8964	.00119760	875	765625	29.5804	.00114286
836	698896	28.9137	.00119617	876	767376	29.5973	.00114155
837	700569	28.9310	.00119474	877	769129	29.6142	.00114025
838	702244	28.9482	.00119332	878	770884	29.6311	.00113895
839	703921	28.9655	.00119190	879	772641	29.6479	.00113766
840	705600	28.9828	.00119048	880	774400	29.6648	.00113636

* Portions of Table II have been reproduced from J. W. Dunlap and A. K. Kurtz. *Handbook of Statistical Nomographs, Tables, and Formulas*, World Book Company, New York (1932), by permission of the authors and publishers.

TABLE II. *Table of Squares, Square Roots, and Reciprocals of Numbers from 1 to 1,000*—Continued*

N	N^2	$\sqrt{N}$	$1/N$	N	N^2	$\sqrt{N}$	$1/N$
881	776161	29.6816	.00113507	921	848241	30.3480	.00108578
882	777924	29.6985	.00113379	922	850084	30.3645	.00108460
883	779689	29.7153	.00113250	923	851929	30.3809	.00108342
884	781456	29.7321	.00113122	924	853776	30.3974	.00108225
885	783225	29.7489	.00112994	925	855625	30.4138	.00108108
886	784996	29.7658	.00112867	926	857476	30.4302	.00107991
887	786769	29.7825	.00112740	927	859329	30.4467	.00107875
888	788544	29.7993	.00112613	928	861184	30.4631	.00107759
889	790321	29.8161	.00112486	929	863041	30.4795	.00107643
890	792100	29.8329	.00112360	930	864900	30.4959	.00107527
891	793881	29.8496	.00112233	931	866761	30.5123	.00107411
892	795664	29.8664	.00112108	932	868624	30.5287	.00107296
893	797449	29.8831	.00111982	933	870489	30.5450	.00107181
894	799236	29.8998	.00111857	934	872356	30.5614	.00107066
895	801025	29.9166	.00111732	935	874225	30.5778	.00106952
896	802816	29.9333	.00111607	936	876096	30.5941	.00106838
897	804609	29.9500	.00111483	937	877969	30.6105	.00106724
898	806404	29.9666	.00111359	938	879844	30.6268	.00106610
899	808201	29.9833	.00111235	939	881721	30.6431	.00106496
900	810000	30.0000	.00111111	940	883600	30.6594	.00106383
901	811801	30.0167	.00110988	941	885481	30.6757	.00106270
902	813604	30.0333	.00110865	942	887364	30.6920	.00106157
903	815409	30.0500	.00110742	943	889249	30.7083	.00106045
904	817216	30.0666	.00110619	944	891136	30.7246	.00105932
905	819025	30.0832	.00110497	945	893025	30.7409	.00105820
906	820836	30.0998	.00110375	946	894916	30.7571	.00105708
907	822649	30.1164	.00110254	947	896809	30.7734	.00105597
908	824464	30.1330	.00110132	948	898704	30.7896	.00105485
909	826281	30.1496	.00110011	949	900601	30.8058	.00105374
910	828100	30.1662	.00109890	950	902500	30.8221	.00105263
911	829921	30.1828	.00109769	951	904401	30.8383	.00105152
912	831744	30.1993	.00109649	952	906304	30.8545	.00105042
913	833569	30.2159	.00109529	953	908209	30.8707	.00104932
914	835396	30.2324	.00109409	954	910116	30.8869	.00104822
915	837225	30.2490	.00109290	955	912025	30.9031	.00104712
916	839056	30.2655	.00109170	956	913936	30.9192	.00104603
917	840889	30.2820	.00109051	957	915849	30.9354	.00104493
918	842724	30.2985	.00108932	958	917764	30.9516	.00104384
919	844561	30.3150	.00108814	959	919681	30.9677	.00104275
920	846400	30.3315	.00108696	960	921600	30.9839	.00104167

* Portions of Table II have been reproduced from J. W. Dunlap and A. K. Kurtz. *Handbook of Statistical Nomographs, Tables, and Formulas*, World Book Company, New York (1932), by permission of the authors and publishers.

TABLE II. *Table of Squares, Square Roots, and Reciprocals of Numbers from 1 to 1,000*—Concluded*

N	N^2	$\sqrt{N}$	$1/N$	N	N^2	$\sqrt{N}$	$1/N$
961	923521	31.0000	.00104058	981	962361	31.3209	.00101937
962	925444	31.0161	.00103950	982	964324	31.3369	.00101833
963	927369	31.0322	.00103842	983	966289	31.3528	.00101729
964	929296	31.0483	.00103734	984	968256	31.3688	.00101626
965	931225	31.0644	.00103627	985	970225	31.3847	.00101523
966	933156	31.0805	.00103520	986	972196	31.4006	.00101420
967	935089	31.0966	.00103413	987	974169	31.4166	.00101317
968	937024	31.1127	.00103306	988	976144	31.4325	.00101215
969	938961	31.1288	.00103199	989	978121	31.4484	.00101112
970	940900	31.1448	.00103093	990	980100	31.4643	.00101010
971	942841	31.1609	.00102987	991	982081	31.4802	.00100908
972	944784	31.1769	.00102881	992	984064	31.4960	.00100806
973	946729	31.1929	.00102775	993	986049	31.5119	.00100705
974	948676	31.2090	.00102669	994	988036	31.5278	.00100604
975	950625	31.2250	.00102564	995	990025	31.5436	.00100503
976	952576	31.2410	.00102459	996	992016	31.5595	.00100402
977	954529	31.2570	.00102354	997	994009	31.5753	.00100301
978	956484	31.2730	.00102249	998	996004	31.5911	.00100200
979	958441	31.2890	.00102145	999	998001	31.6070	.00100100
980	960400	31.3050	.00102041	1000	1000000	31.6228	.00100000

* Portions of Table II have been reproduced from J. W. Dunlap and A. K. Kurtz. *Handbook of Statistical Nomographs, Tables, and Formulas*, World Book Company, New York (1932), by permission of the authors and publishers.

TABLE III. *Areas and Ordinates of the Normal Curve in Terms of x/σ*

(1) z Standard Score $\left(\frac{x}{\sigma}\right)$	(2) A Area from Mean to $\frac{x}{\sigma}$	(3) B Area in Larger Portion	(4) C Area in Smaller Portion	(5) y Ordinate at $\frac{x}{\sigma}$
0.00	.0000	.5000	.5000	.3989
0.01	.0040	.5040	.4960	.3989
0.02	.0080	.5080	.4920	.3989
0.03	.0120	.5120	.4880	.3988
0.04	.0160	.5160	.4840	.3986
0.05	.0199	.5199	.4801	.3984
0.06	.0239	.5239	.4761	.3982
0.07	.0279	.5279	.4721	.3980
0.08	.0319	.5319	.4681	.3977
0.09	.0359	.5359	.4641	.3973
0.10	.0398	.5398	.4602	.3970
0.11	.0438	.5438	.4562	.3965
0.12	.0478	.5478	.4522	.3961
0.13	.0517	.5517	.4483	.3956
0.14	.0557	.5557	.4443	.3951
0.15	.0596	.5596	.4404	.3945
0.16	.0636	.5636	.4364	.3939
0.17	.0675	.5675	.4325	.3932
0.18	.0714	.5714	.4286	.3925
0.19	.0753	.5753	.4247	.3918
0.20	.0793	.5793	.4207	.3910
0.21	.0832	.5832	.4168	.3902
0.22	.0871	.5871	.4129	.3894
0.23	.0910	.5910	.4090	.3885
0.24	.0948	.5948	.4052	.3876
0.25	.0987	.5987	.4013	.3867
0.26	.1026	.6026	.3974	.3857
0.27	.1064	.6064	.3936	.3847
0.28	.1103	.6103	.3897	.3836
0.29	.1141	.6141	.3859	.3825
0.30	.1179	.6179	.3821	.3814
0.31	.1217	.6217	.3783	.3802
0.32	.1255	.6255	.3745	.3790
0.33	.1293	.6293	.3707	.3778
0.34	.1331	.6331	.3669	.3765

TABLE III. *Areas and Ordinates of the Normal Curve in Terms of x/σ—Continued*

(1) z Standard Score $\left(\frac{x}{\sigma}\right)$	(2) A Area from Mean to $\frac{x}{\sigma}$	(3) B Area in Larger Portion	(4) C Area in Smaller Portion	(5) y Ordinate at $\frac{x}{\sigma}$
0.35	.1368	.6368	.3632	.3752
0.36	.1406	.6406	.3594	.3739
0.37	.1443	.6443	.3557	.3725
0.38	.1480	.6480	.3520	.3712
0.39	.1517	.6517	.3483	.3697
0.40	.1554	.6554	.3446	.3683
0.41	.1591	.6591	.3409	.3668
0.42	.1628	.6628	.3372	.3653
0.43	.1664	.6664	.3336	.3637
0.44	.1700	.6700	.3300	.3621
0.45	.1736	.6736	.3264	.3605
0.46	.1772	.6772	.3228	.3589
0.47	.1808	.6808	.3192	.3572
0.48	.1844	.6844	.3156	.3555
0.49	.1879	.6879	.3121	.3538
0.50	.1915	.6915	.3085	.3521
0.51	.1950	.6950	.3050	.3503
0.52	.1985	.6985	.3015	.3485
0.53	.2019	.7019	.2981	.3467
0.54	.2054	.7054	.2946	.3448
0.55	.2088	.7088	.2912	.3429
0.56	.2123	.7123	.2877	.3410
0.57	.2157	.7157	.2843	.3391
0.58	.2190	.7190	.2810	.3372
0.59	.2224	.7224	.2776	.3352
0.60	.2257	.7257	.2743	.3332
0.61	.2291	.7291	.2709	.3312
0.62	.2324	.7324	.2676	.3292
0.63	.2357	.7357	.2643	.3271
0.64	.2389	.7389	.2611	.3251
0.65	.2422	.7422	.2578	.3230
0.66	.2454	.7454	.2546	.3209
0.67	.2486	.7486	.2514	.3187
0.68	.2517	.7517	.2483	.3166
0.69	.2549	.7549	.2451	.3144

TABLE III. *Areas and Ordinates of the Normal Curve in Terms of x/σ—Continued*

(1) z Standard Score $\left(\frac{x}{\sigma}\right)$	(2) A Area from Mean to $\frac{x}{\sigma}$	(3) B Area in Larger Portion	(4) C Area in Smaller Portion	(5) y Ordinate at $\frac{x}{\sigma}$
0.70	.2580	.7580	.2420	.3123
0.71	.2611	.7611	.2389	.3101
0.72	.2642	.7642	.2358	.3079
0.73	.2673	.7673	.2327	.3056
0.74	.2704	.7704	.2296	.3034
0.75	.2734	.7734	.2266	.3011
0.76	.2764	.7764	.2236	.2989
0.77	.2794	.7794	.2206	.2966
0.78	.2823	.7823	.2177	.2943
0.79	.2852	.7852	.2148	.2920
0.80	.2881	.7881	.2119	.2897
0.81	.2910	.7910	.2090	.2874
0.82	.2939	.7939	.2061	.2850
0.83	.2967	.7967	.2033	.2827
0.84	.2995	.7995	.2005	.2803
0.85	.3023	.8023	.1977	.2780
0.86	.3051	.8051	.1949	.2756
0.87	.3078	.8078	.1922	.2732
0.88	.3106	.8106	.1894	.2709
0.89	.3133	.8133	.1867	.2685
0.90	.3159	.8159	.1841	.2661
0.91	.3186	.8186	.1814	.2637
0.92	.3212	.8212	.1788	.2613
0.93	.3238	.8238	.1762	.2589
0.94	.3264	.8264	.1736	.2565
0.95	.3289	.8289	.1711	.2541
0.96	.3315	.8315	.1685	.2516
0.97	.3340	.8340	.1660	.2492
0.98	.3365	.8365	.1635	.2468
0.99	.3389	.8389	.1611	.2444
1.00	.3413	.8413	.1587	.2420
1.01	.3438	.8438	.1562	.2396
1.02	.3461	.8461	.1539	.2371
1.03	.3485	.8485	.1515	.2347
1.04	.3508	.8508	.1492	.2323

TABLE III. *Areas and Ordinates of the Normal Curve in Terms of x/σ—Continued*

(1) z STANDARD SCORE $\left(\frac{x}{\sigma}\right)$	(2) A AREA FROM MEAN TO $\frac{x}{\sigma}$	(3) B AREA IN LARGER PORTION	(4) C AREA IN SMALLER PORTION	(5) y ORDINATE AT $\frac{x}{\sigma}$
1.05	.3531	.8531	.1469	.2299
1.06	.3554	.8554	.1446	.2275
1.07	.3577	.8577	.1423	.2251
1.08	.3599	.8599	.1401	.2227
1.09	.3621	.8621	.1379	.2203
1.10	.3643	.8643	.1357	.2179
1.11	.3665	.8665	.1335	.2155
1.12	.3686	.8686	.1314	.2131
1.13	.3708	.8708	.1292	.2107
1.14	.3729	.8729	.1271	.2083
1.15	.3749	.8749	.1251	.2059
1.16	.3770	.8770	.1230	.2036
1.17	.3790	.8790	.1210	.2012
1.18	.3810	.8810	.1190	.1989
1.19	.3830	.8830	.1170	.1965
1.20	.3849	.8849	.1151	.1942
1.21	.3869	.8869	.1131	.1919
1.22	.3888	.8888	.1112	.1895
1.23	.3907	.8907	.1093	.1872
1.24	.3925	.8925	.1075	.1849
1.25	.3944	.8944	.1056	.1826
1.26	.3962	.8962	.1038	.1804
1.27	.3980	.8980	.1020	.1781
1.28	.3997	.8997	.1003	.1758
1.29	.4015	.9015	.0985	.1736
1.30	.4032	.9032	.0968	.1714
1.31	.4049	.9049	.0951	.1691
1.32	.4066	.9066	.0934	.1669
1.33	.4082	.9082	.0918	.1647
1.34	.4099	.9099	.0901	.1626
1.35	.4115	.9115	.0885	.1604
1.36	.4131	.9131	.0869	.1582
1.37	.4147	.9147	.0853	.1561
1.38	.4162	.9162	.0838	.1539
1.39	.4177	.9177	.0823	.1518

TABLE III. *Areas and Ordinates of the Normal Curve in Terms of x/σ—Continued*

(1) z Standard Score $\left(\frac{x}{\sigma}\right)$	(2) A Area from Mean to $\frac{x}{\sigma}$	(3) B Area in Larger Portion	(4) C Area in Smaller Portion	(5) y Ordinate at $\frac{x}{\sigma}$
1.40	.4192	.9192	.0808	.1497
1.41	.4207	.9207	.0793	.1476
1.42	.4222	.9222	.0778	.1456
1.43	.4236	.9236	.0764	.1435
1.44	.4251	.9251	.0749	.1415
1.45	.4265	.9265	.0735	.1394
1.46	.4279	.9279	.0721	.1374
1.47	.4292	.9292	.0708	.1354
1.48	.4306	.9306	.0694	.1334
1.49	.4319	.9319	.0681	.1315
1.50	.4332	.9332	.0668	.1295
1.51	.4345	.9345	.0655	.1276
1.52	.4357	.9357	.0643	.1257
1.53	.4370	.9370	.0630	.1238
1.54	.4382	.9382	.0618	.1219
1.55	.4394	.9394	.0606	.1200
1.56	.4406	.9406	.0594	.1182
1.57	.4418	.9418	.0582	.1163
1.58	.4429	.9429	.0571	.1145
1.59	.4441	.9441	.0559	.1127
1.60	.4452	.9452	.0548	.1109
1.61	.4463	.9463	.0537	.1092
1.62	.4474	.9474	.0526	.1074
1.63	.4484	.9484	.0516	.1057
1.64	.4495	.9495	.0505	.1040
1.65	.4505	.9505	.0495	.1023
1.66	.4515	.9515	.0485	.1006
1.67	.4525	.9525	.0475	.0989
1.68	.4535	.9535	.0465	.0973
1.69	.4545	.9545	.0455	.0957
1.70	.4554	.9554	.0446	.0940
1.71	.4564	.9564	.0436	.0925
1.72	.4573	.9573	.0427	.0909
1.73	.4582	.9582	.0418	.0893
1.74	.4591	.9591	.0409	.0878

TABLE III. *Areas and Ordinates of the Normal Curve in Terms of x/σ—Continued*

(1) z Standard Score $\left(\frac{x}{\sigma}\right)$	(2) A Area from Mean to $\frac{x}{\sigma}$	(3) B Area in Larger Portion	(4) C Area in Smaller Portion	(5) y Ordinate at $\frac{x}{\sigma}$
1.75	.4599	.9599	.0401	.0863
1.76	.4608	.9608	.0392	.0848
1.77	.4616	.9616	.0384	.0833
1.78	.4625	.9625	.0375	.0818
1.79	.4633	.9633	.0367	.0804
1.80	.4641	.9641	.0359	.0790
1.81	.4649	.9649	.0351	.0775
1.82	.4656	.9656	.0344	.0761
1.83	.4664	.9664	.0336	.0748
1.84	.4671	.9671	.0329	.0734
1.85	.4678	.9678	.0322	.0721
1.86	.4686	.9686	.0314	.0707
1.87	.4693	.9693	.0307	.0694
1.88	.4699	.9699	.0301	.0681
1.89	.4706	.9706	.0294	.0669
1.90	.4713	.9713	.0287	.0656
1.91	.4719	.9719	.0281	.0644
1.92	.4726	.9726	.0274	.0632
1.93	.4732	.9732	.0268	.0620
1.94	.4738	.9738	.0262	.0608
1.95	.4744	.9744	.0256	.0596
1.96	.4750	.9750	.0250	.0584
1.97	.4756	.9756	.0244	.0573
1.98	.4761	.9761	.0239	.0562
1.99	.4767	.9767	.0233	.0551
2.00	.4772	.9772	.0228	.0540
2.01	.4778	.9778	.0222	.0529
2.02	.4783	.9783	.0217	.0519
2.03	.4788	.9788	.0212	.0508
2.04	.4793	.9793	.0207	.0498
2.05	.4798	.9798	.0202	.0488
2.06	.4803	.9803	.0197	.0478
2.07	.4808	.9808	.0192	.0468
2.08	.4812	.9812	.0188	.0459
2.09	.4817	.9817	.0183	.0449

TABLE III. *Areas and Ordinates of the Normal Curve in Terms of x/σ—Continued*

(1) z STANDARD SCORE $\left(\frac{x}{\sigma}\right)$	(2) A AREA FROM MEAN TO $\frac{x}{\sigma}$	(3) B AREA IN LARGER PORTION	(4) C AREA IN SMALLER PORTION	(5) y ORDINATE AT $\frac{x}{\sigma}$
2.10	.4821	.9821	.0179	.0440
2.11	.4826	.9826	.0174	.0431
2.12	.4830	.9830	.0170	.0422
2.13	.4834	.9834	.0166	.0413
2.14	.4838	.9838	.0162	.0404
2.15	.4842	.9842	.0158	.0396
2.16	.4846	.9846	.0154	.0387
2.17	.4850	.9850	.0150	.0379
2.18	.4854	.9854	.0146	.0371
2.19	.4857	.9857	.0143	.0363
2.20	.4861	.9861	.0139	.0355
2.21	.4864	.9864	.0136	.0347
2.22	.4868	.9868	.0132	.0339
2.23	.4871	.9871	.0129	.0332
2.24	.4875	.9875	.0125	.0325
2.25	.4878	.9878	.0122	.0317
2.26	.4881	.9881	.0119	.0310
2.27	.4884	.9884	.0116	.0303
2.28	.4887	.9887	.0113	.0297
2.29	.4890	.9890	.0110	.0290
2.30	.4893	.9893	.0107	.0283
2.31	.4896	.9896	.0104	.0277
2.32	.4898	.9898	.0102	.0270
2.33	.4901	.9901	.0099	.0264
2.34	.4904	.9904	.0096	.0258
2.35	.4906	.9906	.0094	.0252
2.36	.4909	.9909	.0091	.0246
2.37	.4911	.9911	.0089	.0241
2.38	.4913	.9913	.0087	.0235
2.39	.4916	.9916	.0084	.0229
2.40	.4918	.9918	.0082	.0224
2.41	.4920	.9920	.0080	.0219
2.42	.4922	.9922	.0078	.0213
2.43	.4925	.9925	.0075	.0208
2.44	.4927	.9927	.0073	.0203

TABLE III. *Areas and Ordinates of the Normal Curve in Terms of x/σ—Continued*

(1) z Standard Score $\left(\frac{x}{\sigma}\right)$	(2) A Area from Mean to $\frac{x}{\sigma}$	(3) B Area in Larger Portion	(4) C Area in Smaller Portion	(5) y Ordinate at $\frac{x}{\sigma}$
2.45	.4929	.9929	.0071	.0198
2.46	.4931	.9931	.0069	.0194
2.47	.4932	.9932	.0068	.0189
2.48	.4934	.9934	.0066	.0184
2.49	.4936	.9936	.0064	.0180
2.50	.4938	.9938	.0062	.0175
2.51	.4940	.9940	.0060	.0171
2.52	.4941	.9941	.0059	.0167
2.53	.4943	.9943	.0057	.0163
2.54	.4945	.9945	.0055	.0158
2.55	.4946	.9946	.0054	.0154
2.56	.4948	.9948	.0052	.0151
2.57	.4949	.9949	.0051	.0147
2.58	.4951	.9951	.0049	.0143
2.59	.4952	.9952	.0048	.0139
2.60	.4953	.9953	.0047	.0136
2.61	.4955	.9955	.0045	.0132
2.62	.4956	.9956	.0044	.0129
2.63	.4957	.9957	.0043	.0126
2.64	.4959	.9959	.0041	.0122
2.65	.4960	.9960	.0040	.0119
2.66	.4961	.9961	.0039	.0116
2.67	.4962	.9962	.0038	.0113
2.68	.4963	.9963	.0037	.0110
2.69	.4964	.9964	.0036	.0107
2.70	.4965	.9965	.0035	.0104
2.71	.4966	.9966	.0034	.0101
2.72	.4967	.9967	.0033	.0099
2.73	.4968	.9968	.0032	.0096
2.74	.4969	.9969	.0031	.0093
2.75	.4970	.9970	.0030	.0091
2.76	.4971	.9971	.0029	.0088
2.77	.4972	.9972	.0028	.0086
2.78	.4973	.9973	.0027	.0084
2.79	.4974	.9974	.0026	.0081

TABLE III. *Areas and Ordinates of the Normal Curve in Terms of x/σ—Continued*

(1) z Standard Score $\left(\frac{x}{\sigma}\right)$	(2) A Area from Mean to $\frac{x}{\sigma}$	(3) B Area in Larger Portion	(4) C Area in Smaller Portion	(5) y Ordinate at $\frac{x}{\sigma}$
2.80	.4974	.9974	.0026	.0079
2.81	.4975	.9975	.0025	.0077
2.82	.4976	.9976	.0024	.0075
2.83	.4977	.9977	.0023	.0073
2.84	.4977	.9977	.0023	.0071
2.85	.4978	.9978	.0022	.0069
2.86	.4979	.9979	.0021	.0067
2.87	.4979	.9979	.0021	.0065
2.88	.4980	.9980	.0020	.0063
2.89	.4981	.9981	.0019	.0061
2.90	.4981	.9981	.0019	.0060
2.91	.4982	.9982	.0018	.0058
2.92	.4982	.9982	.0018	.0056
2.93	.4983	.9983	.0017	.0055
2.94	.4984	.9984	.0016	.0053
2.95	.4984	.9984	.0016	.0051
2.96	.4985	.9985	.0015	.0050
2.97	.4985	.9985	.0015	.0048
2.98	.4986	.9986	.0014	.0047
2.99	.4986	.9986	.0014	.0046
3.00	.4987	.9987	.0013	.0044
3.01	.4987	.9987	.0013	.0043
3.02	.4987	.9987	.0013	.0042
3.03	.4988	.9988	.0012	.0040
3.04	.4988	.9988	.0012	.0039
3.05	.4989	.9989	.0011	.0038
3.06	.4989	.9989	.0011	.0037
3.07	.4989	.9989	.0011	.0036
3.08	.4990	.9990	.0010	.0035
3.09	.4990	.9990	.0010	.0034
3.10	.4990	.9990	.0010	.0033
3.11	.4991	.9991	.0009	.0032
3.12	.4991	.9991	.0009	.0031
3.13	.4991	.9991	.0009	.0030
3.14	.4992	.9992	.0008	.0029

TABLE III. *Areas and Ordinates of the Normal Curve in Terms of x/σ—Concluded*

(1) z Standard Score $\left(\frac{x}{\sigma}\right)$	(2) A Area from Mean to $\frac{x}{\sigma}$	(3) B Area in Larger Portion	(4) C Area in Smaller Portion	(5) y Ordinate at $\frac{x}{\sigma}$
3.15	.4992	.9992	.0008	.0028
3.16	.4992	.9992	.0008	.0027
3.17	.4992	.9992	.0008	.0026
3.18	.4993	.9993	.0007	.0025
3.19	.4993	.9993	.0007	.0025
3.20	.4993	.9993	.0007	.0024
3.21	.4993	.9993	.0007	.0023
3.22	.4994	.9994	.0006	.0022
3.23	.4994	.9994	.0006	.0022
3.24	.4994	.9994	.0006	.0021
3.30	.4995	.9995	.0005	.0017
3.40	.4997	.9997	.0003	.0012
3.50	.4998	.9998	.0002	.0009
3.60	.4998	.9998	.0002	.0006
3.70	.4999	.9999	.0001	.0004

TABLE IV. *Table of* χ^2*

Degrees of Freedom df	P = .99	.98	.95	.90	.80	.70	.50	.30	.20	.10	.05	.02	.01
1	.000157	.000628	.00393	.0158	.0642	.148	.455	1.074	1.642	2.706	3.841	5.412	6.635
2	.0201	.0404	.103	.211	.446	.713	1.386	2.408	3.219	4.605	5.991	7.824	9.210
3	.115	.185	.352	.584	1.005	1.424	2.366	3.665	4.642	6.251	7.815	9.837	11.341
4	.297	.429	.711	1.064	1.649	2.195	3.357	4.878	5.989	7.779	9.488	11.668	13.277
5	.554	.752	1.145	1.610	2.343	3.000	4.351	6.064	7.289	9.236	11.070	13.388	15.086
6	.872	1.134	1.635	2.204	3.070	3.828	5.348	7.231	8.558	10.645	12.592	15.033	16.812
7	1.239	1.564	2.167	2.833	3.822	4.671	6.346	8.383	9.803	12.017	14.067	16.622	18.475
8	1.646	2.032	2.733	3.490	4.594	5.527	7.344	9.524	11.030	13.362	15.507	18.168	20.090
9	2.088	2.532	3.325	4.168	5.380	6.393	8.343	10.656	12.242	14.684	16.919	19.679	21.666
10	2.558	3.059	3.940	4.865	6.179	7.267	9.342	11.781	13.442	15.987	18.307	21.161	23.209
11	3.053	3.609	4.575	5.578	6.989	8.148	10.341	12.899	14.631	17.275	19.675	22.618	24.725
12	3.571	4.178	5.226	6.304	7.807	9.034	11.340	14.011	15.812	18.549	21.026	24.054	26.217
13	4.107	4.765	5.892	7.042	8.634	9.926	12.340	15.119	16.985	19.812	22.362	25.472	27.688
14	4.660	5.368	6.571	7.790	9.467	10.821	13.339	16.222	18.151	21.064	23.685	26.873	29.141
15	5.229	5.985	7.261	8.547	10.307	11.721	14.339	17.322	19.311	22.307	24.996	28.259	30.578
16	5.812	6.614	7.962	9.312	11.152	12.624	15.338	18.418	20.465	23.542	26.296	29.633	32.000
17	6.408	7.255	8.672	10.085	12.002	13.531	16.338	19.511	21.615	24.769	27.587	30.995	33.409
18	7.015	7.906	9.390	10.865	12.857	14.440	17.338	20.601	22.760	25.989	28.869	32.346	34.805
19	7.633	8.567	10.117	11.651	13.716	15.352	18.338	21.689	23.900	27.204	30.144	33.687	36.191
20	8.260	9.237	10.851	12.443	14.578	16.266	19.337	22.775	25.038	28.412	31.410	35.020	37.566
21	8.897	9.915	11.591	13.240	15.445	17.182	20.337	23.858	26.171	29.615	32.671	36.343	38.932
22	9.542	10.600	12.338	14.041	16.314	18.101	21.337	24.939	27.301	30.813	33.924	37.659	40.289
23	10.196	11.293	13.091	14.848	17.187	19.021	22.337	26.018	28.429	32.007	35.172	38.968	41.638
24	10.856	11.992	13.848	15.659	18.062	19.943	23.337	27.096	29.553	33.196	36.415	40.270	42.980
25	11.524	12.697	14.611	16.473	18.940	20.867	24.337	28.172	30.675	34.382	37.652	41.566	44.314
26	12.198	13.409	15.379	17.292	19.820	21.792	25.336	29.246	31.795	35.563	38.885	42.856	45.642
27	12.879	14.125	16.151	18.114	20.703	22.719	26.336	30.319	32.912	36.741	40.113	44.140	46.963
28	13.565	14.847	16.928	18.939	21.588	23.647	27.336	31.391	34.027	37.916	41.337	45.419	48.278
29	14.256	15.574	17.708	19.768	22.475	24.577	28.336	32.461	35.139	39.087	42.557	46.693	49.588
30	14.953	16.306	18.493	20.599	23.364	25.508	29.336	33.530	36.250	40.256	43.773	47.962	50.892

* Table IV is reprinted from Table III of Fisher: *Statistical Methods for Research Workers*, Oliver & Boyd Ltd., Edinburgh, by permission of the author and publishers.

For larger values of df, the expression $\sqrt{2\chi^2} - \sqrt{2(df) - 1}$ may be used as a normal deviate with unit standard error.

TABLE V. *Table of t**

df	*P* = .9	.8	.7	.6	.5	.4	.3	.2	.1	.05	.02	.01
1	.158	.325	.510	.727	1.000	1.376	1.963	3.078	6.314	12.706	31.821	63.657
2	.142	.289	.445	.617	.816	1.061	1.386	1.886	2.920	4.303	6.965	9.925
3	.137	.277	.424	.584	.765	.978	1.250	1.638	2.353	3.182	4.541	5.841
4	.134	.271	.414	.569	.741	.941	1.190	1.533	2.132	2.776	3.747	4.604
5	.132	.267	.408	.559	.727	.920	1.156	1.476	2.015	2.571	3.365	4.032
6	.131	.265	.404	.553	.718	.906	1.134	1.440	1.943	2.447	3.143	3.707
7	.130	.263	.402	.549	.711	.896	1.119	1.415	1.895	2.365	2.998	3.499
8	.130	.262	.399	.546	.706	.889	1.108	1.397	1.860	2.306	2.896	3.355
9	.129	.261	.398	.543	.703	.883	1.100	1.383	1.833	2.262	2.821	3.250
10	.129	.260	.397	.542	.700	.879	1.093	1.372	1.812	2.228	2.764	3.169
11	.129	.260	.396	.540	.697	.876	1.088	1.363	1.796	2.201	2.718	3.106
12	.128	.259	.395	.539	.695	.873	1.083	1.356	1.782	2.179	2.681	3.055
13	.128	.259	.394	.538	.694	.870	1.079	1.350	1.771	2.160	2.650	3.012
14	.128	.258	.393	.537	.692	.868	1.076	1.345	1.761	2.145	2.624	2.977
15	.128	.258	.393	.536	.691	.866	1.074	1.341	1.753	2.131	2.602	2.947
16	.128	.258	.392	.535	.690	.865	1.071	1.337	1.746	2.120	2.583	2.921
17	.128	.257	.392	.534	.689	.863	1.069	1.333	1.740	2.110	2.567	2.898
18	.127	.257	.392	.534	.688	.862	1.067	1.330	1.734	2.101	2.552	2.878
19	.127	.257	.391	.533	.688	.861	1.066	1.328	1.729	2.093	2.539	2.861
20	.127	.257	.391	.533	.687	.860	1.064	1.325	1.725	2.086	2.528	2.845
21	.127	.257	.391	.532	.686	.859	1.063	1.323	1.721	2.080	2.518	2.831
22	.127	.256	.390	.532	.686	.858	1.061	1.321	1.717	2.074	2.508	2.819
23	.127	.256	.390	.532	.685	.858	1.060	1.319	1.714	2.069	2.500	2.807
24	.127	.256	.390	.531	.685	.857	1.059	1.318	1.711	2.064	2.492	2.797
25	.127	.256	.390	.531	.684	.856	1.058	1.316	1.708	2.060	2.485	2.787
26	.127	.256	.390	.531	.684	.856	1.058	1.315	1.706	2.056	2.479	2.779
27	.127	.256	.289	.531	.684	.855	1.057	1.314	1.703	2.052	2.473	2.771
28	.127	.256	.389	.530	.683	.855	1.056	1.313	1.701	2.048	2.467	2.763
29	.127	.256	.389	.530	.683	.854	1.055	1.311	1.699	2.045	2.462	2.756
30	.127	.256	.389	.530	.683	.854	1.055	1.310	1.697	2.042	2.457	2.750
∞	.12566	.25335	.38532	.52440	.67449	.84162	1.03643	1.28155	1.64485	1.95996	2.32634	2.57582

Additional Values of t at the 5 and the 1 Per Cent Levels of Significance†

df	5%	1%	*df*	5%	1%	*df*	5%	1%
32	2.037	2.739	55	2.005	2.668	125	1.979	2.616
34	2.032	2.728	60	2.000	2.660	150	1.976	2.609
36	2.027	2.718	65	1.998	2.653	175	1.974	2.605
38	2.025	2.711	70	1.994	2.648	200	1.972	2.601
40	2.021	2.704	75	1.992	2.643	300	1.968	2.592
42	2.017	2.696	80	1.990	2.638	400	1.966	2.588
44	2.015	2.691	85	1.989	2.635	500	1.965	2.586
46	2.012	2.685	90	1.987	2.632	1000	1.962	2.581
48	2.010	2.681	95	1.986	2.629	∞	1.960	2.576
50	2.008	2.678	100	1.984	2.626			

* Table V is reprinted from Table IV of Fisher: *Statistical Methods for Research Workers*, Oliver & Boyd Ltd., Edinburgh, by permission of the author and publishers.

† Additional entries were taken from Snedecor: *Statistical Methods*, Iowa State College Press, Ames, Iowa, by permission of the author and publisher. Values for 75, 85, 95, and 175 degrees of freedom were obtained by linear interpolation.

The probabilities given are for a two-tailed test of significance. For a one-tailed test of significance, the tabled probabilities should be halved.

TABLE VI. *Values of the Correlation Coefficient for Different Levels of Significance**

df	*P* = .10	.05	.02	.01
1	.988	.997	.9995	.9999
2	.900	.950	.980	.990
3	.805	.878	.934	.959
4	.729	.811	.882	.917
5	.669	.754	.833	.874
6	.622	.707	.789	.834
7	.582	.666	.750	.798
8	.549	.632	.716	.765
9	.521	.602	.685	.735
10	.497	.576	.658	.708
11	.476	.553	.634	.684
12	.458	.532	.612	.661
13	.441	.514	.592	.641
14	.426	.497	.574	.623
15	.412	.482	.558	.606
16	.400	.468	.542	.590
17	.389	.456	.528	.575
18	.378	.444	.516	.561
19	.369	.433	.503	.549
20	.360	.423	.492	.537
21	.352	.413	.482	.526
22	.344	.404	.472	.515
23	.337	.396	.462	.505
24	.330	.388	.453	.496
25	.323	.381	.445	.487
26	.317	.374	.437	.479
27	.311	.367	.430	.471
28	.306	.361	.423	.463
29	.301	.355	.416	.456
30	.296	.349	.409	.449
35	.275	.325	.381	.418
40	.257	.304	.358	.393
45	.243	.288	.338	.372
50	.231	.273	.322	.354
60	.211	.250	.295	.325
70	.195	.232	.274	.302
80	.183	.217	.256	.283
90	.173	.205	.242	.267
100	.164	.195	.230	.254

Additional Values of r *at the 5 and 1 Per Cent Levels of Significance*

df	.05	.01	*df*	.05	.01	*df*	.05	.01
32	.339	.436	48	.279	.361	150	.159	.208
34	.329	.424	55	.261	.338	175	.148	.193
36	.320	.413	65	.241	.313	200	.138	.181
38	.312	.403	75	.224	.292	300	.113	.148
42	.297	.384	85	.211	.275	400	.098	.128
44	.291	.376	95	.200	.260	500	.088	.115
46	.284	.368	125	.174	.228	1,000	.062	.081

* Table VI is reprinted from Table V.A. of R. A. Fisher, *Statistical Methods for Research Workers*, Oliver & Boyd Ltd., Edinburgh, by permission of the author and publishers.

Additional entries were calculated by means of formula (15.1), using the table of *t*.

The probabilities given are for a two-tailed test of significance, that is with the sign of *r* ignored. For a one-tailed test of significance, the tabled probabilities should be halved.

TABLE VII. *Table of* z′ *Values for* r*

r	z'	r	z'	r	z'	r	z'	r	z'
.000	.000	.200	.203	.400	.424	.600	.693	.800	1.099
.005	.005	.205	.208	.405	.430	.605	.701	.805	1.113
.010	.010	.210	.213	.410	.436	.610	.709	.810	1.127
.015	.015	.215	.218	.415	.442	.615	.717	.815	1.142
.020	.020	.220	.224	.420	.448	.620	.725	.820	1.157
.025	.025	.225	.229	.425	.454	.625	.733	.825	1.172
.030	.030	.230	.234	.430	.460	.630	.741	.830	1.188
.035	.035	.235	.239	.435	.466	.635	.750	.835	1.204
.040	.040	.240	.245	.440	.472	.640	.758	.840	1.221
.045	.045	.245	.250	.445	.478	.645	.767	.845	1.238
.050	.050	.250	.255	.450	.485	.650	.775	.850	1.256
.055	.055	.255	.261	.455	.491	.655	.784	.855	1.274
.060	.060	.260	.266	.460	.497	.660	.793	.860	1.293
.065	.065	.265	.271	.465	.504	.665	.802	.865	1.313
.070	.070	.270	.277	.470	.510	.670	.811	.870	1.333
.075	.075	.275	.282	.475	.517	.675	.820	.875	1.354
.080	.080	.280	.288	.480	.523	.680	.829	.880	1.376
.085	.085	.285	.293	.485	.530	.685	.838	.885	1.398
.090	.090	.290	.299	.490	.536	.690	.848	.890	1.422
.095	.095	.295	.304	.495	.543	.695	.858	.895	1.447
.100	.100	.300	.310	.500	.549	.700	.867	.900	1.472
.105	.105	.305	.315	.505	.556	.705	.877	.905	1.499
.110	.110	.310	.321	.510	.563	.710	.887	.910	1.528
.115	.116	.315	.326	.515	.570	.715	.897	.915	1.557
.120	.121	.320	.332	.520	.576	.720	.908	.920	1.589
.125	.126	.325	.337	.525	.583	.725	.918	.925	1.623
.130	.131	.330	.343	.530	.590	.730	.929	.930	1.658
.135	.136	.335	.348	.535	.597	.735	.940	.935	1.697
.140	.141	.340	.354	.540	.604	.740	.950	.940	1.738
.145	.146	.345	.360	.545	.611	.745	.962	.945	1.783
.150	.151	.350	.365	.550	.618	.750	.973	.950	1.832
.155	.156	.355	.371	.555	.626	.755	.984	.955	1.886
.160	.161	.360	.377	.560	.633	.760	.996	.960	1.946
.165	.167	.365	.383	.565	.640	.765	1.008	.965	2.014
.170	.172	.370	.388	.570	.648	.770	1.020	.970	2.092
.175	.177	.375	.394	.575	.655	.775	1.033	.975	2.185
.180	.182	.380	.400	.580	.662	.780	1.045	.980	2.298
.185	.187	.385	.406	.585	.670	.785	1.058	.985	2.443
.190	.192	.390	.412	.590	.678	.790	1.071	.990	2.647
.195	.198	.395	.418	.595	.685	.795	1.085	.995	2.994

* Table VII was constructed by F. P. Kilpatrick and D. A. Buchanan from formula (15.2).

TABLE VIII. *The 5 (Roman Type) and 1 (Boldface Type) Per Cent Points for the Distribution of* F*

n_2	n_1 degrees of freedom (for greater mean square)																							
	1	2	3	4	5	6	7	8	9	10	11	12	14	16	20	24	30	40	50	75	100	200	500	∞
1	161	200	216	225	230	234	237	239	241	242	243	244	245	246	248	249	250	251	252	253	253	254	254	254
	4,052	**4,999**	**5,403**	**5,625**	**5,764**	**5,859**	**5,928**	**5,981**	**6,022**	**6,056**	**6,082**	**6,106**	**6,142**	**6,169**	**6,208**	**6,234**	**6,258**	**6,286**	**6,302**	**6,323**	**6,334**	**6,352**	**6,361**	**6,366**
2	18.51	19.00	19.16	19.25	19.30	19.33	19.36	19.37	19.38	19.39	19.40	19.41	19.42	19.43	19.44	19.45	19.46	19.47	19.47	19.48	19.49	19.49	19.50	19.50
	98.49	**99.00**	**99.17**	**99.25**	**99.30**	**99.33**	**99.34**	**99.36**	**99.38**	**99.40**	**99.41**	**99.42**	**99.43**	**99.44**	**99.45**	**99.46**	**99.47**	**99.48**	**99.48**	**99.49**	**99.49**	**99.49**	**99.50**	**99.50**
3	10.13	9.55	9.28	9.12	9.01	8.94	8.88	8.84	8.81	8.78	8.76	8.74	8.71	8.69	8.66	8.64	8.62	8.60	8.58	8.57	8.56	8.54	8.54	8.53
	34.12	**30.82**	**29.46**	**28.71**	**28.24**	**27.91**	**27.67**	**27.49**	**27.34**	**27.23**	**27.13**	**27.05**	**26.92**	**26.83**	**26.69**	**26.60**	**26.50**	**26.41**	**26.35**	**26.27**	**26.23**	**26.18**	**26.14**	**26.12**
4	7.71	6.94	6.59	6.39	6.26	6.16	6.09	6.04	6.00	5.96	5.93	5.91	5.87	5.84	5.80	5.77	5.74	5.71	5.70	5.68	5.66	5.65	5.64	5.63
	21.20	**18.00**	**16.69**	**15.98**	**15.52**	**15.21**	**14.98**	**14.80**	**14.66**	**14.54**	**14.45**	**14.37**	**14.24**	**14.15**	**14.02**	**13.93**	**13.83**	**13.74**	**13.69**	**13.61**	**13.57**	**13.52**	**13.48**	**13.46**
5	6.61	5.79	5.41	5.19	5.05	4.95	4.88	4.82	4.78	4.74	4.70	4.68	4.64	4.60	4.56	4.53	4.50	4.46	4.44	4.42	4.40	4.38	4.37	4.36
	16.26	**13.27**	**12.06**	**11.39**	**10.97**	**10.67**	**10.45**	**10.27**	**10.15**	**10.05**	**9.96**	**9.89**	**9.77**	**9.68**	**9.55**	**9.47**	**9.38**	**9.29**	**9.24**	**9.17**	**9.13**	**9.07**	**9.04**	**9.02**
6	5.99	5.14	4.76	4.53	4.39	4.28	4.21	4.15	4.10	4.06	4.03	4.00	3.96	3.92	3.87	3.84	3.81	3.77	3.75	3.72	3.71	3.69	3.68	3.67
	13.74	**10.92**	**9.78**	**9.15**	**8.75**	**8.47**	**8.26**	**8.10**	**7.98**	**7.87**	**7.79**	**7.72**	**7.60**	**7.52**	**7.39**	**7.31**	**7.23**	**7.14**	**7.09**	**7.02**	**6.99**	**6.94**	**6.90**	**6.88**
7	5.59	4.74	4.35	4.12	3.97	3.87	3.79	3.73	3.68	3.63	3.60	3.57	3.52	3.49	3.44	3.41	3.38	3.34	3.32	3.29	3.28	3.25	3.24	3.23
	12.25	**9.55**	**8.45**	**7.85**	**7.46**	**7.19**	**7.00**	**6.84**	**6.71**	**6.62**	**6.54**	**6.47**	**6.35**	**6.27**	**6.15**	**6.07**	**5.98**	**5.90**	**5.85**	**5.78**	**5.75**	**5.70**	**5.67**	**5.65**
8	5.32	4.46	4.07	3.84	3.69	3.58	3.50	3.44	3.39	3.34	3.31	3.28	3.23	3.20	3.15	3.12	3.08	3.05	3.03	3.00	2.98	2.96	2.94	2.93
	11.26	**8.65**	**7.59**	**7.01**	**6.63**	**6.37**	**6.19**	**6.03**	**5.91**	**5.82**	**5.74**	**5.67**	**5.56**	**5.48**	**5.36**	**5.28**	**5.20**	**5.11**	**5.06**	**5.00**	**4.96**	**4.91**	**4.88**	**4.86**
9	5.12	4.26	3.86	3.63	3.48	3.37	3.29	3.23	3.18	3.13	3.10	3.07	3.02	2.98	2.93	2.90	2.86	2.82	2.80	2.77	2.76	2.73	2.72	2.71
	10.56	**8.02**	**6.99**	**6.42**	**6.06**	**5.80**	**5.62**	**5.47**	**5.35**	**5.26**	**5.18**	**5.11**	**5.00**	**4.92**	**4.80**	**4.73**	**4.64**	**4.56**	**4.51**	**4.45**	**4.41**	**4.36**	**4.33**	**4.31**
10	4.96	4.10	3.71	3.48	3.33	3.22	3.14	3.07	3.02	2.97	2.94	2.91	2.86	2.82	2.77	2.74	2.70	2.67	2.64	2.61	2.59	2.56	2.55	2.54
	10.04	**7.56**	**6.55**	**5.99**	**5.64**	**5.39**	**5.21**	**5.06**	**4.95**	**4.85**	**4.78**	**4.71**	**4.60**	**4.52**	**4.41**	**4.33**	**4.25**	**4.17**	**4.12**	**4.05**	**4.01**	**3.96**	**3.93**	**3.91**
11	4.84	3.98	3.59	3.36	3.20	3.09	3.01	2.95	2.90	2.86	2.82	2.79	2.74	2.70	2.65	2.61	2.57	2.53	2.50	2.47	2.45	2.42	2.41	2.40
	9.65	**7.20**	**6.22**	**5.67**	**5.32**	**5.07**	**4.88**	**4.74**	**4.63**	**4.54**	**4.46**	**4.40**	**4.29**	**4.21**	**4.10**	**4.02**	**3.94**	**3.86**	**3.80**	**3.74**	**3.70**	**3.66**	**3.62**	**3.60**
12	4.75	3.88	3.49	3.26	3.11	3.00	2.92	2.85	2.80	2.76	2.72	2.69	2.64	2.60	2.54	2.50	2.46	2.42	2.40	2.36	2.35	2.32	2.31	2.30
	9.33	**6.93**	**5.95**	**5.41**	**5.06**	**4.82**	**4.65**	**4.50**	**4.39**	**4.30**	**4.22**	**4.16**	**4.05**	**3.98**	**3.86**	**3.78**	**3.70**	**3.61**	**3.56**	**3.49**	**3.46**	**3.41**	**3.38**	**3.36**
13	4.67	3.80	3.41	3.18	3.02	2.92	2.84	2.77	2.72	2.67	2.63	2.60	2.55	2.51	2.46	2.42	2.38	2.34	2.32	2.28	2.26	2.24	2.22	2.21
	9.07	**6.70**	**5.74**	**5.20**	**4.86**	**4.62**	**4.44**	**4.30**	**4.19**	**4.10**	**4.02**	**3.96**	**3.85**	**3.78**	**3.67**	**3.59**	**3.51**	**3.42**	**3.37**	**3.30**	**3.27**	**3.21**	**3.18**	**3.16**

* Table VIII is reproduced from Snedecor: *Statistical Methods*, Iowa State College Press, Ames, Iowa, by permission of the author and publisher.

TABLE VIII. *The 5 (Roman Type) and 1 (Boldface Type) Per Cent Points for the Distribution of F*—Continued*

n_2	n_1 degrees of freedom (for greater mean square)																							
	1	2	3	4	5	6	7	8	9	10	11	12	14	16	20	24	30	40	50	75	100	200	500	∞
14	4.60	3.74	3.34	3.11	2.96	2.85	2.77	2.70	2.65	2.60	2.56	2.53	2.48	2.44	2.39	2.35	2.31	2.27	2.24	2.21	2.19	2.16	2.14	2.13
	8.86	**6.51**	**5.56**	**5.03**	**4.69**	**4.46**	**4.28**	**4.14**	**4.03**	**3.94**	**3.86**	**3.80**	**3.70**	**3.62**	**3.51**	**3.43**	**3.34**	**3.26**	**3.21**	**3.14**	**3.11**	**3.06**	**3.02**	**3.00**
15	4.54	3.68	3.29	3.06	2.90	2.79	2.70	2.64	2.59	2.55	2.51	2.48	2.43	2.39	2.33	2.29	2.25	2.21	2.18	2.15	2.12	2.10	2.08	2.07
	8.68	**6.36**	**5.42**	**4.89**	**4.56**	**4.32**	**4.14**	**4.00**	**3.89**	**3.80**	**3.73**	**3.67**	**3.56**	**3.48**	**3.36**	**3.29**	**3.20**	**3.12**	**3.07**	**3.00**	**2.97**	**2.92**	**2.89**	**2.87**
16	4.49	3.63	3.24	3.01	2.85	2.74	2.66	2.59	2.54	2.49	2.45	2.42	2.37	2.33	2.28	2.24	2.20	2.16	2.13	2.09	2.07	2.04	2.02	2.01
	8.53	**6.23**	**5.29**	**4.77**	**4.44**	**4.20**	**4.03**	**3.89**	**3.78**	**3.69**	**3.61**	**3.55**	**3.45**	**3.37**	**3.25**	**3.18**	**3.10**	**3.01**	**2.96**	**2.89**	**2.86**	**2.80**	**2.77**	**2.75**
17	4.45	3.59	3.20	2.96	2.81	2.70	2.62	2.55	2.50	2.45	2.41	2.38	2.33	2.29	2.23	2.19	2.15	2.11	2.08	2.04	2.02	1.99	1.97	1.96
	8.40	**6.11**	**5.18**	**4.67**	**4.34**	**4.10**	**3.93**	**3.79**	**3.68**	**3.59**	**3.52**	**3.45**	**3.35**	**3.27**	**3.16**	**3.08**	**3.00**	**2.92**	**2.86**	**2.79**	**2.76**	**2.70**	**2.67**	**2.65**
18	4.41	3.55	3.16	2.93	2.77	2.66	2.58	2.51	2.46	2.41	2.37	2.34	2.29	2.25	2.19	2.15	2.11	2.07	2.04	2.00	1.98	1.95	1.93	1.92
	8.28	**6.01**	**5.09**	**4.58**	**4.25**	**4.01**	**3.85**	**3.71**	**3.60**	**3.51**	**3.44**	**3.37**	**3.27**	**3.19**	**3.07**	**3.00**	**2.91**	**2.83**	**2.78**	**2.71**	**2.68**	**2.62**	**2.59**	**2.57**
19	4.38	3.52	3.13	2.90	2.74	2.63	2.55	2.48	2.43	2.38	2.34	2.31	2.26	2.21	2.15	2.11	2.07	2.02	2.00	1.96	1.94	1.91	1.90	1.88
	8.18	**5.93**	**5.01**	**4.50**	**4.17**	**3.94**	**3.77**	**3.63**	**3.52**	**3.43**	**3.36**	**3.30**	**3.19**	**3.12**	**3.00**	**2.92**	**2.84**	**2.76**	**2.70**	**2.63**	**2.60**	**2.54**	**2.51**	**2.49**
20	4.35	3.49	3.10	2.87	2.71	2.60	2.52	2.45	2.40	2.35	2.31	2.28	2.23	2.18	2.12	2.08	2.04	1.99	1.96	1.92	1.90	1.87	1.85	1.84
	8.10	**5.85**	**4.94**	**4.43**	**4.10**	**3.87**	**3.71**	**3.56**	**3.45**	**3.37**	**3.30**	**3.23**	**3.13**	**3.05**	**2.94**	**2.86**	**2.77**	**2.69**	**2.63**	**2.56**	**2.53**	**2.47**	**2.44**	**2.42**
21	4.32	3.47	3.07	2.84	2.68	2.57	2.49	2.42	2.37	2.32	2.28	2.25	2.20	2.15	2.09	2.05	2.00	1.96	1.93	1.89	1.87	1.84	1.82	1.81
	8.02	**5.78**	**4.87**	**4.37**	**4.04**	**3.81**	**3.65**	**3.51**	**3.40**	**3.31**	**3.24**	**3.17**	**3.07**	**2.99**	**2.88**	**2.80**	**2.72**	**2.63**	**2.58**	**2.51**	**2.47**	**2.42**	**2.38**	**2.36**
22	4.30	3.44	3.05	2.82	2.66	2.55	2.47	2.40	2.35	2.30	2.26	2.23	2.18	2.13	2.07	2.03	1.98	1.93	1.91	1.87	1.84	1.81	1.80	1.78
	7.94	**5.72**	**4.82**	**4.31**	**3.99**	**3.76**	**3.59**	**3.45**	**3.35**	**3.26**	**3.18**	**3.12**	**3.02**	**2.94**	**2.83**	**2.75**	**2.67**	**2.58**	**2.53**	**2.46**	**2.42**	**2.37**	**2.33**	**2.31**
23	4.28	3.42	3.03	2.80	2.64	2.53	2.45	2.38	2.32	2.28	2.24	2.20	2.14	2.10	2.04	2.00	1.96	1.91	1.88	1.84	1.82	1.79	1.77	1.76
	7.88	**5.66**	**4.76**	**4.26**	**3.94**	**3.71**	**3.54**	**3.41**	**3.30**	**3.21**	**3.14**	**3.07**	**2.97**	**2.89**	**2.78**	**2.70**	**2.62**	**2.53**	**2.48**	**2.41**	**2.37**	**2.32**	**2.28**	**2.26**
24	4.26	3.40	3.01	2.78	2.62	2.51	2.43	2.36	2.30	2.26	2.22	2.18	2.13	2.09	2.02	1.98	1.94	1.89	1.86	1.82	1.80	1.76	1.74	1.73
	7.82	**5.61**	**4.72**	**4.22**	**3.90**	**3.67**	**3.50**	**3.36**	**3.25**	**3.17**	**3.09**	**3.03**	**2.93**	**2.85**	**2.74**	**2.66**	**2.58**	**2.49**	**2.44**	**2.36**	**2.33**	**2.27**	**2.23**	**2.21**
25	4.24	3.38	2.99	2.76	2.60	2.49	2.41	2.34	2.28	2.24	2.20	2.16	2.11	2.06	2.00	1.96	1.92	1.87	1.84	1.80	1.77	1.74	1.72	1.71
	7.77	**5.57**	**4.68**	**4.18**	**3.86**	**3.63**	**3.46**	**3.32**	**3.21**	**3.13**	**3.05**	**2.99**	**2.89**	**2.81**	**2.70**	**2.62**	**2.54**	**2.45**	**2.40**	**2.32**	**2.29**	**2.23**	**2.19**	**2.17**
26	4.22	3.37	2.98	2.74	2.59	2.47	2.39	2.32	2.27	2.22	2.18	2.15	2.10	2.05	1.99	1.95	1.90	1.85	1.82	1.78	1.76	1.72	1.70	1.69
	7.72	**5.53**	**4.64**	**4.14**	**3.82**	**3.59**	**3.42**	**3.29**	**3.17**	**3.09**	**3.02**	**2.96**	**2.86**	**2.77**	**2.66**	**2.58**	**2.50**	**2.41**	**2.36**	**2.28**	**2.25**	**2.19**	**2.15**	**2.13**

* Table VIII is reproduced from Snedecor: *Statistical Methods*, Iowa State College Press, Ames, Iowa, by permission of the author and publisher.

TABLE VIII. *The 5 (Roman Type) and 1 (Boldface Type) Per Cent Points for the Distribution of F*—Continued*

n_2	n_1 degrees of freedom (for greater mean square)																							
	1	2	3	4	5	6	7	8	9	10	11	12	14	16	20	24	30	40	50	75	100	200	500	∞
27	4.21	3.35	2.96	2.73	2.57	2.46	2.37	2.30	2.25	2.20	2.16	2.13	2.08	2.03	1.97	1.93	1.88	1.84	1.80	1.76	1.74	1.71	1.68	1.67
	7.68	**5.49**	**4.60**	**4.11**	**3.79**	**3.56**	**3.39**	**3.26**	**3.14**	**3.06**	**2.98**	**2.93**	**2.83**	**2.74**	**2.63**	**2.55**	**2.47**	**2.38**	**2.33**	**2.25**	**2.21**	**2.16**	**2.12**	**2.10**
28	4.20	3.34	2.95	2.71	2.56	2.44	2.36	2.29	2.24	2.19	2.15	2.12	2.06	2.02	1.96	1.91	1.87	1.81	1.78	1.75	1.72	1.69	1.67	1.65
	7.64	**5.45**	**4.57**	**4.07**	**3.76**	**3.53**	**3.36**	**3.23**	**3.11**	**3.03**	**2.95**	**2.90**	**2.80**	**2.71**	**2.60**	**2.52**	**2.44**	**2.35**	**2.30**	**2.22**	**2.18**	**2.13**	**2.09**	**2.06**
29	4.18	3.33	2.93	2.70	2.54	2.43	2.35	2.28	2.22	2.18	2.14	2.10	2.05	2.00	1.94	1.90	1.85	1.80	1.77	1.73	1.71	1.68	1.65	1.64
	7.60	**5.42**	**4.54**	**4.04**	**3.73**	**3.50**	**3.33**	**3.20**	**3.08**	**3.00**	**2.92**	**2.87**	**2.77**	**2.68**	**2.57**	**2.49**	**2.41**	**2.32**	**2.27**	**2.19**	**2.15**	**2.10**	**2.06**	**2.03**
30	4.17	3.32	2.92	2.69	2.53	2.42	2.34	2.27	2.21	2.16	2.12	2.09	2.04	1.99	1.93	1.89	1.84	1.79	1.76	1.72	1.69	1.66	1.64	1.62
	7.56	**5.39**	**4.51**	**4.02**	**3.70**	**3.47**	**3.30**	**3.17**	**3.06**	**2.98**	**2.90**	**2.84**	**2.74**	**2.66**	**2.55**	**2.47**	**2.38**	**2.29**	**2.24**	**2.16**	**2.13**	**2.07**	**2.03**	**2.01**
32	4.15	3.30	2.90	2.67	2.51	2.40	2.32	2.25	2.19	2.14	2.10	2.07	2.02	1.97	1.91	1.86	1.82	1.76	1.74	1.69	1.67	1.64	1.61	1.59
	7.50	**5.34**	**4.46**	**3.97**	**3.66**	**3.42**	**3.25**	**3.12**	**3.01**	**2.94**	**2.86**	**2.80**	**2.70**	**2.62**	**2.51**	**2.42**	**2.34**	**2.25**	**2.20**	**2.12**	**2.08**	**2.02**	**1.98**	**1.96**
34	4.13	3.28	2.88	2.65	2.49	2.38	2.30	2.23	2.17	2.12	2.08	2.05	2.00	1.95	1.89	1.84	1.80	1.74	1.71	1.67	1.64	1.61	1.59	1.57
	7.44	**5.29**	**4.42**	**3.93**	**3.61**	**3.38**	**3.21**	**3.08**	**2.97**	**2.89**	**2.82**	**2.76**	**2.66**	**2.58**	**2.47**	**2.38**	**2.30**	**2.21**	**2.15**	**2.08**	**2.04**	**1.98**	**1.94**	**1.91**
36	4.11	3.26	2.86	2.63	2.48	2.36	2.28	2.21	2.15	2.10	2.06	2.03	1.98	1.93	1.87	1.82	1.78	1.72	1.69	1.65	1.62	1.59	1.56	1.55
	7.39	**5.25**	**4.38**	**3.89**	**3.58**	**3.35**	**3.18**	**3.04**	**2.94**	**2.86**	**2.78**	**2.72**	**2.62**	**2.54**	**2.43**	**2.35**	**2.26**	**2.17**	**2.12**	**2.04**	**2.00**	**1.94**	**1.90**	**1.87**
38	4.10	3.25	2.85	2.62	2.46	2.35	2.26	2.19	2.14	2.09	2.05	2.02	1.96	1.92	1.85	1.80	1.76	1.71	1.67	1.63	1.60	1.57	1.54	1.53
	7.35	**5.21**	**4.34**	**3.86**	**3.54**	**3.32**	**3.15**	**3.02**	**2.91**	**2.82**	**2.75**	**2.69**	**2.59**	**2.51**	**2.40**	**2.32**	**2.22**	**2.14**	**2.08**	**2.00**	**1.97**	**1.90**	**1.86**	**1.84**
40	4.08	3.23	2.84	2.61	2.45	2.34	2.25	2.18	2.12	2.07	2.04	2.00	1.95	1.90	1.84	1.79	1.74	1.69	1.66	1.61	1.59	1.55	1.53	1.51
	7.31	**5.18**	**4.31**	**3.83**	**3.51**	**3.29**	**3.12**	**2.99**	**2.88**	**2.80**	**2.73**	**2.66**	**2.56**	**2.49**	**2.37**	**2.29**	**2.20**	**2.11**	**2.05**	**1.97**	**1.94**	**1.88**	**1.84**	**1.81**
42	4.07	3.22	2.83	2.59	2.44	2.32	2.24	2.17	2.11	2.06	2.02	1.99	1.94	1.89	1.82	1.78	1.73	1.68	1.64	1.60	1.57	1.54	1.51	1.49
	7.27	**5.15**	**4.29**	**3.80**	**3.49**	**3.26**	**3.10**	**2.96**	**2.86**	**2.77**	**2.70**	**2.64**	**2.54**	**2.46**	**2.35**	**2.26**	**2.17**	**2.08**	**2.02**	**1.94**	**1.91**	**1.85**	**1.80**	**1.78**
44	4.06	3.21	2.82	2.58	2.43	2.31	2.23	2.16	2.10	2.05	2.01	1.98	1.92	1.88	1.81	1.76	1.72	1.66	1.63	1.58	1.56	1.52	1.50	1.48
	7.24	**5.12**	**4.26**	**3.78**	**3.46**	**3.24**	**3.07**	**2.94**	**2.84**	**2.75**	**2.68**	**2.62**	**2.52**	**2.44**	**2.32**	**2.24**	**2.15**	**2.06**	**2.00**	**1.92**	**1.88**	**1.82**	**1.78**	**1.75**
46	4.05	3.20	2.81	2.57	2.42	2.30	2.22	2.14	2.09	2.04	2.00	1.97	1.91	1.87	1.80	1.75	1.71	1.65	1.62	1.57	1.54	1.51	1.48	1.46
	7.21	**5.10**	**4.24**	**3.76**	**3.44**	**3.22**	**3.05**	**2.92**	**2.82**	**2.73**	**2.66**	**2.60**	**2.50**	**2.42**	**2.30**	**2.22**	**2.13**	**2.04**	**1.98**	**1.90**	**1.86**	**1.80**	**1.76**	**1.72**
48	4.04	3.19	2.80	2.56	2.41	2.30	2.21	2.14	2.08	2.03	1.99	1.96	1.90	1.86	1.79	1.74	1.70	1.64	1.61	1.56	1.53	1.50	1.47	1.45
	7.19	**5.08**	**4.22**	**3.74**	**3.42**	**3.20**	**3.04**	**2.90**	**2.80**	**2.71**	**2.64**	**2.58**	**2.48**	**2.40**	**2.28**	**2.20**	**2.11**	**2.02**	**1.96**	**1.88**	**1.84**	**1.78**	**1.73**	**1.70**

*Table VIII is reproduced from Snedecor: *Statistical Methods*, Iowa State College Press, Ames, Iowa, by permission of the author and publisher.

TABLE VIII. *The 5 (Roman Type) and 1 (Boldface Type) Per Cent Points for the Distribution of* F*—*Concluded*

n_2	n_1 degrees of freedom (for greater mean square)																							
	1	2	3	4	5	6	7	8	9	10	11	12	14	16	20	24	30	40	50	75	100	200	500	∞
50	4.03	3.18	2.79	2.56	2.40	2.29	2.20	2.13	2.07	2.02	1.98	1.95	1.90	1.85	1.78	1.74	1.69	1.63	1.60	1.55	1.52	1.48	1.46	1.44
	7.17	**5.06**	**4.20**	**3.72**	**3.41**	**3.18**	**3.02**	**2.88**	**2.78**	**2.70**	**2.62**	**2.56**	**2.46**	**2.39**	**2.26**	**2.18**	**2.10**	**2.00**	**1.94**	**1.86**	**1.82**	**1.76**	**1.71**	**1.68**
55	4.02	3.17	2.78	2.54	2.38	2.27	2.18	2.11	2.05	2.00	1.97	1.93	1.88	1.83	1.76	1.72	1.67	1.61	1.58	1.52	1.50	1.46	1.43	1.41
	7.12	**5.01**	**4.16**	**3.68**	**3.37**	**3.15**	**2.98**	**2.85**	**2.75**	**2.66**	**2.59**	**2.53**	**2.43**	**2.35**	**2.23**	**2.15**	**2.06**	**1.96**	**1.90**	**1.82**	**1.78**	**1.71**	**1.66**	**1.64**
60	4.00	3.15	2.76	2.52	2.37	2.25	2.17	2.10	2.04	1.99	1.95	1.92	1.86	1.81	1.75	1.70	1.65	1.59	1.56	1.50	1.48	1.44	1.41	1.39
	7.08	**4.98**	**4.13**	**3.65**	**3.34**	**3.12**	**2.95**	**2.82**	**2.72**	**2.63**	**2.56**	**2.50**	**2.40**	**2.32**	**2.20**	**2.12**	**2.03**	**1.93**	**1.87**	**1.79**	**1.74**	**1.68**	**1.63**	**1.60**
65	3.99	3.14	2.75	2.51	2.36	2.24	2.15	2.08	2.02	1.98	1.94	1.90	1.85	1.80	1.73	1.68	1.63	1.57	1.54	1.49	1.46	1.42	1.39	1.37
	7.04	**4.95**	**4.10**	**3.62**	**3.31**	**3.09**	**2.93**	**2.79**	**2.70**	**2.61**	**2.54**	**2.47**	**2.37**	**2.30**	**2.18**	**2.09**	**2.00**	**1.90**	**1.84**	**1.76**	**1.71**	**1.64**	**1.60**	**1.56**
70	3.98	3.13	2.74	2.50	2.35	2.23	2.14	2.07	2.01	1.97	1.93	1.89	1.84	1.79	1.72	1.67	1.62	1.56	1.53	1.47	1.45	1.40	1.37	1.35
	7.01	**4.92**	**4.08**	**3.60**	**3.29**	**3.07**	**2.91**	**2.77**	**2.67**	**2.59**	**2.51**	**2.45**	**2.35**	**2.28**	**2.15**	**2.07**	**1.98**	**1.88**	**1.82**	**1.74**	**1.69**	**1.62**	**1.56**	**1.53**
80	3.96	3.11	2.72	2.48	2.33	2.21	2.12	2.05	1.99	1.95	1.91	1.88	1.82	1.77	1.70	1.65	1.60	1.54	1.51	1.45	1.42	1.38	1.35	1.32
	6.96	**4.88**	**4.04**	**3.56**	**3.25**	**3.04**	**2.87**	**2.74**	**2.64**	**2.55**	**2.48**	**2.41**	**2.32**	**2.24**	**2.11**	**2.03**	**1.94**	**1.84**	**1.78**	**1.70**	**1.65**	**1.57**	**1.52**	**1.49**
100	3.94	3.09	2.70	2.46	2.30	2.19	2.10	2.03	1.97	1.92	1.88	1.85	1.79	1.75	1.68	1.63	1.57	1.51	1.48	1.42	1.39	1.34	1.30	1.28
	6.90	**4.82**	**3.98**	**3.51**	**3.20**	**2.99**	**2.82**	**2.69**	**2.59**	**2.51**	**2.43**	**2.36**	**2.26**	**2.19**	**2.06**	**1.98**	**1.89**	**1.79**	**1.73**	**1.64**	**1.59**	**1.51**	**1.46**	**1.43**
125	3.92	3.07	2.68	2.44	2.29	2.17	2.08	2.01	1.95	1.90	1.86	1.83	1.77	1.72	1.65	1.60	1.55	1.49	1.45	1.39	1.36	1.31	1.27	1.25
	6.84	**4.78**	**3.94**	**3.47**	**3.17**	**2.95**	**2.79**	**2.65**	**2.56**	**2.47**	**2.40**	**2.33**	**2.23**	**2.15**	**2.03**	**1.94**	**1.85**	**1.75**	**1.68**	**1.59**	**1.54**	**1.46**	**1.40**	**1.37**
150	3.91	3.06	2.67	2.43	2.27	2.16	2.07	2.00	1.94	1.89	1.85	1.82	1.76	1.71	1.64	1.59	1.54	1.47	1.44	1.37	1.34	1.29	1.25	1.22
	6.81	**4.75**	**3.91**	**3.44**	**3.14**	**2.92**	**2.76**	**2.62**	**2.53**	**2.44**	**2.37**	**2.30**	**2.20**	**2.12**	**2.00**	**1.91**	**1.83**	**1.72**	**1.66**	**1.56**	**1.51**	**1.43**	**1.37**	**1.33**
200	3.89	3.04	2.65	2.41	2.26	2.14	2.05	1.98	1.92	1.87	1.83	1.80	1.74	1.69	1.62	1.57	1.52	1.45	1.42	1.35	1.32	1.26	1.22	1.19
	6.76	**4.71**	**3.88**	**3.41**	**3.11**	**2.90**	**2.73**	**2.60**	**2.50**	**2.41**	**2.34**	**2.28**	**2.17**	**2.09**	**1.97**	**1.88**	**1.79**	**1.69**	**1.62**	**1.53**	**1.48**	**1.39**	**1.33**	**1.28**
400	3.86	3.02	2.62	2.39	2.23	2.12	2.03	1.96	1.90	1.85	1.81	1.78	1.72	1.67	1.60	1.54	1.49	1.42	1.38	1.32	1.28	1.22	1.16	1.13
	6.70	**4.66**	**3.83**	**3.36**	**3.06**	**2.85**	**2.69**	**2.55**	**2.46**	**2.37**	**2.29**	**2.23**	**2.12**	**2.04**	**1.92**	**1.84**	**1.74**	**1.64**	**1.57**	**1.47**	**1.42**	**1.32**	**1.24**	**1.19**
1000	3.85	3.00	2.61	2.38	2.22	2.10	2.02	1.95	1.89	1.84	1.80	1.76	1.70	1.65	1.58	1.53	1.47	1.41	1.36	1.30	1.26	1.19	1.13	1.08
	6.66	**4.62**	**3.80**	**3.34**	**3.04**	**2.82**	**2.66**	**2.53**	**2.43**	**2.34**	**2.26**	**2.20**	**2.09**	**2.01**	**1.89**	**1.81**	**1.71**	**1.61**	**1.54**	**1.44**	**1.38**	**1.28**	**1.19**	**1.11**
∞	3.84	2.99	2.60	2.37	2.21	2.09	2.01	1.94	1.88	1.83	1.79	1.75	1.69	1.64	1.57	1.52	1.46	1.40	1.35	1.28	1.24	1.17	1.11	1.00
	6.64	**4.60**	**3.78**	**3.32**	**3.02**	**2.80**	**2.64**	**2.51**	**2.41**	**2.32**	**2.24**	**2.18**	**2.07**	**1.99**	**1.87**	**1.79**	**1.69**	**1.59**	**1.52**	**1.41**	**1.36**	**1.25**	**1.15**	**1.00**

* Table VIII is reproduced from Snedecor: *Statistical Methods*, Iowa State College Press, Ames, Iowa, by permission of the author and publisher.

TABLE IX. *Table of Four-Place Logarithms**

N	0	1	2	3	4	5	6	7	8	9	1	2	3	4	5	6	7	8	9
1.0	.0000	.0043	.0086	.0128	.0170	.0212	.0253	.0294	.0334	.0374	4	8	12	17	21	25	29	33	37
1.1	.0414	.0453	.0492	.0531	.0569	.0607	.0645	.0682	.0719	.0755	4	8	11	15	19	23	26	30	34
1.2	.0792	.0828	.0864	.0899	.0934	.0969	.1004	.1038	.1072	.1106	3	7	10	14	17	21	24	28	31
1.3	.1139	.1173	.1206	.1239	.1271	.1303	.1335	.1367	.1399	.1430	3	6	10	13	16	19	23	26	29
1.4	.1461	.1492	.1523	.1553	.1584	.1614	.1644	.1673	.1703	.1732	3	6	9	12	15	18	21	24	27
1.5	.1761	.1790	.1818	.1847	.1875	.1903	.1931	.1959	.1987	.2014	3	6	8	11	14	17	20	22	25
1.6	.2041	.2068	.2095	.2122	.2148	.2175	.2201	.2227	.2253	.2279	3	5	8	11	13	16	18	21	24
1.7	.2304	.2330	.2355	.2380	.2405	.2430	.2455	.2480	.2504	.2529	2	5	7	10	12	15	17	20	22
1.8	.2553	.2577	.2601	.2625	.2648	.2672	.2695	.2718	.2742	.2765	2	5	7	9	12	14	16	19	21
1.9	.2788	.2810	.2833	.2856	.2878	.2900	.2923	.2945	.2967	.2989	2	4	7	9	11	13	16	18	20
2.0	.3010	.3032	.3054	.3075	.3096	.3118	.3139	.3160	.3181	.3201	2	4	6	8	11	13	15	17	19
2.1	.3222	.3243	.3263	.3284	.3304	.3324	.3345	.3365	.3385	.3404	2	4	6	8	10	12	14	16	18
2.2	.3424	.3444	.3464	.3483	.3502	.3522	.3541	.3560	.3579	.3598	2	4	6	8	10	12	14	15	17
2.3	.3617	.3636	.3655	.3674	.3692	.3711	.3729	.3747	.3766	.3784	2	4	6	7	9	11	13	15	17
2.4	.3802	.3820	.3838	.3856	.3874	.3892	.3909	.3927	.3945	.3962	2	4	5	7	9	11	12	14	16
2.5	.3979	.3997	.4014	.4031	.4048	.4065	.4082	.4099	.4116	.4133	2	3	5	7	9	10	12	14	15
2.6	.4150	.4166	.4183	.4200	.4216	.4232	.4249	.4265	.4281	.4298	2	3	5	7	8	10	11	13	15
2.7	.4314	.4330	.4346	.4362	.4378	.4393	.4409	.4425	.4440	.4456	2	3	5	6	8	9	11	13	14
2.8	.4472	.4487	.4502	.4518	.4533	.4548	.4564	.4579	.4594	.4609	2	3	5	6	8	9	11	12	14
2.9	.4624	.4639	.4654	.4669	.4683	.4698	.4713	.4728	.4742	.4757	1	3	4	6	7	9	10	12	13
3.0	.4771	.4786	.4800	.4814	.4829	.4843	.4857	.4871	.4886	.4900	1	3	4	6	7	9	10	11	13
3.1	.4914	.4928	.4942	.4955	.4969	.4983	.4997	.5011	.5024	.5038	1	3	4	6	7	8	10	11	12
3.2	.5051	.5065	.5079	.5092	.5105	.5119	.5132	.5145	.5159	.5172	1	3	4	5	7	8	9	11	12
3.3	.5185	.5198	.5211	.5224	.5237	.5250	.5263	.5276	.5289	.5302	1	3	4	5	6	8	9	10	12
3.4	.5315	.5328	.5340	.5353	.5366	.5378	.5391	.5403	.5416	.5428	1	3	4	5	6	8	9	10	11
3.5	.5441	.5453	.5465	.5478	.5490	.5502	.5514	.5527	.5539	.5551	1	2	4	5	6	7	9	10	11
3.6	.5563	.5575	.5587	.5599	.5611	.5623	.5635	.5647	.5658	.5670	1	2	4	5	6	7	8	10	11
3.7	.5682	.5694	.5705	.5717	.5729	.5740	.5752	.5763	.5775	.5786	1	2	3	5	6	7	8	9	10
3.8	.5798	.5809	.5821	.5832	.5843	.5855	.5866	.5877	.5888	.5899	1	2	3	5	6	7	8	9	10
3.9	.5911	.5922	.5933	.5944	.5955	.5966	.5977	.5988	.5999	.6010	1	2	3	4	5	7	8	9	10
4.0	.6021	.6031	.6042	.6053	.6064	.6075	.6085	.6096	.6107	.6117	1	2	3	4	5	6	8	9	10
4.1	.6128	.6138	.6149	.6160	.6170	.6180	.6191	.6201	.6212	.6222	1	2	3	4	5	6	7	8	9
4.2	.6232	.6243	.6253	.6263	.6274	.6284	.6294	.6304	.6314	.6325	1	2	3	4	5	6	7	8	9
4.3	.6335	.6345	.6355	.6365	.6375	.6385	.6395	.6405	.6415	.6425	1	2	3	4	5	6	7	8	9
4.4	.6435	.6444	.6454	.6464	.6474	.6484	.6493	.6503	.6513	.6522	1	2	3	4	5	6	7	8	9
4.5	.6532	.6542	.6551	.6561	.6571	.6580	.6590	.6599	.6609	.6618	1	2	3	4	5	6	7	8	9
4.6	.6628	.6637	.6646	.6656	.6665	.6675	.6684	.6693	.6702	.6712	1	2	3	4	5	6	7	7	8
4.7	.6721	.6730	.6739	.6749	.6758	.6767	.6776	.6785	.6794	.6803	1	2	3	4	5	5	6	7	8
4.8	.6812	.6821	.6830	.6839	.6848	.6857	.6866	.6875	.6884	.6893	1	2	3	4	4	5	6	7	8
4.9	.6902	.6911	.6920	.6928	.6937	.6946	.6955	.6964	.6972	.6981	1	2	3	4	4	5	6	7	8
5.0	.6990	.6998	.7007	.7016	.7024	.7033	.7042	.7050	.7059	.7067	1	2	3	3	4	5	6	7	8
5.1	.7076	.7084	.7093	.7101	.7110	.7118	.7126	.7135	.7143	.7152	1	2	3	3	4	5	6	7	8
5.2	.7160	.7168	.7177	.7185	.7193	.7202	.7210	.7218	.7226	.7235	1	2	2	3	4	5	6	7	7
5.3	.7243	.7251	.7259	.7267	.7275	.7284	.7292	.7300	.7308	.7316	1	2	2	3	4	5	6	6	7
5.4	.7324	.7332	.7340	.7348	.7356	.7364	.7372	.7380	.7388	.7396	1	2	2	3	4	5	6	6	7

* Table IX is reprinted from D. E. Smith, W. D. Reeve, and E. L. Morss: *Elementary Mathematical Tables*, Ginn and Company, by permission of the authors and publishers.

To obtain the mantissa for a four-digit number, find in the body of the table the mantissa for the first three digits and then, neglecting the decimal point temporarily, add the number in the proportional-parts table at the right which is on the same line as the mantissa already obtained and in the column corresponding to the fourth digit.

TABLE IX. *Table of Four-Place Logarithms*—Concluded*

N	0	1	2	3	4	5	6	7	8	9	1	2	3	4	5	6	7	8	9
5.5	.7404	.7412	.7419	.7427	.7435	.7443	.7451	.7459	.7466	.7474	1	2	2	3	4	5	5	6	7
5.6	.7482	.7490	.7497	.7505	.7513	.7520	.7528	.7536	.7543	.7551	1	2	2	3	4	5	5	6	7
5.7	.7559	.7566	.7574	.7582	.7589	.7597	.7604	.7612	.7619	.7627	1	2	2	3	4	5	5	6	7
5.8	.7634	.7642	.7649	.7657	.7664	.7672	.7679	.7686	.7694	.7701	1	1	2	3	4	4	5	6	7
5.9	.7709	.7716	.7723	.7731	.7738	.7745	.7752	.7760	.7767	.7774	1	1	2	3	4	4	5	6	7
6.0	.7782	.7789	.7796	.7803	.7810	.7818	.7825	.7832	.7839	.7846	1	1	2	3	4	4	5	6	6
6.1	.7853	.7860	.7868	.7875	.7882	.7889	.7896	.7903	.7910	.7917	1	1	2	3	4	4	5	6	6
6.2	.7924	.7931	.7938	.7945	.7952	.7959	.7966	.7973	.7980	.7987	1	1	2	3	3	4	5	6	6
6.3	.7993	.8000	.8007	.8014	.8021	.8028	.8035	.8041	.8048	.8055	1	1	2	3	3	4	5	5	6
6.4	.8062	.8069	.8075	.8082	.8089	.8096	.8102	.8109	.8116	.8122	1	1	2	3	3	4	5	5	6
6.5	.8129	.8136	.8142	.8149	.8156	.8162	.8169	.8176	.8182	.8189	1	1	2	3	3	4	5	5	6
6.6	.8195	.8202	.8209	.8215	.8222	.8228	.8235	.8241	.8248	.8254	1	1	2	3	3	4	5	5	6
6.7	.8261	.8267	.8274	.8280	.8287	.8293	.8299	.8306	.8312	.8319	1	1	2	3	3	4	5	5	6
6.8	.8325	.8331	.8338	.8344	.8351	.8357	.8363	.8370	.8376	.8382	1	1	2	3	3	4	4	5	6
6.9	.8388	.8395	.8401	.8407	.8414	.8420	.8426	.8432	.8439	.8445	1	1	2	2	3	4	4	5	6
7.0	.8451	.8457	.8463	.8470	.8476	.8482	.8488	.8494	.8500	.8506	1	1	2	2	3	4	4	5	6
7.1	.8513	.8519	.8525	.8531	.8537	.8543	.8549	.8555	.8561	.8567	1	1	2	2	3	4	4	5	5
7.2	.8573	.8579	.8585	.8591	.8597	.8603	.8609	.8615	.8621	.8627	1	1	2	2	3	4	4	5	5
7.3	.8633	.8639	.8645	.8651	.8657	.8663	.8669	.8675	.8681	.8686	1	1	2	2	3	4	4	5	5
7.4	.8692	.8698	.8704	.8710	.8716	.8722	.8727	.8733	.8739	.8745	1	1	2	2	3	4	4	5	5
7.5	.8751	.8756	.8762	.8768	.8774	.8779	.8785	.8791	.8797	.8802	1	1	2	2	3	3	4	5	5
7.6	.8808	.8814	.8820	.8825	.8831	.8837	.8842	.8848	.8854	.8859	1	1	2	2	3	3	4	5	5
7.7	.8865	.8871	.8876	.8882	.8887	.8893	.8899	.8904	.8910	.8915	1	1	2	2	3	3	4	4	5
7.8	.8921	.8927	.8932	.8938	.8943	.8949	.8954	.8960	.8965	.8971	1	1	2	2	3	3	4	4	5
7.9	.8976	.8982	.8987	.8993	.8998	.9004	.9009	.9015	.9020	.9025	1	1	2	2	3	3	4	4	5
8.0	.9031	.9036	.9042	.9047	.9053	.9058	.9063	.9069	.9074	.9079	1	1	2	2	3	3	4	4	5
8.1	.9085	.9090	.9096	.9101	.9106	.9112	.9117	.9122	.9128	.9133	1	1	2	2	3	3	4	4	5
8.2	.9138	.9143	.9149	.9154	.9159	.9165	.9170	.9175	.9180	.9186	1	1	2	2	3	3	4	4	5
8.3	.9191	.9196	.9201	.9206	.9212	.9217	.9222	.9227	.9232	.9238	1	1	2	2	3	3	4	4	5
8.4	.9243	.9248	.9253	.9258	.9263	.9269	.9274	.9279	.9284	.9289	1	1	2	2	3	3	4	4	5
8.5	.9294	.9299	.9304	.9309	.9315	.9320	.9325	.9330	.9335	.9340	1	1	2	2	3	3	4	4	5
8.6	.9345	.9350	.9355	.9360	.9365	.9370	.9375	.9380	.9385	.9390	1	1	2	2	3	3	4	4	5
8.7	.9395	.9400	.9405	.9410	.9415	.9420	.9425	.9430	.9435	.9440	0	1	1	2	2	3	3	4	4
8.8	.9445	.9450	.9455	.9460	.9465	.9469	.9474	.9479	.9484	.9489	0	1	1	2	2	3	3	4	4
8.9	.9494	.9499	.9504	.9509	.9513	.9518	.9523	.9528	.9533	.9538	0	1	1	2	2	3	3	4	4
9.0	.9542	.9547	.9552	.9557	.9562	.9566	.9571	.9576	.9581	.9586	0	1	1	2	2	3	3	4	4
9.1	.9590	.9595	.9600	.9605	.9609	.9614	.9619	.9624	.9628	.9633	0	1	1	2	2	3	3	4	4
9.2	.9638	.9643	.9647	.9652	.9657	.9661	.9666	.9671	.9675	.9680	0	1	1	2	2	3	3	4	4
9.3	.9685	.9689	.9694	.9699	.9703	.9708	.9713	.9717	.9722	.9727	0	1	1	2	2	3	3	4	4
9.4	.9731	.9736	.9741	.9745	.9750	.9754	.9759	.9763	.9768	.9773	0	1	1	2	2	3	3	4	4
9.5	.9777	.9782	.9786	.9791	.9795	.9800	.9805	.9809	.9814	.9818	0	1	1	2	2	3	3	4	4
9.6	.9823	.9827	.9832	.9836	.9841	.9845	.9850	.9854	.9859	.9863	0	1	1	2	2	3	3	4	4
9.7	.9868	.9872	.9877	.9881	.9886	.9890	.9894	.9899	.9903	.9908	0	1	1	2	2	3	3	4	4
9.8	.9912	.9917	.9921	.9926	.9930	.9934	.9939	.9943	.9948	.9952	0	1	1	2	2	3	3	4	4
9.9	.9956	.9961	.9965	.9969	.9974	.9978	.9983	.9987	.9991	.9996	0	1	1	2	2	3	3	3	4

* Table IX is reprinted from D. E. Smith, W. D. Reeve, and E. L. Morss: *Elementary Mathematical Tables*, Ginn and Company, by permission of the authors and publishers.

To obtain the mantissa for a four-digit number, find in the body of the table the mantissa for the first three digits and then, neglecting the decimal point temporarily, add the number in the proportional-parts table at the right which is on the same line as the mantissa already obtained and in the column corresponding to the fourth digit.

TABLE X. *Values of Estimated* r_t, *Based upon Pearson's "Cosine Method," for Various Values of* $\frac{bc^*}{ad}$

r_t	$\frac{bc}{ad}$	r_t	$\frac{bc}{ad}$	r_t	$\frac{bc}{ad}$
.00	0–1.00	.35	2.49–2.55	.70	8.50– 8.90
.01	1.01–1.03	.36	2.56–2.63	.71	8.91– 9.35
.02	1.04–1.06	.37	2.64–2.71	.72	9.36– 9.82
.03	1.07–1.08	.38	2.72–2.79	.73	9.83– 10.33
.04	1.09–1.11	.39	2.80–2.87	.74	10.34– 10.90
.05	1.12–1.14	.40	2.88–2.96	.75	10.91– 11.51
.06	1.15–1.17	.41	2.97–3.05	.76	11.52– 12.16
.07	1.18–1.20	.42	3.06–3.14	.77	12.17– 12.89
.08	1.21–1.23	.43	3.15–3.24	.78	12.90– 13.70
.09	1.24–1.27	.44	3.25–3.34	.79	13.71– 14.58
.10	1.28–1.30	.45	3.35–3.45	.80	14.59– 15.57
.11	1.31–1.33	.46	3.46–3.56	.81	15.58– 16.65
.12	1.34–1.37	.47	3.57–3.68	.82	16.66– 17.88
.13	1.38–1.40	.48	3.69–3.80	.83	17.89– 19.28
.14	1.41–1.44	.49	3.81–3.92	.84	19.29– 20.85
.15	1.45–1.48	.50	3.93–4.06	.85	20.86– 22.68
.16	1.49–1.52	.51	4.07–4.20	.86	22.69– 24.76
.17	1.53–1.56	.52	4.21–4.34	.87	24.77– 27.22
.18	1.57–1.60	.53	4.35–4.49	.88	27.23– 30.09
.19	1.61–1.64	.54	4.50–4.66	.89	30.10– 33.60
.20	1.65–1.69	.55	4.67–4.82	.90	33.61– 37.79
.21	1.70–1.73	.56	4.83–4.99	.91	37.80– 43.06
.22	1.74–1.78	.57	5.00–5.18	.92	43.07– 49.83
.23	1.79–1.83	.58	5.19–5.38	.93	49.84– 58.79
.24	1.84–1.88	.59	5.39–5.59	.94	58.80– 70.95
.25	1.89–1.93	.60	5.60–5.80	.95	70.96– 89.01
.26	1.94–1.98	.61	5.81–6.03	.96	89.02–117.54
.27	1.99–2.04	.62	6.04–6.28	.97	117.55–169.67
.28	2.05–2.10	.63	6.29–6.54	.98	169.68–293.12
.29	2.11–2.15	.64	6.55–6.81	.99	293.13–923.97
.30	2.16–2.22	.65	6.82–7.10	1.00	923.98–
.31	2.23–2.28	.66	7.11–7.42		
.32	2.29–2.34	.67	7.43–7.75		
.33	2.35–2.41	.68	7.76–8.11		
.34	2.42–2.48	.69	8.12–8.49		

* Table X is reprinted from M. D. Davidoff and H. W. Goheen, A table for the rapid determination of the tetrachoric correlation coefficient. *Psychometrika*, 1953, **18,** 115-121, by permission of the authors and the editors of *Psychometrika*.

To use the table, set the data up in a 2 × 2 table as shown in the text, page 191. Enter the table with bc/ad or its reciprocal, whichever is the larger, and read the corresponding value of r_t. The accuracy of the values given for r_t does not extend beyond the second decimal, and interpolation between the values listed for bc/ad is not recommended.

TABLE XI. *Table of* T *Scores**

PROPORTION	*T* SCORE	PROPORTION	*T* SCORE
.001	20	.540	51
.002	21	.579	52
.003	22	.618	53
.004	23	.655	54
.005	24	.692	55
.006	25	.726	56
.008	26	.758	57
.011	27	.788	58
.014	28	.816	59
.018	29	.841	60
.023	30	.864	61
.029	31	.885	62
.036	32	.903	63
.045	33	.919	64
.055	34	.933	65
.067	35	.945	66
.081	36	.955	67
.097	37	.964	68
.115	38	.971	69
.136	39	.977	70
.159	40	.982	71
.184	41	.986	72
.212	42	.989	73
.242	43	.992	74
.274	44	.994	75
.308	45	.995	76
.345	46	.996	77
.382	47	.997	78
.421	48	.998	79
.460	49	.999	80
.500	50		

* Table XI is modified from a table published by the Air Training Command in ATRC Manual 50-900-9 prepared under the direction of J. R. Berkshire.

The proportions refer to the proportion of the total frequency below a given score plus ½ the frequency of that score. *T* scores are read directly from the given proportions.

TABLE XII. T *Scores Corresponding to Ranks**

Number of Persons or Objects Ranked

Rank	5	6	7	8	9	10	11	12	13	14	15	16	17	18	19	20	21	22	23	24	25
1	63	64	65	65	66	66	67	67	68	68	68	69	69	69	69	70	70	70	70	70	71
2	55	57	58	59	60	60	61	62	62	62	63	63	64	64	64	64	65	65	65	65	66
3	50	52	54	55	56	57	57	58	59	59	60	60	60	61	61	62	62	62	62	63	63
4	45	48	50	52	53	54	55	55	56	57	57	58	58	59	59	59	60	60	60	61	61
5	37	43	46	48	50	51	52	53	54	55	55	56	56	57	57	58	58	58	59	59	59
6		36	42	45	47	49	50	51	52	53	53	54	55	55	56	56	56	57	57	57	58
7			35	41	44	46	48	49	50	51	52	52	53	54	54	55	55	55	56	56	56
8				35	40	43	45	47	48	49	50	51	51	52	53	53	54	54	55	55	55
9					34	40	43	45	46	47	48	49	50	51	51	52	52	53	53	54	54
10						34	39	42	44	45	47	48	49	49	50	51	51	52	52	53	53
11							33	38	41	43	45	46	47	48	49	49	50	51	51	52	52
12								33	38	41	43	44	45	46	47	48	49	49	50	51	51
13									32	38	40	42	44	45	46	47	48	48	49	49	50
14										32	37	40	42	43	44	45	46	47	48	48	49
15											32	37	40	41	43	44	45	46	47	47	48
16												31	36	39	41	42	44	45	45	46	47
17													31	36	39	41	42	43	44	45	46
18														31	36	38	40	42	43	44	45
19															31	36	38	40	41	43	44
20																30	35	38	40	41	42
21																	30	35	38	39	41
22																		30	35	37	39
23																			30	35	37
24																				30	34
25																					29

26	27	28	29	30	31	32	33	34	35	36	37	38	39	40	41	42	43	44	45	Rank
71	71	71	71	71	71	71	72	72	72	72	72	72	72	72	72	73	73	73	73	1
66	66	66	66	66	67	67	67	67	67	67	67	68	68	68	68	68	68	68	68	2
63	63	63	64	64	64	64	64	64	65	65	65	65	65	65	65	66	66	66	66	3
61	61	62	62	62	62	62	62	63	63	63	63	63	63	64	64	64	64	64	64	4
59	60	60	60	60	61	61	61	61	61	62	62	62	62	62	62	62	63	63	63	5
58	58	59	59	59	59	59	60	60	60	60	60	61	61	61	61	61	61	62	62	6
57	57	57	58	58	58	58	59	59	59	59	59	60	60	60	60	60	60	60	61	7
56	56	56	57	57	57	57	57	58	58	58	58	59	59	59	59	59	59	60	60	8
54	55	55	55	55	56	56	56	57	57	57	57	58	58	58	58	58	58	59	59	9
53	54	54	55	55	55	55	56	56	56	56	57	57	57	57	57	58	58	58	58	10
52	53	53	54	54	54	54	55	55	55	55	56	56	56	56	56	57	57	57	57	11
51	52	52	53	53	53	54	54	54	54	55	55	55	55	56	56	56	56	56	57	12
50	51	51	52	52	52	53	53	53	54	54	54	54	55	55	55	55	56	56	56	13
50	50	50	51	51	52	52	52	53	53	53	53	54	54	54	54	55	55	55	55	14
49	49	50	50	50	51	51	52	52	52	52	53	53	53	54	54	54	54	54	55	15
48	48	49	49	50	50	50	51	51	51	52	52	52	53	53	53	53	54	54	54	16
47	47	48	48	49	49	50	50	50	51	51	51	52	52	52	52	53	53	53	53	17
46	46	47	47	48	48	49	49	50	50	50	51	51	51	52	52	52	52	53	53	18
44	45	46	46	47	48	48	48	49	49	50	50	50	51	51	51	51	52	52	52	19
43	44	45	45	46	47	47	48	48	49	49	49	50	50	50	51	51	51	52	52	20
42	43	44	45	45	46	46	47	47	48	48	49	49	49	50	50	50	51	51	51	21
41	42	43	43	45	45	46	46	47	47	48	48	48	49	49	49	50	50	50	51	22
39	40	41	42	43	44	45	45	46	46	47	47	48	48	48	49	49	49	50	50	23
37	39	40	41	42	43	44	44	45	46	46	47	47	47	48	48	49	49	49	49	24
34	37	38	40	41	42	43	44	44	45	45	46	46	47	47	48	48	48	49	49	25
29	34	37	38	40	41	42	43	43	44	45	45	46	46	46	47	47	48	48	48	26
	29	34	36	38	39	41	41	42	43	44	44	45	45	46	46	47	47	47	48	27
		29	34	36	38	39	40	41	42	43	43	44	45	45	46	46	46	47	47	28
			29	34	36	38	39	40	41	42	43	43	44	44	45	45	46	46	47	29
				29	33	36	38	39	40	41	42	42	43	44	44	45	45	46	46	30
					29	33	36	37	39	40	41	41	42	43	44	44	44	45	45	31
						29	33	36	37	38	40	40	41	42	43	43	44	44	45	32
							28	33	35	37	38	39	40	41	42	42	43	44	44	33
								28	33	35	37	38	39	40	41	42	42	43	43	34
									28	33	35	37	38	39	40	41	42	42	43	35
										28	33	35	37	37	39	40	41	41	42	36
											28	32	35	36	38	39	40	40	41	37
												28	32	35	37	38	39	40	40	38
													28	32	35	36	37	38	39	39
														28	32	34	36	37	38	40
															28	32	34	36	37	41
																27	32	34	36	42
																	27	32	34	43
																		27	32	44
																			27	45

This table converts rankings to a normalized standard score scale with a mean of 50 and a standard deviation of 10. To use the table, first determine the number of persons or objects ranked. Then, enter the table with the rank of the individual or object. (A rank of 3 indicates a person who is third from the top.) At the intersection of the row indicating rank, and the column indicating number of persons or objects ranked will be found the standard score. For example, the 4th person in a group of 22 would have a score of 60. While the 17th person in a group of 30 would have a score of 49.

* Table XII is reprinted from a table published by the Air Training Command in ATRC Manual 50-900-9 prepared under the direction of J. R. Berkshire.

TABLE XIII. *Values of the Rank Correlation Coefficient* r′ *at Selected Significance Points**

n	r'	p
4	1.000	.0417
5	1.000	.0083
5	.900	.0417
5	.800	.0667
5	.700	.1167
6	.943	.0083
6	.886	.0167
6	.829	.0292
6	.771	.0514
6	.657	.0875
7	.857	.0119
7	.786	.0240
7	.750	.0331
7	.714	.0440
7	.679	.0548
7	.643	.0694
7	.571	.1000
8	.810	.0108
8	.738	.0224
8	.690	.0331
8	.643	.0469
8	.619	.0550
8	.595	.0639
8	.524	.0956
9	.767	.0106
9	.700	.0210
9	.650	.0323
9	.617	.0417
9	.583	.0528
9	.550	.0656
9	.467	.1058
10	.733	.0100
10	.661	.0210
10	.612	.0324
10	.576	.0432
10	.552	.0515
10	.527	.0609
10	.442	.1021

* Values of r' were computed from Table IV of E. G. Olds, Distributions of sums of squares of rank differences for small numbers of individuals. *Annals of Mathematical Statistics*, 1938, 9, 133–148, by permission of the author and the editors of the *Annals of Mathematical Statistics*.

The probabilities given are for a one-tailed test of significance. For a two-tailed test of significance, the tabled probabilities should be doubled.

TABLE XIV. *The 5 (Roman Type) and 1 (Boldface Type) Per Cent Points for the Distribution of W_c**

m	n = 3	4	5	6	7
3			.689	.645	.615
			.811	**.764**	**.727**
4		.591	.540	.505	.480
		.737	**.669**	**.621**	**.587**
5		.485	.442	.413	.392
		.626	**.563**	**.520**	**.488**
6		.410	.373	.349	.331
		.541	**.484**	**.445**	**.417**
8	.362	.313	.285	.266	.252
	.506	**.424**	**.376**	**.345**	**.323**
10	.292	.253	.230	.214	.203
	.416	**.347**	**.307**	**.281**	**.263**
15	.196	.170	.155	.145	.137
	.288	**.239**	**.211**	**.192**	**.179**
20	.148	.128	.117	.109	.103
	.219	**.181**	**.160**	**.146**	**.136**

* Values of W_c were computed from Table II of M. Friedman, A comparison of alternative tests of significance for the problem of m rankings. *Annals of Mathematical Statistics*, 1940, 11, 86–92, by permission of the author and the editors of the *Annals of Mathematical Statistics*.

The probabilities given are for obtaining a value of W_c equal to or greater than the tabled value.

For n greater than 7 and for values of m not given, the significance of W may be tested by means of the F distribution or the χ^2 distribution as described in the text, pp. 410–411.

TABLE XV. *Values of T or T′, Whichever Is the Smaller, Significant at the 5 and 1 Per Cent Levels**

n_2 \ n_1	2	3	4	5	6	7	8	9	10	11	12	13	14	15
	5 Per Cent Level													
4			10											
5		6	11	17										
6		7	12	18	26									
7		7	13	20	27	36								
8	3	8	14	21	29	38	49							
9	3	8	15	22	31	40	51	63						
10	3	9	15	23	32	42	53	65	78					
11	4	9	16	24	34	44	55	68	81	96				
12	4	10	17	26	35	46	58	71	85	99	115			
13	4	10	18	27	37	48	60	73	88	103	119	137		
14	4	11	19	28	38	50	63	76	91	106	123	141	160	
15	4	11	20	29	40	52	65	79	94	110	127	145	164	185
16	4	12	21	31	42	54	67	82	97	114	131	150	169	
17	5	12	21	32	43	56	70	84	100	117	135	154		
18	5	13	22	33	45	58	72	87	103	121	139			
19	5	13	23	34	46	60	74	90	107	124				
20	5	14	24	35	48	62	77	93	110					
21	6	14	25	37	50	64	79	95						
22	6	15	26	38	51	66	82							
23	6	15	27	39	53	68								
24	6	16	28	40	55									
25	6	16	28	42										
26	7	17	29											
27	7	17												
28	7													

n_2 \ n_1	2	3	4	5	6	7	8	9	10	11	12	13	14	15
	1 Per Cent Level													
5				15										
6			10	16	23									
7			10	17	24	32								
8			11	17	25	34	43							
9		6	11	18	26	35	45	56						
10		6	12	19	27	37	47	58	71					
11		6	12	20	28	38	49	61	74	87				
12		7	13	21	30	40	51	63	76	90	106			
13		7	14	22	31	41	53	65	79	93	109	125		
14		7	14	22	32	43	54	67	81	96	112	129	147	
15		8	15	23	33	44	56	70	84	99	115	133	151	171
16		8	15	24	34	46	58	72	86	102	119	137	155	
17		8	16	25	36	47	60	74	89	105	122	140		
18		8	16	26	37	49	62	76	92	108	125			
19	3	9	17	27	38	50	64	78	94	111				
20	3	9	18	28	39	52	66	81	97					
21	3	9	18	29	40	53	68	83						
22	3	10	19	29	42	55	70							
23	3	10	19	30	43	57								
24	3	10	20	31	44									
25	3	11	20	32										
26	3	11	21											
27	4	11												
28	4													

* Table XV is reprinted from C. White, The use of ranks in a test of significance for comparing two treatments. *Biometrics*, 1952, 8, 33–41, by permission of the author and editors of *Biometrics*.

n_1 and n_2 are the numbers of cases in the two groups. If the groups are unequal in size, n_1 refers to the smaller.

The probabilities given are for a two-tailed test of significance. For a one-tailed test of significance, the probability should be halved.

Answers to Examples

CHAPTER TWO, *page 29*

2.1 (*a*) -11 (*b*) 2 (*c*) -1 (*d*) 10
(*e*) 2 (*f*) -4 (*g*) -3 (*h*) -8
(*i*) -16 (*j*) -6 (*k*) 3

2.2 (*a*) -5 (*b*) 6 (*c*) 17 (*d*) 30
(*e*) 18 (*f*) -4 (*g*) -3 (*h*) -8
(*i*) 16 (*j*) -2 (*k*) -11

2.3 (*a*) 24 (*b*) -10 (*c*) -6 (*d*) 6
(*e*) 0 (*f*) .0004 (*g*) .01 (*h*) .183
(*i*) $-.00168$ (*j*) .00008 (*k*) .00088 (*l*) $-.012$

2.4 (*a*) -4 (*b*) -4 (*c*) -3 (*d*) 2
(*e*) 20 (*f*) .02 (*g*) 40 (*h*) .6
(*i*) 2 (*j*) 800 (*k*) 42.3 (*l*) -21

2.5 (*a*) 49 (*b*) 1 (*c*) 9 (*d*) 2
(*e*) -3 (*f*) 32 (*g*) $\frac{7}{8}$ (*h*) 0
(*i*) $-\frac{1}{6}$ (*j*) $\frac{1}{8}$ (*k*) 10 (*l*) 32
(*m*) 12 (*n*) 15 (*o*) 0 (*p*) 2

2.6 (*a*) 581 (*b*) 276 (*c*) 27.9 (*d*) 3.91
(*e*) .2 (*f*) .04 (*g*) .005 (*h*) .68
(*i*) .94868 (*j*) 32 (*k*) 2.44 (*l*) 3.17
(*m*) .3 (*n*) .094868 (*o*) 6.1 (*p*) 197
(*q*) 174 (*r*) 983

2.7 (*a*) 2.8319 (*b*) .9053 (*c*) −3.5315 (*d*) 1.7486
(*e*) −4.6405 (*f*) 2.9272 (*g*) 1.8811 (*h*) 2.8762

2.8 (*a*) 8.51 (*b*) 5.50 (*c*) 55.2 (*d*) 305
(*e*) .0859 (*f*) .479

2.9 (*a*) 2 (*b*) 2 (*c*) 2 (*d*) 1
(*e*) 1 (*f*) 1 (*g*) 1 (*h*) 2
(*i*) 2 (*j*) 1 (*k*) 1 (*l*) 2
(*m*) 2 (*n*) 1 (*o*) 1 (*p*) 2
(*q*) 2 (*r*) 1 (*s*) 1 (*t*) 1
(*u*) 1 (*v*) 1 (*w*) 1 (*x*) 1
(*y*) 1

2.10 (*a*) c/b (*b*) bx
(*c*) bx/y (*d*) xy/bcn
(*e*) $y\sqrt{1 - r^2}$ (*f*) $(x^2 - 4a)/9$
(*g*) $(28a/3) - 40$ (*h*) $\sqrt{16x^2 + 4c^2}$ or $2\sqrt{4x^2 + c^2}$
(*i*) $\frac{1}{5}\sqrt{c^2 + 16b^2}$ (*j*) $(r/6) - 2x$
(*k*) -155

2.11 .25 **2.12** .75 **2.13** 120

CHAPTER THREE, *page 51*

3.1 $\bar{X} = 24.0$

3.2 (*a*) 16.9 (*b*) 17.0 (*c*) 9.0
(*d*) 16.5 (*e*) 31.5 (*f*) 86.0
(*g*) 9.2 (*h*) 158.0 (*i*) 21.25
(*j*) 38.0 (*k*) 3.64 (*l*) 14.0
(*m*) 5.0

3.3 $\bar{X} = 20.0$ $s^2 = 10.45$ $s = 3.23$

3.4 $Mdn = 20.12$ $Q_1 = 17.75$ $Q_3 = 22.42$

3.5 $Mdn = 21.5$ $C_{60} = 22.77$ $C_{13} = 13.84$

3.6 (*a*)

Section 1	*Section 2*
$\bar{X}_1 = 82.0$	$\bar{X}_2 = 74.0$
$AD_1 = 3.6$	$AD_2 = 5.4$
$s_1^2 = 19.7895$	$s_2^2 = 45.0526$
$s_1 = 4.45$	$s_2 = 6.71$

(*b*) Section 1 (*c*) Section 1 (*d*) None

3.7 (*a*) x

(*b*) $n\bar{X}$ or $X_1 + X_2 + \cdots + X_n$

(*c*) $(n-1)s^2$ or $\Sigma(X - \bar{X})^2$

(*d*) $\dfrac{\Sigma X}{n}$

(*e*) x^2

(*f*) $\dfrac{\Sigma x^2}{n-1}$ or $\dfrac{\Sigma(X - \bar{X})^2}{n-1}$

(*g*) Σx^2 or $\Sigma(X - \bar{X})^2$

(*h*) $\bar{X}$

(*i*) $\sqrt{\dfrac{\Sigma x^2}{n-1}}$ or $\sqrt{\dfrac{\Sigma(X - \bar{X})^2}{n-1}}$

(*j*) ΣX

(*k*) $X - \bar{X}$

(*l*) s^2 or $\dfrac{\Sigma(X - \bar{X})^2}{n-1}$

(*m*) Σx or 0

3.8 See text, page 38

3.9 Given:

$$D = X_1 - X_2 \tag{1}$$

Summing both sides of (1)

$$\Sigma D = \Sigma X_1 - \Sigma X_2 \tag{2}$$

Dividing both sides of (2) by n

$$\frac{\Sigma D}{n} = \frac{\Sigma X_1}{n} - \frac{\Sigma X_2}{n}$$

or $$\bar{D} = \bar{X}_1 - \bar{X}_2$$

which was to be proved

3.10 $$\bar{X} = \frac{\Sigma X_1 + \Sigma X_2}{n_1 + n_2} = \frac{n_1\bar{X}_1 + n_2\bar{X}_2}{n_1 + n_2}$$

3.11 (*a*) $\Sigma(X - \bar{X})^2 = (n - 1)s^2$
(*b*) $\Sigma(X - \bar{X}) = 0$
(*c*) $\dfrac{\Sigma(X - 10)}{n} = \bar{X} - 10$
(*d*) $\Sigma(X + 1)^2 = \Sigma X^2 + 2\Sigma X + n$
(*e*) $(X - \bar{X})^2 = X^2 - 2X\bar{X} + \bar{X}^2$
(*f*) $\Sigma kX = k\Sigma X$

CHAPTER FOUR, *page 76*

4.1 (*a*) $\bar{X} = 25.0 \qquad \Sigma x^2 = 64.0$
(*b*) $\bar{X} = 22 + \dfrac{21}{7} = 25.0 \qquad \Sigma x^2 = 127 - \dfrac{(21)^2}{7} = 64.0$
(*c*) $\Sigma x^2 = 4{,}439 - \dfrac{(175)^2}{7} = 64.0$

4.2 (*a*) $\bar{X} = 22.17 \qquad s = 7.4$
(*b*) $\Sigma fx'' = 1{,}090 = 910 + 180$
$\Sigma fx''^2 = 7{,}700 = 5{,}700 + (2)(910) + 180$

4.3 $\bar{X} = 46.79 \qquad Mdn = 46.75 \qquad s = 5.9$

4.4 $\bar{X} = 18.1 \qquad Mdn = 18.7 \qquad s = 5.5$

4.5 $\bar{X} = 31.3 \qquad Mdn = 32.8 \qquad C_{30} = 26.5 \qquad s = 8.2$

4.6 $\bar{X} = 7.25 \qquad s = 3.1$

4.7 $\bar{X} = 72.3 \qquad s = 12.5$

4.8 See text, page 61

4.9 See text, page 59

4.10 Given:
$$\Sigma X^2 = \Sigma X'^2 + 2M'\Sigma X' + nM'^2 \tag{1}$$
$$\frac{(\Sigma X)^2}{n} = \frac{(\Sigma X' + nM')^2}{n} \tag{2}$$
$$\Sigma x^2 = \Sigma X^2 - \frac{(\Sigma X)^2}{n} \tag{3}$$

Expanding (2)
$$\frac{(\Sigma X)^2}{n} = \frac{(\Sigma X')^2 + 2\Sigma X'nM' + n^2M'^2}{n}$$

or
$$\frac{(\Sigma X)^2}{n} = \frac{(\Sigma X')^2}{n} + 2\Sigma X'M' + nM'^2 \tag{4}$$

Substituting the right sides of (1) and (4) in (3)
$$\Sigma x^2 = \Sigma X'^2 + 2M'\Sigma X' + nM'^2 - \frac{(\Sigma X')^2}{n} - 2\Sigma X'M' - nM'^2$$

or
$$\Sigma x^2 = \Sigma X'^2 - \frac{(\Sigma X')^2}{n}$$

which was to be proved

4.11 Given:
$$\Sigma x'^2 = \frac{\Sigma X^2}{i^2} \tag{1}$$
$$\frac{(\Sigma x')^2}{n} = \frac{(\Sigma X)^2}{ni^2} \tag{2}$$

From (1) and (2)
$$\Sigma x'^2 - \frac{(\Sigma x')^2}{n} = \frac{\Sigma X^2}{i^2} - \frac{(\Sigma X)^2}{ni^2} \tag{3}$$

Multiplying both sides of (3) by i^2
$$\left[\Sigma x'^2 - \frac{(\Sigma x')^2}{n}\right] i^2 = \Sigma X^2 - \frac{(\Sigma X)^2}{n} \tag{4}$$

We know that
$$\Sigma x^2 = \Sigma X^2 - \frac{(\Sigma X)^2}{n} \tag{5}$$

Substituting from (5) in (4)
$$\Sigma x^2 = \left[\Sigma x'^2 - \frac{(\Sigma x')^2}{n}\right] i^2$$

which was to be proved

4.12 Given:
$$x' = \frac{(X - M')}{i} \tag{1}$$

Summing both sides of (1)
$$\Sigma x' = \frac{\Sigma X - nM'}{i} \tag{2}$$

Multiplying both sides of (2) by i
$$i\Sigma x' = \Sigma X - nM' \tag{3}$$

Dividing both sides of (3) by n
$$i\left(\frac{\Sigma x'}{n}\right) = \bar{X} - M' \tag{4}$$

or
$$\bar{X} = M' + \left(\frac{\Sigma x'}{n}\right)i$$

which was to be proved

4.13 (*a*) Given:
$$x'' = x' + 1 \tag{1}$$

Multiplying both sides of (1) by the appropriate frequencies
$$fx'' = fx' + f \tag{2}$$

Summing both sides of (2)
$$\Sigma fx'' = \Sigma fx' + \Sigma f \tag{3}$$

or
$$\Sigma fx'' = \Sigma fx' + n$$

which was to be proved

(*b*) Squaring both sides of (1)
$$x''^2 = x'^2 + 2x' + 1 \tag{4}$$

Multiplying both sides of (4) by the appropriate frequencies
$$fx''^2 = fx'^2 + 2fx' + f \tag{5}$$

Summing both sides of (5)
$$\Sigma fx''^2 = \Sigma fx'^2 + 2\Sigma fx' + \Sigma f$$

or
$$\Sigma fx''^2 = \Sigma fx'^2 + 2\Sigma fx' + n$$

which was to be proved

4.14 Given:

$$X' = X - M' \quad (1)$$

$$x = X - \bar{X} \quad (2)$$

$$d = \bar{X} - M' \quad (3)$$

Subtracting (2) from (1)

$$X' - x = (X - M') - (X - \bar{X})$$

or

$$X' = x + \bar{X} - M' \quad (4)$$

Substituting from (3) in (4)

$$X' = x + d \quad (5)$$

Squaring and summing both sides of (5)

$$\Sigma X'^2 = \Sigma x^2 + 2d\Sigma x + nd^2 \quad (6)$$

We know that $\Sigma x = 0$, hence (6) becomes

$$\Sigma X'^2 = \Sigma x^2 + nd^2 \quad (7)$$

If d is positive or negative in sign, d^2 is positive and $\Sigma X'^2 > \Sigma x^2$. Only if $d = 0$, can $\Sigma X'^2 = \Sigma x^2$ and because of (3) this can be true only when $M' = \bar{X}$.

CHAPTER FIVE, *page 99*

5.3 (*a*) $X = 50$ (*b*) $X = 30$ (*c*) $X = 56$

CHAPTER SIX, *page 114*

6.1 See text, page 103

6.2 See text, page 103

6.3 Given:

$$Z = a + bz \quad (1)$$

Summing both sides of (1)

$$\Sigma Z = na + b\Sigma z \quad (2)$$

We know that $\Sigma z = 0$, hence (2) becomes

$$\Sigma Z = na \quad (3)$$

Dividing both sides of (3) by n

$$\frac{\Sigma Z}{n} = a$$

or

$$\bar{Z} = a \tag{4}$$

which was to be proved

From (4) and (1) we obtain

$$Z - \bar{Z} = a + bz - a$$

or

$$Z - \bar{Z} = bz \tag{5}$$

Squaring both sides of (5) and summing

$$\Sigma(Z - \bar{Z})^2 = b^2 \Sigma z^2 \tag{6}$$

Dividing both sides of (6) by $n - 1$

$$\frac{\Sigma(Z - \bar{Z})^2}{n - 1} = b^2 \frac{\Sigma z^2}{n - 1} \tag{7}$$

We know that $\dfrac{\Sigma z^2}{n - 1} = 1.00$, hence (7) becomes

$$\frac{\Sigma(Z - \bar{Z})^2}{n - 1} = b^2$$

or

$$s_Z^2 = b^2$$

which was to be proved

6.4 (*a*) C_{50} (*b*) C_{77} (*c*) C_{25} (*d*) C_{33}
(*e*) C_{16} (*f*) C_{85} (*g*) C_{89} (*h*) C_{99}

6.7 (*a*) $R = (6.1)(s) = (6.1)(10) = 61$

(*b*) $z = -.67 = Q_1$ and $-.67 = \dfrac{X - 50}{10}$

Solving for X and rounding we obtain a score of 43

(*c*) Approximately $\frac{2}{3}$ or more precisely .6826

(*d*) The distribution is normal and the mean and median will coincide. Therefore, $Mdn = 50$

CHAPTER SEVEN, *page 138*

7.1 Given: $$\Sigma xy = \Sigma(X - \bar{X})(Y - \bar{Y}) \qquad (1)$$

Expanding the right side of (1)

$$\Sigma xy = \Sigma(XY - X\bar{Y} - Y\bar{X} + \bar{X}\bar{Y}) \qquad (2)$$

Carrying out the summation on the right of (2)

$$\Sigma xy = \Sigma XY - \bar{Y}\Sigma X - \bar{X}\Sigma Y + n\bar{X}\bar{Y} \qquad (3)$$

or $$\Sigma xy = \Sigma XY - \bar{Y}n\bar{X} - \bar{X}n\bar{Y} + n\bar{X}\bar{Y}$$
$$= \Sigma XY - n\bar{X}\bar{Y}$$
$$= \Sigma XY - \frac{(\Sigma X)(\Sigma Y)}{n}$$

which was to be proved

7.2 Given: $$\Sigma Y = na + b\Sigma X \qquad (1)$$

Dividing both sides of (1) by n

$$\frac{\Sigma Y}{n} = a + b\bar{X} \qquad (2)$$

Solving for a we get $a = \bar{Y} - b\bar{X}$

7.3 Given: $$a = \bar{Y} - b\bar{X} \qquad (1)$$
$$\Sigma XY = a\Sigma X + b\Sigma X^2 \qquad (2)$$

Substituting (1) in (2)

$$\Sigma XY = b\Sigma X^2 + (\bar{Y} - b\bar{X})\Sigma X$$

or $$\Sigma XY = b\Sigma X^2 + \bar{Y}\Sigma X - b\bar{X}\Sigma X \qquad (3)$$

Subtracting $\bar{Y}\Sigma X$ from both sides of (3)

$$\Sigma XY - \bar{Y}\Sigma X = b\Sigma X^2 - b\bar{X}\Sigma X$$

or $$\Sigma XY - \bar{Y}\Sigma X = b(\Sigma X^2 - \bar{X}\Sigma X) \qquad (4)$$

Dividing both sides of (4) by $(\Sigma X^2 - \bar{X}\Sigma X)$

$$\frac{\Sigma XY - \bar{Y}\Sigma X}{\Sigma X^2 - \bar{X}\Sigma X} = b$$

or
$$b = \frac{\Sigma XY - \frac{(\Sigma X)(\Sigma Y)}{n}}{\Sigma X^2 - \frac{(\Sigma X)^2}{n}}$$
$$= \frac{\Sigma xy}{\Sigma x^2}$$

7.4 See text, page 125 **7.5** See text, page 126

7.6 $a = 10$ and $b = -.5$ **7.7** $a = 3.62$ and $b = .483$

7.9 $Y = 2X^2$ **7.10** $Y = 2\frac{1}{\sqrt{X}}$

7.11 $Y = 2\sqrt{X}$ **7.12** $Y = 2\frac{1}{X^2}$

7.13 If $Y = a10^{bX}$, then $\log Y = \log a + bX$, and the plot of Y against X on semilogarithmic paper should be linear

7.14 If $Y = aX^b$, then $\log Y = \log a + b \log X$, and the plot of Y against X on logarithmic paper should be linear

7.15 If $Y = a + b \log X$, then the plot of Y against X on semilogarithmic paper should be linear

CHAPTER EIGHT, *page 164*

8.1 $r = .94$ **8.2** $r = .71$ **8.3** $r = .92$

8.4 $r = -.86$ **8.5** $r = .89$ **8.6** $b_{yx} = 1.00$ and $b_{xy} = .79$

8.7 $r = .99$ **8.8** $r = .12$ **8.9** $r = .73$

8.10 $b_{yx} = .58$
(*a*) 56 (*b*) 60 (*c*) 70 (*d*) 76 (*e*) 80

8.11 $b_{xy} = .93$
(*a*) 58 (*b*) 70 (*c*) 75 (*d*) 78 (*e*) 92

8.12 $s_{y \cdot x} = 6.90$ and $s_{x \cdot y} = 8.75$

8.13 See text, page 154

8.14 See text, page 160

8.15 See text, page 162

8.16 See text, page 163

8.17 $r = -.59$

CHAPTER NINE, *page 179*

9.1 See text, page 171

9.2 See text, page 172

9.3 See text, page 174

9.4 See text, page 177

9.5 $r_{kk} = .89$

9.6 $r_{xy} = .72$

9.7 $r_{y_1y_2} = 1.00$

9.8 $r_{kk} = .75$

9.9 Solve

$$k = n\left[\frac{r_{kk}(1 - r_{nn})}{r_{nn}(1 - r_{kk})}\right]$$

with $n = 10$, $r_{kk} = .90$, and $r_{nn} = .60$. Then $k = 60$

CHAPTER TEN, *page 206*

10.1 $r_b = .36$

10.2 $r' = .13$

10.3 $r_\phi = .41$

10.4 $r_b = -.09$

10.5 $r_\phi = .20$

10.6 $\eta_{yx} = .41$

10.7 $\eta_{yx} = .82$

10.8 $r_t = .57$

10.9 $r_t = .34$

10.10 $r' = .27$

10.11 $r_\phi = .41$

10.12 $r_{pb} = .56$

10.13 $r_{pb} = .25$

10.14 $\eta_{yx} = .83$

10.15 $r_\phi = .30$

10.16 $r_\phi = .42$

10.17 Given: $p_1 = n_1/n$, and $q = 1 - p_1$ or n_0/n.

Then
$$n_1 - \frac{(n_1)^2}{n} = n_1 - \frac{n_1 n_1}{n}$$
$$= n_1 - n_1 p_1$$
$$= n_1(1 - p_1)$$
$$= n_1 q$$
$$= \frac{n_0 n_1}{n}$$

which was to be proved

10.18 Given: $p_1 = n_1/n$, and $q = n_0/n$, and formula (10.4) or

$$r_{pb} = \frac{n\Sigma Y_1 - n_1 \Sigma Y}{\sqrt{(n_0 n_1)[n\Sigma Y^2 - (\Sigma Y)^2]}} \tag{1}$$

Dividing both numerator and denominator of (1) by nn_1

$$r_{pb} = \frac{\bar{Y}_1 - \bar{Y}}{\sqrt{\left(\frac{n_0 n_1}{n_1{}^2}\right)\left(\frac{n\Sigma Y^2 - (\Sigma Y)^2}{n^2}\right)}}$$

or
$$r_{pb} = \frac{\bar{Y}_1 - \bar{Y}}{\sqrt{\frac{n_0}{n_1}}\sqrt{\frac{\Sigma Y^2}{n} - \frac{(\Sigma Y)^2}{n^2}}} \tag{2}$$

We know that

$$\frac{\Sigma y^2}{n} = \frac{\Sigma Y^2 - \frac{(\Sigma Y)^2}{n}}{n} = \frac{\Sigma Y^2}{n} - \frac{(\Sigma Y)^2}{n^2} \tag{3}$$

Substituting from (3) in (2)

$$r_{pb} = \frac{\bar{Y}_1 - \bar{Y}}{\sqrt{\frac{n_0}{n_1}}\sqrt{\frac{\Sigma y^2}{n}}} \tag{4}$$

Multiplying both numerator and denominator of (4) by $\sqrt{\frac{n_1}{n}}$

$$r_{pb} = \frac{(\bar{Y}_1 - \bar{Y})\sqrt{\frac{n_1}{n}}}{\sqrt{\frac{n_0}{n}}\sqrt{\frac{\Sigma y^2}{n}}}$$

or
$$r_{pb} = \left(\frac{\bar{Y}_1 - \bar{Y}}{\sqrt{\frac{\Sigma y^2}{n}}}\right)\frac{\sqrt{p_1}}{\sqrt{q}} \tag{5}$$

which was to be proved

Multiplying (5) by $\dfrac{\sqrt{p_1 q}}{y_p}$ we get

$$r_b = \left(\frac{\bar{Y}_1 - \bar{Y}}{\sqrt{\frac{\Sigma y^2}{n}}}\right)\left(\frac{\sqrt{p_1}}{\sqrt{q}}\right)\left(\frac{\sqrt{p_1 q}}{y_p}\right)$$

or
$$r_b = \left(\frac{\bar{Y}_1 - \bar{Y}}{\sqrt{\frac{\Sigma y^2}{n}}}\right)\frac{p_1}{y_p}$$

which was to be proved

CHAPTER ELEVEN, *page 226*

11.1 (a) $p = \dfrac{1}{4{,}096} = .0002$

(b) $p = \dfrac{220}{4{,}096} = .0537$

(c) $p = \dfrac{299}{4{,}096} = .0730$

11.2 (a) $z = 3.18, \quad p = .0007$
(b) $p = .0532$
(c) $z = 1.44, \quad p = .0749$

11.3 $z = 1.75, \quad p = .0401$

11.4 (a) 15 trials
(b) $z = 1.76, \quad p = .0392$
(c) 153 ways

11.5 (a) $p = \dfrac{26}{32} = .8125$

(b) $p = \dfrac{10}{32} = .3125$

11.6 (a) $p = \left(\dfrac{1}{4}\right)^6 = \dfrac{1}{4{,}096} = .0002$

(b) $p = \left(\dfrac{1}{4}\right)^6 + 6\left(\dfrac{1}{4}\right)^5\left(\dfrac{3}{4}\right) = \dfrac{19}{4{,}096} = .0046$

11.7 (a) $p = \left(\dfrac{1}{2}\right)^8 = \dfrac{1}{256} = .0039$

(b) $p = \dfrac{37}{256} = .1445$

11.8 (*a*) 84 ways
(*b*) 20 ways
(*c*) $p = \frac{20}{84} = .2381$

11.9 (*a*) 252 ways
(*b*) $p = \frac{1}{252} = .004$

11.10 $m = 50$ and $\sigma = 5$

11.11 (*a*) The expectation is 1/3 of the 105 subjects or 35
(*b*) $\sigma = 4.83$
(*c*) Yes. We have $z = \frac{21.5}{4.83} = 4.45$, $p < .0001$

11.12 (*a*) The expectation is 1/2 of the 69 subjects tested
(*b*) $\sigma = 4.15$
(*c*) $z = \frac{8.0}{4.15} = 1.93$, $p = .0268$

11.13 $z = 1.64$, $p = .0505$

11.14 $m = 5.00$ $\sigma = 1.58$

CHAPTER TWELVE, *page 245*

12.3 (*a*) 10 (*b*) 4 (*c*) 2

12.5 $n = 40$

12.6 $n = 160$

CHAPTER THIRTEEN, *page 275*

13.1 (*a*) $F = 1.05$, $df = 6$ and 6, $p > .10$
(*b*) $t = 3.60$, $df = 12$, $p < .01$

13.2 (*a*) $F = 2.66$, $df = 38$ and 39, $p < .02$
(*b*) $t = 5.94$, $df = 72$, $p < .01$

13.3 (*a*) $F = 1.11$, $df = 199$ and 199, $p > .10$
(*b*) $t = 4.55$, $df = 398$, $p < .01$

13.4 $t = 2.33$, $df = 18$, $p < .05$

13.5 (*a*) $F = 2.51$, $df = 19$ and 9, $p > .10$
(*b*) $t = 5.03$, $df = 28$, $p < .01$

13.6 (*a*) $m_1 = 18.27$ and $m_2 = 26.53$
(*b*) $m_1 = 20.42$ and $m_2 = 24.38$

13.7 (*a*) $F = 1.38$, $df = 19$ and 19, $p > .10$
(*b*) $t = 2.88$, $df = 38$, $p < .01$

CHAPTER FOURTEEN, *page 296*

14.1 $t = 8.1$, $df = 7$, $p < .01$

14.2 $t = 2.55$, $df = 9$, $p < .05$

14.3 $t = 2.11$, $df = 19$, $p < .05$

14.4 $z = 2.345$, $p < .02$

14.5 $t = 2.72$, $df = 8$, $p < .05$

14.6 $t = 4.04$, $df = 23$, $p < .01$

14.7 $z = 2.03$, $p = (2)(.0212) = .0424$

CHAPTER FIFTEEN, *page 313*

15.1 (*a*) $r = .82$ with fiducial limits of .63 and .92
(*b*) $z = .25$, $p = (2)(.4013) = .8026$, $r_1 = .876$, $r_2 = .899$
(*c*) $b_{yx} = 1.03$, $df = 23$, $t = 6.9$, $p < .01$
(*d*) $b_{y_1x} = 1.06$ and $b_{y_2x} = .94$, $s_{y \cdot x}{}^2 = 2.03$,
$df = 21$, $t = .51$, $p > .50$

15.2 Table VI shows that with 8 *df* an *r* of .765 will be significant at the 1 per cent level.

15.3 No. Table VI shows that with 8 *df* an *r* of .632 would be required for significance at the 5 per cent level.

15.4 Table VI shows that an *r* of .27 would be significant at the 5 per cent level if 48 *df* are available.

15.5 (*a*) Table VI shows that 62 pairs of observations would be needed for significance at the 5 per cent level.
(*b*) Table VI shows that 37 pairs of observations would be needed for significance at the 5 per cent level.

CHAPTER SIXTEEN, *page 338*

16.1 (*a*) *Total* = 666, *Between groups* = 120, *Within groups* = 546
(*b*) The sums of squares are the same. The value of $F = 1.10$ also remains unchanged.

16.2

Source of Variation	*Sum of Squares*	*df*	*Mean Square*	*F*
Between groups	314.4	4	78.60	3.25
Within groups	846.0	35	24.17	
Total	1,160.4	39		

16.3 (*a*) $t = 2.99$, $t^2 = 8.94$
(*b*) $F = 8.95$

16.4

Source of Variation	*Sum of Squares*	*df*	*Mean Square*	*F*
Between groups	110.0	3	36.67	11.79
Within groups	112.0	36	3.11	
Total	222.0	39		

CHAPTER SEVENTEEN, *page 363*

17.1

(*a*)

Source of Variation	*Sum of Squares*	*df*	*Mean Square*	*F*
Between groups	260.0	8	32.50	13.16
Within groups	200.0	81	2.47	
Total	460.0	89		

(*b*)

Methods	26.67	2	13.34	5.40
Age levels	6.67	2	3.34	1.35
Methods × Age levels	226.66	4	56.67	22.94
Within groups	200.00	81	2.47	
Total	460.00	89		

17.2

(a)

Source of Variation	*Sum of Squares*	*df*	*Mean Square*	*F*
Between columns	20.00	2	10.00	1.98
Within columns	136.00	27	5.04	
Total	156.00	29		

(b)

Source of Variation	*Sum of Squares*	*df*	*Mean Square*	*F*
Between columns	20.00	2	10.00	22.73
Between rows	128.00	9	14.22	
Rows × columns	8.00	18	.44	
Total	156.00	29		

17.3

Source of Variation	*Sum of Squares*	*df*
Between columns	24.0	2
Within columns	84.0	6
Total	108.0	8

$$\textit{Sum of squares for linear regression} = \frac{(\Sigma xy)^2}{\Sigma x^2} = \frac{(12)^2}{6} = 24$$

17.4

Source of Variation	*Sum of Squares*	*df*	*Mean Square*	*F*
Between columns	27.81	4	6.95	4.02
Within columns	25.94	15	1.73	
Total	53.75	19		

Source of Variation	*Sum of Squares*	*df*	*Mean Square*	*F*
Linear regression	20.12	1	20.12	
Deviations from regression	7.69	3	2.56	1.48
Within columns	25.94	15	1.73	
Total	53.75	19		

17.5

(*a*)

Source of Variation	Sum of Squares	df	Mean Square	F
Between columns	25.0	3	8.33	3.33
Within columns	40.0	16	2.50	
Total	65.0	19		

(*b*)

Source of Variation	Sum of Squares	df	Mean Square	F
Between columns	25.0	3	8.33	3.33
Between rows	10.0	4	2.50	
Rows × columns	30.0	12	2.50	
Total	65.0	19		

CHAPTER EIGHTEEN, *page 393*

18.1 $\chi^2 = 11.21$, $df = 1$, $p < .01$

18.2 $\chi^2 = 3.76$, $df = 1$, $p > .05$

18.3 $\chi^2 = 4.51$, $df = 1$, $p < .05$

18.4 $\chi^2 = 14.00$, $df = 2$, $p < .01$

18.5 $\chi^2 = 64.50$, $df = 4$, $p < .01$

18.6 $\chi^2 = 18.89$, $df = 2$, $p < .01$

18.7 $\chi^2 = 12.25$, $df = 1$, $p < .01$

18.8 $\chi^2 = 8.76$, $df = 2$, $p < .02$

18.9 $\chi^2 = 2.02$, $df = 1$, $p > .10$

18.10 $\chi^2 = 11.28$, $df = 1$, $p < .01$

18.11 $\chi^2 = 3.86$, $df = 1$, $p < .05$

18.12 $\chi^2 = 5.15$, $df = 3$, $p > .10$

18.13 $\chi^2 = 53.38$, $df = 5$, $p < .01$

18.14 $\chi^2 = 23.64$, $df = 1$, $p < .01$

18.15 $\chi^2 = 4.9$, $df = 1$, $p < .05$

18.16 $\chi^2 = 15.65$, $df = 6$, $p < .02$

CHAPTER NINETEEN, *page 433*

19.1 (*a*) $W = .762$ and $W_c = .752$
(*b*) According to Table XIV a value of W_c equal to .727 would be significant with $p = .01$, if $m = 3$ and $n = 7$. For the obtained value of $W_c = .752$, therefore, we have $p < .01$.
(*c*) $r_{\bar{x}\bar{x}} = .84$

19.2 (*a*) $W = .554$
(*b*) $\chi_r^2 = 38.81$, $df = 10$, $p < .01$
(*c*) $r_{\bar{x}\bar{x}} = .87$
(*d*) $\bar{r}' = .48$
(*e*) $r_{\bar{x}\bar{x}} = .87$

19.3 (*a*) $r_{12}' = .81$ $r_{13}' = .65$ $r_{23}' = .82$
(*b*) $W = .838$
(*c*) $\chi_r^2 = 60.37$, $df = 24$, $p < .01$
(*d*) $\bar{r}' = .76$

19.4 (*a*) $r_{12}' = .80$ $r_{13}' = .89$ $r_{23}' = .70$ $r_{45}' = .79$
(*b*) $W = .696$
(*c*) $\chi_r^2 = 45.23$, $df = 13$, $p < .01$
(*d*) $r_{\bar{x}\bar{x}} = .89$

19.5 (*a*) The value of r' without any correction for tied ranks is .911. If the correction is applied, then $r' = .910$.
(*b*) Table VI shows that $p < .01$

19.6 (*a*) $W = .559$
(*b*) $\chi_r^2 = 22.36$, $df = 5$, $p < .01$

19.7 (*b*) Table XV shows that $p < .01$ for $T = 56.5$
(*c*) $z = -3.667$
(*d*) $z^2 = 13.45$ and $H = 13.44$

19.8 Table XV shows that $p > .05$ for $T = 99$

19.9 Making a continuity correction, we have $z = 1.77$ and
$p = (2)(.0384) = .0768$

19.10 $H = 21.97, \quad df = 3, \quad p < .01$

19.11 $H = 4.46, \quad df = 2, \quad p > .10$

19.12 Ignoring the continuity corrections, we are given:

$$F = \frac{(m-1)W}{1-W} \tag{1}$$

Substituting an identity for W in (1)

$$F = \frac{(m-1)\dfrac{\textit{Sum of squares between columns}}{\textit{Total sum of squares}}}{1 - \dfrac{\textit{Sum of squares between columns}}{\textit{Total sum of squares}}} \tag{2}$$

Multiplying both numerator and denominator of the right side of (2) by the *Total sum of squares*

$$F = \frac{(m-1)\ \textit{Sum of squares between columns}}{\textit{Total} - \textit{Sum of squares between columns}}$$

or $$F = \frac{(m-1)\ \textit{Sum of squares between columns}}{\textit{Sum of squares within columns}} \tag{3}$$

Dividing both numerator and denominator of the right side of (3) by $(m-1)(n-1)$

$$F = \frac{\textit{Sum of squares between columns}/(n-1)}{\textit{Sum of squares within columns}/(m-1)(n-1)}$$

which was to be proved

Index of Names

Index of Subjects